Gift

$$x = \frac{-b \pm \sqrt{b^2 - 4ac}}{2a}$$ *prog*

$$ax^2 + bx + c = 0$$

$$a = 1 \qquad b = -3 \qquad c = 2$$

$$x = \frac{-(-3) \pm \sqrt{(-3)^2 - 4 \cdot 1 \cdot 2}}{2 \cdot 1}$$

$$= \frac{3 \pm \sqrt{9-8}}{2} = \frac{3 \pm 1}{2} = 2 \text{ or } 1$$

$$x = \frac{-b \pm \sqrt{b^2 - 4ac}}{2a}$$

To E. and to V.

PRE-CALCULUS

MERRILL E. SHANKS
Purdue University

CHARLES F. BRUMFIEL
University of Michigan

CHARLES R. FLEENOR
Ball State University

ROBERT E. EICHOLZ
Ball State University

MATHEMATICS

 ADDISON-WESLEY PUBLISHING COMPANY, INC.
READING, MASSACHUSETTS • PALO ALTO • LONDON
New York • Dallas • Atlanta

This book is in the
ADDISON-WESLEY SERIES
IN SCIENCE AND MATHEMATICS EDUCATION

Consulting Editors:

Richard S. Pieters   Paul Rosenbloom
George B. Thomas, Jr.   John Wagner

PREFACE

PRE-CALCULUS MATHEMATICS covers topics which tradition-
ally follow an intermediate algebra course (space geometry
and trigonometry). However, it extends beyond the traditional
course and provides a full course in analytic geometry, with
use of vectors. Central themes of function, vector, and graph
pervade the book. It can be used successfully following any
reasonably modern, intermediate algebra text.

Features of the book are clear definitions, logical development, historical notes that illuminate the development of
mathematical concepts, and chapter summaries with review
problems after each chapter. The text is meant to be *read*.
Attention is given to proofs, since this text is more than a source
of formulas to be applied in problems. Because progress in
mathematics is highly dependent on ability to read mathematical exposition, we have promoted this skill.

The text gives students the mathematics that is represented
in the new College Entrance Examination Board Test. Furthermore, it meets the general recommendations of the Committee
on the Undergraduate Program in Mathematics for the mathematical content that should constitute pre-calculus mathematics. Finally, this book closely follows the spirit and philosophy of the School Mathematics Study Group's Course in
the elementary functions.

A Teachers' Commentary, which provides teaching suggestions, mathematical remarks on the text, and sample test
problems, is available. The Teachers' Commentary also shows
how this text can be used for a variety of courses by omitting
chapters or changing the order of chapters. Three possible
alternative chapter sequences are as follows (see Teachers'
Commentary for more detail):

> 1, 2, 3, 4, 7, 8, 9, 10, 11, 5, 6, 12, 13, 14, 15
>
> 1, 3, 6, 7, 8, 9, 10, 2, 4, 5, 11, 12, 13, 14, 15
>
> 1, 3, 5, 6, 12, 13, 14, 2, 4, 7, 8, 9, 10, 11, 15

We are indebted to Dr. Curtis Howd of Ball State University,
who made it possible for us to test our material, and to Mr.
Donald Foss, who made numerous suggestions for improve-
ments. Finally, we owe much to the students who, by their
insistence on clarity of concept, have guided our exposition.

November 1964   M.E.S., C.F.B., C.R.F., R.E.E.

v

FOREWORD TO THE STUDENT

With this book you are beginning a study of mathematics that thoroughly combines algebra and geometry. Since functions are the foundations of calculus, this text has been specifically designed to give you an understanding of the so-called elementary functions. Thus polynomial, rational, exponential, logarithmic, and trigonometric (or circular) functions, as well as some of their properties and graphs, are discussed in detail.

Since many of the important properties of functions have a strong geometric flavor, we have included the geometric interpretation of ideas that actually involve only numbers and their relations. This interplay between number and geometry, frequently called "analytic geometry," has many different aspects and ramifications. In this text we combine the properties of numbers and number systems with the properties of lines, triangles, circles, etc. which were deduced from a few postulated properties. In spite of this step, no new postulates are needed, since the development of each topic is based on the known properties of numbers and the known theorems of geometry. Thus proofs will rest, as always, on postulates, previous theorems, definitions, and logic. However, quite a few proofs will be given in sketchy form, and you will be asked to supply most of the missing details.

Good luck!
The Authors

CONTENTS

CONTENTS

CONTENTS

X

1

THE PLANE

1-1. INTRODUCTION

You know from your previous mathematics courses that in geometry the center of attention was the Euclidean plane, and in the plane, lines were of paramount importance. In algebra, the center of attention was number systems and, in particular, the real number system. Now we shall unify these two branches of mathematics by using more fully the real numbers to deal with lines, and by using geometry to illustrate and clarify properties of numbers.

Later in this book we shall investigate many curves and surfaces, using algebraic tools. However, at the moment we are concerned with the plane and with lines in the plane.

1-2. COORDINATIZATION OF A LINE

The basic relation between the field of real numbers and geometry is that given by a coordinate system on a line or a coordinatization of a line. We review briefly this mapping of the reals on a line.

Fig. 1-1

Given a line, let us *choose* a point P_0 on it (Fig. 1-1). This point will be called the *origin* of coordinates. Next we *select* a segment which shall be of unit length. We then *choose* one of the rays from P_0 on the line and call this the positive side of P_0. The other ray from P_0 is called the negative side. We choose the point P_1 on the positive side of P_0 such that the segment $\overline{P_0P_1}$ is congruent to the unit segment. The point P_2 is chosen such that P_1 is between P_0 and P_2, and such that $\overline{P_1P_2}$ is congruent to the unit segment. Continuing in this way, we obtain a point P_n for each positive integer n, and in the same way on the negative side of P_0 for each negative integer. We now have a one-to-one mapping,† $i \rightarrow P_i$, of the integers onto some points of the line (zero corresponds to the point P_0) such that the distance from P_i to $P_j = |P_iP_j| = |i - j| = |j - i|$.

To show the correspondence between the rational numbers and the points of a line, we choose a rational number x (Fig. 1-2). Now, if x is a positive rational number, then

$$x = n + p,$$

where n is a nonnegative integer and p is a nonnegative rational number r/s, where r and s are integers and $0 \leq r < s$, so that $r/s < 1$.

---

† A mapping is a *function*. See Chapter 6. In this case the function assigns to each integer a certain point on the line.

2

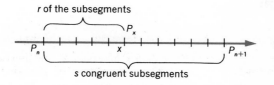

r of the subsegments

s congruent subsegments

Fig. 1-2

We subdivide $\overline{P_n P_{n+1}}$ into subsegments that are congruent to $1/s$ of a unit segment. Let P_x be the point on the line at the end of the rth subsegment such that the length

$$|P_n P_x| = p = \frac{r}{s}.$$

In this manner we obtain a unique point P_x on the line for each positive rational number x. Similarly, if x is a negative rational number, we obtain a unique point P_x on the negative side of P_0. We now have a one-to-one mapping, $x \to P_x$, of the rational numbers onto some points of the line such that

$$\text{distance } P_x P_{x'} = |P_x P_{x'}| = |x - x'|.$$

Figure 1-3 shows the points corresponding to the rational numbers -2, -1, $-\frac{1}{3}$, 0, 1, $\frac{3}{2}$, 2, $\frac{11}{4}$. It remains now to specify the correspondence between *real* numbers and points of the line.

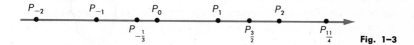

Fig. 1-3

It is a natural reaction to suppose that the points corresponding to the rational numbers comprise *all* points on the line. However, even after all rational numbers have been assigned points on the number line, there are still points left over which correspond to the irrational numbers.

We will assume that the following idea is familiar and will accept it as a fundamental postulate of geometry that there is a one-to-one correspondence,

$$x \to P_x,$$

of the real numbers onto all points of the line. This correspondence maps each real number x into a unique point P_x on the line—on the positive side of P_0 if $x > 0$, and on the negative side if $x < 0$, such that

$$\text{distance } P_x P_{x'} = |P_x P_{x'}| = |x - x'|. \tag{1}$$

Furthermore, the order of the points P_x, P_y, P_z on the line is the same as the order of the real numbers x, y, z. That is, if $x < y < z$, then P_y is between P_x and P_z.

3

DEFINITION 1-1

A *coordinatization* of (or a *coordinate system* on) a line is a one-to-one mapping of the real numbers onto the line with the property described in equation (1). A line with such a mapping is called a *coordinate line*.

Remark

There are many coordinate systems on a line because several choices are available, and a decision must be made about: (a) an origin P_0, (b) a unit of length, (c) one side of P_0 as the positive side. With these choices the coordinate system is fixed.

To *plot a real number x* on a coordinate line is to mark on the line, as closely as you can, the point P_x corresponding to x. We say that x is the coordinate of P_x. For brevity we shall often refer simply to "the point x" when we mean the point P_x.

Usually, instead of indicating the point corresponding to x by P, it is simpler just to write the number next to the point to which it corresponds, as in Fig. 1-4.

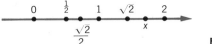

Fig. 1-4

Often it is useful to be able to speak of the directed distance from a first point to a second on a coordinate line. All we need do is use the difference of the coordinates.

DEFINITION 1-2

The directed distance from P_x to $P_{x'}$ is denoted by $P_x P_{x'}$, and is given by
$$P_x P_{x'} = x' - x.$$

Remark

The directed distance is a positive number if $P_{x'} \neq P_x$ and is on the positive ray from P_x; otherwise it is negative or zero. Observe that it is the first coordinate which is subtracted from the second.

Problems

1. (a) A and B are points on a line with coordinates 6 and 14, respectively. Show that 10 is the coordinate of a point C equidistant from A to B.
   (b) A and B are points on a line with coordinates -7 and 9, respectively. Determine the coordinate of a point C such that $|AC| = |BC|$.

2. Let A, B, and C be points on a line with coordinates -6, -2, and 3, respectively. Determine the possible coordinates of a point D if $|AC| = |BD|$.

4

3. Plot the following pairs of real numbers, x_1, x_2. Find the directed distance from the first to the second. Show in each case that $P_{x_1}P_{x_2} = -P_{x_2}P_{x_1}$.

(a) $x_1 = -3$, $x_2 = 6$ (b) $x_1 = -2$, $x_2 = -7$

(c) $x_1 = 0$, $x_2 = \pi$ (d) $x_1 = \pi$, $x_2 = 0$

(e) $x_1 = \sqrt{3} - 2$, $x_2 = 2\sqrt{3} - 1$ (f) $x_1 = -7\pi$, $x_2 = -6\pi$

(g) $x_1 = a$, $x_2 = b$, $a < 0$, $b > 0$

4. Suppose the coordinates of A, B, and C are a, b, and c, respectively, and B is between A and C. If D is a point such that $|AC| = |BD|$, show that the coordinate of D is

$$b - (c - a) \quad \text{or} \quad b + (c - a).$$

5. A, B, and C are points on a coordinate line with coordinates a, b, and c.

(a) Prove that $AB + BC + CA = 0$.
(b) Can $|AB| + |BC| + |CA| = 0$?

6. Plot on the real number line the set of points whose coordinates, x, satisfy the following sentences.

(a) $x \leq -1$ or $x \geq 1$ (b) $x < 5$ and $x > -2$

(c) $|x - 2| = 6$ (d) $|x - 2| < 6$

(e) $|x - 2| > 6$ (f) $-4 \leq x \leq -1$

(g) $|x| < 1$ (h) $|x| < 1/x$

7. Show that $|x - a| < 3$ is equivalent to

$$a - 3 < x < a + 3.$$

8. What are the two different coordinate systems on a line which have the same origin and the same unit of length? If x_1 and x_2 are the real numbers corresponding to a certain point on the line in these two coordinate systems, how are x_1 and x_2 related?

9. A line is assigned coordinates in two ways but with the same origin P_0 and the same positive side of P_0. The unit of length in the second coordinate system has length a with respect to the first unit. If x_1 and x_2 are respectively the coordinates of a point in the two coordinate systems, how are x_1 and x_2 related?

10. A coordinate system is a certain mapping (or function) from real numbers to the points of a line: $x \rightarrow P_x$. Let c be a fixed real number and consider the mapping $x \rightarrow P_{x+c}$. Show that this is a coordinate system and find its origin, positive ray, and unit of length.

*11. Given the coordinate system $x \rightarrow P_x$, when is the mapping $x \rightarrow P_{ax+b}$ a coordinate system?

*12. Given the coordinate system $x \rightarrow P_x$, consider the mapping $x \rightarrow P_{(x^3)}$. Is this a coordinate system? Why or why not?

5

*13. Using a coordinate system, argue geometrically that

$$|x - y| \leq |x - z| + |z - y|.$$

[*Hint:* Consider the possible orders of P_x, P_y, P_z.]

*14. Use the result of Exercise 13 to show that

$$|x + y| \leq |x| + |y|.$$

*15. Establish $|x + y| \leq |x| + |y|$ from arithmetic properties of the real numbers.

1-3. COORDINATIZATION OF A PLANE

We shall now use coordinate systems on lines to define coordinate systems in the plane. Given a plane, a number of choices must be made.

Let us choose a point 0 in the plane, called the *origin of coordinates*. Next we select two *perpendicular* lines through 0. Then we choose positive sides of 0 on these two lines and decide on a unit length. We call one line the *first axis* and the other the *second axis*. Our next step is to coordinatize† each of the axes, with the point 0 as origin, P_0, for each coordinate system.

We now consider an arbitrary point P and the (unique) lines through P parallel to the axes. (These parallels might coincide with an axis if P is on an axis.) The line through P parallel to the second axis will intersect the first axis at a point corresponding to some real number a. This number is called the *first coordinate* (or *abscissa*) of P. The line through P parallel to the first axis will intersect the second axis at a point corresponding to some real number b. This number is called the *second coordinate* of P (or *ordinate*).

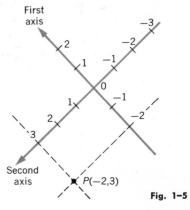

Fig. 1-5

The real numbers a and b are the coordinates of P and we indicate the point and coordinates by $P(a, b)$, or by (a, b). In Fig. 1–5 the point $P(-2, 3)$ is plotted.

Frequently we shall refer to the ordered pair of real numbers (a, b) as a point.

---

† Ordinarily we use the same unit segment for both axes, but this is not necessary in order to set up a coordinate system on a plane.

A convention. Usually one gives names to the two axes related to the variables which are used to denote the coordinates. Thus, if we use x to denote any first coordinate, it is convenient to call the first axis the x-axis. And so if y denotes any second coordinate, we call the second axis the y-axis. In this way it becomes natural to speak of the x- and y-coordinates of a point. Because the axes were chosen to be perpendicular, the coordinates, x and y, of a point (x, y) are called *rectangular coordinates*, and the coordinate system is called a *rectangular coordinate system*. Since we have called the axes the x-axis and y-axis, we call the plane the xy-plane.

Of course there is nothing special about the letters x and y. Any other letters would do as well. Furthermore, as indicated in Fig. 1–5, there is no single way to orient the axes in a plane. But in textbooks, one commonly finds the figure drawn so that, as you view the page, the positive x-axis is to the right and the positive y-axis upward.

The coordinate axes separate the plane into four sets of points, called quadrants, that are numbered I, II, III, and IV as in Fig. 1–6. But the definition of the quadrants does not depend upon this particular picture. Thus, the first quadrant consists of the set of all points for which both coordinates are positive. The second quadrant consists of points whose first coordinate is negative and whose second coordinate is positive. Similar definitions are made for the other quadrants.

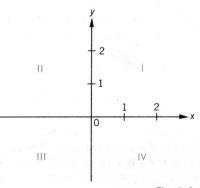

Fig. 1–6

To *plot a point*, with given coordinates, in the coordinate plane is to mark on your paper as nearly as possible the point with the given coordinates.

A coordinate system on the plane is a one-to-one mapping of the set of ordered pairs of real numbers onto the set of points in the plane.

Problems

1. Plot the points: $(0, 0)$, $(0, -1)$, $(-1, 0)$, $(-\frac{3}{2}, \frac{7}{3})$, $\left(\pi, \frac{\pi}{2}\right)$, $\left(-\frac{1}{\sqrt{2}}, \frac{1}{\sqrt{2}}\right)$, $\left(\frac{\sqrt{3}}{2}, -\frac{1}{2}\right)$, and (a, b) where $a > 0$ and $b < 0$.

2. A point is on the second axis. What can you say about its first coordinate? What can you say about its second coordinate if the point is on the same side of the first axis as $(5, -3)$?

3. A point is in the same half-plane determined by the x-axis as is the point $(0, 1)$. What can you say about the second coordinate of $P(x, y)$ in this half-plane?

7

4. A point is on a line which is parallel to the y-axis and passes through the point $(-2, 7)$. What is the x-coordinate of the point? Conversely, what is the set of all points (x, y) for which $x = -2$? What is the set of all points (x, y) for which $x = 0$? for which $x = \pi$?

5. A point $P(x, y)$ lies on a line parallel to, and 3 units from, the x-axis. What is an equation satisfied by the coordinates of P?

6. What is the set of all points (x, y) for which $x + 2 < 0$? for which $x + 2 \le 0$?

7. What is the set of all points (x, y) for which $x^2 > 0$?

8. Draw a graph of the set of points (x, y) whose coordinates satisfy the statement $|x| > 1$ or $|y| > 1$. Do the same for the statement $|x| < 1$ and $|y| < 1$.

9. Give an algebraic definition for each of the four quadrants.

10. What is the distance between $(-1, 3)$ and $(-1, -4)$? between $(-1, a)$ and $(-1, a - 7)$? between $(-1, a)$ and $(-1, b)$?

11. Two points lie on a line parallel to the second axis. Explain how to find the distance between them. What is a formula for this distance if the points are (x_1, y_1) and (x_1, y_2)?

12. Suppose two points are on a line parallel to the x-axis. Choose a notation for the coordinates of these points and write a formula for the distance between them.

*13. Sketch the set of points (x, y) whose coordinates satisfy the following statement. $x = \pm 3$ and $-3 \le y \le 3$, or $y = \pm 3$ and $-3 \le x \le 3$, or $-2 < x < -1$ and $y = 2$, or $1 < x < 2$ and $y = 2$, or $x = \pm\frac{3}{2}$ and $1 < y < 2$, or $-1 < x < 1$ and $y = -1$, or $-2 < x < 2$ and $y = -2$.

*14. It is not necessary, in coordinatizing the plane, to choose axes at right angles. Describe how one can assign coordinates for the plane using any two intersecting lines as axes.

Remark

We have started with a geometric object, namely the plane of Euclidean geometry, and have then put coordinates in the plane, that is, ordered pairs of real numbers. In many situations, however, it is the converse situation that prevails. We are given ordered pairs of real numbers and use the plane to illustrate graphically relations between these ordered pairs. In these situations, the variables x and y may refer to different kinds of things (possibly physical measurements). For example, x could refer to time and y to distance. In such cases there is no need to choose the same unit segment for the two axes. Furthermore, only a portion of the plane may make sense for the application at hand. Figure 1-7 shows such an application to radio. In the figure we have plotted points (t, V) showing the voltage V at time t. We

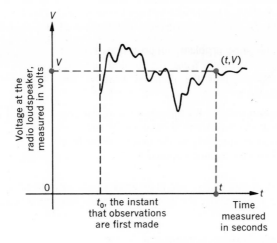

Fig. 1-7

say that we have plotted *V against t.* There is no connection between the units used on the two axes. The choice is made according to the problem at hand, and for expediency in getting the relevant part of the graph on the paper.

In some problems, one will not be interested in all values of the first (or second) coordinate. For example, to illustrate wheat production per year in the United States, one would use only a finite set of first coordinates, one for each year for which records exist.

Problems

1. A block slides down an inclined plane, starting from rest at the top. (See figure.) A record of its motion is obtained by taking a motion picture. Discuss how to plot distance x against time t, suitable units, and the portion of the tx-plane to use. What does the graph of the motion look like?

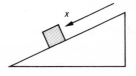

2. Suppose that from the film data we can compute the speed v of the block. What is the relevant portion of the xv-plane?

3. First-class postage is 5¢ per ounce, or fraction thereof. Discuss units and the relevant portion of the plane for illustration of this postage function. (Note that the graph of this function is discontinuous; that is, it is a set of unconnected line segments.)

4. Work (in some units) must be done in order to pump water into a cylindrical tank, such as that in the figure. Discuss the relevant portion of the plane to illustrate the relation between work done, W, and the depth d of water in the tank.

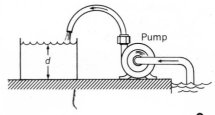

9

5. A body falls from a height of h feet above the ground. (See figure.) Given that x is the distance it falls in t seconds, discuss how to plot x against t.

Now, in the same problem, suppose that distance is measured positively from the ground upward. Discuss how to plot the distance x above the ground against t.

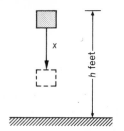

Finally, in this same problem, suppose that distance is measured positively upward but consider the original position of the body as the origin. Now how does the plot of x against t appear?

6. A projectile is shot from a gun at an angle of 45° with the horizontal. Discuss the plot of height above the ground against the horizontal distance traveled.

1-4. THE DISTANCE FORMULA

We shall see how to find the distance between two points $P(x_1, y_1)$ and $P(x_2, y_2)$ with given coordinates. We assume that $x_1 \neq x_2$, $y_1 \neq y_2$, and the same unit segment is chosen for both axes.

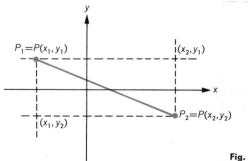

Fig. 1-8

Through the two points consider the four lines parallel to the two axes, as shown in Fig. 1-8. Two pairs of these will be parallel and two of the pairs will intersect in the points (x_1, y_2) and (x_2, y_1). Then the two given points form a right triangle with either one of the points (x_1, y_2) or (x_2, y_1). The lengths of the sides of this triangle are $|x_1 - x_2|$ and $|y_1 - y_2|$. Finally, from the Pythagorean Theorem, we obtain

[distance from (x_1, y_1) to $(x_2, y_2)]^2 = |x_1 - x_2|^2 + |y_1 - y_2|^2$,

or the desired *distance formula:*

$$|P_1P_2| = \sqrt{(x_1 - x_2)^2 + (y_1 - y_2)^2}.$$

(Remember that $\sqrt{a^2} = |a|$ for all real numbers a.)

10

EXAMPLE

The distance between $(-3, -2)$ and $(-1, 5)$ is

$$\sqrt{(-3 + 1)^2 + (-2 - 5)^2} = \sqrt{53} = 7.42, \quad \text{approximately.}$$

Problems

1. Find the distance between:
   (a) $(-4, 2)$ and $(0, 5)$ (b) $(-2, -4)$ and $(-7, 1)$
   (c) $(2, -2)$ and $(2, 7)$
   (d) $(1 - \sqrt{2}, 1 - \sqrt{3})$ and $(1 + \sqrt{2}, 1 + \sqrt{3})$
   (e) $\left(\pi, \dfrac{\pi}{2}\right)$ and $(1, 1)$ (f) (a, b) and $(a + c, b + d)$

2. Using the distance formula show that $|P_1 P_2| = |P_2 P_1|$.

3. Show that the distance formula gives the correct number $|y_2 - y_1|$ as the distance between (x_1, y_1) and (x_1, y_2).

4. Show that the points $(-3, 1)$, $(2, 4)$, and $(0, -4)$ are vertices of a right triangle. What geometric theorem must you use?

5. Is the point $(0, 4)$ inside or outside the circle of radius 4 with center at $(-3, 1)$? Draw a figure.

6. Determine y so that $(0, y)$ shall be on the circle of radius 4 with center at $(-3, 1)$.

7. Show that a triangle with vertices at $(0, 0)$, $(3, 3)$, $(7, 0)$ is congruent to a triangle whose vertices are $(0, 0)$, $(-3, -4)$, and $(-3, 3)$.

8. Show that the point $(3, \sqrt{7})$ is on a circle with center at the origin and radius 4.

9. Using the circle of Problem 8, determine the coordinates of the point of intersection of the x-axis and the tangent to the circle through $(3, \sqrt{7})$.

*10. Show that if the line through (x_1, y_1) and (x_2, y_2) is perpendicular to the line through (x_1, y_1) and (x_3, y_3), then

$$(y_2 - y_1)(y_1 - y_3) + (x_2 - x_1)(x_1 - x_3) = 0.$$

Remark

In Section 1-7 we will find a condition for perpendicularity in terms of *slope*. This new condition will be equivalent to the one you have developed in this problem.

*11. Consider the circle with center at the origin and radius r. Show that if (x, y) is on this circle, then the line through $(-r, 0)$ and (x, y) is perpendicular to the line through (x, y) and $(r, 0)$. What geometric theorem does this prove?

1–5. LINES

Everyone is familiar with locating towns on a map by giving distance, in miles, along a road. Figure 1–9 shows a road running approximately northeast. If we wish to find the location of Town B with respect to the crossroads through 0, we must obviously have a way of describing the direction of the road.

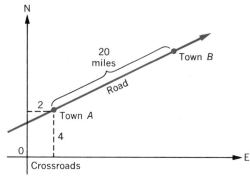

Fig. 1–9

Suppose that for every 5 miles traveled along the road one moves 3 miles north. Then Town B must be 12 miles north of Town A. It would also follow that traveling 5 miles along the road would take one 4 miles east. Then Town B would be 16 miles east of Town A. The north and east coordinates of B from the crossroads are

$$N = 4 + \tfrac{3}{5} \cdot 20 = 16,$$
$$E = 2 + \tfrac{4}{5} \cdot 20 = 18.$$

We can apply the idea of this example to any line.

Let l be any line in the plane and (x_0, y_0) a point on it. We choose a direction on l so that l becomes a directed line. (See Fig. 1–10.) Each point

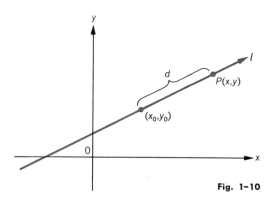

Fig. 1–10

12

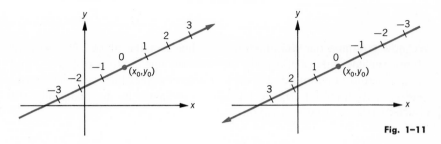

Fig. 1-11

(x, y) of l is uniquely determined by giving the directed distance from (x_0, y_0) to (x, y). In other words, we assign coordinates for l, with (x_0, y_0) as origin of the coordinates and with the same choice of unit as on the x- and y-axes.

The two coordinatizations of l, depending on which way l is directed, are shown in Fig. 1-11.

Remark

Observe that there are *two coordinate systems* involved: the rectangular coordinates, x and y, in the plane, and the coordinate system on l which gives the directed distance from (x_0, y_0) on l.

Problems

1. A line through 0 bisects the first and third quadrants. Find the rectangular coordinates of the two points on the line at a distance 5 from the origin. Find the coordinates of the two points on the line at a distance 5 from $(1, 1)$.

2. A line passes through $(0, 0)$ and $(3, 4)$ and is positively directed from $(0, 0)$ to $(3, 4)$. Find the rectangular coordinates of the point whose directed distance from $(0, 0)$ is 10. Find the coordinates of the point whose directed distance from $(0, 0)$ is -5. Find the coordinates of the point whose directed distance from $(3, 4)$ is -5. Find the coordinates of the point whose directed distance from $(3, 4)$ is -10.

3. For the directed line in Problem 2, obtain a formula for the rectangular coordinates of:

   (a) The point at directed distance d from $(0, 0)$

   (b) The point at directed distance d from $(3, 4)$

4. How are the answers to Problems 2 and 3 affected if the line is oppositely directed?

5. A line passes through $(0, 0)$ and $(-3, 4)$, and is positively directed from $(0, 0)$ to $(6, -8)$. Determine the rectangular coordinates of the point whose directed distance from $(0, 0)$ is 10; whose directed distance from $(0, 0)$ is -10; whose directed distance from $(-3, 4)$ is -10.

13

1-6. LINES (Cont.)

We now continue our examination of a line l in the plane. We wish to express the coordinates of a point (x, y) on the line in terms of (x_0, y_0) and the directed-distance coordinate on l. Remember that there are *two* coordinate systems involved: the rectangular coordinates in the plane and the directed distance from (x_0, y_0) on l.

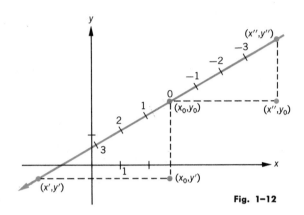

Fig. 1-12

Examine the line of Fig. 1-12, directed as shown. For the point (x', y') which, with respect to distance along the line is on the positive side of (x_0, y_0), we find, in this particular case, that both

$$x' - x_0 \quad \text{and} \quad y' - y_0$$

are negative numbers. For the point (x'', y'') on the negative side of (x_0, y_0), both

$$x'' - x_0 \quad \text{and} \quad y'' - y_0$$

are positive numbers. Let d' and d'' be the directed distances from (x_0, y_0) to (x', y') and (x'', y''), respectively. Then, because of the *similar triangles* shown in Fig. 1-12,

$$\frac{x_0 - x'}{d'} = \frac{x'' - x_0}{-d''}$$

or

$$\frac{x' - x_0}{d'} = \frac{x'' - x_0}{d''} ;$$

similarly,

$$\frac{y' - y_0}{d'} = \frac{y'' - y_0}{d''} .$$

14

In fact, if (x, y) is any point of the line other than (x_0, y_0), with directed distance d, the ratios

$$\begin{cases} \dfrac{x - x_0}{d} = c_1, \\[2mm] \dfrac{y - y_0}{d} = c_2 \end{cases} \qquad (1)$$

are always the same numbers c_1 and c_2. Note that for the line of Fig. 1–12 directed as shown, both c_1 and c_2 are negative numbers.

Remark

The numbers c_1 and c_2 will be encountered again later. They are *direction cosines* of the positive ray from (x_0, y_0) on l. In other words, they are the cosines of the angles between this ray and rays from (x_0, y_0) in the directions of the positive x- and y-axes. At the moment, since we do not suppose any familiarity with trigonometry, we content ourselves with the observation that the numbers c_1 and c_2 in formulas (1) exist. One can describe c_1 as "the horizontal change" divided by the directed distance, and c_2 as the "vertical change" divided by the directed distance.

From equations (1) we obtain the result we have been seeking. The next theorem states our conclusion.

THEOREM 1–1

Given a directed line l with direction cosines c_1 and c_2, then a point $P(x, y)$ at a directed distance d from (x_0, y_0) on l has coordinates

$$\begin{cases} x = x_0 + c_1 d, \\ y = y_0 + c_2 d. \end{cases} \qquad (2)$$

Conversely, if x and y are given by (2), then the point (x, y) is on l.

Proof. If $d \neq 0$, then equations (1) are equivalent to (2). If $d = 0$, then $(x, y) = (x_0, y_0)$.

Conversely, if equations (2) are satisfied, and $d \neq 0$, then the point (x, y) is on l because the distance from (x, y) to (x_0, y_0) is $|d|$ and the direction cosines of the ray from $P(x_0, y_0)$ through $P(x, y)$ are c_1, c_2.

Equations (2) are *parametric equations*† of the line, with *parameter d*. A *parameter* is merely a variable. The domain of the parameter is just the domain of the variable. It can be any nonempty set. In the parametric equations (2) the domain of the parameter d is the set of all real numbers.

---

† Parametric equations of a line represent the line as a mapping of the real numbers into the plane. Other curves may also be represented by parametric equations. See Chapter 14. In general, as the parameter varies, the point in the plane "moves" along the curve.

15

EXAMPLE

Find parametric equations of the line through $(-1, 3)$ and $(1, 1)$.

First we observe that there are several different sets of parametric equations. Either $(-1, 3)$ or $(1, 1)$ could be used as the origin of coordinates on l. Let us select $(1, 1)$. Now we must choose a direction on l as positive. Let us select the ray downward and to the right as the positive direction. (See Fig. 1-13.)

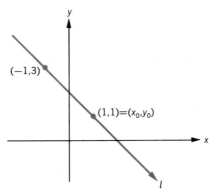

Fig. 1-13

Next we must determine the numbers c_1 and c_2. Because we have two points on the line and can compute the distance between $(-1, 3)$ and $(1, 1)$, we can find c_1 and c_2 from equations (2). The distance from $(-1, 3)$ to $(1, 1)$ is

$$\sqrt{(-1 - 1)^2 + (3 - 1)^2} = \sqrt{8} = 2\sqrt{2}.$$

Then the parameter d for the point $(-1, 3)$ is $-2\sqrt{2}$ because $(-1, 3)$ is on the negative side of $(1, 1)$ on l. Hence

$$\frac{-1 - 1}{-2\sqrt{2}} = c_1 = \frac{1}{\sqrt{2}}, \qquad \frac{3 - 1}{-2\sqrt{2}} = c_2 = -\frac{1}{\sqrt{2}}.$$

Parametric equations of the line therefore are

$$\begin{cases} x = 1 + \dfrac{1}{\sqrt{2}} d, \\[2mm] y = 1 - \dfrac{1}{\sqrt{2}} d. \end{cases}$$

By using these equations we can find coordinates of as many points of the line as we like. Thus, using $d = 1$ we get the point $\left(1 + \dfrac{1}{\sqrt{2}}, 1 - \dfrac{1}{\sqrt{2}}\right)$.

16

For $d = 2\sqrt{2}$, we get the point $(3, -1)$. For $d = -2\sqrt{2}$, we get the given point $(-1, 3)$. For $d = \sqrt{2}$, we get the point $(2, 0)$. (See Fig. 1-14.)

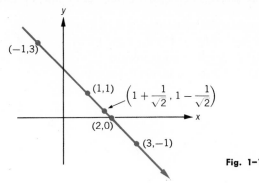

Fig. 1-14

You should verify that if the other ray from $(1, 1)$ had been selected as the positive direction on l, then the parametric equations would have been

$$\begin{cases} x = 1 - \dfrac{1}{\sqrt{2}}\, d, \\[2mm] y = 1 + \dfrac{1}{\sqrt{2}}\, d. \end{cases}$$

Likewise, if the point $(-1, 3)$ were selected as origin on l, we would obtain the two sets of parametric equations:

$$\begin{cases} x = -1 + \dfrac{1}{\sqrt{2}}\, d, \\[2mm] y = 3 - \dfrac{1}{\sqrt{2}}\, d; \end{cases} \qquad \begin{cases} x = -1 - \dfrac{1}{\sqrt{2}}\, d, \\[2mm] y = 3 + \dfrac{1}{\sqrt{2}}\, d. \end{cases}$$

There is an important relation between the numbers c_1 and c_2 given in the following theorem.

THEOREM 1-2

If c_1 and c_2 are direction cosines of a line, then $c_1^2 + c_2^2 = 1$.

A proof based on the Pythagorean Theorem is left as an exercise.

Let us suppose that we have a pair of real numbers, r and s, such that $r^2 + s^2 = 1$. Is there a line such that r and s are the direction cosines of the line? The answer to this question is "yes." Indeed, there are infinitely many lines such that r and s are the direction cosines of the lines.

17

THEOREM 1-3

If r and s are real numbers and $r^2 + s^2 = 1$, then there is a directed line whose direction cosines are the real numbers r and s.

Proof. It is necessary to find only one such line. Consider the line (Fig. 1-15) through $(0, 0)$ and (r, s), and directed from 0 toward (r, s). The point (r, s) is at distance 1 from 0; therefore

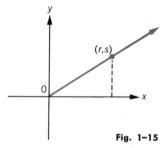

$$c_1 = \frac{r}{1} = r$$

and

$$c_2 = \frac{s}{1} = s.$$

Fig. 1-15

Problems

1. Find parametric equations for the lines through the following pairs of points. Assume that the first point is (x_0, y_0).

   (a) $(0, 0)$ and $(3, 4)$ (b) $(0, 0)$ and $(-3, 4)$

   (c) $(1, -2)$ and $(-4, -7)$ (d) $(-3, -5)$ and $(-5, 2)$

   (e) $(-1, 1)$ and $(10, 3)$ (f) (a, b) and $(a + e, b + f)$

2. If parametric equations of a line are

$$\begin{cases} x = 6 + \dfrac{4d}{5}, \\[2mm] y = -8 + \dfrac{3d}{5}, \end{cases}$$

   then what are the rectangular coordinates of a point that is 5 units from $(6, -8)$? -5 units from $(6, -8)$? 5 units from $(2, -11)$? -5 units from $(2, -11)$?

3. (a) If a line is parallel to the x-axis, show that $c_2 = 0$ and $c_1 = 1$ or -1. What are c_1 and c_2 for a line parallel to the y-axis?

   (b) Find parametric equations of the line through $(2, -3)$ and parallel to the x-axis; parallel to the y-axis.

4. Show that, for any line, $c_1^2 + c_2^2 = 1$.

5. Let a and b be any two real numbers where a and b are not both zero. Show that

$$\frac{a}{\sqrt{a^2 + b^2}} \quad \text{and} \quad \frac{b}{\sqrt{a^2 + b^2}}$$

   are direction cosines of a directed line. Show this in two ways: (1) Use Theorem 1-3. (2) Consider the line through $(0, 0)$ and (a, b).

18

6. Equations $x = -2 + \frac{1}{3}d$ and $y = 3 - \frac{2\sqrt{2}}{3}d$ are parametric equations of a line.

(a) Verify that $c_1^2 + c_2^2 = 1$.   (b) Find several points on the line.

(c) Find the coordinates of the point where the line intersects the y-axis.

(d) Give two other pairs of parametric equations for the line.

(e) Draw the line.

7. A line has parametric equations $x = a$ and $y = b + d$, where d is the parameter. Draw the line.

8. What is the set of points (x, y) such that $x = -2 + \frac{3}{5}d$, $y = 3 - \frac{4}{5}d$, if d is restricted to the interval $-1 \le d \le 4$?

*9. What is the set of points (x, y) such that $x = x_0 + c_1 d$, $y = y_0 + c_2 d$ if $a \le d \le b$?

*10. Consider the line l shown in the figure, with (x_0, y_0) in the second quadrant. By considering separately the cases where (x, y) is on the positive or the negative side of (x_0, y_0) on l, show that the ratios

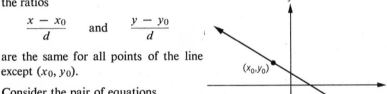

$$\frac{x - x_0}{d} \quad \text{and} \quad \frac{y - y_0}{d}$$

are the same for all points of the line except (x_0, y_0).

*11. Consider the pair of equations,

$$\begin{cases} x = 2 - 2t, \\ y = -1 + 3t, \end{cases}$$

where t is a variable representing any real number.

(a) Find three ordered pairs of real numbers, (x, y), determined by this pair of equations by choosing three values for t.

(b) Show that the three points having the coordinates determined are collinear points.

(c) What are direction cosines of the line?

*12. Consider the equations

$$\begin{cases} x = x_0 + At, \\ y = y_0 + Bt, \end{cases}$$

where t is a parameter whose domain is the set of real numbers and A and B are given real numbers, not both zero.

(a) Do these equations represent a line?

(b) Find three points determined by the equations and show that the points are collinear.

(c) What are direction cosines of the line?

(d) How is the parameter t related to the distance parameter d?

19

1-7. SLOPE

We have seen that direction cosines tell us which "way" a line goes. There is another related concept, called *slope*, which is applicable to all lines not parallel to the y-axis (see Fig. 1–16) and more convenient for many purposes. Recall that c_1 and c_2 are horizontal and vertical changes per unit of directed distance along the line. The slope of a line is *the vertical change divided by the horizontal change*. We shall usually represent slope by the letter m. It is defined by

$$\text{slope} = m = \frac{y_2 - y_1}{x_2 - x_1}.$$

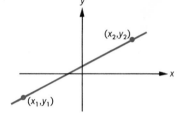

Fig. 1–16

Remarks

1. Vertical lines do not have slope, for the denominator, $x_2 - x_1$, would vanish if the line were vertical.

2. The formula for slope, above, is independent of which point is considered first, because

$$\frac{y_2 - y_1}{x_2 - x_1} = \frac{y_1 - y_2}{x_1 - x_2}.$$

3. It should be geometrically clear to you that one obtains the same number m regardless of which two points one chooses on the line. In order that slope be a property of the line and not of the particular pair of points chosen, we need the following result.

THEOREM 1–4

> If $(x_1, y_1) \neq (x_2, y_2)$, and $(x_3, y_3) \neq (x_4, y_4)$, and all are points on one line not parallel to the y-axis, then
>
> $$\frac{y_2 - y_1}{x_2 - x_1} = \frac{y_4 - y_3}{x_4 - x_3}.$$

Proof. Figure 1–17 can be used to supply a proof based on the similarity of the right triangles with dashed sides.

An easier proof follows from use of the parametric equations of the line. We have

$$\begin{aligned}
x_1 &= x_0 + c_1 d_1, & y_1 &= y_0 + c_2 d_1; \\
x_2 &= x_0 + c_1 d_2, & y_2 &= y_0 + c_2 d_2; \\
x_3 &= x_0 + c_1 d_3, & y_3 &= y_0 + c_2 d_3; \\
x_4 &= x_0 + c_1 d_4, & y_4 &= y_0 + c_2 d_4.
\end{aligned}$$

20

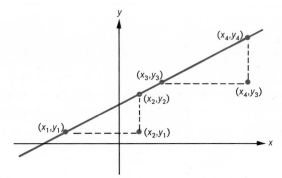

Fig. 1-17

Observe that $c_1 \neq 0$ because the line is not parallel to the y-axis. Therefore

$$\frac{y_2 - y_1}{x_2 - x_1} = \frac{c_2 d_2 - c_2 d_1}{c_1 d_2 - c_1 d_1} = \frac{c_2}{c_1},$$

and

$$\frac{y_4 - y_3}{x_4 - x_3} = \frac{c_2 d_4 - c_2 d_3}{c_1 d_4 - c_1 d_3} = \frac{c_2}{c_1}.$$

EXAMPLE

Draw the line through $(2, -1)$ with slope $\frac{-3}{2}$, such as that in Fig. 1-18.

Since the slope is $\frac{-3}{2}$, the vertical change is -3 for a horizontal change of 2. Also, the vertical change is 3 for a horizontal change of -2. Therefore the points $(0, 2)$ and $(4, -4)$ must be on the line. Why are the points $(1, \frac{1}{2})$ and $(3, -\frac{5}{2})$ also on the line?

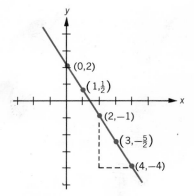

Fig. 1-18

Problems

1. Find the slopes (if any) of the lines through the following pairs of points. Draw the lines.

   (a) $(0, 0)$ and $(2, 3)$ (b) $(0, 0)$ and $(-2, -3)$

   (c) $(0, 0)$ and $(-2, 3)$ (d) $(-1, 1)$ and $(3, 3)$

   (e) $(3, -4)$ and $(-4, -4)$ (f) $(-2, 5)$ and $(-2, -3)$

   (g) (x_0, y_0) and $(x_0 + l, y_0 + m)$

2. Draw a line through the given point with the slope indicated.

(a) $(2, 3)$, $m = 1$ (b) $(-1, 2)$, $m = -1$

(c) $(-2, 4)$, $m = 3$ (d) $(7, 0)$, $m = -\frac{1}{2}$

(e) $(4, -1)$, $m = \frac{2}{3}$ (f) $(0, 0)$, $m = k$

3. By using slope, show that the points P_1, P_2, and P_3 are collinear if the co-ordinates of the points are $(-4, 6)$, $(-1, 12)$, and $(-7, 0)$, respectively.

4. From each of the figures (a) through (d), estimate the slope of the line.

(a)
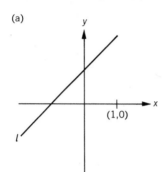

(b)
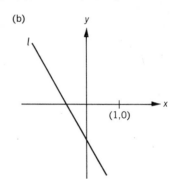

(c)
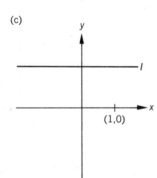

(d)
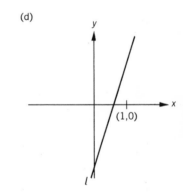

5. Describe a line that has

(a) a positive slope;   (b) a negative slope;   (c) slope zero;   (d) no slope.

*6. If c_1 and c_2 are direction cosines of a line, prove that the line has slope if and only if $c_1 \neq 0$. If it has slope, show that $m = c_2/c_1$.

1-8. SOME EQUATIONS OF LINES

While for many purposes parametric equations are convenient (certainly they give a natural way of describing lines), in many situations the algebraic description of a line is best given by a single equation. This will be an equation in x and y, of the first degree, which is satisfied by the coordinates of

22

those points (x, y) on the line, and only those points. The line is the graph of the equation.

If the line is not parallel to the y-axis, it will have a slope and an equation is easy to find, as we shall see.

But let us first dispose of lines parallel to the y-axis. Such a line will meet the x-axis in a point $(a, 0)$. (See Fig. 1–19.) Every point on the line has its x-coordinate equal to a. Conversely, if a point has its x-coordinate equal to a, then the point is on the line through $(a, 0)$ parallel to the y-axis. Therefore the line has the equation

$$x = a.$$

Other equations equivalent to $x = a$ are

$$kx = ka,$$

where

$$k \neq 0.$$

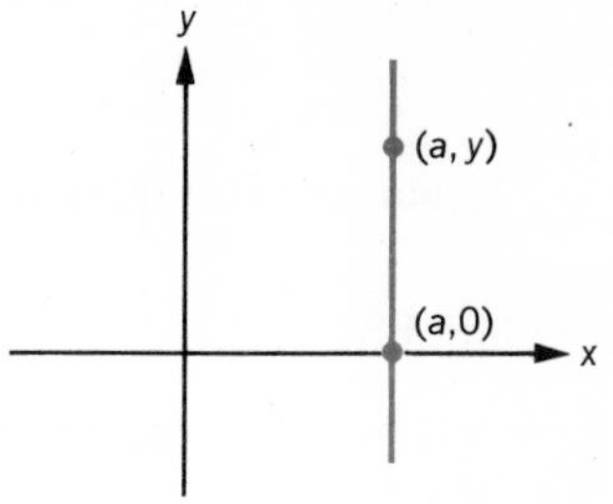

Fig. 1–19

Now let us consider lines with slope. The following theorem is basic.

THEOREM 1–5

The point (x, y) is on the line with slope m through (x_1, y_1) if and only if

$$y - y_1 = m(x - x_1). \tag{1}$$

Proof. We prove first that if (x, y) is on the line, then x and y satisfy equation (1). If $(x, y) = (x_1, y_1)$, then (1) becomes $0 = m \cdot 0$, which is certainly true. If $(x, y) \neq (x_1, y_1)$, then the slope of the line is

$$m = \frac{y - y_1}{x - x_1},$$

and so $y - y_1 = m(x - x_1)$. This proves that (1) is satisfied if (x, y) is on the line.

Now suppose that x and y are such that $y - y_1 = m(x - x_1)$. If $x = x_1$, then $y = y_1$ and $(x, y) = (x_1, y_1)$, so the point (x, y) is on the line. If $x \neq x_1$, then

$$\frac{y - y_1}{x - x_1} = m,$$

and we see that (x, y) is a point on the line with slope m through (x_1, y_1). This proves that if x and y satisfy (1), then (x, y) is on the line. The proof is complete.

Equation (1) is called the *point-slope* form for an equation of a line.

23

Formula (1) takes a particularly simple form if (x_1, y_1) is the point where the line intersects the y-axis. This point is called the *y-intercept*. It is customary to denote this point by $(0, b)$. Frequently, for brevity, the number b is called the y-intercept.

Corollary

The line with slope m and y-intercept b has an equation

$$y = mx + b. \tag{2}$$

Equation (2) is often referred to as the *slope-intercept form* for the line.

EXAMPLES

1. A line has slope $-\frac{1}{2}$ and passes through $(-2, 3)$. Find an equation of the line.

From Theorem 1–5 its equation is

$$y - 3 = -\tfrac{1}{2}(x + 2),$$

or an equivalent equation

$$x + 2y - 4 = 0.$$

(*Note:* Two equations are equivalent if they have the same solution sets.)

2. Find an equation of the line with slope $-\frac{2}{3}$ passing through $(0, 3)$. (See Fig. 1–20.)

Using the Corollary we get

$$y = -\tfrac{2}{3}x + 3,$$

or the equivalent equation

$$2x + 3y = 9.$$

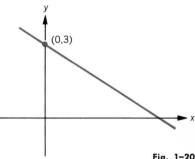

Fig. 1-20

3. We can use formula (1) to quickly obtain an equation for the line through two points. Suppose the points are $(-1, 2)$ and $(3, -4)$. Then

$$m = \frac{2 - (-4)}{-1 - 3} = -\frac{3}{2},$$

and the line is given by

$$y - 2 = -\tfrac{3}{2}(x + 1)$$

or

$$3x + 2y - 1 = 0.$$

24

Remark

To abbreviate, one often speaks of "the line $3x + 2y - 1 = 0$" instead of the longer "the line whose equation is $3x + 2y - 1 = 0$."

4. Sketch the graph of $2x - 5y + 7 = 0$.
An equivalent equation is

$$y = \tfrac{2}{5}x + \tfrac{7}{5}.$$

We see from the Corollary that this is an equation for the line with slope $\tfrac{2}{5}$ and y-intercept $\tfrac{7}{5}$. (See Fig. 1–21.)

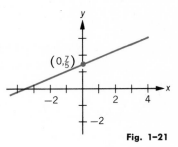

Fig. 1–21

Problems

1. Find equations for the lines described. Sketch the line in each case.
   (a) Through $(4, 2)$ and $(-5, -1)$
   (b) Through $(-1, 2)$ and $(3, -1)$
   (c) Through $(2, -4)$ with slope 2
   (d) Through $(-1, -1)$ with slope $-\tfrac{1}{2}$
   (e) Through $(0, 0)$ with slope $-\tfrac{2}{5}$
   (f) Through $(-4, -\tfrac{7}{2})$ with slope 0
   (g) Through $(-\tfrac{3}{2}, \tfrac{5}{4})$ with slope $\tfrac{3}{4}$
   (h) Through $(-2, -\tfrac{2}{3})$ and $(3, -\tfrac{3}{2})$
   (i) Through $(-2, 1)$ and $(3, 4)$
   (j) Through $(-\tfrac{7}{3}, 0)$ and $(-\tfrac{5}{2}, 0)$
   (k) Through $(0, 0)$ and (a, b) where $a \neq 0$
   (l) Through $(0, b)$ with slope m
   (m) Through (x_0, y_0) and $(x_0 + a, y_0 + b)$, $a \neq 0$

2. Find the slope and the y-intercept, and draw the lines.
   (a) $3x - y = 6$
   (b) $2x + 3y = 6$
   (c) $y = 2x + 2$
   (d) $x + y = 0$
   (e) $x + \pi y = 2$
   (f) $ax + by = b, b \neq 0$
   (g) $3x + 4y = k$, k is arbitrary
   (h) $\sqrt{2}\,x + (1 - \sqrt{2})y = 2$

3. Show that the points $(1, 0)$, $(4, -12)$, and $(2, -4)$ are collinear.

1–9. THE GENERAL LINEAR EQUATION

First we must have a definition.

DEFINITION 1–3

A *linear* equation in x and y is an equation of the form

$$Ax + By = C, \tag{1}$$

where A and B are given real numbers and A and B are not both zero.

25

An equation of the form (1) is called "linear" because the graph of such an equation is always a straight line. Recall that the graph of any equation in x and y is the set of *all* points (x, y) and *only* those points whose coordinates satisfy the equation.

THEOREM 1-6

Every straight line is the graph of a linear equation. Conversely, every linear equation has a graph which is a straight line.

Proof. If a line is vertical, it has an equation $x = a$. This is a linear equation with $A = 1$, $B = 0$, and $C = a$. If a line is not vertical, it has a slope m and a y-intercept b, and is, by the corollary to Theorem 1–5, the graph of

$$y = mx + b.$$

This equation is equivalent to the equation

$$-mx + y = b,$$

which is a linear equation with $A = -m$, $B = 1$, and $C = b$. Therefore a line is the graph of a linear equation, and the first part of the theorem is proved.

Now, suppose we have a linear equation

$$Ax + By = C.$$

If $B = 0$, then $A \neq 0$ and the equation is $Ax = C$, which is equivalent to

$$x = \frac{C}{A}.$$

The graph of this equation is a line parallel to the y-axis.

If $B \neq 0$, then the linear equation is equivalent to

$$y = -\frac{A}{B}x + \frac{C}{B}.$$

By the corollary to Theorem 1–5 we recognize that the graph of this last equation is the straight line with slope $m = -\frac{A}{B}$ and y-intercept $b = \frac{C}{B}$. Therefore, in all cases, the graph of $Ax + By = C$ is a straight line.

EXAMPLES

1. Draw the graph of $3x - 2y = 7$.

From Theorem 1–6 we know that the graph is a straight line. To draw the line it would suffice to find two points on the line. It is easily seen that $(0, -\frac{7}{2})$ and $(\frac{7}{3}, 0)$ are on the graph of the given equation. Therefore the graph appears as in Fig. 1–22.

26

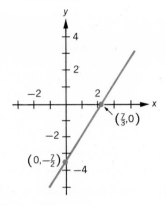

Fig. 1-22

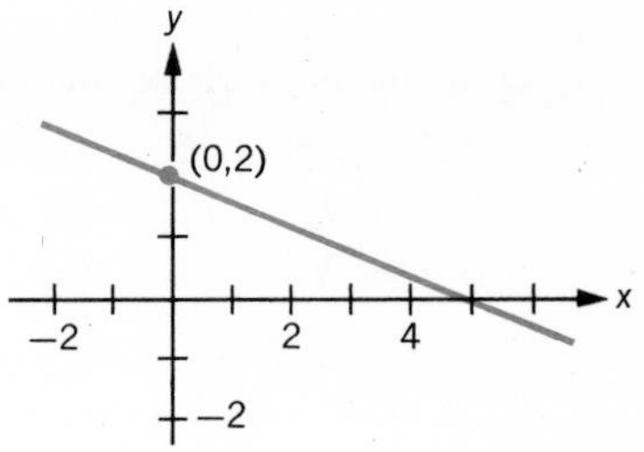

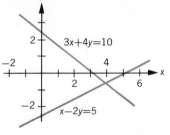

Fig. 1-23

2. Find the slope of the line which has the equation $2x + 5y = 10$.

The equation is equivalent to $y = -\frac{2}{5}x + 2$. We recognize this equation as the slope-intercept form for the line with y-intercept 2 and slope $-\frac{2}{5}$. (See Fig. 1–23.)

Of course, one could also find the slope by getting two points on the line and then using the formula for slope. If this were done and one selected the points $(0, 2)$ and $(5, 0)$, then the slope would be

$$m = \frac{2 - 0}{0 - 5} = -\frac{2}{5}.$$

3. Find the point of intersection of the lines

$$3x + 4y = 10 \quad \text{and} \quad x - 2y = 5.$$

The graphs of the equations are shown in Fig. 1–24. From the graph we might *estimate* the coordinates of the point of intersection. We can be more precise by attacking the problem algebraically.

We seek all those points and only those points (x, y) that satisfy

$$3x + 4y = 10 \quad (2)$$

and

$$x - 2y = 5. \quad (3)$$

From (3) we have $x = 5 + 2y$, and substituting in (2), we have

$$3(5 + 2y) + 4y = 10.$$

Fig. 1-24

Solving this equation for y, we find $y = -\frac{1}{2}$. Hence in (2) we must have $3x + 4(-\frac{1}{2}) = 10$ and therefore $x = 4$. Observe that the pair $(4, -\frac{1}{2})$ satisfies both equations (2) and (3), and so the point of intersection of the lines must be $(4, -\frac{1}{2})$.

27

Problems

1. Draw the lines whose equations are:

(a) $2x - 3y = 6$ (b) $2x - \sqrt{3}\,y = \pi$ (c) $x + y = \sqrt{7}$

(d) $x + 7y = 1$ (e) $y = 3x$ (f) $y = -3x$

(g) $y = \frac{1}{3}x$ (h) $y = -\frac{1}{3}x$ (i) $2x = -5$

(j) $y = -\dfrac{\pi}{2}$ (k) $x = 2\pi$ (l) $y = \dfrac{\sqrt{3}}{2}$

*(m) $mx - y = 2$. Draw several of these lines for different values of m.

*(n) $y + 2x = b$. Draw several of these lines for different values of b.

2. Find a linear equation for the lines through the following pairs of points. Draw the lines.

(a) $(-1, 1)$ and $(-2, 5)$ (b) $(2, -1)$ and $(5, 1)$

(c) $(-1, -\sqrt{2}, 2 + \sqrt{2})$ and $(\sqrt{2}, \sqrt{2} - 1)$

(d) $(\pi, 7)$ and $(\pi, -\sqrt{2})$ (e) $(0, 0)$ and $(1, m)$

(f) $(a, 0)$ and $(0, b)$, where $a \neq 0 \neq b$

(g) (x_1, y_1) and (x_2, y_2) (h) (x_0, y_0) and $(x_0 + 1, y_0 + 1)$

3. Find the slope and sketch the line whose equation is

(a) $x + y = 9$ (b) $x - y = 9$

(c) $3x + y = -2$ (d) $x + y = -2$

(e) $6x - 5y = 15$ (f) $\dfrac{2x}{3} + \dfrac{5y}{6} = \dfrac{1}{4}$

(g) $\sqrt{3}\,x + \sqrt{6}\,y = \sqrt{2}$

4. At what point do the lines with equations $x = 2$ and $y = 3$ meet? Sketch the lines.

5. Show algebraically that the lines with equations $2x + 3y = 5$ and $4x + 6y + 7 = 0$ do not intersect. Then sketch the lines.

6. Find the points of intersection of the following pairs of lines. Sketch the lines in parts a, b, c, and d.

(a) $3x - 2y = 5$ and $5x + 7y = -2$

(b) $y = 2x - 7$ and $x + 2y = 5$

(c) $7x - 3y = 11$ and $21x - 9y = 30$

(d) $x = 5$ and $2x + 3y = 5$ (e) $x = a$ and $y = b$

(f) $ax + by = c$ and $Ax + By = C$, where $aB - Ab \neq 0$

7. Show that the equations $x - 3y = 7$ and $2x - 6y - 14 = 0$ are equivalent. In other words, if x and y satisfy either of these equations then they satisfy the other.

8. Show that the equations $Ax + By = C$ and $kAx + kBy = kC$, where $k \neq 0$, are equivalent. Prove that if one equation represents a straight line, so also does the other.

28

9. Find two points on the line whose parametric equations are

$$\begin{cases} x = 4 + \dfrac{2}{\sqrt{5}}d, \\[2mm] y = -2 + \dfrac{1}{\sqrt{5}}d. \end{cases}$$

What is a linear equation of the line?

10. Eliminate the parameter d from the pair of parametric equations

$$\begin{cases} x = -1 + \dfrac{1}{\sqrt{2}}d, \\[2mm] y = 5 + \dfrac{-1}{\sqrt{2}}d, \end{cases}$$

to get a linear equation of the same line.

11. Show that if parametric equations of a line are

$$\begin{cases} x = x_0 + c_1d, \\ y = y_0 + c_2d, \end{cases}$$

then $c_2x - c_1y = c_2x_0 - c_1y_0$ is a linear equation of the line.

12. A linear equation of a line is $3x + 4y = 12$. What are direction cosines of the line? What are a pair of parametric equations for the line?

1-10. PARALLEL AND PERPENDICULAR LINES

The concept of slope is a convenient tool for studying parallel and perpendicular lines. The main objection to its use is that not all lines have slope, so that vertical lines must be discussed separately. However, since vertical lines have such simple equations there is no real problem.

THEOREM 1-7

If l_1 and l_2 are nonvertical lines and have respective equations

$$a_1x + b_1y + c_1 = 0, \qquad a_2x + b_2y + c_2 = 0,$$

then they are parallel or coincide if and only if they have the same slope. That is, if m_1 and m_2 are the slopes of l_1 and l_2, respectively, then

$$m_1 = -\frac{a_1}{b_1} = -\frac{a_2}{b_2} = m_2.$$

29

A proof, based on the properties of similar triangles, is left to the student. A separate argument must be made for vertical lines. Suppose l_1 is vertical. How do you tell whether or not l_2 is parallel to l_1?

Consider now perpendicular lines. A horizontal and a vertical line are perpendicular, and this is the only pair of perpendicular lines, where one of the lines does not have slope.

THEOREM 1-8

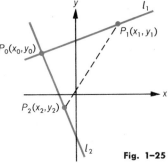

Suppose that lines l_1 and l_2 have slopes m_1 and m_2, respectively. Then l_1 is perpendicular to l_2 if and only if

$$m_1 = -\frac{1}{m_2}$$

or, equivalently, $m_1 m_2 = -1$.

Fig. 1–25

Proof. We shall use the idea of Problem 10, p. 11, to make a proof. Let $P_0 = P(x_0, y_0)$ be the point of intersection of l_1 and l_2, as in Fig. 1–25. Choose P_1 on l_1 so that $P_1 \neq P_0$ and $P_1 = P(x_1, y_1)$. Choose P_2 on l_2 so that $P_2 \neq P_0$ and $P_2 = P(x_2, y_2)$. The slopes of l_1 and l_2 are, respectively,

$$m_1 = \frac{y_1 - y_0}{x_1 - x_0} \quad \text{and} \quad m_2 = \frac{y_2 - y_0}{x_2 - x_0}.$$

If $l_1 \perp l_2$, then by the Pythagorean Theorem

$$|P_0 P_1|^2 + |P_0 P_2|^2 = |P_1 P_2|^2. \tag{1}$$

By the distance-formula equation, (1) can be expressed as

$$(x_1 - x_0)^2 + (y_1 - y_0)^2 + (x_2 - x_0)^2 + (y_2 - y_0)^2 = (x_2 - x_1)^2 + (y_2 - y_1)^2. \tag{2}$$

Squaring the differences in (2) and simplifying, we get

$$-x_1 x_0 + x_0^2 - y_1 y_0 + y_0^2 - x_2 x_0 - y_2 y_0 = -x_2 x_1 - y_2 y_1. \tag{3}$$

By the distributive property, we obtain

$$(x_1 - x_0)(x_2 - x_0) + (y_1 - y_0)(y_2 - y_0) = 0. \tag{4}$$

Equation (4) can then be written as

$$\frac{(y_1 - y_0)}{(x_1 - x_0)} \frac{(y_2 - y_0)}{(x_2 - x_0)} = -1 \quad \text{or} \quad m_1 m_2 = -1. \tag{5}$$

This proves that if $l_1 \perp l_2$, then $m_1 m_2 = -1$.

30

We leave it to the student to show that each step of the proof is reversible so that equation (5) implies equation (1). This will show that if $m_1 m_2 = -1$, then $l_1 \perp l_2$. Note that $x_1 - x_0$ and $x_2 - x_0$ are not zero. Why?

EXAMPLES

1. A line is parallel to the line $2x + 3y = 5$ and passes through $(-1, 3)$. (See Fig. 1–26.) Find an equation for the line.

The slope of the line is $-\frac{2}{3}$. Hence the desired line has an equation

$$y - 3 = -\tfrac{2}{3}(x + 1)$$

or, equivalently,

$$2x + 3y = 7.$$

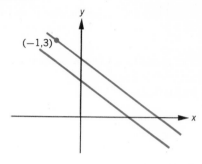

Fig. 1–26

2. The lines $3x - 5y = 1$ and $6x - 10y + 7 = 0$ are parallel because both have slope $\frac{3}{5}$. (See Fig. 1–27.) The first line has an equation

$$y = \tfrac{3}{5}x - \tfrac{1}{5},$$

and the second has

$$y = \tfrac{3}{5}x + \tfrac{7}{10}.$$

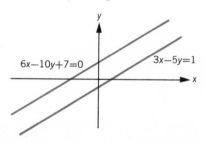

Fig. 1–27

3. Find an equation of the line that contains $(1, 5)$ and is perpendicular to the line $2x - 3y + 6 = 0$, as shown in Fig. 1–28.

The given line has slope $\frac{2}{3}$. By Theorem 1–8, a perpendicular to this line must have slope $-\frac{3}{2}$. Hence the line through $(1, 5)$ perpendicular to the given line is

$$y - 5 = -\tfrac{3}{2}(x - 1)$$

or

$$3x + 2y = 13.$$

The two previous theorems imply the following theorem, which includes the cases of horizontal and vertical lines.

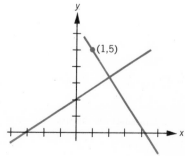

Fig. 1–28

31

THEOREM 1-9

The lines l_1 and l_2,

$$l_1: \quad a_1x + b_1y + c_1 = 0, \qquad l_2: \quad a_2x + b_2y + c_2 = 0,$$

are parallel (or identical) if and only if there is a number $k \neq 0$ such that

$$a_2 = ka_1 \quad \text{and} \quad b_2 = kb_1.$$

They are perpendicular if and only if

$$a_1a_2 + b_1b_2 = 0.$$

The proof is left to the student.

EXAMPLES

4. The lines $7x + 5y = 3$ and $10x - 14y = 0$ are perpendicular because

$$(7)(10) + (5)(-14) = 0.$$

5. The line $ax + by = k$ is parallel (or identical) to $ax + by = c$, regardless of what number k is.

Similarly, $bx - ay = k$ is perpendicular to $ax + by = c$, regardless of what number k is.

6. Find the line which is perpendicular to the line $4x + 7y = 5$ and which passes through $(-1, 2)$.

The line $7x - 4y = k$ is perpendicular to the given line. If it passes through $(-1, 2)$, then

$$7(-1) - 4(2) = k = -15.$$

Hence the desired line has an equation

$$7x - 4y = -15.$$

Problems

1. Sketch the graphs of the following lines. Which pairs are parallel? perpendicular? identical?

(a) $3x + 2y = 0$ (b) $2x - 3y = 7$ (c) $4x + 6y = 5$

(d) $6x = -4y$ (e) $3x + 7y = 6$ (f) $15x + 35y = 31$

(g) $x = 5$ (h) $x = k$ (i) $y = -3$

(j) $7y + 21 = 0$ (k) $7x = 3y$ (l) $4x - 6y = 0$

2. Sketch some of the lines with an equation $3x - 4y = k$, for different values of k.

3. Consider all the lines $ax + by = k$, where a and b are fixed, given numbers and k can have different values. How do these lines compare with all the lines $bx - ay = k$?

4. Using slope, show that the points $(1, -1)$, $(-\frac{39}{25}, 7)$, and $(\frac{29}{4}, 1)$ are vertices of a right triangle.

5. Show that the lines $2x + 3y = 0$, $2x + 3y = 5$, $x - y = 1$, and $3x = 3y - 8$ meet in four points which are vertices of a parallelogram.

6. The line $5y + 3x = 47$ is tangent to a circle with center at $(1, 2)$. Find the point of tangency.

7. The hypotenuse of a right triangle is a subset of the line $2x + 3y = 5$. The right angle has its vertex at $(1, -1)$. If one of the other vertices is at $(-2, 3)$, find the third vertex.

8. What is the perpendicular distance from $y = 7x + 7$ to $(6\frac{1}{2}, 4\frac{1}{2})$?

*9. Prove Theorem 1–9.

*10. Use the distance formula to prove that the lines $y = m_1x$ and $y = m_2x$ are perpendicular, where $m_1 \neq 0 \neq m_2$, if and only if $m_1m_2 = -1$. (See accompanying figure.) [*Hint:* Consider the triangle with vertices $(0, 0)$, $(1, m_1)$, $(1, m_2)$.]

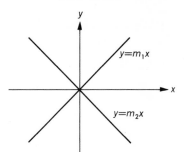

*11. Show that if $a > b > 0$, then

$$(0, 0), \quad (a, 0), \quad (a + \sqrt{a^2 - b^2}, b), \quad (\sqrt{a^2 - b^2}, b)$$

are vertices of a rhombus. Then show that the diagonals are perpendicular.

*12. A triangle has vertices $(2, -1)$, $(-2, 3)$, and $(0, -3)$. Find its area by finding the length of a base and an altitude.

*13. Show that the altitudes of the triangle whose vertices are $(-1, 2)$, $(4, 3)$, and $(1, -2)$ intersect in a point. Find the coordinates of the point of intersection.

*14. Find the perpendicular distance from (x_1, y_1) to the line $ax + by + c = 0$.

*15. Find equations of the three altitudes of the triangle whose vertices are (x_1, y_1), (x_2, y_2), and (x_3, y_3).

SUMMARY

In this chapter we have concerned ourselves with the plane and plane geometric figures. One of the aims of the chapter is to show the relation between geometry and algebra. This relation is made possible by coordinatization of the line and the plane. In your previous study of geometry, line and point were considered to be undefined objects. Here we have identified "point" with an ordered pair (x, y) of real numbers by establishing a one-to-one correspondence between the set of points in the plane and the set of ordered pairs of real numbers. Briefly we have an algebraic model of geometry, or if you prefer, a geometric model of algebra, as shown by the correspondences on the following page.

33

Geometry		Algebra
Line	$\longleftrightarrow$	{Real numbers {A coordinate system on a line
Point	$\longleftrightarrow$	{An ordered pair of real numbers {The coordinates of the point
Plane	$\longleftrightarrow$	{Ordered pairs of real numbers {A coordinate system on a plane

We list below some of the most important formulas, theorems, and definitions.

1. The distance formula: $|P_1P_2| = \sqrt{(x_1 - x_2)^2 + (y_1 - y_2)^2}$.

2. x-direction cosine $= \dfrac{x_1 - x_0}{d} = c_1,$ y-direction cosine $= \dfrac{y_1 - y_0}{d} = c_2,$

   where d is the directed distance.

3. $c_1^2 + c_2^2 = 1$.

4. Parametric equations of a line with origin (x_0, y_0) and parameter d:

$$\begin{cases} x = x_0 + c_1 d, \\ y = y_0 + c_2 d. \end{cases}$$

5. Linear equation of a line: $Ax + By + C = 0$.

6. Slope of a line: $m = \dfrac{y_2 - y_1}{x_2 - x_1}$.

7. Two lines are parallel or identical if and only if they have the same slope.

8. Two lines both of which have slopes are perpendicular if and only if the product of their slopes is -1.

9. Equation of a line containing (x_0, y_0) with slope m: $y - y_0 = m(x - x_0)$.

10. Slope-intercept form of a line: $y = mx + b$, where $m = $ slope, $b = $ y-intercept.

Review Problems

1. What are parametric equations of a line containing the points $(5, -4)$ and $(-2, 3)$?

2. A line contains the point $(7, -3)$; $c_1 = 0$. What is a linear equation of the line?

3. Determine the slope and y-intercept of the lines whose equations are:

   (a) $5x - 4y = 10$ (b) $y = -2$

   (c) $\frac{1}{4}x + \frac{8}{3}y = \frac{3}{8}$ (d) $ax + by = c, b \neq 0$

4. Write an equation of the line parallel to $2x - 7y = 8$ and containing the origin.

5. What is an equation of a line perpendicular to $5x - y = 4$ and containing the point $(2, 3)$?

6. Find the point of intersection of the perpendicular lines in Problem 5.

7. A line has y-intercept b and x-intercept a where neither a nor b are zero. Show that an equation of the line has the form $x/a + y/b = 1$.

8. What are the x- and y-intercepts of $3x + 4y = 12$?

9. Prove that if (x_0, y_0) is a point on the line $ax + by + c = 0$, then so are $(x_0 + b, y_0 - a)$ and $(x_0 - b, y_0 + a)$.

10. A line has y-intercept 3 and is perpendicular to the line $x + 2y = 7$. Find an equation of the line.

11. Use the formula for the distance between two points and the triangle inequality to argue that the points $(-4, 4)$, $(-2, 1)$, and $(6, -11)$ are collinear.

12. If l is a line with direction cosines

$$c_1 = \frac{2\sqrt{5}}{5}, \qquad c_2 = \frac{-\sqrt{5}}{5},$$

what is the slope of the line?

13. Find the intersection of the lines $3y + x + 6 = 0$ and $5y + 2x - 4 = 0$.

14. Find the intersection of the lines $a_1x + b_1y + c_1 = 0$ and $a_2x + b_2y + c_2 = 0$. State the condition under which the lines will be parallel.

15. Determine the real number k so that the two lines, $5x - 3y = 12$ and $kx - y = 2$, will be

(a) parallel.   (b) perpendicular.

16. Show that the set of all points equidistant from $(-1, 2)$ and $(2, -3)$ is a straight line. Find its equation and draw the line.

*17. Find the equations of the medians of the triangle with vertices $(-4, -6)$, $(0, 10)$, $(4, 2)$. Show that the medians meet in a point.

*18. A triangle has vertices at $(0, 0)$, (a, b), and (c, d). (See accompanying figure.) Prove analytically that a line containing the midpoints of two of the sides of the triangle is parallel to the third side.

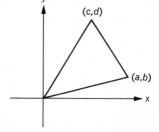

*19. A line that contains the origin is perpendicular to and intersects a second line at the point $(-2, 3)$. What is an equation of the second line?

*20. Find the coordinates of the points that trisect the segment whose endpoints are (a, b) and (c, d).

HISTORICAL NOTE

René Descartes (1596–1650)

Descartes is universally acclaimed as the founder of analytic geometry. He is also a central figure in philosophy, where his writings (principally his *Discourse on Method*) have had a lasting effect. He lived during a period of intense intellectual ferment. A few of the great whose lives overlapped his are Fermat, Pascal, Galileo, Newton, and Leibniz. In philosophy he was apparently much influenced by the mathematics and the science of his day, for he attempted to formulate a philosophy with a logical flavor based on a minimum of assumptions. The phrase, *Cogito ergo sum* (I think, therefore I am), expresses his goal of starting from a point grounded in experience.

His one book on mathematics, *Geometry*, was published in 1637 as an appendix to the *Discourse on Method*. Its main purpose was to show

how a systematic use of coordinates (real numbers) could vastly simplify geometric arguments. In it he gave a simple technique of great flexibility for the solution of a variety of problems.

One should realize, with all deference to Descartes, that the idea of coordinates was not conceived by him in one magnificent stroke. He had numerous predecessors who had made partial use of algebra in geometry. One can find instances of the use of coordinates in Greek geometry, and his contemporary, the great Pierre Fermat, was accustomed to using algebra and coordinates. Nevertheless, the main idea of fixing each point in the plane by specifying its coordinates was all Descartes' own. His book was tremendously influential, since it opened the door to new problems. Without analytic geometry it is inconceivable that physics could have advanced as it did, or that calculus could have been invented as early (by Isaac Newton in 1666 and Gottfried Leibniz a bit later).

Moreover, he greatly simplified algebraic notation, improving upon the already quite modern notation of Francois Viète. Descartes was the first to consider curves with an arbitrary equation.

37

VECTORS IN

2

THE PLANE

2-1. INTRODUCTION

In this chapter we shall use the ideas of Chapter 1 concerning the plane to help develop a new mathematical concept, *vector*. If you have studied physics, you have encountered this concept in that part of physics concerned with forces and equilibrium.

Physicists were responsible for first conceiving the idea of a vector, but the mathematical concept of vectors has become important in its own right and has extremely wide application, not only in the sciences but in mathematics as well.

2-2. ARROWS

Imagine a picture of a line segment with endpoints P_1 and P_2 and with the point of an arrow at P_2, as in Fig. 2-1. There are several interpretations that we may give to the arrow. First, the arrow suggests *motion*. We might think of an object which *moves* or is *displaced* from the position P_1 to the position P_2. Second, we might think of the arrow as giving the position of P_2 with respect to P_1. Third, we might think of the arrow as a *force*, namely a force applied at P_1 in the direction of P_2 and whose magnitude is proportional to the length of the arrow. Finally, we may think of the arrow as a *velocity*, that is, if a point moves with constant speed along a line and at some instant is at P_1 and at a *unit time* later is at P_2, then the arrow denotes the velocity of the moving point. All of these applications arise in mathematics and physics. Other applications occur in chemistry, biology, economics, and psychology.

DEFINITION 2-1

If P_1 and P_2 are points, then the ordered pair of points (P_1, P_2) is called an *arrow*. The first point of the ordered pair is the *initial point* of the arrow and the second point is the *terminal point* or *endpoint* of the arrow. The magnitude of an arrow (P_1, P_2) is the length $|P_1P_2|$ of the segment $\overline{P_1P_2}$.

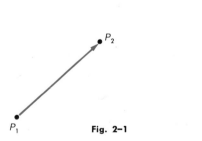

Fig. 2-1

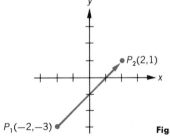

Fig. 2-2

EXAMPLE 1

The arrow (P_1, P_2) has initial point $P_1 = P(-2, -3)$ and endpoint $P_2 = P(2, 1)$. (See Fig. 2-2.) The magnitude of (P_1, P_2) is

$$|P_1P_2| = \sqrt{[2 - (-2)]^2 + [1 - (-3)]^2} = \sqrt{4^2 + 4^2} = 4\sqrt{2}.$$

Next consider two arrows, (P_1, P_2) and (Q_1, Q_2), as in Fig. 2-3, and suppose that these two arrows have the same direction and the same magnitude. Are these arrows to be regarded as *equal* in some sense? Clearly they are not equal in the strict sense, since the arrows are two different ordered pairs of points. If the arrows are interpreted as forces, they have different physical effects because they are applied at different points. Since we want to reserve equality to mean identity, we shall say that these arrows are *equivalent*.

DEFINITION 2-2

Two arrows are *equivalent* if they have the same direction and the same magnitude. The set of all arrows equivalent to a given arrow is an *equivalence class* of arrows.

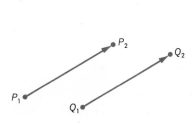

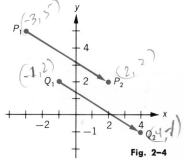

Fig. 2-3

Fig. 2-4

EXAMPLE 2

The arrows $(P_1, P_2) = ((-3, 5), (2, 2))$ and $(Q_1, Q_2) = ((-1, 2), (4, -1))$ are equivalent arrows. (See Fig. 2-4.) To prove this, we observe that

$$|P_1P_2| = |Q_1Q_2| = \sqrt{34}.$$

Furthermore, choosing P_1 as the origin and the distance from P_1 to P_2 positive, we find that the direction cosines of (P_1, P_2) are

$$c_1 = \frac{2 - (-3)}{\sqrt{34}} = \frac{5}{\sqrt{34}} \quad \text{and} \quad c_2 = \frac{2 - 5}{\sqrt{34}} = \frac{-3}{\sqrt{34}}.$$

Similarly, for the arrow (Q_1, Q_2) with Q_1 as the origin and the distance from Q_1 to Q_2 positive, we find that

$$c_1 = \frac{4 - (-1)}{\sqrt{34}} = \frac{5}{\sqrt{34}} \quad \text{and} \quad c_2 = \frac{-1 - 2}{\sqrt{34}} = \frac{-3}{\sqrt{34}}.$$

41

Since the arrows have the same magnitude and the same direction (the same direction cosines), they are equivalent arrows and are in the same equivalence class.

Figure 2–5 illustrates several arrows, (A, B), (C, D), (E, F), (G, H), (H, I), and (J, K), which are equivalent to one another.

It is helpful to conceive of an arrow whose initial point and endpoint are the same. Such an arrow has zero magnitude and its direction is undefined. Such an arrow might be called a *zero arrow* or a *null arrow*.

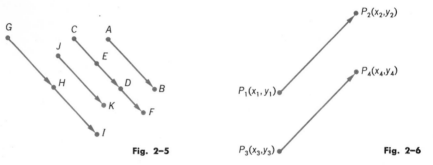

Fig. 2–5 Fig. 2–6

The following theorem is fundamental because it tells, in terms of the coordinates of points, when two arrows are equivalent.

THEOREM 2–1

If the points P_1, P_2, P_3, P_4 have the coordinates shown in Fig. 2–6, then the arrows (P_1, P_2) and (P_3, P_4) are equivalent if and only if

$$x_2 - x_1 = x_4 - x_3,$$
$$y_2 - y_1 = y_4 - y_3. \tag{1}$$

Proof. Suppose that equations (1) are true. Then the magnitudes of the arrows are the same, that is

$$d = \sqrt{(x_2 - x_1)^2 + (y_2 - y_1)^2} = \sqrt{(x_4 - x_3)^2 + (y_4 - y_3)^2}. \tag{2}$$

The direction cosines are also the same:

$$c_1 = \frac{x_2 - x_1}{d} = \frac{x_4 - x_3}{d},$$
$$c_2 = \frac{y_2 - y_1}{d} = \frac{y_4 - y_3}{d}. \tag{3}$$

Therefore the two arrows are equivalent.

Conversely, suppose the two arrows are equivalent. Then they will have the same magnitude and direction. Therefore, equations (2) and (3) will be true, and these equations imply equations (1).

42

Problems

1. (a) The arrow (P_1, P_2) is the ordered pair of points $((2, 3), (-1, 4))$. Represent this arrow in the plane and draw pictures of several other arrows that are in the equivalence class of arrows determined by the arrow (P_1, P_2).

   (b) Represent the arrow $(P_3, P_4) = ((3, 7), (8, -1))$ in the plane and draw pictures of several other arrows that are in this equivalence class of arrows.

2. The arrow (P, Q) is the ordered pair of points $((1, -2), (5, 4))$. (R, S) is an arrow equivalent to (P, Q), and R has coordinates $(-4, 1)$. What are the coordinates of S? Draw (R, S).

3. $(P, Q) = ((2, 3), (-2, 1))$. (X, Y) is equivalent to (P, Q), and Y has coordinates $(7, 0)$. Determine the coordinates of X.

4. What are the coordinates of the terminal point of an arrow equivalent to the arrows in Problem 3 if the initial point of the arrow is $(0, 0)$?

5. $(P_1, P_2) = ((-1, 2), (5, 6))$ and $(P_3, P_4) = ((2, -2), (8, 2))$. Is (P_1, P_2) equivalent to (P_3, P_4)? Draw a picture of the arrows.

6. Show that $(P_1, P_2) = ((1, 1), (4, 5))$ and $(P_3, P_4) = ((-2, 2), (-5, -2))$ have the same magnitude and lie on parallel lines but are not equivalent. Draw a picture.

7. An arrow has initial point $(3, 4)$ and direction cosines, $\check{c}_1 = \frac{3}{5}$ and $c_2 = \frac{4}{5}$. If the arrow has magnitude 5, what are the coordinates of the terminal point? Sketch the arrow.

8. How would you define *equal* arrows? Are equal arrows equivalent arrows? Are equivalent arrows necessarily equal arrows?

9. How many arrows are determined by 3 noncollinear points? How many arrows are determined by 4 points, no three of which are collinear?

10. Give a geometric argument that if two arrows have the same initial point and are not collinear, then they determine a unique parallelogram in which the two arrows form a pair of adjacent sides of the parallelogram.

11. Show that if (P_1, P_2) and (Q_1, Q_2) are equivalent, then so are (P_1, Q_1) and (P_2, Q_2). (See figure.)

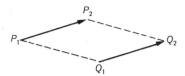

2-3. VECTORS

It is evident that given an arrow, there are infinitely many arrows equivalent to the given one. Furthermore, there are infinitely many different equivalence classes of arrows. Because all arrows in an equivalence class have the same direction and magnitude, we shall regard each equivalence class as a single object which we call a *vector*.

DEFINITION 2–3

A *vector* is an equivalence class of arrows. Any arrow of an equivalence class of arrows may represent the vector. The *magnitude* of a vector is the magnitude of any arrow in the equivalence class, which represents the vector.

Sometimes, for simplicity, we shall refer to an arrow as a *vector* instead of using the lengthy phrase, "*the vector represented by the arrow.*"

Notation. We shall denote vectors by letters in boldface type, for example, **a**, **b**, **r**, **s**, and **v**. The vector represented by the arrow (P_1, P_2) will be denoted by $\overrightarrow{P_1P_2}$. The magnitude of **a** will be denoted by $|\mathbf{a}|$.

Therefore a vector is a whole equivalence class of arrows. Each vector contains arrows of the same magnitude and direction. We can now say what we mean by the statement, *two vectors*, **u** *and* **v**, *are equal*; **u** = **v**. We mean that they contain the same arrows, that is, the two sets of arrows are the same. Another way of saying this is that the arrows of **u** and the arrows of **v** have the same direction and magnitude.

DEFINITION 2–4

The *null vector* is the vector whose magnitude is zero. We denote the null vector by **0**.

The null vector is the set of all null arrows, that is, the set of all arrows of zero magnitude.

The arrow most commonly used to represent a vector is the arrow whose initial point is the origin. This arrow is given the special name *position vector* (see Fig. 2–7).

DEFINITION 2–5

The *position vector* for any given vector is the arrow, in the vector, whose initial point is at the origin.

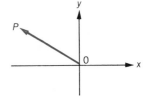

Fig. 2–7

Since we can visualize a vector by picturing any arrow in its equivalence class, it is convenient to visualize a vector by picturing its position vector (**v** in Fig. 2–8). That is, we think of a vector as described by an arrow emanating from the origin. Figure 2–8 illustrates this concept. We will sometimes use vector notation for the position vector.

44

Vectors as we have defined them are called *free vectors*. They are called free vectors because any arrow in a vector can be "moved" to coincide with any other arrow in the vector.

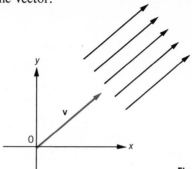

Fig. 2-8

Problems

1. Vectors are represented by the following ordered pairs of points. Determine the magnitude of each vector. Sketch each arrow.

(a) $((7, -1), (4, 3))$ (b) $((0, 0), (1, 0))$ (c) $((0, 1), (1,0))$

(d) $((3, -4), (3, 5))$ (e) $((6, 5), (-1, 5))$ (f) $((11, -2), (51, 7))$

2. Represent each vector in Problem 1 by a position vector. What are the coordinates of the endpoint of each position vector?

3. What is the magnitude of a position vector $\overrightarrow{OP}$ if $P = (12, 5)$? What are the coordinates of point P' if $\overrightarrow{OP}$ and $\overrightarrow{OP'}$ have the same magnitude but are opposite in direction?

4. The vector $\mathbf{v}$ is represented by the arrow (P_1, P_2), and $\mathbf{r}$ is represented by the arrow (Q_1, Q_2). If $\mathbf{v} = \mathbf{r}$, what can you conclude?

5. If (X, Y) represents $\mathbf{a}$, (R, S) represents $\mathbf{b}$, and (X, Y) is equivalent to (R, S), what can you conclude?

6. Suppose that O, P_1, and P_2 are points, as shown in the figure. How does $|\overrightarrow{OP_2}|$ compare with $|\overrightarrow{OP_1}| + |\overrightarrow{P_1P_2}|$?

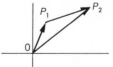

7. Is it possible for the points O, P_1, and P_2 in Problem 6 to be such that $|\overrightarrow{OP_2}| = 0$?

8. What must be the condition for the points of Problem 6 to be such that $|\overrightarrow{OP_1}| + |\overrightarrow{P_1P_2}| = |\overrightarrow{OP_2}|$?

9. Show that if (P_1, P_2) is an arrow and P_1 and P_2 are the points (x_1, y_1) and (x_2, y_2), then (P_1, P_2) is equivalent to the position vector, $\overrightarrow{OP}$, where $P = (x_2 - x_1, y_2 - y_1)$.

45

2-4. ADDITION OF VECTORS

In this section we shall see that vectors have many algebraic properties similar to the properties of the real numbers. One can add and subtract vectors and multiply them by real numbers.

If $\mathbf{v}$ is any vector and P is any point, then there is a unique point Q such that $\mathbf{v} = \overrightarrow{PQ}$. We shall use this fact in our definition of *addition* of vectors.

DEFINITION 2-6

Suppose $\mathbf{a}$ and $\mathbf{b}$ are any two vectors. Choose point A so that $\mathbf{a} = \overrightarrow{OA}$. Choose point C so that $\mathbf{b} = \overrightarrow{AC}$. The *sum*, $\mathbf{a} + \mathbf{b}$, of $\mathbf{a}$ and $\mathbf{b}$ is the vector $\overrightarrow{OC}$ (Fig. 2-9).

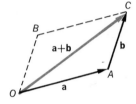

Fig. 2-9

Remarks

1. If O, A, and C are not collinear, they are three of the vertices of a parallelogram $OACB$ such that $\mathbf{b} = \overrightarrow{OB}$ and the segment OC is a diagonal of the parallelogram. Because vectors can represent forces in physics, our definition of addition of vectors corresponds to the "parallelogram law" for the addition of forces. Sometimes the sum of two vectors is called the *resultant* of the vectors, a terminology borrowed from physics.

2. Although we denote the sum of $\mathbf{a}$ and $\mathbf{b}$ by $\mathbf{a} + \mathbf{b}$, using the familiar $+$ sign, you should realize that this is not ordinary addition of real numbers.

3. It would be possible at this point to prove that vector addition is commutative, but we shall not do so, since commutativity will follow from the next theorem.

4. Definition 2-6 applies even if $\mathbf{a}$ or $\mathbf{b}$ is the null vector $\mathbf{0}$, or if they have either the same direction or opposite directions.

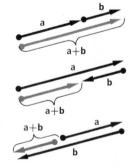

Figure 2-10 shows $\mathbf{a} + \mathbf{b}$ when the vectors $\mathbf{a}$ and $\mathbf{b}$ have either the same direction or opposite directions.

Fig. 2-10

The following theorem is fundamental in problems dealing with vector addition.

THEOREM 2-2

If $\overrightarrow{OP_1}$ and $\overrightarrow{OP_2}$ are vectors represented by position vectors (O, P_1) and (O, P_2), with endpoints (x_1, y_1) and (x_2, y_2), respectively (as in Fig. 2–11), then $\overrightarrow{OP_1} + \overrightarrow{OP_2}$ is represented by the position vector with endpoint P whose coordinates are $(x_1 + x_2, y_1 + y_2)$.

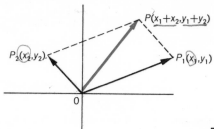

Fig. 2–11

Proof. Let $\overrightarrow{OP}$ be the sum of $\overrightarrow{OP_1}$ and $\overrightarrow{OP_2}$ and suppose that P has coordinates (x, y). We must have $\overrightarrow{OP_1} = \overrightarrow{P_2P}$.

Therefore by Theorem 2–1,

$$x_1 - 0 = x - x_2, \quad y_1 - 0 = y - y_2;$$

and hence

$$x = x_1 + x_2, \quad y = y_1 + y_2.$$

Corollary

Addition of vectors is commutative,

$$\mathbf{a} + \mathbf{b} = \mathbf{b} + \mathbf{a}.$$

Proof. If $\mathbf{a} = \overrightarrow{OP_1}$ and $\mathbf{b} = \overrightarrow{OP_2}$, in the notation of the theorem, then $\mathbf{a} + \mathbf{b} = \overrightarrow{OP}$ and $\mathbf{b} + \mathbf{a} = \overrightarrow{OP}$.

Sometimes we will want to discuss a vector that is three times as long, or k times as long, as another vector. To be able to do this we need the following definition.

DEFINITION 2-7

If k is a real number and $\mathbf{v}$ is any vector then $k\mathbf{v} = \mathbf{v}k$ is the vector such that

(a) $k\mathbf{v} = \mathbf{0}$ if $k = 0$.

(b) $k\mathbf{v}$ is a vector in the *same* direction as $\mathbf{v}$ and with magnitude $k|\mathbf{v}|$ if $k > 0$.

(c) $k\mathbf{v}$ is a vector in the *opposite* direction from $\mathbf{v}$ and with magnitude $|k|\,|\mathbf{v}|$ if $k < 0$.

47

Remarks

1. The vector $(-1)\mathbf{v}$ is denoted by $-\mathbf{v}$.

2. The real number k of Definition 2-7 is often called a *scalar*.

EXAMPLE

In Fig. 2-12 arrows representing $\mathbf{v}$, $\frac{1}{2}\mathbf{v}$, $-\mathbf{v}$, $-2\mathbf{v}$, and $3\mathbf{v}$ are shown.

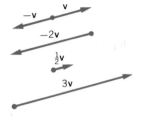

Fig. 2-12

Problems

1. One vector has magnitude 2. A second vector has magnitude 5 and direction opposite to the first vector. What is the magnitude of their sum? What can you say about the direction of the sum of the vectors?

2. The arrows representing two vectors are at right angles to each other. One vector has magnitude 4 and the other has magnitude 5. What is the magnitude of their sum?

3. $\overrightarrow{OP}$ is a position vector to the point $P = (3, 0)$. What is the terminal point of the position vector for $4\overrightarrow{OP}$? What is the terminal point of the position vector for $-3\overrightarrow{OP}$? What is the terminal point of the position vector for $(4\overrightarrow{OP} + -3\overrightarrow{OP})$?

4. $\overrightarrow{OQ}$ has a position vector with terminal point $Q = (2, 3)$. What are the coordinates of the terminal point for the position vectors for

   (a) $2\overrightarrow{OQ}$?   (b) $-5\overrightarrow{OQ}$?   (c) $k\overrightarrow{OQ}$, where k is a real number?

5. If $\mathbf{v}$ is any vector, is there always a vector $\mathbf{r}$ such that $\mathbf{v} + \mathbf{r} = \mathbf{0}$? How would you define the vector $\mathbf{r}$, if it exists?

6. Draw a picture of two position vectors for $\mathbf{a}$ and $\mathbf{b}$. Sketch the arrows representing $-\mathbf{b}$ and $[\mathbf{a} + (-\mathbf{b})]$. What is $[\mathbf{a} + (-\mathbf{b})] + \mathbf{b}$?

7. If $\mathbf{r}$ and $\mathbf{t}$ are any vectors, is there a vector $\mathbf{s}$ such that $\mathbf{r} + \mathbf{s} = \mathbf{t}$?

8. Define subtraction for vectors.

9. If A, B, and C are points as in the figure at the right, give an argument that shows that $(\overrightarrow{AB} + \overrightarrow{BC}) + \overrightarrow{CA} = 0$.

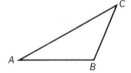

10. In the figure at the right, which of the following statements are true?

   (a) $\overrightarrow{XY} + \overrightarrow{YZ} = \overrightarrow{XZ}$
   (b) $\overrightarrow{XY} - \overrightarrow{XZ} = \overrightarrow{YZ}$
   (c) $\overrightarrow{XZ} - \overrightarrow{YZ} = \overrightarrow{XY}$

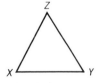

48

11. Points P_1 and P_2 have coordinates $(2, -8)$ and $(-5, 10)$, respectively. P is a point such that

$$\overrightarrow{OP_1} + \overrightarrow{OP_2} = \overrightarrow{OP}.$$

What are the coordinates of P?

12. Q and R are points whose coordinates are $(11, 2)$ and $(8, 5)$, respectively. Determine the coordinates of a point X such that $\overrightarrow{OQ} + \overrightarrow{OX} = \overrightarrow{OR}$.

13. If $P_1 = P(-5, 1)$, $P_2 = P(2, 6)$, and $P_3 = P(6, 2)$, find the coordinates of a point P such that

$$(\overrightarrow{OP_1} + \overrightarrow{OP_2}) + \overrightarrow{OP_3} = \overrightarrow{OP}.$$

*14. If **a** and **b** are vectors which have either the same or opposite directions, and **a** $\neq$ **0**, prove that there is a unique real number k such that $k\mathbf{a} = \mathbf{b}$.

2-5. UNIT VECTORS

One of the most important theorems concerning vectors is that every vector in the plane can be represented as the sum of multiples of two fixed vectors which do not have either the same direction or opposite directions.

THEOREM 2-3

If **a** and **b** are two nonzero vectors which do not have either the same or opposite directions, and **c** is any other vector, then there exist unique real numbers p and q such that

$$\mathbf{c} = p\mathbf{a} + q\mathbf{b}.$$

Proof. Let **a** and **b** have two nonzero position vectors with endpoints A and B, respectively. (See Fig. 2–13.) By hypothesis, $\overrightarrow{OA}$ and $\overrightarrow{OB}$ do not have either the same or opposite directions. Let **c** have a position vector with endpoint C. Consider a line through C parallel to $\overrightarrow{OA}$. This line intersects line OB at Q. Consider a line through C parallel to $\overrightarrow{OB}$. The line meets line OA at P. Then $\overrightarrow{OC} = \overrightarrow{OQ} + \overrightarrow{OP}$. Since **a** and $\overrightarrow{OP}$ have either the same or opposite directions, and **b** and $\overrightarrow{OQ}$ have either the same or opposite directions, then $\overrightarrow{OP} = p\mathbf{a}$ for some unique real number p and $\overrightarrow{OQ} = q\mathbf{b}$ for some unique real number q. (Recall Definition 2–7.) Hence

$$\overrightarrow{OC} = \mathbf{c} = p\mathbf{a} + q\mathbf{b}.$$

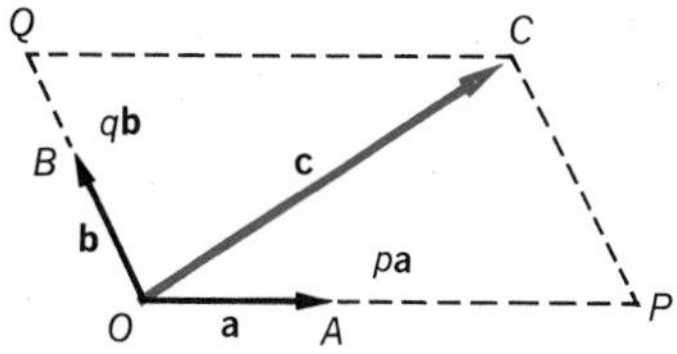

Fig. 2–13

EXAMPLE 1

The real numbers of Theorem 2–3 may be positive, negative, or zero. Figure 2–14 illustrates a situation in which q is evidently some negative real number. What must be the situation if one of the real numbers, p or q, is zero?

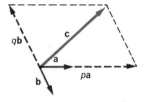

Fig. 2–14

The fixed vectors, **a** and **b**, of Theorem 2–3 are said to be a *base* for all vectors in the plane. While many pairs of vectors may be chosen as base vectors, the usual and most convenient choice of base vectors is a pair of *unit vectors* (vectors of unit length) directed, respectively, along the positive x- and y-axes. Let **i** denote the unit vector with the same direction as the positive x-axis and let **j** denote the unit vector with the same direction as the positive y-axis, as in Fig. 2–15. Then the position vector to any point $P(x, y)$ in the plane is (see Fig. 2–16)

$$\overrightarrow{OP} = \mathbf{r} = x\mathbf{i} + y\mathbf{j}.$$

DEFINITION 2–8

The *components* of **r** are the real numbers x and y such that $\mathbf{r} = x\mathbf{i} + y\mathbf{j}$. The component in the **i**-direction is x, while the component in the **j**-direction is y.

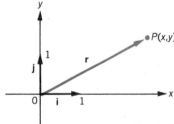

Fig. 2–15

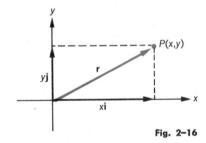

Fig. 2–16

EXAMPLE 2

The vector represented by the position vector to the point $(4, -3)$ is $4\mathbf{i} + (-3)\mathbf{j}$. The **i**-direction component is 4 and the **j**-direction component is -3.

THEOREM 2–4

Two vectors are equal if and only if they have the same components.

The proof of this theorem is left to the student.

EXAMPLE 3

If $3\mathbf{i} + y\mathbf{j} = x\mathbf{i} - \mathbf{j}$, then by Theorem 2–4 we must have $x = 3$ and $y = -1$.

THEOREM 2–5

If $\mathbf{r}_1 = x_1\mathbf{i} + y_1\mathbf{j}$ and $\mathbf{r}_2 = x_2\mathbf{i} + y_2\mathbf{j}$, then

$$\mathbf{r}_1 + \mathbf{r}_2 = (x_1 + x_2)\mathbf{i} + (y_1 + y_2)\mathbf{j}.$$

The proof is left to the student.

Problems

1. Sketch the following pairs of vectors, add them, and sketch their sum.
   - (a) $2\mathbf{i} + 3\mathbf{j}, \mathbf{i} + \mathbf{j}$
   - (b) $2\mathbf{i} + 3\mathbf{j}, -4\mathbf{i} + 2\mathbf{j}$
   - (c) $-\mathbf{i} - \mathbf{j}, -\mathbf{i} + 3\mathbf{j}$
   - (d) $\pi\mathbf{i} + \sqrt{3}\,\mathbf{j}, -2\mathbf{i} - 4\mathbf{j}$
   - (e) $\dfrac{-1}{\sqrt{2}}\mathbf{j} + \mathbf{i}, \sqrt{2}\,\mathbf{i} + \mathbf{j}$

2. What is the magnitude of each of the following vectors?
   - (a) $\mathbf{i}$
   - (b) $\mathbf{i} + \mathbf{j}$
   - (c) $\mathbf{i} + \mathbf{i}$
   - (d) $2\mathbf{i} - 3\mathbf{j}$

3. Determine x and y so that $\mathbf{v} = x\mathbf{i} + y\mathbf{j}$ satisfies $\mathbf{v} + (2\mathbf{i} - 3\mathbf{j}) = -4\mathbf{i} - 5\mathbf{j}$.

4. Solve the vector equations
   - (a) $5(\alpha\mathbf{i} + \beta\mathbf{j}) = 3\mathbf{i} - 2\mathbf{j}$
   - (b) $((2u\mathbf{i} + 3w\mathbf{j}) - \pi\mathbf{i}) + \sqrt{2}\,\mathbf{j} = -4\mathbf{i} + \mathbf{j}$

5. The coordinates of the endpoints of a segment are $(1, 5)$ and $(7, 7)$. What are the position vectors to these points? What is the sum of these two vectors? What is the position vector to the midpoint of the segment?

6. Vector $\mathbf{c}$ has a position vector to the point $(2, 7)$, $\mathbf{a}$ has a position vector to the point $(4, -1)$ and $\mathbf{b}$ has a position vector to the point $(-2, 3)$. Determine real numbers p and q such that $p\mathbf{a} + q\mathbf{b} = \mathbf{c}$. Sketch the arrows.

7. If $\mathbf{r} = \mathbf{i} - 9\mathbf{j}$, $\mathbf{a} = \mathbf{i} + 2\mathbf{j}$, and $\mathbf{b} = 5\mathbf{i} - \mathbf{j}$, determine the real numbers s and t such that

$$\mathbf{r} = s\mathbf{a} + t\mathbf{b}.$$

8. Prove Theorem 2–4.

9. Prove Theorem 2–5.

*10. Prove that if $\mathbf{v}$ is a vector of length L, and c_1 and c_2 are the direction cosines of $\mathbf{v}$, then

$$\mathbf{v} = L(c_1\mathbf{i} + c_2\mathbf{j}).$$

*11. Prove that if $\mathbf{u} = a\mathbf{i} + b\mathbf{j}$ and $\mathbf{v} = x\mathbf{i} + y\mathbf{j}$ are perpendicular, then $ax + by = 0$.

51

2-6. THEOREMS OF VECTOR ALGEBRA

We list below several important facts concerning vectors. Some are direct consequences of the definitions. Others are easily proved by means of Theorems 2–4 and 2–5. Note the similarity between these assertions for vectors and corresponding ones for real numbers.

1. The sum of two vectors is another vector and the product of a real number and a vector is another vector.

2. Vector addition is commutative, that is, if $\mathbf{a}$ and $\mathbf{b}$ are any vectors, then
$$\mathbf{a} + \mathbf{b} = \mathbf{b} + \mathbf{a}.$$

3. Multiplication of a vector by a real number is commutative:
$k\mathbf{v} = \mathbf{v}k,$ where $\mathbf{v}$ is any vector and k is a real number.

4. Vector addition is associative; that is, if $\mathbf{a}$, $\mathbf{b}$, and $\mathbf{c}$ are any vectors, then
$$\mathbf{a} + (\mathbf{b} + \mathbf{c}) = (\mathbf{a} + \mathbf{b}) + \mathbf{c}.$$

5. If r and s are real numbers, and $\mathbf{v}$ is any vector, then
$$r(s\mathbf{v}) = (rs)\mathbf{v}.$$

6. If $\mathbf{v}$ is any vector, then
$$\mathbf{v} + \mathbf{0} = \mathbf{v} \quad \text{and} \quad 1\mathbf{v} = \mathbf{v}.$$

7. Multiplication of a sum of vectors by a real number is distributive; that is, if $\mathbf{a}$ and $\mathbf{b}$ are any vectors and k is a real number, then
$$k(\mathbf{a} + \mathbf{b}) = k\mathbf{a} + k\mathbf{b}.$$

8. Multiplication of a vector by a sum of real numbers is distributive; that is, if r and s are real numbers and $\mathbf{v}$ is any vector, then
$$(r + s)\mathbf{v} = r\mathbf{v} + s\mathbf{v}.$$

9. For each vector $\mathbf{v}$ there exists a vector $\mathbf{r}$ such that
$$\mathbf{v} + \mathbf{r} = \mathbf{0}.$$

Problems

1. Sketch a picture of arrows illustrating the associative law for vector addition.

2. List the key definitions or theorems that imply Assertion 4 of Section 2–6.

3. List the key definitions or theorems that imply Assertion 5 of Section 2–6.

4. Sketch a picture of the arrows illustrating Assertion 7.

5. List the key definitions or theorems that imply Assertion 7 of Section 2–6.

6. List the key definitions or theorems that imply Assertion 8 of Section 2–6.

7. List the key definitions or theorems that imply Assertion 9 of Section 2–6.

8. If $k\mathbf{a} + 4\mathbf{a} = (-3)\mathbf{a}$, where $\mathbf{a} \neq \mathbf{0}$, what real number is k?

9. Show that $\mathbf{v} + (-1)\mathbf{v} = \mathbf{0}$.

10. Prove that $(3\mathbf{v})(-2) = (-6)\mathbf{v}$ for every vector $\mathbf{v}$.

2–7. VECTOR EQUATIONS OF LINES

In Chapter 1 we studied parametric and rectangular equations of lines. In this section we shall use vectors to represent lines. First we consider some examples.

EXAMPLES

1. A line is given by the rectangular equation $x + 2y = 6$ (Fig. 2–17). Several points on this line are

$$P_1 = P(2, 2), \qquad P_2 = P(4, 1), \qquad \text{and} \qquad P_3 = P(-2, 4).$$

Let $\mathbf{r}_1$, $\mathbf{r}_2$, and $\mathbf{r}_3$ be the vectors $\overrightarrow{OP_1}$, $\overrightarrow{OP_2}$, and $\overrightarrow{OP_3}$, respectively. Then

$$\mathbf{r}_1 = 2\mathbf{i} + 2\mathbf{j}, \qquad \mathbf{r}_2 = 4\mathbf{i} + \mathbf{j}, \qquad \text{and} \qquad \mathbf{r}_3 = -2\mathbf{i} + 4\mathbf{j}.$$

Clearly, if $P(x, y)$ is any point on the line, then the position vector to the point P is $\overrightarrow{OP} = \mathbf{r} = x\mathbf{i} + y\mathbf{j}$.

Let us consider the set of all position vectors having endpoints on the line $x + 2y = 6$, as shown in Fig. 2–18. We want to think of this set of vectors as representing the line. Our problem is that of finding a way of representing this set of vectors for any line.

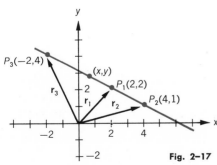

Fig. 2–17

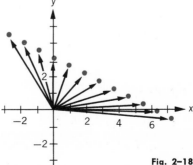

Fig. 2–18

53

2. Suppose that l is a vertical line that contains the point $(a, 0)$. (See Fig. 2-19.) Then any point on the line has coordinates of the form (a, y), and a position vector $\mathbf{r}$ to any point of the line is $\mathbf{r} = a\mathbf{i} + y\mathbf{j}$, where y is any real number and a is a fixed real number.

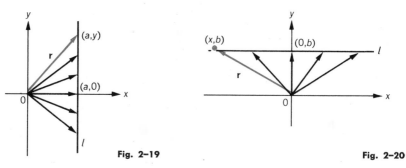

Fig. 2-19   Fig. 2-20

3. If l is a horizontal line containing the point $(0, b)$, as in Fig. 2-20, then the position vector $\mathbf{r}$ to any point (x, b) on l is $\mathbf{r} = x\mathbf{i} + b\mathbf{j}$.

Problems

1. A line has a rectangular equation $2x + 3y = 12$. Find three points on the line and write expressions for the position vectors whose endpoints are the three points selected.

2. A line contains the points $(1, 3)$ and $(4, 7)$. Determine the coordinates of another point on the line and write an expression denoting the position vector to this point.

3. A line contains the point $(7, 4)$ and is parallel to the y-axis. Find another point on the line and represent the position vector to this point.

4. A line contains the point $(0, 0)$. Sketch a picture showing the set of position vectors to points on the line.

5. A line l contains the point (x_0, y_0) and has direction cosines c_1 and c_2. Let (x, y) be another point on the line and d the directed distance from (x_0, y_0) to (x, y). Show that the position vector $\mathbf{r}$ to (x, y) is

$$\mathbf{r} = (x_0 + c_1 d)\mathbf{i} + (y_0 + c_2 d)\mathbf{j}.$$

2-8. VECTOR EQUATIONS OF LINES (Cont.)

Now return to the general problem of representing lines by means of vectors. Suppose l is a line containing two points, $P_0 = P(x_0, y_0)$ and $P_1 = P(x_1, y_1)$, as in Fig. 2-21. Let $\mathbf{r}_0$ and $\mathbf{r}_1$ be the position vectors to these two points. By the definition of vector addition,

$$\mathbf{r}_1 = \mathbf{r}_0 + \overrightarrow{P_0P_1}. \tag{1}$$

54

If $P(x, y)$ is any point on l, then there is a unique real number t such that $\overrightarrow{P_0P} = t\overrightarrow{P_0P_1}$ because the vectors $\overrightarrow{P_0P}$ and $\overrightarrow{P_0P_1}$ have either the same or opposite direction. Then the position vector $\mathbf{r}$ to $P(x, y)$ is

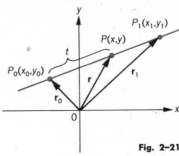

$$\mathbf{r} = \mathbf{r}_0 + t\overrightarrow{P_0P_1}. \qquad (2)$$

From (1) we have $\overrightarrow{P_0P_1} = \mathbf{r}_1 - \mathbf{r}_0$, and hence (2) can be written as

$$\mathbf{r} = \mathbf{r}_0 + t(\mathbf{r}_1 - \mathbf{r}_0). \qquad (3)$$

Fig. 2-21

Equation (3) represents the position vector to any point $P(x, y)$ on the line l. By choosing different real values for t, we get position vectors to different points on the line. If we think of t as a parameter whose domain is the set of real numbers, then equation (3) represents the set of position vectors to all points of the line l. We shall refer to (3) or any equivalent statement as a *vector equation* of the line.

Note that in (3), if $t = 0$, we get $\mathbf{r} = \mathbf{r}_0$, the position vector to P_0. If $t = 1$, we get $\mathbf{r} = \mathbf{r}_1$, the position vector to P_1. If $0 < t < 1$, we get position vectors to points between P_0 and P_1. If $t > 1$, then (3) represents position vectors to points P such that P_1 is between P_0 and P. If $t < 0$, then (3) represents position vectors to points P such that P_0 is between P_1 and P.

From (3) we may find the coordinates of the midpoint of segment $\overline{P_0P_1}$. Choosing $t = \frac{1}{2}$, we have

$$\mathbf{r} = \mathbf{r}_0 + \tfrac{1}{2}(\mathbf{r}_1 - \mathbf{r}_0) = \tfrac{1}{2}(\mathbf{r}_0 + \mathbf{r}_1).$$

If $P_0 = (x_0, y_0)$ and $P_1 = (x_1, y_1)$, then expressing each vector in terms of components, we have

$$\mathbf{r} = x\mathbf{i} + y\mathbf{j},$$
$$\mathbf{r}_0 = x_0\mathbf{i} + y_0\mathbf{j},$$

and

$$\mathbf{r}_1 = x_1\mathbf{i} + y_1\mathbf{j},$$

so that

$$x\mathbf{i} + y\mathbf{j} = \tfrac{1}{2}(x_0\mathbf{i} + y_0\mathbf{j} + x_1\mathbf{i} + y_1\mathbf{j})$$
$$= \tfrac{1}{2}(x_0 + x_1)\mathbf{i} + \tfrac{1}{2}(y_0 + y_1)\mathbf{j}.$$

Since two vectors are equal if and only if their components are equal, it follows that

$$x = \tfrac{1}{2}(x_0 + x_1) \qquad \text{and} \qquad y = \tfrac{1}{2}(y_0 + y_1).$$

Problems

1. Find the midpoints of the segments whose endpoints are given below.
   (a) $(-1, 7)$ and $(-3, 5)$
   (b) $(\pi, \pi/2)$ and $(\sqrt{2}, -\sqrt{2})$ (c) $(-1, 5)$ and $(8, 2)$
   (d) $(-a, b)$ and $(a, -b)$, where $a < 0$ and $b < 0$
   (e) $(a, 0)$ and $(b, 0)$, where $a > 0$ and $b > 0$
   (f) $(a, 0)$ and $(b, 0)$, where $a < 0$ and $b > 0$
   (g) $(a, 0)$ and $(0, b)$, where $a > 0$ and $b > 0$

2. A point on the segment whose endpoints are $(-1, 3)$ and $(5, 2)$, is twice as far from the point $(-1, 3)$ as from $(5, 2)$. Find its coordinates.

3. What is a vector equation of the y-axis?

4. A line contains the points $(-7, 5)$ and $(3, 5)$. What is a vector equation of the line?

5. What is a vector equation of the line that bisects the first and third quadrant?

6. Determine a vector equation for each of the following lines.
   (a) The line containing $(3, 4)$ and $(0, -2)$
   (b) The line containing $(1, -3)$ and $(5, 0)$
   (c) The line containing $(-4, -1)$ and $(-1, -2)$
   (d) The line containing $(5, -3)$ and $(-5, 3)$

7. Determine a vector equation of each of the following lines.
   (a) A line that has a rectangular equation of $x - 2y = 10$
   (b) A line that has a rectangular equation of $3x - y = 12$
   (c) A line that has a rectangular equation of $2x + y = 6$
   (d) A line that has a rectangular equation of $5x + 2y = 10$

8. A line has parametric equations
$$\begin{cases} x = 3 + \tfrac{1}{3}d, \\ y = -2 + \dfrac{2\sqrt{2}\,d}{3}. \end{cases}$$

   Write a vector equation of the line.

9. Obtain a formula for the coordinates of the points which trisect the segment between (x_1, y_1) and (x_2, y_2).

10. Given P_1 and P_2 as below, determine the coordinates of the point P satisfying the condition indicated.
    (a) $P_1 = (-2, 3)$, $P_2 = (5, -1)$. The points P_1, P_2, and P are in the order P_1PP_2 and $|\overrightarrow{P_1P}| = \tfrac{1}{3}|\overrightarrow{P_1P_2}|$.
    (b) Same as part (a) except that P_1, P_2, and P are in the order PP_1P_2.
    (c) Same as part (a) except that P_1, P_2, and P are in the order P_1P_2P.

56

11. A point moves along a line with constant speed. At time $t = 0$ it is at $(-1, 2)$. At the end of one second it is at $(2, 4)$. See figure on the right.

    Show that the position vector to the point at t seconds is

    $$\mathbf{r} = \mathbf{r}_0 + t(\mathbf{r}_1 - \mathbf{r}_0)$$

    or

    $$x\mathbf{i} + y\mathbf{j} = (-1 + 3t)\mathbf{i} + (2 + 2t)\mathbf{j}.$$

    What is the speed in the x-direction? the y-direction? along the line?

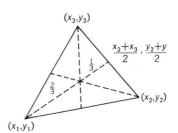

12. The points $(1, 3)$, $(4, -1)$, and $(-2, -2)$ are the midpoints of the sides of a triangle. Find the vertices of the triangle.

*13. Show that the medians of the triangle with vertices (x_1, y_1), (x_2, y_2), and (x_3, y_3) meet at a point two-thirds the distance from a vertex to the midpoint of the opposite side. (See figure.) This point is called the centroid of the triangle. Its coordinates are

$$\left(\frac{x_1 + x_2 + x_3}{3}, \frac{y_1 + y_2 + y_3}{3} \right).$$

*14. The points (a_1, b_1), (a_2, b_2), and (a_3, b_3) are the midpoints of the sides of a triangle. Find the vertices of the triangle.

SUMMARY

In this chapter we have studied vectors in the plane. Beginning with the simple idea of an *arrow* as an ordered pair of points, we have built a mathematical system containing elements called *vectors*. We have seen that vectors, while quite different from real numbers, have properties similar to some of the properties of real numbers. We have observed that vector addition is associative and commutative, that vectors may be multiplied by real numbers, and that multiplication by a real number is distributive with respect to vector addition.

The most important aid to computation with vectors is the theorem that every vector is the sum of multiples of two unit vectors directed along the positive x-axis and positive y-axis. Thus if $\mathbf{r}$ is any vector, then there exist unique real numbers x and y such that

$$\mathbf{r} = x\mathbf{i} + y\mathbf{j}.$$

In a later chapter we shall see that we can easily extend our concept of vectors in the plane to vectors in space. Still later we shall define some new operations for vectors. At the present, for example, we add vectors, but we have not defined any operations corresponding to multiplication for a pair of vectors. We shall defer such a definition until we have studied some trigonometry.

57

Review Problems

1. Solve the following vector equations.

    (a) $x\mathbf{i} + (-4)\mathbf{j} = 7\mathbf{i} + y\mathbf{j}$

    (b) $5(\mathbf{i} + \mathbf{j}) - \mathbf{i} + y\mathbf{j} = x\mathbf{i} - 4\mathbf{j}$

2. Given: $\mathbf{r} = x\mathbf{i} + y\mathbf{j}$ is the sum of vectors $\overrightarrow{P_1P_2}$ and $\overrightarrow{P_3P_4}$, where $P_1 = (-1, 5)$, $P_2 = (-5, 2)$, $P_3 = (2, 3)$, and $P_4 = (5, 2)$. Determine the components x and y of $\mathbf{r}$.

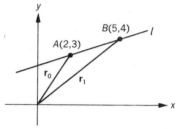

3. Suppose that l is a line containing the points A and B whose coordinates are $(2, 3)$ and $(5, 4)$. (See figure.)

    (a) Write a vector equation of line l.

    (b) What are a pair of parametric equations of the line?

    (c) What is a rectangular equation of the line?

    (d) What are the components of vector $\overrightarrow{AB}$?

    (e) What are the coordinates of the midpoint of $\overline{AB}$?

    (f) What are the coordinates of a point C such that the order is CAB, and $\overline{CA} \cong \overline{AB}$?

4. What conclusion would you draw from the following statements?

    (a) $x\mathbf{i} + y\mathbf{j} = \mathbf{0}$

    (b) $x\mathbf{i} + y\mathbf{j} = a\mathbf{i} + b\mathbf{j}$

    (c) $m\mathbf{a} = \mathbf{0}$, m a real number

    (d) $\mathbf{r} = \mathbf{r}_1 t + (1 - t)\mathbf{r}_0$ and parameter $t = 0$

    (e) $\mathbf{r} = \mathbf{r}_1 t + (1 - t)\mathbf{r}_0$ and parameter $t = 1$

    (f) $\mathbf{a} + \mathbf{c} = \mathbf{c} + \mathbf{b}$

5. If $\mathbf{a}$ and $\mathbf{b}$ are vectors, we may show that

$$|\mathbf{a} + \mathbf{b}| \leq |\mathbf{a}| + |\mathbf{b}|.$$

    (a) When will equality hold?

    (b) To what geometric theorem does this vector theorem correspond?

6. What vector added to $x\mathbf{i} + y\mathbf{j}$ gives $a\mathbf{i} + b\mathbf{j}$?

7. Determine the real numbers k and s such that

$$4\mathbf{i} + 3\mathbf{j} = k(\mathbf{i} - \mathbf{j}) + s(2\mathbf{i} + 5\mathbf{j}).$$

Draw a picture of the position vectors involved.

8. For each of the pairs of points below, write a vector equation of the line determined by these points.

(a) $(6, 6)$, $(-4, 3)$ (b) $(2, 2)$, $(-3, 3)$

(c) $(\pi, 1)$, $(\pi/2, 4)$ (d) (a, b), (c, d)

(e) $(\sqrt{2}, 0)$, $(0, \sqrt{2})$ (f) $(0, 0)$, (a, b)

9. If $k(3\mathbf{i} - 5\mathbf{j}) = 4\mathbf{i} + y\mathbf{j}$, determine the real numbers k and y.

10. A and B are points on a line and have coordinates $(-1, 5)$ and $(4, 6)$, respectively. Determine the coordinates of a point C on this line, given that

(a) $|\overrightarrow{AC}| = 4|\overrightarrow{BC}|$ and B is between A and C.

(b) $|\overrightarrow{AC}| = 4|\overrightarrow{BC}|$ and C is between A and B.

(c) $|\overrightarrow{BC}| = 4|\overrightarrow{AC}|$ and A is between B and C.

(d) $|\overrightarrow{BC}| = 4|\overrightarrow{AC}|$ and C is between B and A.

HISTORICAL NOTE

John Wallis (1649–1703)

Historically, the concept of a vector (from the Latin *vehere*, "to carry") has its origin in the attempts to represent complex numbers geometrically. We know that complex numbers can be represented by points in a coordinate plane, as is shown in Fig. 2–22. The complex number $a + bi$ is represented by the arrow $(\overrightarrow{OP})$. The idea of representing complex numbers by points in a coordinate plane (Fig. 2–22) was first conceived by John Wallis (1649–1703), professor of mathematics at Oxford University, who discussed

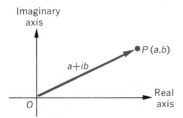

Fig. 2–22

it in his *Algebra*, published in 1673. However, a full description of this relation was not given until 1798 by the Norwegian surveyor Caspar Wessel.

Two remarks are appropriate. In the first place, complex numbers are *not* our vectors in the plane. That is, $a + bi \neq a\mathbf{i} + b\mathbf{j}$. The two concepts are only related. Both are represented by the arrow $(\overrightarrow{OP})$. In the second place, complex numbers can be multiplied to give complex numbers, whereas we have not (as yet) defined a product of two vectors.

3

Introduction

SPACE

3-1. INTRODUCTION

In this chapter we shall see that we can coordinatize space in much the same way we did a plane. We shall also see further similarities: Parametric equations of a line in space are quite similar to those of a line in the plane. The distance formula is a simple extension of the formula in the plane. And finally, planes in space can be described simply by means of equations.

In this discussion we shall use certain facts about lines and planes in space which will be familiar to you if you have studied space geometry. However, since this is not always the case, we shall explicitly state the required properties of space as *Space Assumptions*. Our conclusions will then follow logically from these few statements. You are encouraged to use your intuition freely to devise short cuts or alternative methods of attacking problems.

3-2. SPACE ASSUMPTIONS

It may come as a surprise but most of the essential difficulties in geometry occur in plane geometry. The hard theorems are those of plane geometry. Furthermore, very few additional assumptions, or postulates, are needed to establish all theorems of space geometry. These postulates are given below. We are assuming familiarity with the theorems of *plane geometry*.

POSTULATES FOR SPACE

1. There is a set of points called *euclidean space*. Certain subsets of space are called *lines*. Certain other subsets of space are called *planes*. Space contains at least four points not in any one plane.

2. There is exactly one plane containing any three noncollinear points (Fig. 3–1).

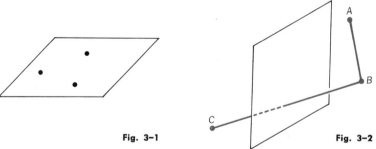

Fig. 3–1 Fig. 3–2

3. Each plane satisfies all the postulates for euclidean plane geometry. In particular, the line joining two points of a plane lies in that plane, and the postulates for congruence of segments and angles apply whether or not the segments and angles are in the same plane.

4. Each plane separates space (Fig. 3–2). This means that the set of points not in the plane consists of two subsets on either side of the plane, called half-spaces, with the following properties: (a) If two points are in the same subset, the segment joining them *does not* intersect the plane. (b) If two points are in different subsets, the segment joining them *does* intersect the plane.

Remarks about the postulates

The first postulate asserts that no plane fills up space. We have a geometry of more than two dimensions.

The second postulate gives a simple condition for determining a definite plane.

The third postulate makes our planes like those familiar from plane geometry, and requires that all planes be alike.

Finally, the fourth postulate is suggested by our experience with the physical world. We observe that a wall between neighbors separates them. It is this postulate which makes space three-dimensional.

From these few postulates all the theorems of space, or *solid*, geometry can be derived. The ones which we particularly need will be given in this section and the next. We are not particularly concerned with proofs of these theorems, although they are arranged in logical order, and most of the proofs are not difficult. In this section, we are more concerned that you understand the theorems and are able to draw figures representing points and lines. Observe that the drawing problem is one of representing three-dimensional relations in a plane, in fact, in only a portion of a plane, namely a sheet of paper. Planes will be indicated by a drawing of a parallelogram, suggesting a portion of a plane. Lines that are behind planes as viewed by the observer (you) are dashed, as in Fig. 3–3.

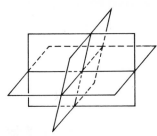

Fig. 3–3

Five theorems concerning lines and planes are given below. The first four theorems have simple proofs. The fifth theorem will require a little more thought. The figure accompanying each theorem illustrates the theorem and may also suggest a proof of the theorem.

THEOREM 3-1

If a line l does not lie in a plane π and contains at least one point of π, then l and π have exactly one point in common (Fig. 3-4).

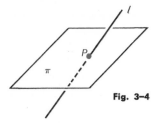

Fig. 3-4

THEOREM 3-2

There is a unique plane containing a given line and a point not on the line (Fig. 3-5).

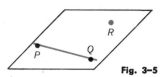

Fig. 3-5

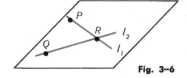

Fig. 3-6

THEOREM 3-3

There is a unique plane containing two distinct intersecting lines (Fig. 3-6).

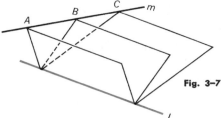

Fig. 3-7

THEOREM 3-4

There are infinitely many planes containing a given line (Fig. 3-7).

THEOREM 3-5

If two distinct planes have at least one point in common, they have exactly one line in common (Fig. 3-8).

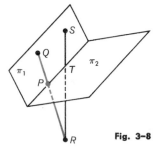

Fig. 3-8

Discussion. Choose Q on π_1 and not on π_2. Select R so that the common point, P, is between Q and R. Choose S on π_1 so that S is not on the line of P and Q. Then either S is also on π_2 and the line PS is on both planes, or S is on the same side of π_2 as R and $\overline{SQ}$ meets π_2 in $T \neq P$, or else S is on the side of π_2 opposite R, and hence $\overline{SR}$ meets π_2 in $T \neq P$. The line of T and P is in both planes.

66

Problems

1. Draw a picture of two intersecting planes, with a line intersecting each in distinct points.

2. Draw a picture of three planes with only one point in common. Extend the picture of each plane so that part is on each side of the line of intersection with any of the other two. How many lines of intersection are there? Draw a line meeting each of the three planes.

3. Prove Theorem 3–1. [*Hint:* Suppose there were a second point.]

4. Prove Theorem 3–2.   5. Prove Theorem 3–3.

6. Postulates 1, 2, and 4 for space should remind you of similar properties for the plane. State the corresponding properties for plane geometry.

7. Which postulate for space assures us that planes do *not* have boundaries, as might be suggested by our drawings?

8. Draw a *tetrahedron*. This is the space analogue of a triangle. It is made of portions of four planes; each portion is a triangle plus the interior of the triangle. The four planes meet, three at a time in four points, A, B, C, and D, called the *vertices* of the tetrahedron.

9. Give a definition of the interior of a tetrahedron.

10. Draw a picture of two rays from a point. Do they lie in a plane? Do they form an angle?

11. Lines p and q are two lines in space that do not intersect. Must p and q necessarily be *parallel?*

12. Prove Theorem 3–4. [*Hint:* If l is the given line, choose a point A not on l. Choose B not on the plane of l and A. Consider points C, on the line through A and B.]

13. Prove Theorem 3–5.

14. Use only Postulates 1 and 2 to prove that there are at least four planes.

15. Prove that there are at least two points which are on opposite sides of a given plane.

3–3. CONGRUENCE, PARALLELISM, AND PERPENDICULARITY

Congruent segments, angles, and triangles are familiar from plane geometry. Postulate 3 states that congruence relations are the same for all planes. For example, all right angles are congruent whether or not they are in the same plane. Also, for an angle A in a plane π and a ray r' from a point O' in a plane π', there is, on a given side of the line of r', a unique ray s' in plane π' forming with r' an angle which is congruent to angle A (Fig. 3–9).

67

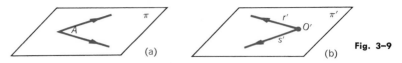

Fig. 3-9

We shall be concerned for some time with parallel and perpendicular lines and planes. Some definitions are needed.

DEFINITIONS 3-1

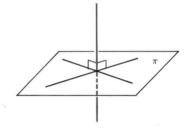

1. A line *l* and a plane π are *perpendicular* ($l \perp \pi$ or $\pi \perp l$) if *l* intersects π at a point and *l* is perpendicular to every line of π through that point (Fig. 3-10).

Fig. 3-10

2. Two lines are *parallel* if they are in the same plane (*coplanar*) and do not intersect.

3. Two lines which are not coplanar are *skew*.

4. Two planes are *parallel* if they do not intersect.

5. A line and a plane are *parallel* if they do not intersect.

The theorems that follow deal with lines perpendicular to planes, parallel lines, and parallel planes.

THEOREM 3-6

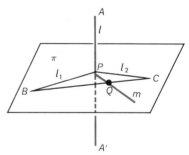

If a line *l* is perpendicular to two intersecting lines, l_1 and l_2, then the given line is perpendicular to the plane containing l_1 and l_2.

Fig. 3-11

Discussion. One must show that $l \perp m$, where *m* is any line in π through the intersection of the two lines, *P*, as shown in Fig. 3-11. To do this, we proceed as follows: We choose *A* and *A'* such that $\overline{AP} \cong \overline{A'P}$. Next we select *B* and *C* and prove that $\triangle ABC \cong \triangle A'BC$. Finally, we prove that that $\triangle ABQ \cong \triangle A'BQ$. Since $\overline{AQ} \cong \overline{A'Q}$ it follows that $l \perp m$.

68

THEOREM 3-7

There is exactly one plane perpendicular to a line l at a point P of the line.

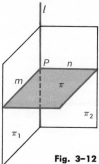

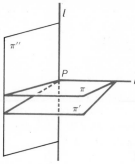

Fig. 3-12

Fig. 3-13

Proof. Choose two planes π_1 and π_2 containing l (Fig. 3-12). Let m and n be lines in π_1 and π_2, respectively, which are perpendicular to l at P. Then m and n lie in a plane π which is perpendicular to l.

To see that there is a *unique* plane perpendicular to l, suppose that there are two planes, π and π'. These planes meet in a line r, as shown in Fig. 3-13. If π'' is a plane containing l but not r, then the two planes π and π' would meet π'' in two lines of π'' both perpendicular to l at P. Since this contradicts a theorem of plane geometry, π' cannot exist.

THEOREM 3-8

There is a unique plane perpendicular to a line l and containing a point P not on l.

Discussion. Consider the plane containing l and P not on the line. In this plane there is a unique line perpendicular to l through P. Let this perpendicular meet l at O. Consider the plane through O which is perpendicular to l.

THEOREM 3-9

All the perpendiculars to a given line l through a point P of l lie in the plane perpendicular to l at P.

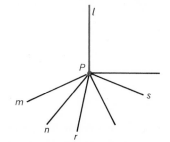

Fig. 3-14

Discussion. If m, n, r, and s are lines through P perpendicular to l (Fig. 3-14), then by Theorems 3-6 and 3-7, the plane of m and n must be the same as the plane of r and s.

69

THEOREM 3-10

If two lines are perpendicular to the same plane, they are parallel.

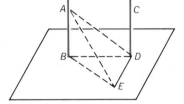

Fig. 3-15

Discussion. The difficult part of the theorem is to show that the two lines are coplanar. We choose $\overline{DE}$ so that $\overline{DE} \perp \overline{BD}$ and $\overline{DE} \cong \overline{AB}$, as shown in Fig. 3-15. Next, by congruent triangles, we show that $\overline{DE}$ is perpendicular to the segments $\overline{CD}$, $\overline{BD}$, and $\overline{AD}$. Finally, we appeal to Theorem 3-9 to complete the proof.

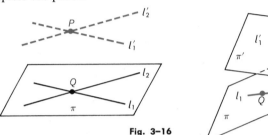

Fig. 3-16

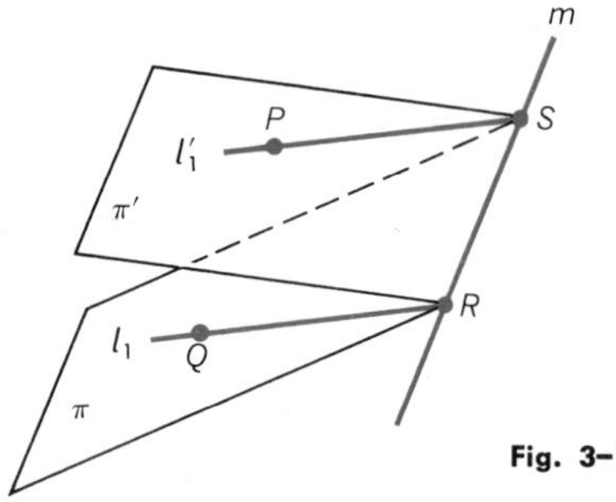

Fig. 3-17

THEOREM 3-11

Through a point P not in a plane π, there is exactly one plane parallel to π.

Discussion. Choose l_1 and l_2 in π intersecting at Q (Fig. 3-16). Select l_1' and l_2' through P and parallel to l_1 and l_2, respectively. Then l_1' and l_2' determine a plane π'.

To see that π' and π must be parallel, we proceed as shown in Fig. 3-17. Let us suppose that π and π' intersect in a line m. Then one of the lines l_1 or l_2 meets m. Suppose that it is l_1 which meets m in R. Then l_1' must meet m in a point $S \neq R$. Then through the points P, S, and R there are two planes, the plane π' and the plane of l_1 and l_1'. This is impossible.

Uniqueness remains to be proved.

THEOREM 3-12

Two distinct planes perpendicular to the same line are parallel (Fig. 3-18).

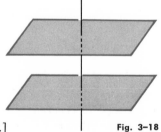

[*Hint:* Suppose that the planes are not parallel.]

Fig. 3-18

70

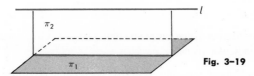

Fig. 3–19

THEOREM 3-13

If a line l is parallel to a plane π_1, and plane π_2 contains l and intersects π_1, then l is parallel to the line of intersection of π_1 and π_2 (Fig. 3–19).

THEOREM 3-14

If two distinct lines l_1 and l_2 are parallel to a line l, then l_1 and l_2 are parallel.

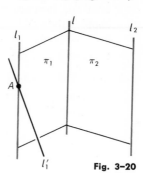

Fig. 3–20

*Proof. For lines l_1, l_2, and l that are coplanar, the theorem is known from plane geometry. Hence let us suppose that the plane π_1 of l_1 and l is distinct from the plane π_2 of l_2 and l, and that l_1 is *not* parallel to l_2 (Fig. 3–20).

We now choose a point, A, on l_1 and assume that l_1' is the line through A parallel to l_2. Then l_1' cannot lie in π_1, for if it did, l_1' would meet l in a point B, and through B there would be two lines, l_1' and l, parallel to l_2. Also, the line l_2 does not meet π_1, for if it did, l_2 would lie in π_1, contrary to assumption. Now, the plane of l_1' and l_2 meets π_1 at A and so meets π_1 in a line m. The line $m \neq l_1$, for if $m = l_1$, then l_1 would meet l_2 and hence l_2 would meet π_1, which it does not. Since $m \neq l_1$ and m is in the plane of l_1' and l_2, m must meet l_2 in a point C. But then C is in π_1 and on l_2, which is impossible. This contradiction completes the proof that l_1 is parallel to l_2.

Problems

1. Place your pencil point down on your desk so that the line of the pencil is perpendicular to two selected lines through this point in the plane of your desk. Convince yourself that this fixes the position of your pencil and observe that the pencil appears perpendicular to any other line through the point and in the plane of the desk.

2. Prove Theorem 3–6.

3. Prove Theorem 3–8.

4. State two theorems analogous to Theorems 3–7 and 3–8 concerning the existence of lines perpendicular to planes. Draw pictures to illustrate the theorems.

5. Prove the analog of Theorem 3–7, which you stated for Problem 4.

71

6. Prove that three mutually perpendicular lines exist in space.

7. How would you define perpendicular planes? Give some physical examples of perpendicular planes.

8. The fourth space postulate says that each plane separates the points of space not in the plane into two sets. If two planes intersect, into how many parts is space divided?

9. If three planes have a common point of intersection and do not contain the same line, then into how many parts is space divided by these planes? What happens for 4 and 5 planes? Can you generalize this problem for n planes if no three contain the same line but have one point in common?

10. Prove Theorem 3-9.   11. Prove Theorem 3-10.

12. Prove Theorem 3-11.   13. Prove Theorem 3-12.

14. Prove Theorem 3-13.

3-4. DIHEDRAL ANGLES AND PERPENDICULAR PLANES

One of the basic assumptions of *plane* geometry is that every line l in a plane π separates the points of π other than the points of l, into two disjoint sets. Each of the two sets is called a *half-plane* (Fig. 3-21).

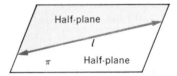

Fig. 3-21

Let us consider two distinct intersecting planes, π_1 and π_2, with l the line of intersection (Fig. 3-22). We choose a point A, not on l, in π_1 and a point B, not on l, in π_2. The set of points in the half-plane containing A, or in the half-plane containing B, or on the line l is called a *dihedral angle*. The line l is called the *edge* of the dihedral angle, and each half-plane is called a *side* or *face* of the dihedral angle. If P and Q are two points on the edge of a dihedral angle and A and B are points in each face, then we denote the dihedral angle by writing $\angle A\text{-}PQ\text{-}B$.

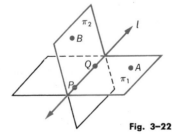

Fig. 3-22

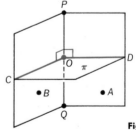

Fig. 3-23

Let us suppose that ∠*A-PQ-B* is a dihedral angle and π is a plane perpendicular to the edge at a point *O*, as in Fig. 3–23. The intersection of π and ∠*A-PQ-B* is a *plane angle* of the dihedral angle (∠*COD* in Fig. 3–23).

We state an important theorem concerning dihedral angles.

THEOREM 3-15

Any two plane angles of the same dihedral angle are congruent.

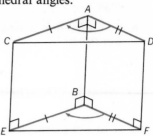

Fig. 3–24

The theorem may be proved by choosing lines *EC* and *FD* as shown in Fig. 3–24 and then proving that △*ACD* ≅ △*BEF*.

Theorem 3–15 allows us to define *right dihedral angles* and *perpendicular planes*. In some of the problems, you will be asked to formulate these definitions.

THEOREM 3-16

Two angles whose sides are parallel and in the same direction, in pairs, are congruent.

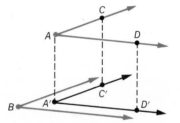

Fig. 3–25

Proof (sketch). For angles that are in the same plane, the theorem is familiar from plane geometry. Therefore, let us suppose that the angles are in different planes (necessarily parallel) and have vertices at *A* and *B* (Fig. 3–25). We consider the line through *A* perpendicular to the plane of angle *A*, which meets the plane of angle *B* in *A'*. Angle *A* and the line through *A* and *A'* determine a dihedral angle. By Theorem 3–15, the two plane angles of this dihedral angle at *A* and *A'* are congruent. Then the angles at *A'* and *B* will be in the same plane and either be identical or their sides, in pairs, will be in the same direction. Thus ∠*A* ≅ ∠*A'* ≅ ∠*B*.

Problems

1. How many dihedral angles are formed by two distinct intersecting planes?

2. Explain why a dihedral angle is completely determined by naming a point in a face, two points on the edge, and another point in the other face.

3. Prove Theorem 3–15.

4. Define a *right dihedral angle*.   5. Define *perpendicular planes*.

73

6. The plane angles of two dihedral angles are congruent angles. Would you say that the dihedral angles are congruent?

7. Draw a picture of a dihedral angle. Show a plane that *bisects* the dihedral angle.

8. If ∠*A-PQ-B* is a dihedral angle, how would you define the interior of ∠*A-PQ-B*?

3-5. SPACE COORDINATIZATION

Just as in the plane we defined a one-to-one mapping of ordered pairs of real numbers onto the points of the plane, so for space we analogously define a one-to-one mapping of ordered *triples* of real numbers onto space.

As was the case in the plane, the assigning of coordinates to space also depends on certain choices. These choices can be made in different ways.

Let us choose a unit of length and a point O, called the *origin of coordinates* (Fig. 3–26a). Next, let us choose three mutually perpendicular lines through O. We call any one of these lines the *first axis*, either of the other two the *second axis*, and the remaining line the *third axis*. The planes containing pairs of coordinate axes are called the *coordinate planes*.

Next we coordinatize each axis (Fig. 3–26b). This step involves choosing a positive direction on each axis. We can now define a mapping from the points of space to ordered triples of real numbers (Fig. 3–26c). For each point P, we consider the plane through P parallel to the coordinate plane of the second and third axes. This plane meets the first axis in a point with coordinate a_1, called the *first coordinate* of P. In the same manner, planes parallel to the other coordinate planes determine the second and third coordinates, a_2 and a_3, of P. We indicate the point and its coordinates by

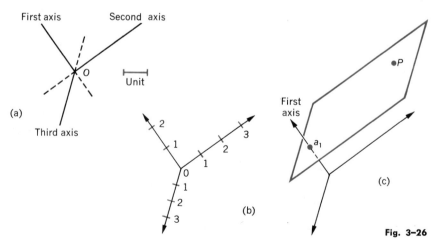

Fig. 3–26

$P(a_1, a_2, a_3)$. Frequently we simply refer to the ordered triple (a_1, a_2, a_3) as a point.

Because the planes through P parallel to the coordinate planes are unique, the definition of coordinates given above defines a function, or mapping, of points of space into ordered triples of real numbers. This mapping is one-to-one. Since we know that for each point there is only one triple (a_1, a_2, a_3), it remains to show that each triple corresponds to exactly one point. This converse is left to the student.

A coordinate system provides a one-to-one mapping between the points of space and the set of all ordered triples of real numbers. The coordinates of a point are called *rectangular Cartesian coordinates.* The word *rectangular* comes from our choice of axes which are mutually perpendicular. This choice is not necessary but is highly convenient (see Problem 15 of the next problem set).

A Convention. Usually we give names to the three axes, which are related to the variable used to denote the coordinate. Thus, if we use x to denote any first coordinate, and y and z to denote the second and third coordinates, respectively, then it is natural to speak of the x, y, and z coordinates of a point, as well as the x-, y-, and z-axes. Of course, there is nothing compulsory about the use of the letters x, y, and z. Any letters would do as well. We could also have a-, b-, and c-axes, or u-, v-, and w-axes, etc.

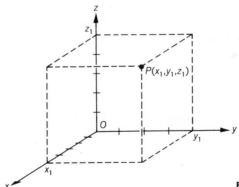

Fig. 3–27

Furthermore, there is no definite way to orient the axes, but it is customary in textbooks to picture the axes as shown in Fig. 3–27. The y- and z-axes are in the plane of the page, and the positive x-axis extends out from the page toward the reader. In the drawing, the x-axis is at an angle which is intended to convey a feeling of perspective, and the unit of length is shortened along the x-axis to enhance this effect. But these drawings are *not* perspective drawings, since parallel lines are not drawn to converge. Lines parallel in space are parallel in these drawings.

The plane containing the x- and y-axes is the *xy-coordinate plane*, or simply, the *xy*-plane. Likewise there are *yz*- and *xz*-coordinate planes. The coordinate planes separate space into eight *octants*. Usually only one of them is given a name; this is the *first octant*, which consists of the set of all points having positive coordinates only.

Each plane separates space. The two sides of a plane are called *half-spaces*.

Problems

1. Plot the points $(0, 0, 0)$, $(0, 1, 2)$, $(0, -1, 2)$, $(1, -1, 2)$, $(-2, 2, -3)$, $(4, 0, 3)$, $(4, 0, -3)$, $(\pi, \pi/2, 0)$, $(-\sqrt{2}, \sqrt{2}, 0)$.

2. A point is on the *y*-axis. What can you say about its *x*- and *z*-coordinates? What equations in *x*, *y*, and *z* are satisfied if and only if the point (x, y, z) is on the *y*-axis?

3. Describe the eight octants in terms of the coordinates of points in them. Also describe the octants in terms of the half-spaces formed by the coordinate planes.

4. A plane is parallel to the *xz*-coordinate plane and passes through $(-1, 3, -4)$. What can you say about the coordinates of any point (x, y, z) on the plane?

5. What is the set of all points (x, y, z) for which $x = -2$? the set of all points (x, y, z) for which $x = 1$ and $y = -2$?

6. A point lies in the half-space formed by the *yz*-plane which contains the point $(-3, 4, 5)$. What can you say about the coordinates of any point (x, y, z) in this half-space?

7. What is the set of all points (x, y, z) for which $y < 0$?

8. What is the set of all points (x, y, z) for which $x + 2 \leq 0$?

9. What is the set of all points (x, y, z) for which $x^2 > 0$?

10. Draw a picture of the set of all points (x, y, z) for which $0 \leq x \leq 1$, $0 \leq y \leq 1$, and $0 \leq z \leq 1$.

11. A line is parallel to the *z*-axis and passes through $(-1, -2, -3)$. Find several other points on the line.

12. Plot the following pairs of points. Then draw the line segment connecting them. Draw a plane containing the segment that is parallel to the *y*-axis. Draw a second plane containing the segment parallel to the *z*-axis.

    (a) $(2, -2, 0)$, $(-1, 2, 3)$ (b) $(3, 0, 2)$, $(0, 3, 3)$

    (c) $(3, 0, 3)$, $(0, 2, -1)$ (d) $(2, 0, -2)$, $(0, 3, 1)$

*13. A line passes through $(-1, -2, 3)$ and $(3, -2, 1)$. Find a pair of equations, one in *x* and *z* and the other in *y*, which are satisfied if and only if the point (x, y, z) is on the line.

*14. What is the set of all points (x, y, z) such that $2x + 3y = 6$?

*15. In assigning coordinates for space, it is not necessary to choose mutually perpendicular axes. Describe how to set up a coordinate system for space using any three concurrent noncoplanar lines as axes.

*16. Show that to each ordered triple of real numbers, (a_1, a_2, a_3), there corresponds a unique point P in space.

Remark

We have started with a geometric object, namely euclidean space, and have given it coordinates. Often it is the converse situation that prevails. We are given an ordered triple of real numbers and use space to graphically illustrate the relations between the ordered triples. Because in these cases the variables x, y, and z could represent quite different quantities, there is no need to choose the same unit for all axes.

Problems

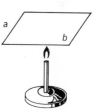

1. A rectangular plate is heated, but not uniformly. Consider the temperature at each point of the plate. Discuss the problem of plotting temperature as a function of position. What is the relevant portion of space?

2. A particle moves along a straight line subject to a force which depends on its position and the time t. If the force is always in one direction and no greater than 100 pounds, discuss the portion of space relevant to plotting force as a function of distance and time.

3. The internal energy E of a given quantity of a gas depends upon the pressure p and temperature T. What is the relevant portion of space?

3–6. THE DISTANCE FORMULA

Let us consider any two points

$$P_1 = P(x_1, y_1, z_1) \quad \text{and} \quad P_2 = (x_2, y_2, z_2).$$

We choose $P_3 = P(x_2, y_2, z_1)$ (Fig. 3–28). Then the points P_1 and P_3 are in the plane parallel to the xy-coordinate plane where $z = z_1$. The distance $|P_1P_3|$ is given by the distance formula in the plane,

$$|P_1P_3| = \sqrt{(x_1 - x_2)^2 + (y_1 - y_2)^2}.$$

The points P_2 and P_3 are on a line parallel to the z-axis and

$$|P_2P_3| = \sqrt{(z_1 - z_2)^2} = |z_1 - z_2|.$$

77

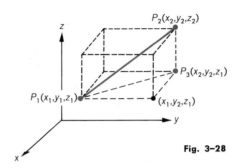

Fig. 3-28

The triangle $\triangle P_1P_2P_3$ is a right triangle; hence by the Pythagorean Theorem,

$$|P_1P_2|^2 = |P_1P_3|^2 + |P_2P_3|^2$$
$$= (x_1 - x_2)^2 + (y_1 - y_2)^2 + (z_1 - z_2)^2,$$

and we obtain the *distance formula*

$$|P_1P_2| = \sqrt{(x_1 - x_2)^2 + (y_1 - y_2)^2 + (z_1 - z_2)^2}.$$

The distance formula in three dimensions is an extension of the distance formula in two dimensions. There is one extra term. If both P_1 and P_2 lie in the xy-plane, then $z_1 = z_2 = 0$ and we get the two-dimensional formula.

Problems

1. Plot the following point pairs and find the distance between them.

   (a) $(2, 0, 1)$, $(10, 1, 5)$ (b) $(0, 0, 0)$, $(2, -9, 6)$

   (c) $(3, 2, 0)$, $(0, 0, 6)$ (d) (a, b, c), $(a + d, b + e, c + f)$

   (e) $(1 - \sqrt{2}, 1 + \sqrt{3}, 5)$, $(1 + \sqrt{2}, 1 - \sqrt{3}, 1)$

   (f) $(2, -1, -1)$, $(-1, 3, 3)$

2. Using the distance formula, show that $|P_1P_2| = |P_2P_1|$.

3. A room has dimensions 12 ft $\times$ 18 ft $\times$ 8 ft. What is the distance between a point on the floor in one corner and a point on the ceiling in the far opposite corner?

4. Is the point $(1, 0, 4)$ inside or outside the sphere of radius π with center at $(2, 3, 3)$?

5. Determine x such that $(x, 0, 0)$ shall be on the sphere of radius $3\sqrt{3}$ and center at $(2, 3, 3)$.

6. Give an equation in x, y, and z which is satisfied if and only if the point (x, y, z) is on the sphere of radius r with center at the origin. Explain your reasoning.

7. Are the points $(1, -1, 1)$, $(2, 2, 2)$, and $(4, -2, 1)$ vertices of a right triangle?

8. Show that $(2, 6, -3)$, $(-4, 3, -3)$, and $(-2, 7, 2)$ are vertices of an isosceles triangle.

9. Find an equation in x, y, and z satisfied by the coordinates of all points $P(x, y, z)$ that are equidistant from $(2, 3, -2)$ and $(6, 11, 8)$.

10. Find the points on the y-axis at a distance 6 from the point $(2, 1, 4)$.

*11. Show that if the line through (x_1, y_1, z_1) and (x_2, y_2, z_2) is perpendicular to the line through (x_1, y_1, z_1) and (x_3, y_3, z_3), then

$$(x_2 - x_1)(x_1 - x_3) + (y_2 - y_1)(y_1 - y_3) + (z_2 - z_1)(z_1 - z_3) = 0.$$

3-7. LINES

We shall obtain parametric equations for a line in space quite analogous to parametric equations for a line in the plane.

We let l be any line and (x_0, y_0, z_0) a point on it. Next we coordinatize the line with point (x_0, y_0, z_0) as the origin (Fig. 3–29). Then each point of l has associated with it a unique real number, d, the directed distance from (x_0, y_0, z_0).

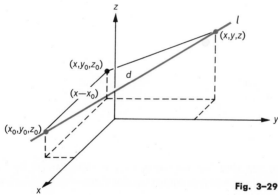

Fig. 3–29

As in the development of parametric equations for a line in a plane, there are two coordinate systems associated with the parametric equations of a line in space. One is the rectangular coordinate system represented by the ordered triple (x, y, z) and the other is the coordinate system represented by the directed distance d.

We wish to express the coordinates of any point (x, y, z) of l in terms of x_0, y_0, z_0 and the real number d. Consider a plane through (x, y, z) and perpendicular to the x-axis. A perpendicular from (x_0, y_0, z_0) to this plane meets the plane in (x, y_0, z_0) and has length $|x - x_0|$. Consider different positions of $P(x, y, z)$ on l. With each choice of $P(x, y, z) \neq P(x_0, y_0, z_0)$ there is a triangle with vertices (x_0, y_0, z_0), (x, y, z), and (x, y_0, z_0). All these right triangles are similar. Hence the ratio $|x - x_0|/|d|$ is the same for

79

all points $(x, y, z) \neq (x_0, y_0, z_0)$ on l. Therefore the ratio

$$\frac{x - x_0}{d} = c_1$$

is also the same for all points of l other than (x_0, y_0, z_0), because both $(x - x_0)$ and d change sign at (x_0, y_0, z_0). We shall denote this ratio by c_1 and call it the "*x-direction cosine* of the directed line l."

In the same manner one can establish that the ratios

$$\frac{y - y_0}{d} = c_2 \quad \text{and} \quad \frac{z - z_0}{d} = c_3$$

are the same for all points of l except (x_0, y_0, z_0). These numbers are the y- and z-direction cosines of the directed line l. The corresponding triangle is shown for the case of the y-direction cosine in Fig. 3–30.

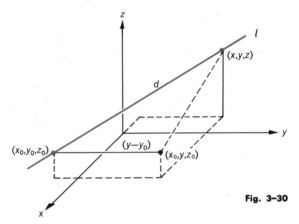

Fig. 3–30

Therefore we see that the direction of l is determined by the numbers c_1, c_2, and c_3, and parametric equations for l are

$$\begin{cases} x = x_0 + c_1 d, \\ y = y_0 + c_2 d, \\ z = z_0 + c_3 d, \end{cases}$$

where d is a parameter which can be any real number.

There is an important relation connecting the direction cosines of any line in space, which we state as a theorem.

THEOREM 3–17

If c_1, c_2, and c_3 are the direction cosines of a line, then

$$c_1^2 + c_2^2 + c_3^2 = 1.$$

The proof, which is quite similar to the proof of the corresponding theorem in the plane, is left to the student.

EXAMPLE

Find parametric equations for the line through $(1, 3, 1)$ and $(3, 0, 5)$.

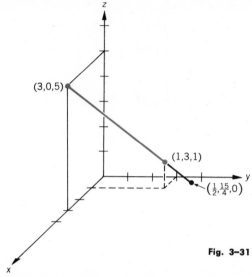

Fig. 3-31

We must first decide which point to use for (x_0, y_0, z_0). Let us suppose that $(1, 3, 1)$ is selected (Fig. 3–31). Then the positive direction on l must be chosen. Suppose that we select $(3, 0, 5)$ to be on the positive side. Then the distance between $(3, 0, 5)$ and $(1, 3, 1)$ is $\sqrt{29}$, and the direction cosines of the directed line are

$$c_1 = \frac{3-1}{\sqrt{29}} = \frac{2}{\sqrt{29}}, \qquad c_2 = \frac{0-3}{\sqrt{29}} = \frac{-3}{\sqrt{29}}, \qquad c_3 = \frac{5-1}{\sqrt{29}} = \frac{4}{\sqrt{29}}.$$

Had we selected the other ray from $(1, 3, 1)$ to be the positive side of l, the direction cosines would all have been opposite in sign.

Parametric equations of the line are therefore

$$\begin{cases} x = 1 + \dfrac{2}{\sqrt{29}}\, d, \\[2mm] y = 3 - \dfrac{3}{\sqrt{29}}\, d, \\[2mm] z = 1 + \dfrac{4}{\sqrt{29}}\, d. \end{cases}$$

81

Other points of the line are easily found by using different values for d. The point where the line pierces the xy-plane is found by setting

$$z = 1 + \frac{4}{\sqrt{29}} d = 0.$$

From this we conclude that $d = -\sqrt{29}/4$, and the x- and y-coordinates are

$$x = 1 + \left(\frac{2}{\sqrt{29}} \cdot \frac{-\sqrt{29}}{4} \right) = \frac{1}{2},$$

$$y = 3 - \left(\frac{3}{\sqrt{29}} \cdot \frac{-\sqrt{29}}{4} \right) = \frac{15}{4}.$$

The point where the line pierces the plane is $(\frac{1}{2}, \frac{15}{4}, 0)$.

THEOREM 3-18

If a, b, and c are real numbers and $a^2 + b^2 + c^2 = 1$, then there is at least one line whose x-, y-, and z-direction cosines are a, b, and c, respectively.

The proof of the theorem is left to you and can easily be made by considering the line through $(0, 0, 0)$ and (a, b, c).

Problems

1. What are parametric equations of the line of the above example (see also Fig. 3-31) if the initial point is $(3, 0, 5)$ and the same direction is positive? if the initial point is $(3, 0, 5)$ and the opposite direction is positive?

2. Find parametric equations for the lines through the following pairs of points. Use the first point as (x_0, y_0, z_0). Plot the pairs of points and find one other point on each line. Sketch the lines in parts a, b, c, and d.

   (a) $(0, 0, 0)$, $(3, 2, 6)$ (b) $(2, -1, 2)$, $(-1, 2, -1)$

   (c) $(2, 4, 0)$, $(4, 0, 5)$ (d) $(2, 2, -2)$, $(2, 5, 3)$

   (e) $(0, 0, 0)$, (e, f, g) (f) (a, b, c), $(a + e, b + f, c + g)$

3. A line is parallel to the z-axis and passes through $(2, -3, -2)$. Find parametric equations for the line.

4. A line is parallel to the x-axis. Write parametric equations for the line.

5. A line is parallel to the xy-plane. Show that $c_3 = 0$. What are parametric equations of such a line? Compare with lines in the plane.

6. Prove that for any line $c_1^2 + c_2^2 + c_3^2 = 1$.

7. A line has parametric equations

$$x = 3 + \frac{2}{\sqrt{17}}d, \qquad y = -1 - \frac{3}{\sqrt{17}}d, \qquad \text{and} \qquad z = 3 + \frac{2}{\sqrt{17}}d.$$

(a) Find several points on the line.

(b) Verify that $c_1^2 + c_2^2 + c_3^2 = 1$.

(c) Find the point where the line pierces each of the coordinate planes.

(d) Give two other sets of parametric equations of the line.

(e) Describe the positive direction on the line.

8. A line has parametric equations

$$x = 5, \qquad y = 2 + \frac{1}{\sqrt{2}}d, \qquad \text{and} \qquad z = -2 - \frac{1}{\sqrt{2}}d.$$

Draw the line.

9. A line has parametric equations $x = x_0$, $y = y_0$, and $z = z_0 + d$. Sketch the line. Show that the distance from (x, y, z) to (x_0, y_0, z_0) is $|d|$.

*10. In this section the parameter has been the directed distance along the line, but this restriction is not necessary. Show that $x = x_0 + At$, $y = y_0 + Bt$, and $z = z_0 + Ct$ are parametric equations for a line, where t is a parameter whose domain is the set of all real numbers, and A, B, C are arbitrary given numbers, not all zero. Show that the distance from (x, y, z) to (x_0, y_0, z_0) is $|t|\sqrt{A^2 + B^2 + C^2}$. Finally, give a geometric interpretation for the parameter t.

*11. A point moves with uniform speed v along a line. If t is the time elapsed since the point was at (x_0, y_0, z_0), write parametric equations for the line in terms of the parameter t.

3–8. PLANES

We shall return to the study of planes again in Chapter 11, where we shall prove that if A, B, C are real numbers, not all zero, then the set of points (x, y, z) such that

$$Ax + By + Cz + D = 0 \qquad (1)$$

is a plane. Equation (1) is called an equation of the plane, and sometimes we simply say "the plane $Ax + By + Cz + D = 0$." Conversely, every plane has an equation of the form (1).

For now, we shall take this basic theorem for granted. We shall plot some planes and find equations for some. At the moment, however, we are more concerned with lines as the intersections of planes than with the planes themselves.

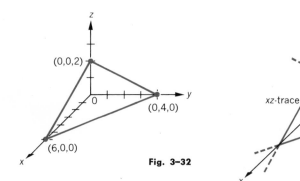

Fig. 3-32   Fig. 3-33

EXAMPLES

1. To sketch the plane $2x + 3y + 6z = 12$, it will suffice to find three points on the plane. Then we can "see" where it goes. If the plane is not parallel to any of the axes, it will cut each axis. These three *intercepts* are easy to obtain. For the given plane (Fig. 3–32) they are $(6, 0, 0)$, $(0, 4, 0)$, and $(0, 0, 2)$. The plane, or rather a triangular portion of the plane, is then easy to draw.

Another way of looking at the same problem is to examine the *traces* of the given plane in each of the coordinate planes (Fig. 3–33). The trace in any coordinate plane is the line of intersection of the given plane and that coordinate plane. Thus from Fig. 3–33 we see that the trace in the xy-plane is the intersection of the planes

$$z = 0, \qquad 2x + 3y = 12;$$

the trace in the yz-plane is the intersection of the planes

$$x = 0, \qquad 3y + 6z = 12;$$

the trace in the zx-plane is the intersection of the planes

$$y = 0, \qquad 2x + 6z = 12.$$

2. Sketch the plane $3x + 2z = 6$.

What is striking here is that the variable y is missing from the equation. The x- and z-intercepts are at $(2, 0, 0)$ and $(0, 0, 3)$. There is no y-intercept because x and z cannot both be zero. Since the plane does not cut the y-axis, it is parallel to the y-axis and the plane appears as in Fig. 3–34.

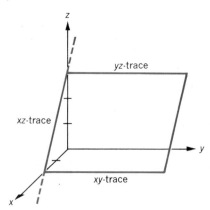

Fig. 3-34

3. Find an equation of the plane through the points $(0, -1, 1)$, $(6, 2, 1)$, and $(2, 1, 2)$.

Our first remark is that if the three points are collinear, there will be many planes through them. However, by finding direction cosines, it is easy to see that the three given points are *not* collinear, and so there is a unique plane. Therefore we wish to determine constants A, B, C, D such that the equation $Ax + By + Cz + D = 0$ is satisfied by the coordinates of all three points:

$$A(0) + B(-1) + C(1) + D = 0, \tag{2}$$

$$A(6) + B(2) + C(1) + D = 0, \tag{3}$$

$$A(2) + B(1) + C(2) + D = 0. \tag{4}$$

Although it may turn out that any one of A, B, C, or D is zero, we know that not all of A, B, C are zero because the unique plane through the given points has an equation of the type we seek.

Let us see what we can discover about the relations of A, B, C, and D from equations (2), (3), and (4). From equations (2) and (3) we obtain by subtraction

$$6A + 3B = 0,$$

where $A = -\frac{1}{2}B$. If we use $-\frac{1}{2}B$ for A in equation (4), we obtain

$$-B + B + 2C + D = 0,$$

where $C = -\frac{1}{2}D$. Then equation (2) gives

$$B = C + D = -\frac{1}{2}D + D = \frac{1}{2}D.$$

Therefore

$$A = -\tfrac{1}{2}B = -\tfrac{1}{4}D,$$
$$B = \tfrac{1}{2}D, \tag{5}$$
$$C = -\tfrac{1}{2}D,$$

and the plane has an equation

$$-\tfrac{1}{4}Dx + \tfrac{1}{2}Dy + (-\tfrac{1}{2}Dz) + D = 0. \tag{6}$$

Certainly $D \neq 0$, for otherwise equation (6) is the triviality, $0 = 0$, and does not represent a plane. Hence equation (6) is equivalent to

$$x - 2y + 2z - 4 = 0,$$

and this is an equation of the plane we sought.

Remarks

1. What we have done in the above solution is to solve for three of the constants in terms of the fourth. We cannot tell in advance which one to select for the fourth; however, in practice this causes no trouble. We simply successively eliminate A, B, C, or D until we obtain a solution analogous to equation (5).

2. Equations (2), (3), and (4) are three equations in four unknowns. We are not actually interested in these numbers A, B, C, and D, but only in their ratios. In equation (6), D can be any nonzero number. In other words, the plane

$$Ax + By + Cz + D = 0 \tag{1}$$

is also represented by

$$\frac{A}{D}x + \frac{B}{D}y + \frac{C}{D}z + 1 = 0$$

if $D \neq 0$. Then the three ratios,

$$\frac{A}{D}, \frac{B}{D}, \frac{C}{D},$$

can be found from equations (2), (3), and (4), and the plane is determined.

But what happens if $D = 0$? Then we cannot divide equation (1) by D. Yet, there is a plane, $Ax + By + Cz = 0$, through the three given points, for which at least one of A, B, or C is not zero. Thus we may divide in equation (1) by any one of A, B, or C which is not zero. More generally, we can multiply equation (1) by any number $k \neq 0$ to obtain the equivalent equation

$$kAx + kBy + kCz + kD = 0. \tag{7}$$

If $k = 1/D$, we have the situation of the example. If $k = 1/A$ ($A \neq 0$), then we would solve for the three ratios B/A, C/A, D/A.

Problems

1. Sketch the following planes. In each case find the intercepts and the traces in the coordinate planes.

(a) $x - y + 2z = 3$

(b) $x + y + z = a$, $a > 0$

(c) $x - 2y - z + 4 = 0$

(d) $x + 2y = 5$

(e) $2y + 3z = 10$

(f) $2x - 2z + 5 = 0$

(g) $2x = 5$

2. Find the point or points of intersection, if any, of the following sets of three planes.†

   (a) $x + y + z = 5,\quad 2x - y + z = 0,\quad 3x - 4y + 5z + 4 = 0$

   (b) $x + 2y = 6,\quad 2x = y,\quad z = 3$ (Draw the planes.)

   (c) $x = a,\quad y = b,\quad z = c$ (Draw the planes.)

   (d) $x + 2y - 3z = 5,\quad 2x + y + z = 6,\quad 3x - y + 4z = -1$

   (e) $x + y + z = 5,\quad x - y - z + 5 = 0,\quad 3x - y - z + 5 = 0$
   (Draw the planes.)

   (f) $x - y + 2x = 6,\quad 2x - 2y + 4z = -4,\quad 5x - 5y + 10z = 15$
   (Draw the planes.)

3. Traces of a plane in each of the coordinate planes are given by

$$3x + 5z = 15,\qquad 2x - 5y = 10,\qquad \text{and} \qquad 2z - 3y = 6.$$

   Sketch a portion of the plane and find an equation of the plane with these traces.

4. Find an equation of the plane passing through the points:

   (a) $(1, 2, 2),\quad (3, 3, -1),\quad (-1, 5, 1)$

   (b) $(0, -1, 0),\quad (2, 1, -2),\quad (1, 0, -1)$

   (c) $(1, 1, 0),\quad (3, 0, 1),\quad (-1, 2, -1)$

   (d) $(1, 1, 1),\quad (2, 4, -2),\quad (5, 1, 0)$

   (e) $(2, 0, 0),\quad (0, 3, 0),\quad (0, 0, 4)$

   (f) $(2, 2, 1),\quad (4, 2, -1),\quad (6, -3, 2)$

5. Show that if not all of A, B, and C are zero, then

$$A(x - x_0) + B(y - y_0) + C(z - z_0) = 0$$

   is an equation of a plane through (x_0, y_0, z_0).

*6. Given distinct planes $A_1x + B_1y + C_1z + D_1 = 0$ and $A_2x + B_2y + C_2z + D_2 = 0$ which are not parallel, and given a real number k, show that the set of all points (x, y, z) for which

$$A_1x + B_1y + C_1z + D_1 + k(A_2x + B_2y + C_2z + D_2) = 0$$

   is a plane through the line of intersection of the given planes.

*7. Use Problem 6 to obtain an equation for the plane through the line of intersection of the planes $x - 3y + z = 5$ and $2x - y - z = 5$, and containing the point $(1, 1, 1)$.

---

† For the solution of three linear equations in three unknowns by determinants, see Appendix A.

*3-9. PROJECTING PLANES OF A LINE

The *projecting planes of a line* are planes containing the line which are perpendicular to the coordinate planes. These planes are frequently con- venient for sketching the line.

EXAMPLES

1. Find equations for the xy and the xz projecting planes of the line through $(3, 1, 1)$ and $(-1, 3, 3)$. Dropping perpendiculars from these points to the xy-plane, we get the points $(3, 1, 0)$ and $(-1, 3, 0)$. The trace in the xy-plane is then

$$\frac{y-3}{x+1} = \frac{1-3}{3+1} \quad \text{or} \quad x + 2y - 5 = 0.$$

Dropping perpendiculars to the xz-plane, we get the points $(3, 0, 1)$ and $(-1, 0, 3)$. The trace in the xz-plane is then

$$\frac{z-1}{x-3} = \frac{3-1}{-1-3} \quad \text{or} \quad x + 2z - 5 = 0.$$

These projecting planes and the line l are shown in Fig. 3–35.

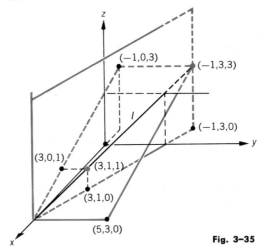

Fig. 3–35

2. The line of the previous example has parametric equations

$$x = 3 + \frac{2d}{\sqrt{6}}, \quad y = 1 - \frac{d}{\sqrt{6}}, \quad z = 1 - \frac{d}{\sqrt{6}}.$$

Solving each of these equations for d, we find

$$d = \frac{\sqrt{6}\,(x-3)}{2} = -\sqrt{6}\,(y-1) = -\sqrt{6}\,(z-1),$$

88

from which we obtain the three equations

$$x + 2y = 5, \qquad y - z = 0, \qquad x + 2z = 5.$$

These are equations of the three projecting planes.

3. The equations of two intersecting planes are

$$2x - y + z = 10 \qquad \text{and} \qquad x + y - 3z = 4.$$

Find the equations of the projecting planes of their line of intersection. If (x, y, z) is a point on the line of intersection of the planes, then both equations are satisfied simultaneously. Therefore, if we eliminate y between the two equations (by adding), we get the equation

$$3x - 2z = 14.$$

This is an equation satisfied by the coordinates of all points on the line of intersection. But it is also a plane parallel to the y-axis. It is therefore the xz projecting plane.

Similarly, if we eliminate z between the two equations, we get the xy projecting plane:

$$7x - 2y = 34.$$

If we eliminate x between the two equations, we obtain the yz projecting plane:

$$-3y + 7z = 2.$$

Problems

1. Given the following parametric equations of lines, find equations of the projecting planes, draw two of these planes and the line, and find two of the points of intersection of the line with the coordinate planes.

(a) $x = -1 + \dfrac{2d}{\sqrt{5}}, \quad y = 2, \quad z = 2 - \dfrac{d}{\sqrt{5}}$

(b) $x = \dfrac{2d}{3}, \quad y = 1 - \dfrac{2d}{3}, \quad z = 2 + \dfrac{d}{3}$

(c) $x = 1 - \dfrac{d}{\sqrt{3}}, \quad y = -1 + \dfrac{d}{\sqrt{3}}, \quad z = 1 - \dfrac{d}{\sqrt{3}}$

(d) $x = 1 + \dfrac{d}{\sqrt{11}}, \quad y = \dfrac{3d}{\sqrt{11}}, \quad z = 1 - \dfrac{d}{\sqrt{11}}$

2. Find two of the projecting planes and draw the line determined by the following pairs of points.

(a) $(4, 0, 4), (0, 2, 2)$ (b) $(0, -3, 0), (1, 3, 3)$ (c) $(1, 1, 7), (3, 7, 1)$

89

3. Find the equations of the projecting planes of the lines of intersection of the following planes. Draw two of the projecting planes and the line in each case.

(a) $x + y + 3z = 9$, $2x + y + 2z = 10$

(b) $x + 3z = 6$, $x + y + z = 9$

(c) $x + y + z = 6$, $y = 2x$

4. Draw a picture of the two planes

$$x + 2z = 4 \quad \text{and} \quad x + y = 4.$$

Show the line of intersection and determine direction cosines of this line.

5. Draw a picture of the line of intersection of the two planes $x + y + z = 6$ and $y + 2z = 4$. Find two points on this line and determine its direction cosines.

SUMMARY

In this chapter we have studied some geometry of euclidean space. First we stated four assumptions, or postulates, for space and then proved a few theorems that follow from these assumptions. Using the theorems for space and the fact that a line can be assigned coordinates, we were able to coordinatize space; that is, to show the existence of a one-to-one correspondence between the points of space and the set of ordered triples (x, y, z) of real numbers. A distance formula between pairs of points in space was developed as a result of the establishment of a coordinate system.

Parametric equations for a line in space were derived in a manner analogous to that used for a line in the plane. In the plane, each line can be represented by two parametric equations. In space, a set of three parametric equations are needed to represent a line.

Finally, we considered rectangular equations of planes and observed that by considering the intercepts of a plane or the traces of the plane in the coordinate planes, it is quite easy to draw pictures of planes.

Some of the more important relations developed in this chapter are listed below.

1. *The distance between two points:*

$$d = \sqrt{(x_2 - x_1)^2 + (y_2 - y_1)^2 + (z_2 - z_1)^2}.$$

2. *Direction cosines of a line:* If d is the directed distance from (x_0, y_0, z_0) to (x_1, y_1, z_1), then the line containing these points has direction cosines

$$c_1 = \frac{x_1 - x_0}{d}, \qquad c_2 = \frac{y_1 - y_0}{d}, \qquad c_3 = \frac{z_1 - z_0}{d}.$$

3. *Parametric equations of a line:*

$$x = x_0 + c_1 d, \qquad y = y_0 + c_2 d, \qquad z = z_0 + c_3 d,$$

where d is the parameter and is the directed distance along the line.

4. *Rectangular equation of a plane:* Every plane has an equation of the form

$$Ax + By + Cz + D = 0,$$

where not all of the real numbers A, B, and C are zero. The set of all points (x, y, z) satisfying $Ax + By + Cz + D = 0$ is a plane.

5. *Intercepts and traces of planes:* The plane $Ax + By + Cz + D = 0$ has intercepts

$$\left(\frac{-D}{A}, 0, 0\right), \quad \left(0, \frac{-D}{B}, 0\right), \quad \text{and} \quad \left(0, 0, \frac{-D}{C}\right)$$

if A, B, and C are not zero.

Traces of the plane are given by

$$Ax + By + D = 0, \quad By + Cz + D = 0, \quad \text{and} \quad Ax + Cz + D = 0.$$

Review Problems

1. Prove that if a plane intersects one of two parallel planes, then it must intersect the other plane.

2. Prove that if a plane intersects two parallel planes, then the lines of intersection are parallel.

3. Show that if a line is perpendicular to a plane, then any plane containing the line is perpendicular to the given plane.

4. Show that the points $(-2, 4, -1)$, $(0, 8, 3)$, and $(-3, 2, -3)$ are collinear by using the distance formula.

5. What is the length of the diagonal of a cube which is four inches on an edge?

6. Find the length of the shortest path *on the surface of the cube* between diagonally opposite corners of a four-inch cube.

7. If the coordinates of two points on a line are known, how many different sets of parametric equations of the line can be written using one of the points as (x_0, y_0, z_0)?

8. Parametric equations of a line are

$$x = 1 + \frac{3d}{5}, \quad y = 4 - \frac{3d}{5}, \quad \text{and} \quad z = -2 + \frac{\sqrt{7}\,d}{5}.$$

Find the coordinates of the points of intersection of the line with each of the coordinate planes. Draw the line.

9. A point "moves" at constant velocity along a line toward the xy-plane as follows: At a time t_0, it is at $(-3, 5, 4)$. One second later, it is at $(-1, 2, 2)$.

   (a) What point in the xy-plane will it reach?
   (b) How long from time t_0 will it take the point to reach the plane?
   (c) Compute the speed of the point in units per second.

10. The traces of a plane are

$$2x + 5y = 10, \qquad 3x + 5z = 15, \qquad \text{and} \qquad 3y + 2z = 6.$$

   (a) Sketch each line in the proper coordinate plane.
   (b) What are the intercepts of the plane?
   (c) What is a rectangular equation of the plane?

11. Show that if $(a, 0, 0)$, $(0, b, 0)$, and $(0, 0, c)$ are the intercepts of a plane, then the plane has an equation of the form

$$\frac{x}{a} + \frac{y}{b} + \frac{z}{c} = 1.$$

12. A line has parametric equations

$$x = 1 + \frac{2}{\sqrt{62}} d, \qquad y = -2 + \frac{-7}{\sqrt{62}} d, \qquad \text{and} \qquad z = 1 + \frac{-3}{\sqrt{62}} d.$$

   Find an equation of a plane that contains this line and the point $(7, 0, 0)$.

13. Parametric equations of a line are

$$x = 1 + \frac{5}{\sqrt{59}} d, \qquad y = 1 + \frac{5}{\sqrt{59}} d, \qquad \text{and} \qquad z = 4 - \frac{3}{\sqrt{59}} d.$$

   Sketch the line and its projecting planes.

14. The three planes $2x + y + 2z = 7$, $x + y + z = 3$, and $x - y - z = 5$ have exactly one point in common. Find this point of intersection.

15. Sketch the planes $10x + 12y + 15z = 60$ and $x - y + 2z = 4$ and the line of their intersection. Draw the xy projecting plane of the intersection line and determine an equation of the projecting plane.

16. Find an equation of the plane through $(4, 2, 1)$, $(0, 4, 0)$, and $(2, -2, 2)$.

*17. The line through $(4, 4, 1)$ is perpendicular to a plane at $(3, 2, -1)$. Find an equation of the plane.

*18. Show that if a line contains a point (a, b, c) and is perpendicular to a plane at (d, e, f), then

$$(a - d)x + (b - e)y + (c - f)z$$
$$+ (d^2 + e^2 + f^2 - ad - be - cf) = 0$$

   is an equation of the plane.

92

HISTORICAL NOTE

Adaptation of the title page of the first English translation of Euclid's *Elements*, printed in London in 1570.

Little is known of Euclid the man. The information we have is by inference from comments by other writers concerning his mathematics. What seems to be certain is that he lived around 300 B.C., that he learned his mathematics from pupils of Plato, and that he lived much of his life in Alexandria, where he taught and founded a school. His major work, *The Elements*,† consists of thirteen "books," parts of which are familiar to high school students from either geometry or algebra. Of these books only XI and XIII are concerned with solid geometry.

Most of the theorems presented in Sections 3–1 through 3–4 are to be found in Book XI among the first 19 Propositions. The remaining propositions (20 to 39) of Book XI are concerned with solid polyhedra and their volumes. It should be noted that Euclid used (erroneously) no additional postulates for his geometry of space—whereas we, in conformity to modern insight, require four additional postulates. Book XIII is devoted to propositions about the five regular polyhedra.

---

† The word "elements" should not be construed in its common current sense as meaning simple, or elementary. Rather, the word means *foundations* or the basic building blocks from which the entire edifice of mathematics (of his day) was to be constructed.

VECTORS

4

N SPACE

4-1. INTRODUCTION

In Chapter 2 we discussed vectors in the plane. In this chapter we again consider vectors, but vectors in space. We shall see that lines in space can be represented by vector equations, and we shall also show that planes can be represented by vector equations.

4-2. DEFINITIONS: ARROWS, VECTORS

The definitions for vectors in space are essentially the same as those for vectors in the plane. The same physical interpretations that were given for plane vectors may be made for vectors in space. We shall again denote vectors by boldface type. For example, $\mathbf{a}$, $\mathbf{v}$, $\mathbf{r}$, $\mathbf{s}$, and $\mathbf{u}$. The vector represented by the arrow (P_1, P_2) will be denoted by $\overrightarrow{P_1P_2}$. The magnitude of $\mathbf{a}$ will be denoted by $|\mathbf{a}|$.

DEFINITION 4-1

If P_1 and P_2 are points, the ordered pair of points (P_1, P_2) is called an *arrow*. The point P_1 is the *initial point* of the arrow. The point P_2 is the *terminal point* of the arrow. The *magnitude* of the arrow (P_1, P_2) is the length, $|P_1P_2|$, of the segment $\overline{P_1P_2}$. The direction of the arrow is given by the direction cosines of the line directed from P_1 through P_2.

If $P_1 = P_2$, the arrow is called a *null arrow*. It has magnitude zero but no direction.

DEFINITION 4-2

Two arrows are *equivalent* if they have the same magnitude and direction. The set of all arrows equivalent to a given arrow is an *equivalence class* of arrows.

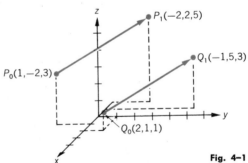

Fig. 4-1

EXAMPLE

The ordered pair of points $(P_0, P_1) = \big((1, -2, 3), (-2, 2, 5)\big)$ and $(Q_0, Q_1) = \big((2, 1, 1), (-1, 5, 3)\big)$ are equivalent arrows since each arrow has magnitude $\sqrt{29}$, and the ray from P_0 to P_1 has the same direction cosines as the ray from Q_0 to Q_1 (Fig. 4-1).

96

THEOREM 4-1

If the points P_1, P_2, P_3, and P_4 have the coordinates shown in Fig. 4-2, then the arrows (P_1, P_2) and (P_3, P_4) are equivalent if and only if

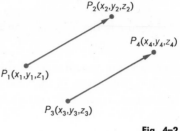

$$x_2 - x_1 = x_4 - x_3,$$
$$y_2 - y_1 = y_4 - y_3, \qquad (1)$$
$$z_2 - z_1 = z_4 - z_3.$$

Fig. 4-2

Proof. We suppose that equations (1) are true. The magnitudes of the arrows are the same,

$$\sqrt{(x_2 - x_1)^2 + (y_2 - y_1)^2 + (z_2 - z_1)^2}$$
$$= \sqrt{(x_4 - x_3)^2 + (y_4 - y_3)^2 + (z_4 - z_3)^2}, \qquad (2)$$

and the direction cosines are also the same,

$$c_1 = \frac{x_2 - x_1}{d} = \frac{x_4 - x_3}{d},$$
$$c_2 = \frac{y_2 - y_1}{d} = \frac{y_4 - y_3}{d}, \qquad (3)$$
$$c_3 = \frac{z_2 - z_1}{d} = \frac{z_4 - z_3}{d}.$$

Therefore the two arrows are equivalent.

Conversely, let us suppose that the two arrows are equivalent. Then they have the same magnitude and direction. Therefore equations (2) and (3) will be true, and these equations imply equations (1).

DEFINITION 4-3

A *vector* is an equivalence class of arrows. Any arrow in an equivalence class of arrows may represent the vector. The magnitude and direction of a vector are the same as the magnitude and direction of an arrow representing the vector.

Thus a vector is a set of arrows. Each vector contains all arrows of the same magnitude and direction. Therefore two vectors **u** and **v** are *equal* if they are the same set of arrows, **u** = **v**. This will be true if and only if arrows of **u** and arrows of **v** have the same direction and magnitude.

DEFINITION 4-4

The *null vector* is the vector whose magnitude is zero. It is the equivalence class of null arrows. The null vector is denoted by **0**.

97

DEFINITION 4-5

> *The position vector* for any given vector is the arrow in the vector whose initial point is at the origin.

Since we can visualize any vector by picturing any arrow in the vector, it is convenient to visualize vectors by picturing their position vectors (Fig. 4–3).

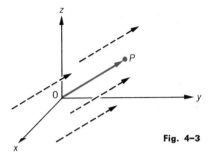

Fig. 4-3

Problems

1. Sketch each of the arrows given below and determine the magnitude and direction cosines.

   (a) $((0, 0, 0), (4, 4, 2))$
   (b) $((5, 4, 1), (1, -3, 3))$
   (c) $((-3, -3, 4), (0, 0, 0))$
   (d) $((0, a, 0), (b, 0, 0)), \quad a > 0, b > 0$.

2. Sketch several arrows that are in the same equivalence class as the arrow $((3, 3, 4), (5, -2, 1))$.

3. What is the endpoint of the position vector for each of the equivalence classes of arrows in Problems 1 and 2?

4. Distinguish between *equivalent arrows* and *equal arrows*.

5. $\mathbf{a} \neq \mathbf{b}$. Could arrows representing these vectors be equivalent arrows?

6. If, in the figure,

   $(P_0, P_1) = ((x_0, y_0, z_0), (x_1, y_1, z_1))$,

   what are the coordinates of the endpoint of a position vector, $\overrightarrow{OP}$, such that $\overrightarrow{P_0P_1} = \overrightarrow{OP}$?

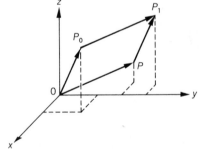

7. Show that the arrows (O, P_0) and (P, P_1) in Problem 6 are equivalent arrows, and hence represent the same vector.

8. An arrow has initial point $(-1, -2, 1)$ and direction cosines $c_1 = -\frac{1}{3}$, $c_2 = \frac{2}{3}$, $c_3 = \frac{2}{3}$. If the arrow has magnitude 6, what are the coordinates of the endpoint of the arrow?

9. If $P = (6, -6, -2)$ and $\overrightarrow{OP'}$ has the same magnitude as $\overrightarrow{OP}$ but is opposite in direction, what are the coordinates of P'? Sketch the arrows.

10. $|\overrightarrow{OP}| = 1$, and $\overrightarrow{OP}$ has direction cosines

$$\left(\frac{3}{\sqrt{14}}, \frac{-2}{\sqrt{14}}, \frac{1}{\sqrt{14}}\right).$$

What are the coordinates of P?

*11. If $P_1 = (3, -2, 2)$ and $P_2 = (4, 5, -1)$, show that $\overrightarrow{OP_1} \perp \overrightarrow{OP_2}$. [*Hint:* Use the distance formula and the converse of the Pythagorean Theorem.]

4-3. ALGEBRA OF VECTORS

In this section we define addition of vectors. Our definition for addition of vectors is the same as that given for plane vectors except that we are now considering vectors in space.

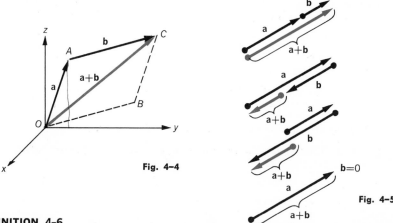

Fig. 4-4

Fig. 4-5

DEFINITION 4-6

If **a** and **b** are vectors and A and C are points such that $\mathbf{a} = \overrightarrow{OA}$ and $\mathbf{b} = \overrightarrow{AC}$, then

$$\mathbf{a} + \mathbf{b} = \overrightarrow{OC}.$$

Observe that C is the fourth vertex of the parallelogram (possibly degenerate) whose other vertices are O, A, and B (see Fig. 4-4). Cases for which **a** and **b** have the same direction or opposite directions are illustrated in Fig. 4-5.

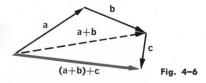

Fig. 4-6

The sum of three vectors is illustrated in Fig. 4-6.

99

We also define multiplication of a vector by a real number just as we did for vectors in the plane.

DEFINITION 4-7

If **v** is any vector and k is a real number, then $k\mathbf{v} = \mathbf{v}k$ is a vector with magnitude $|k| \cdot |\mathbf{v}|$. If $k > 0$, then $k\mathbf{v}$ has the same direction as **v**; if $k < 0$, then $k\mathbf{v}$ has direction opposite to that of **v**. In particular, $(-1)\mathbf{v} = -\mathbf{v}$.

The real number k in Definition 4-7 is often called a *scalar*, and we speak of "multiplication of a vector by a scalar."

If **p** is any vector in the same direction as, or in opposite direction to, **v**, then a real number k can be found so that $\mathbf{p} = k\mathbf{v}$.

The following theorem is fundamental in vector addition.

THEOREM 4-2

If $\mathbf{v}_1 = \overrightarrow{OP_1}$ and $\mathbf{v}_2 = \overrightarrow{OP_2}$, where P_1 and P_2 are points with coordinates as shown in Fig. 4-7, then

$$\mathbf{v}_1 + \mathbf{v}_2 = \overrightarrow{OP},$$

where P is the point $(x_1 + x_2, y_1 + y_2, z_1 + z_2)$.

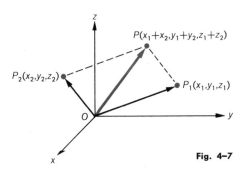

Fig. 4-7

Proof. Suppose that P has coordinates (x, y, z). Then (P_2, P) is equivalent to (O, P_1), and by Theorem 4-1,

$$x - x_2 = x_1 - 0,$$
$$y - y_2 = y_1 - 0,$$
$$z - z_2 = z_1 - 0.$$

Therefore, $(x, y, z) = (x_1 + x_2, y_1 + y_2, z_1 + z_2)$.

Corollary

Vector addition is commutative.

100

Problems

1. The endpoints of two position vectors are given below. Draw the arrows and determine the sum of the vectors by completing the parallelogram.

   (a) $(0, 2, 3)$ and $(3, 1, 0)$ (b) $(-1, 5, 1)$ and $(4, 1, 1)$

   (c) $(-2, -2, 4)$ and $(5, 6, -2)$ (d) $(-2, 4, 4)$ and $(1, -2, -1)$

2. What are the coordinates of the endpoint of the position vector that is the sum of the vectors in each part of Problem 1?

3. Vectors v_1 and v_2 have position vectors to points $(3, -4, 2)$ and $(-3, 4, -2)$, respectively. What are the coordinates of the point P such that

$$\overrightarrow{OP} = v_1 + v_2?$$

4. Does each vector in space have an additive inverse? That is, if v is any vector, is there a vector r such that $v + r = 0$?

5. If r and t are any vectors, is there a vector s such that $r + s = t$?

6. Define subtraction for vectors.

7. Show that $v + v = 2v$ for every vector v.

8. If $a = \overrightarrow{OA}, b = \overrightarrow{OB},$ and $c = \overrightarrow{OC},$ where $A = P(3, 1, 2), B = P(-2, 2, -1)$ and $C = P(4, 0, 3)$, find the coordinates of the point P such that $\overrightarrow{OP} = (a + b) + c$. Find the coordinates of the point Q such that $\overrightarrow{OQ} = a + (b + c)$. Is addition of vectors associative?

9. If r has a position vector with endpoint at $(3, -2, 1)$, what is the endpoint of the position vector for $4r$? What is the endpoint of $(-3)r$? What is the endpoint of $4r + (-3)r$?

10. In the figure, c is the difference of two vectors. Write the proper subtraction statement for each picture.

 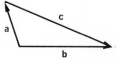

4-4. UNIT BASE VECTORS

In Chapter 2 we saw that each vector in the plane can be represented as a sum of multiples of two unit vectors directed along the positive x- and positive y-axes. In a similar manner, we may show that every vector in space can be represented as a sum of multiples of three unit vectors. A most convenient choice of the unit vectors is the three unit vectors directed along the positive x-, y-, and z-axes, as shown in Fig. 4-8. We shall use $i, j,$ and k to denote these unit vectors.

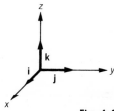

Fig. 4-8

101

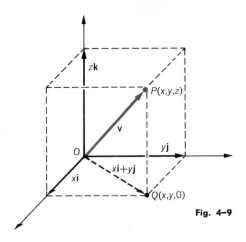

Fig. 4–9

Let us consider a vector $\mathbf{v} = \overrightarrow{OP}$ as in Fig. 4–9. Then $x\mathbf{i}$, $y\mathbf{j}$, and $z\mathbf{k}$ are vectors directed along the axes, and

$$x\mathbf{i} + y\mathbf{j} = \overrightarrow{OQ}.$$

Because $\overrightarrow{QP} = z\mathbf{k}$,

$$\overrightarrow{OP} = \overrightarrow{OQ} + \overrightarrow{QP}$$

and

$$\mathbf{v} = \overrightarrow{OP} = (x\mathbf{i} + y\mathbf{j}) + z\mathbf{k}. \tag{1}$$

In the same way,

$$\mathbf{v} = x\mathbf{i} + (y\mathbf{j} + z\mathbf{k}). \tag{2}$$

Thus, if $P' \neq P$, then $\overrightarrow{OP'} \neq \overrightarrow{OP}$, and it follows that every vector is a sum of unique vectors directed along the axes. From equations (1) and (2), we see that the way in which the vectors are grouped, or associated, is immaterial. We therefore write

$$\mathbf{v} = x\mathbf{i} + y\mathbf{j} + z\mathbf{k}.$$

DEFINITION 4–8

The *components* of $\mathbf{v} = x\mathbf{i} + y\mathbf{j} + z\mathbf{k}$ are the real numbers x, y, and z. The vectors $\mathbf{i}$, $\mathbf{j}$, and $\mathbf{k}$ are the *unit base vectors* for this coordinate system.

THEOREM 4–3

Two vectors are equal if and only if the corresponding components of these vectors are equal relative to the same coordinate system.

Proof. The coordinates of P, which are the components of $\overrightarrow{OP}$, uniquely determine the vector $\overrightarrow{OP}$.

102

THEOREM 4-4

If $v_1 = x_1 i + y_1 j + z_1 k$ and $v_2 = x_2 i + y_2 j + z_2 k$, then

$$v_1 + v_2 = (x_1 + x_2)i + (y_1 + y_2)j + (z_1 + z_2)k.$$

Proof. This is simply Theorem 4-2 expressed in terms of the unit base vectors.

The following theorem exhibits several properties of vector addition. These properties are either immediate consequences of Definitions 4-6 and 4-7 or easy deductions from Theorem 4-4.

THEOREM 4-5

For all vectors **a**, **b**, **c** and real numbers r and s:

(1) $a + b = b + a$.   (2) $a + (b + c) = (a + b) + c$.

(3) $a + 0 = a$.   (4) $r(a + b) = ra + rb$.

(5) $(r + s)a = ra + sa$.   (6) $(rs)a = r(sa)$.

(7) $0a = 0$.   (8) $1 \cdot a = a$.

Proofs of the various parts of Theorem 4-5 are left to the student.

Problems

1. Sketch a picture as in Fig. 4-9 to show that a position vector $\overrightarrow{OP}$ may be represented as $\overrightarrow{OP} = (xi + zk) + yj$.

2. If $P_1 = P(7, 4, -1)$ and $P_2 = P(3, -5, 4)$, what are the components of $\overrightarrow{P_1P_2}$? Express $\overrightarrow{P_1P_2}$ in terms of **i**, **j**, and **k**.

3. Find the magnitude of the following vectors.

   (a) $v = i + j + k$ (b) $a = a_1 i + a_2 j + a_3 k$

   (c) $r = 3i + (-4)j + k$ (d) $u = \frac{3}{5}i + \frac{(-2)}{5}j + \frac{2\sqrt{3}}{5}k$

   (e) $t = xi + yj + zk$

4. Sketch the following vectors, add them, and sketch their sum.

   (a) $2i + 3j, \quad j + k$ (b) $2i + j + (-1)k, \quad -i + j + 2k$

   (c) $3i, \quad -2k$ (d) $4i, \quad -2j + 2k$

5. Find real numbers x, y, and z such that

   (a) $xi + 2yj - zk + 3i - j = 4i + 3k$

   (b) $7xi + (y - 3)j + 6k = 10i + 8j - 3zk$

   (c) $(x + 4)i + (y - 5)j + (z - 1)k = 0$

6. Show that $(0, 0, 0)$, (x_1, y_1, z_1), (x_2, y_2, z_2), and $(x_1 + x_2, y_1 + y_2, z_1 + z_2)$ are the vertices of a parallelogram, possibly degenerate.

103

7. Prove parts (1), (2), and (4) of Theorem 4–5.

8. Let $\mathbf{v}$ be a position vector such that $|\mathbf{v}| = L$. If the direction cosines of $\mathbf{v}$ are c_1, c_2, and c_3, show that $\mathbf{v} = L(c_1\mathbf{i} + c_2\mathbf{j} + c_3\mathbf{k})$.

9. In the figure,

$$\mathbf{r}_1 = x_1\mathbf{i} + y_1\mathbf{j} + z_1\mathbf{k}$$

and

$$\mathbf{r}_2 = x_2\mathbf{i} + y_2\mathbf{j} + z_2\mathbf{k}.$$

What are the components of the vector $\frac{1}{2}(\mathbf{r}_1 + \mathbf{r}_2)$? What is this vector, geometrically?

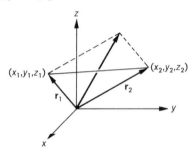

10. Explain how the figure on the right illustrates the associative property of vector addition.

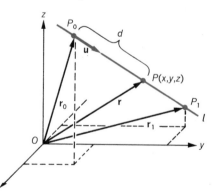

11. Three vectors with magnitudes 5, 12, and 13 have a sum equal to $\mathbf{0}$. Illustrate how this is possible.

12. If $\mathbf{u} = \mathbf{a} + \mathbf{b}$ and $\mathbf{v} = \mathbf{a} - \mathbf{b}$ are given, show how to find $\mathbf{a}$ and $\mathbf{b}$ geometrically.

4–5. VECTOR EQUATIONS OF LINES

In Chapter 2 we used vectors to represent lines in the plane. Here, we repeat the same argument for lines in space. As in Chapter 2, a vector equation of a line is an equation for the position vectors of all points on the line.

Let l be the line through $P_0 = P(x_0, y_0, z_0)$ and $P_1 = P(x_1, y_1, z_1)$, and let $\mathbf{r}_0 = \overrightarrow{OP_0}$ and $\mathbf{r}_1 = \overrightarrow{OP_1}$ (Fig. 4–10). Choose a positive direction on l, say from P_0 to P_1, and let $\mathbf{u}$ be a unit vector in that direction.

If $P(x, y, z)$ is any point on l, let

$$\mathbf{r} = \overrightarrow{OP} = x\mathbf{i} + y\mathbf{j} + z\mathbf{k}.$$

If d is the directed distance along l from P_0, then

$$\mathbf{r} = \mathbf{r}_0 + d\mathbf{u}. \qquad (1)$$

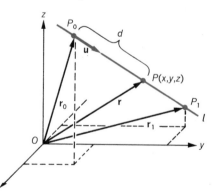

Fig. 4–10

If c_1, c_2, and c_3 are the direction cosines of $\mathbf{u}$, then $\mathbf{u} = c_1\mathbf{i} + c_2\mathbf{j} + c_3\mathbf{k}$ so that equation (1) may be written

$$
\begin{aligned}
\mathbf{r} &= x\mathbf{i} + y\mathbf{j} + z\mathbf{k} \\
&= x_0\mathbf{i} + y_0\mathbf{j} + z_0\mathbf{k} + d(c_1\mathbf{i} + c_2\mathbf{j} + c_3\mathbf{k}) \qquad (2) \\
&= (x_0 + c_1 d)\mathbf{i} + (y_0 + c_2 d)\mathbf{j} + (z_0 + c_3 d)\mathbf{k}.
\end{aligned}
$$

It follows from Theorem 4-3 that

$$
x = x_0 + c_1 d, \qquad y = y_0 + c_2 d, \qquad \text{and} \qquad z = z_0 + c_3 d.
$$

These three equations are parametric equations of l. Thus the single vector equation (1) is equivalent to three parametric equations.

We may also write equation (1) in another way. Observe that for any point P on l, we have $d\mathbf{u} = \overrightarrow{P_0P}$; and since $\overrightarrow{P_0P}$ and $\overrightarrow{P_0P_1}$ have the same or opposite directions it follows that $\overrightarrow{P_0P} = t\overrightarrow{P_0P_1}$, where t is a real number. Thus equation (1) can be written as

$$
\mathbf{r} = \mathbf{r}_0 + t\overrightarrow{P_0P_1}. \qquad (3)
$$

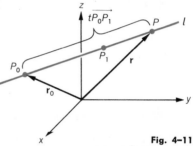

Note that if $0 < t < 1$, then P lies between P_0 and P_1, that is, P_0PP_1. If $t < 0$, then the order of the points will be PP_0P_1. If $t > 1$, then P_0P_1P. Figure 4-11 illustrates the case for $t > 1$.

Fig. 4-11

Problems

1. The coordinates of P_0 and P_1 are $(3, -2, 4)$ and $(-1, 3, 7)$, respectively. Show that a vector equation of the line through P_0 and P_1 is

$$
\mathbf{r} = (3 - 4t)\mathbf{i} + (-2 + 5t)\mathbf{j} + (4 + 3t)\mathbf{k},
$$

where t is any real number.

2. Given the vector equation of Problem 1, find the coordinates of the endpoint of $\mathbf{r}$ for the following values of the parameter t. Sketch the line.
   (a) 0   (b) 1   (c) -1 (d) 2   (e) $\frac{1}{2}$ (f) $\frac{2}{3}$

3. Determine the vector equation for the line through each of the following pairs of points. (Let P_0 be the first point listed.)
   (a) $(0, 1, 2)$, $(3, 0, 2)$ (b) $(3, -1, 5)$, $(2, 0, -5)$
   (c) $(4, 4, -2)$, $(-3, 2, -1)$ (d) $(-3, -1, -3)$, $(3, 1, 3)$
   (e) (a_1, b_1, c_1), (a_2, b_2, c_2)

105

4. Prove that the coordinates of the midpoint of a segment $\overline{P_1P_2}$, where $P_1 = P(x_1, y_1, z_1)$ and $P_2 = P(x_2, y_2, z_2)$, are

$$\left(\frac{x_1 + x_2}{2}, \frac{y_1 + y_2}{2}, \frac{z_1 + z_2}{2} \right).$$

5. Find the midpoints of the segments whose endpoints are:
   (a) $(-1, 5, 2)$ and $(-3, 2, 7)$ (b) $(1, 2, 3)$ and $(4, 5, 6)$
   (c) $(\pi, \pi/2, 2)$ and $(3, \sqrt{3}, \sqrt{2})$ (d) $(a, -b, c)$ and $(-a, b, -c)$
   (e) $(a, 0, 0)$ and $(0, b, 0)$

6. A point P is between $P_0 = P(-1, 3, 2)$ and $P_1 = P(5, 2, 5)$ and is twice as far from P_0 as P_1. Find the coordinates of P.

7. A point P is on the line containing $P_0 = P(-2, -4, 1)$ and $P_1 = P(3, 2, 2)$. If P_1 is the midpoint of the segment $\overline{P_0P}$, what are the coordinates of P?

8. A line contains the points $P_0 = P(5, 5, 3)$ and $P_1 = P(1, -3, 8)$. Find all possible coordinates of a point P which is twice as far from P_1 as it is from P_0.

9. Obtain the coordinates of the points which trisect the segment whose endpoints are (x_1, y_1, z_1) and (x_2, y_2, z_2).

10. Parametric equations of a line are

$$x = -2 + \tfrac{2}{3}d, \qquad y = 5 + \tfrac{1}{3}d, \qquad z = 1 - \tfrac{2}{3}d.$$

Write a vector equation of the line.

11. A point "moves" on a line with constant speed. At time $t = 0$, it is at $(0, 0, 0)$. At the end of one second it is at $(2, 4, \sqrt{5})$. Give a formula for the position vector to the point at the end of t seconds. What is the speed in the x-direction? in the y-direction? in the z-direction?

12. The midpoints of the sides of a triangle are (a_1, b_1, c_1), (a_2, b_2, c_2), and (a_3, b_3, c_3). Using vectors, find the coordinates of the vertices of the triangle.

4–6. VECTOR REPRESENTATION OF PLANES

We now turn to the vector representation of planes. Let us consider any plane π and a point $P_0 = P(x_0, y_0, z_0)$ in π (Fig. 4–12). Let $\mathbf{u}$ and $\mathbf{v}$ be unit vectors (not necessarily perpendicular) in π which are not collinear. Let P be any point in the plane π and let $\mathbf{r}_0 = \overrightarrow{OP_0}$ and $\mathbf{r} = \overrightarrow{OP}$. Then

$$\mathbf{r} = \mathbf{r}_0 + \overrightarrow{P_0P}.$$

But $\overrightarrow{P_0P}$ is a sum of multiples of the unit vectors $\mathbf{u}$ and $\mathbf{v}$, that is, $\overrightarrow{P_0P} = s\mathbf{u} + t\mathbf{v}$, where s and t are real numbers uniquely associated with P. The

106

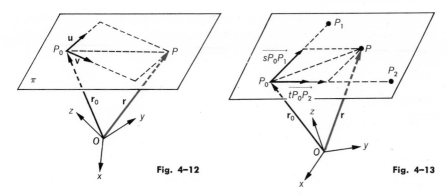

Fig. 4-12   Fig. 4-13

real numbers s and t are the directed lengths of the sides of the parallelogram whose opposite vertices are P_0 and P. Thus

$$\mathbf{r} = \mathbf{r}_0 + s\mathbf{u} + t\mathbf{v}. \tag{1}$$

Now, if we think of s and t as parameters, that is, as variables that can be any real numbers, then the vector equation (1) represents the plane π. Note that the parameters have a simple geometric interpretation as lengths of the sides of parallelograms.

We have seen that three noncollinear points determine a unique plane. When we are given three such points, say P_0, P_1, and P_2, with coordinates (x_0, y_0, z_0), (x_1, y_1, z_1), and (x_2, y_2, z_2), respectively, it is convenient to use the vectors $\overrightarrow{P_0 P_1}$ and $\overrightarrow{P_0 P_2}$ instead of the unit vectors $\mathbf{u}$ and $\mathbf{v}$. Referring to Fig. 4-13, we then have

$$\mathbf{r} = \mathbf{r}_0 + s\overrightarrow{P_0 P_1} + t\overrightarrow{P_0 P_2}, \tag{2}$$

where s and t are parameters. Note that s and t do not represent the directed lengths of the sides of the parallelogram, as before. Considering the components of the vectors in equation (2), we find that

$$
\begin{aligned}
x &= x_0 + s(x_1 - x_0) + t(x_2 - x_0), \\
y &= y_0 + s(y_1 - y_0) + t(y_2 - y_0), \\
z &= z_0 + s(z_1 - z_0) + t(z_2 - z_0).
\end{aligned} \tag{3}
$$

Equations (3) are parametric equations of the plane through P_0, P_1, and P_2.

Remarks

1. In equations (1), (2), and (3), there are *two* parameters. Assigning values to these parameters determines a unique point in the plane and conversely. Thus we see that for a line, a single parameter covers all points of the line, whereas for a plane, two parameters are needed. This distinction is reflected in the common language that "a line is one-dimensional and a plane is two-dimensional."

107

2. A rectangular equation of the plane can be obtained by eliminating s and t from equations (3). One can solve the first pair of equations (3) for s and t and substitute the result in the third equation.

Problems

1. A vector equation of a plane is given by

$$\mathbf{r} = (2 + 3s + 4t)\mathbf{i} + (-1 + 2s - 5t)\mathbf{j} + (4 - s + t)\mathbf{k}.$$

Find the coordinates of points in the plane determined by the following values of the parameters s and t.

(a) $s = 0$ and $t = 0$ (b) $s = 0$ and $t = 1$

(c) $s = 1$ and $t = 0$ (d) $s = 1$ and $t = 1$

(e) $s = -1$ and $t = 0$ (f) $s = 0$ and $t = -1$

2. Write parametric equations for the planes through each of the following triples of points. Find several other points on the planes.

(a) $(1, 0, 0)$, $(0, 1, 0)$, $(0, 0, 1)$ (b) $(1, 1, 1)$, $(3, 0, 0)$, $(0, 2, 1)$

(c) $(0, 0, 0)$, $(0, 2, 0)$, $(1, 0, 2)$ (d) $(0, 1, 4)$, $(1, -2, 0)$, $(3, 0, 0)$

3. Eliminate the parameters s and t in the parametric equations determined in Problem 2 to obtain rectangular equations for the planes.

4. Show how equations (3) are derived from equation (2).

5. Sketch the planes having the following vector representations.

(a) $\mathbf{r} = 3\mathbf{i} + s\mathbf{j} + t\mathbf{k}$

(b) $\mathbf{r} = \mathbf{i} + \mathbf{j} + s\mathbf{j} + t\mathbf{k}$

(c) $\mathbf{r} = \mathbf{i} + \mathbf{j} + (-\mathbf{i} + \mathbf{j})s + t\mathbf{k}$

(d) $\mathbf{r} = (\mathbf{i} + 2\mathbf{j}) + s\mathbf{k} + t(-\mathbf{i} - \mathbf{j})$

(e) $\mathbf{r} = 2\mathbf{k} - s\mathbf{k} + t(2\mathbf{i} + \mathbf{j})$

(f) $\mathbf{r} = -2\mathbf{j} + s(2\mathbf{j} + \mathbf{k}) + t(3\mathbf{i} + 2\mathbf{j})$

6. Write parametric equations for each of the planes in Problem 5. Eliminate the parameters to obtain rectangular equations of the planes.

*7. Parametric equations of a line l are

$$x = 3 + \frac{2}{\sqrt{17}}d, \quad y = -5 + \frac{2}{\sqrt{17}}d, \quad z = 4 + \frac{3}{\sqrt{17}}d.$$

Let $P(2, 1, 1)$ be a point not on l.

(a) Write a vector equation of the plane determined by l and P.

(b) Write parametric equations of this plane.

(c) Write a rectangular equation of the plane.

108

*4–7. VECTORS AND VECTOR SPACES

The properties of vectors which have been studied so far do not cover all the properties possessed by vectors. We have not yet discussed the angles that a vector makes with another vector or with a plane. Discussion of these properties is deferred until the trigonometric functions have been treated. In Chapter 11 we shall return to this aspect of vectors and show that vectors in space have additional algebraic properties.

In our discussion we have outlined the main algebraic properties of vectors in space, namely:

1. Vectors can be *added*. This addition is commutative and associative; the zero vector has special properties. Thus

$$\mathbf{a} + \mathbf{b} = \mathbf{b} + \mathbf{a},$$
$$\mathbf{a} + (\mathbf{b} + \mathbf{c}) = (\mathbf{a} + \mathbf{b}) + \mathbf{c},$$
$$\mathbf{a} + \mathbf{0} = \mathbf{a}.$$

For every vector $\mathbf{a}$ there is a vector $-\mathbf{a}$ (called the additive, inverse, or opposite of $\mathbf{a}$) such that

$$\mathbf{a} + (-\mathbf{a}) = \mathbf{0}.$$

2. Vectors can be *multiplied by real numbers to give vectors*. This multiplication by real numbers has the properties

$$\alpha(\mathbf{a} + \mathbf{b}) = \alpha\mathbf{a} + \alpha\mathbf{b},$$
$$(\alpha + \beta)\mathbf{a} = \alpha\mathbf{a} + \beta\mathbf{a},$$
$$\alpha(\beta\mathbf{a}) = (\alpha\beta)\mathbf{a},$$
$$0 \cdot \mathbf{a} = \mathbf{0},$$
$$1 \cdot \mathbf{a} = \mathbf{a},$$

where α and β are real numbers.

3. Each vector can be *uniquely represented as a sum of multiples of three base vectors:*

$$\mathbf{v} = v_1\mathbf{i} + v_2\mathbf{j} + v_3\mathbf{k}.$$

Now it so happens that one encounters in mathematics and in its applications many sets of things with the three properties listed above—and yet these are not vectors as we have defined them, that is, equivalence classes of ordered pairs of points. However, any set of things which has these three properties listed above is called a *three-dimensional vector space* over the real numbers. The set of vectors in the plane is a two-dimensional vector space over the real numbers.

Properties 2 and 3 can be generalized. For instance, you will remember that the real numbers are only one of many mathematical systems that are called *fields*. The rational numbers comprise a field. The generalization of property 2 is that the scalars which are used as multipliers need not be the real numbers, but may be the objects in any field.

Property 3 is generalized in the natural way by having each vector uniquely represented as a sum of multiples of n base vectors:

$$\mathbf{v} = v_1\mathbf{i}_1 + v_2\mathbf{i}_2 + \cdots + v_n\mathbf{i}_n,$$

where the base vectors are $\mathbf{i}_1, \ldots, \mathbf{i}_n$.

Any set of things having these generalized properties is called an *n-dimensional vector space*. Here n can be any natural number. When $n = 2$, the situation is the same as in the plane, discussed in Chapter 2. When $n = 3$, we have vectors in space. When $n > 3$, we cannot visualize these objects any longer, and must learn to use them by relying only on their assumed algebraic properties. However, although we cannot visualize these objects for $n > 3$, we can carry over much of the geometric language which is natural to us for $n = 3$, to the case $n > 3$. Thus we speak of a vector as the position vector of a point. And we speak of $v_1, v_2, \ldots, v_n$ as the coordinates of this point, just as we speak of $v_1, v_2, \ldots, v_n$ as the components of the vector.

SUMMARY

The development of vectors in space is quite analogous to that of plane vectors in Chapter 2. The main topics are as follows.

1. We began with the concept of *arrow*, that is an ordered pair (P_1, P_2) of points in space. An arrow has a magnitude equal to the distance between the two points, and a direction given by the direction cosines of the ray from P_1 through P_2.

2. Two arrows are *equivalent* if they have the same magnitude and direction. Hence it is true that the arrows (P_1, P_2) and (Q_1, Q_2) are equivalent if and only if the coordinate differences are the same for the two arrows (Theorem 4–1).

3. A *vector* is an equivalence class of arrows. It is the set of all arrows equivalent to a given arrow. Vectors are denoted by $\mathbf{u}$, $\mathbf{v}$, or $\overrightarrow{P_1P_2}$, etc. The *position vector* of $\overrightarrow{OP}$ is the arrow (O, P).

4. The *sum* of two vectors $\mathbf{a}$ and $\mathbf{b}$ is obtained by "tacking on" an arrow representing $\mathbf{b}$ to an arrow representing $\mathbf{a}$.

5. If $\mathbf{v}$ is a vector and k a real number, then $k\mathbf{v}$ is a vector with magnitude $|k|$ times the magnitude of $\mathbf{v}$ and is in the same or opposite direction according as k is positive or negative. Then if $\mathbf{v}$ and $\mathbf{w}$ are in the same direction or in opposite directions, there is a unique real number k such that $\mathbf{v} = k\mathbf{w}$.

6. Every vector can be represented as a sum of multiples of three noncoplanar vectors. Usually we choose these three noncoplanar vectors to be the unit vectors **i**, **j**, **k** with directions along the coordinate axes. Then, if

$$\mathbf{v} = x\mathbf{i} + y\mathbf{j} + z\mathbf{k},$$

the numbers x, y, and z are the *components* of **v** with respect to the *base vectors* **i**, **j**, **k**.

7. If $\mathbf{a} = a_1\mathbf{i} + a_2\mathbf{j} + a_3\mathbf{k}$ and $\mathbf{b} = b_1\mathbf{i} + b_2\mathbf{j} + b_3\mathbf{k}$, then

$$\mathbf{a} + \mathbf{b} = (a_1 + b_1)\mathbf{i} + (a_2 + b_2)\mathbf{j} + (a_3 + b_3)\mathbf{k}.$$

8. Vectors have many (but not all) algebraic properties that the real numbers have. For all vectors **a**, **b**, and **c** and for all real numbers r and s, we have

$$\mathbf{a} + \mathbf{b} = \mathbf{b} + \mathbf{a},$$
$$\mathbf{a} + (\mathbf{b} + \mathbf{c}) = (\mathbf{a} + \mathbf{b}) + \mathbf{c},$$
$$\mathbf{a} + 0 = \mathbf{a},$$
$$r(\mathbf{a} + \mathbf{b}) = r\mathbf{a} + r\mathbf{b},$$
$$(r + s)\mathbf{a} = r\mathbf{a} + s\mathbf{a},$$
$$(rs)\mathbf{a} = r(s\mathbf{a}),$$
$$0\mathbf{a} = 0,$$
$$1\mathbf{a} = \mathbf{a}.$$

9. If P_0 and P_1 are points on a line l, and $\mathbf{r}_0 = \overrightarrow{OP_0}$ then a vector equation of the line l is

$$\mathbf{r} = \mathbf{r}_0 + t\overrightarrow{P_0P_1}.$$

10. If P_0, P_1, P_2 are three noncollinear points on a plane π, and $\mathbf{r}_0 = \overrightarrow{OP_0}$, then a vector equation of the plane π is

$$\mathbf{r} = \mathbf{r}_0 + s\overrightarrow{P_0P_1} + t\overrightarrow{P_0P_2}.$$

Review Problems

1. If $P_1 = P(3, 5, 7)$ and $P_2 = P(4, 4, 4)$, $P_3 = P(5, -2, 4)$, and $\overrightarrow{P_1P_2} = \overrightarrow{P_3P_4}$, what are the coordinates of P_4?

2. $\overrightarrow{OP_1}$ is a position vector with endpoint at $(2, 4, 3)$. The coordinates of a point P_2 are $(1, -2, 2)$. What is the sum of $\overrightarrow{OP_1}$ and $\overrightarrow{P_1P_2}$ in terms of components and unit base vectors? Sketch the arrows.

3. A line contains the point $(2, 3, 0)$ and is perpendicular to the xy-plane. What are parametric equations of the line?

4. A line contains the origin of the coordinate axes and the point $(2, 5, 3)$. Write a vector equation of the line.

5. If $(5\mathbf{i} - \mathbf{j} + 2\mathbf{k}) + \mathbf{b} = 4\mathbf{i} + 3\mathbf{j} - \mathbf{k}$, what are the components of $\mathbf{b}$?

6. Determine the real numbers x, y, and z such that

$$x\mathbf{i} + 4\mathbf{j} + z\mathbf{k} = -3\mathbf{i} + y\mathbf{j} + \mathbf{k}.$$

7. Write a vector equation of the plane containing the three points whose coordinates are $(2, 4, 2)$, $(3, 1, 1)$, and $(5, 3, 2)$.

*8. Lines l_1 and l_2 are parallel and have the following equations:

$$l_1: \begin{cases} x = 4 + \dfrac{-2}{\sqrt{14}}\,d, \\[2mm] y = \dfrac{1}{\sqrt{14}}\,d, \\[2mm] z = \dfrac{3}{\sqrt{14}}\,d. \end{cases} \qquad l_2: \begin{cases} x = 2 + \dfrac{-2}{\sqrt{14}}\,d, \\[2mm] y = -2 + \dfrac{1}{\sqrt{14}}\,d, \\[2mm] z = 2 + \dfrac{3}{\sqrt{14}}\,d. \end{cases}$$

Find parametric equations of the plane determined by l_1 and l_2. What is a rectangular equation of the plane?

*9. $\mathbf{v}_1 = 2\mathbf{i} - 3\mathbf{j} + 4\mathbf{k}$, $\mathbf{v}_2 = \mathbf{i} + 2\mathbf{j} + \mathbf{k}$, $\mathbf{v}_3 = 3\mathbf{i} - \mathbf{j} - \mathbf{k}$, and $\mathbf{r} = 10\mathbf{i} - 15\mathbf{j} + 8\mathbf{k}$. Determine real numbers a, b, and c such that $a\mathbf{v}_1 + b\mathbf{v}_2 + c\mathbf{v}_3 = \mathbf{r}$.

*10. A vector equation of a plane is

$$\mathbf{r} = (3\mathbf{i} + 2\mathbf{j}) + s(\mathbf{i} + 3\mathbf{j} + \mathbf{k}) + t(2\mathbf{i} - 2\mathbf{j}).$$

A vector equation of a line is

$$\mathbf{v} = (3\mathbf{i} + 6\mathbf{j} + \mathbf{k}) + d(5\mathbf{i} + 7\mathbf{j} + 3\mathbf{k}).$$

Show that the line lies in the plane.

*11. Find a vector equation of the plane containing the points $(3, 1, 0)$, $(0, 3, 0)$, and $(2, 2, 3)$. Sketch the plane. What is a vector equation of its trace in the xz-plane? Where does the plane meet the x- and z-axes?

HISTORICAL NOTE

Sir William Rowan Hamilton (1805-1865)

In the Historical Note at the end of Chapter 2, we observed that the additive properties of complex numbers were essentially the same as the additive properties of vectors in the plane. Both can be represented by arrows, and both use the "parallelogram law" for addition.

However, complex numbers can not only be added, they can be multiplied, and form a *field*. It is natural, therefore, to look for an extended field which would do for vectors in space what complex numbers do for vectors in the plane. We shall see, shortly, how this can be done.

First we remark that vectors in space were familiar to the nineteenth-century physicists. Velocities, accelerations, and forces are all represented by vectors. In the early nineteenth century these were handled by writing out their components, for example, 2, 3, -5 instead of $2\mathbf{i} + 3\mathbf{i} - 5\mathbf{k} = \mathbf{v}$. There was no formal vector algebra.

113

Second, we remark that there exists a method of multiplying vectors *in space* to obtain a product which is also a vector. We shall discuss this in Chapter 11. At the moment, we simply note that such a product is possible and that it has applications in physics and in geometry. The nineteenth-century physicists knew how to find this product, called the *vector product*.

Although we have yet to define this vector product, we can, nevertheless, ask the following *purely algebraic* question: "Is there a way of defining objects akin to vectors in space which can be added and multiplied, and which, together with these two operations, form a field?"

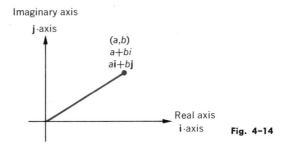

Fig. 4-14

In trying to generalize complex numbers from objects in the plane to objects in space, the natural first guess is to add to them another component. One would then have objects of the form

$$a + bi + cj,$$

where j is a new unit. Unfortunately, this natural attempt is doomed to failure. It *cannot* succeed because it is not complete.

It was Sir William Rowan Hamilton (Irish, 1805–1865) who found the answer (and the only one) to our question. Hamilton, who was professor of astronomy at the University of Dublin, is famous for his work in theoretical mechanics as well as for his solution to our problem. He presented his generalization of complex numbers, called *quaternions*, to the Irish Academy in 1843. We give below a sketch of the essential features of the algebra of quaternions.

It turns out that to solve our algebraic problem one needs *four components* instead of three, and even then one *must* give up the commutativity of multiplication. It is also interesting to observe that although Hamilton was vitally concerned with the application of quaternions to physics, in the solution of this problem he was guided principally by a feeling for algebraic relations—and our point of view here is algebraic.

The form of a quaternion is $r + ai + bj + ck$ where r, a, b, and c are real numbers. Then i, j and k are called quaternion unit vectors and r, a, b, and c are called the *components* of the quaternion. Two quaternions are equal if and only if their components are respectively equal. Quaternions are

114

added by adding components. Multiplication of quaternions is performed by means of the distributive property and the products of the units:

$$i^2 = j^2 = k^2 = -1,$$
$$i \cdot j = k, \qquad j \cdot k = i, \qquad k \cdot i = j,$$
$$j \cdot i = -k, \qquad k \cdot j = -i, \qquad i \cdot k = -j.$$

(Observe that we do not have commutativity of multiplication.)

To be sure that you understand how products are formed, you may verify that

$$(l + 2i - 3j + k)(2 - i - j + 2k) = -l - 2i - 12j - k.$$

It is now possible to show, in quite the same way as one shows that complex numbers form a commutative field, that the quaternions form a *noncommutative field*.

CIRCLES, CYLINDERS

5

AND SPHERES

5-1. INTRODUCTION

Rectilinear figures, namely lines and planes, are the simplest of all geometric figures. Circles, spheres, and cylinders are, perhaps, the next simplest. In this chapter we shall obtain equations for these latter figures and examine some of their simpler properties.

5-2. CIRCLES

In this section we shall always consider figures in a fixed coordinate plane with coordinates x and y. Recall that a circle is the set of all points in a plane at a fixed distance, called the *radius*, from a fixed point, called the *center*.

An equation of a circle is an equation in x and y which is satisfied by the coordinates of a point if and only if the point is on the circle.

THEOREM 5-1

An equation of a circle with radius r and with center at (h, k) is

$$(x - h)^2 + (y - k)^2 = r^2 \qquad (1)$$

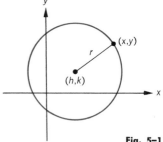

Fig. 5-1

The proof is left to the student (see Fig. 5-1).

Because any equation equivalent to equation (1) is also an equation of the circle, it is convenient to recognize some of these equivalent equations. The most common variant of equation (1) is the equation which results from expanding the squares in (1) and collecting the constant terms. If

$$(x - h)^2 + (y - k)^2 = r^2,$$

then

$$x^2 - 2hx + h^2 + y^2 - 2ky + k^2 = r^2,$$

or

$$x^2 + y^2 - 2hx - 2ky + (h^2 + k^2 - r^2) = 0.$$

THEOREM 5-2

The graph of the equation $x^2 + y^2 + ax + by + c = 0$

(a) is a circle if $\qquad \dfrac{a^2}{4} + \dfrac{b^2}{4} - c > 0$;

118

(b) is a point if $\qquad \dfrac{a^2}{4} + \dfrac{b^2}{4} - c = 0;$

(c) is empty if $\qquad \dfrac{a^2}{4} + \dfrac{b^2}{4} - c < 0.$

Proof. The equation is equivalent to

$$\left(x + \frac{a}{2}\right)^2 + \left(y + \frac{b}{2}\right)^2 = \frac{a^2}{4} + \frac{b^2}{4} - c.$$

Therefore, if

$$\frac{a^2}{4} + \frac{b^2}{4} - c > 0,$$

the graph is a circle with center at $(-a/2, -b/2)$ and radius

$$\sqrt{\frac{a^2}{4} + \frac{b^2}{4} - c}.$$

The other assertions of the theorem should be obvious. When

$$\frac{a^2}{4} + \frac{b^2}{4} - c = 0,$$

we often speak of a circle of zero radius, or a *degenerate circle*. And when

$$\frac{a^2}{4} + \frac{b^2}{4} - c < 0,$$

the term *imaginary circle* is sometimes used.

EXAMPLES

1. Find the center and radius, and sketch the circle

$$x^2 + y^2 + x - 4y - \tfrac{7}{4} = 0.$$

We have

$$x^2 + x + y^2 - 4y = \tfrac{7}{4},$$
$$(x + \tfrac{1}{2})^2 + (y - 2)^2 = \tfrac{7}{4} + \tfrac{1}{4} + 4,$$
$$(x + \tfrac{1}{2})^2 + (y - 2)^2 = 6.$$

Hence the center is at $(-\tfrac{1}{2}, 2)$, and the radius is $\sqrt{6}$ (Fig. 5–2).

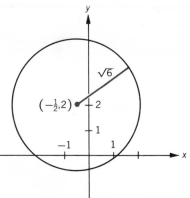

Fig. 5–2

2. Find an equation of the circle passing through $(9, -7)$, $(-3, -1)$, and $(6, 2)$.

119

There are at least two ways of proceeding.

METHOD I. The circle has an equation

$$x^2 + y^2 + ax + by + c = 0.$$

We must determine the numbers a, b, and c.

The requirement that the circle pass through the three given points leads to three linear equations in a, b, and c.

$$9^2 + (-7)^2 + 9a + (-7)b + c = 0, \tag{2}$$
$$(-3)^2 + (-1)^2 + (-3)a + (-1)b + c = 0, \tag{3}$$
$$6^2 + (2)^2 + 6a + 2b + c = 0. \tag{4}$$

Equivalent equations are

$$9a - 7b + c = -130, \tag{2'}$$
$$-3a - b + c = -10, \tag{3'}$$
$$6a + 2b + c = -40. \tag{4'}$$

Solving this system of equations for a, b, and c, we find that $a = -6$, $b = 8$, and $c = -20$. Therefore an equation of the circle is

$$x^2 + y^2 - 6x + 8y - 20 = 0.$$

This method has the disadvantage that we must do more work to find the center and radius of the circle.

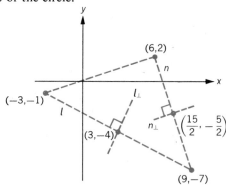

Fig. 5-3

METHOD II. This method is more geometric in character. It depends on the geometric fact that the center of the circle is at the intersection of the perpendicular bisectors of segments joining the three given points. It suffices to use only two of those perpendicular bisectors.

As we can see from Fig. 5-3, the slope of l is

$$\frac{-1 + 7}{-3 - 9} = \frac{6}{-12} = -\frac{1}{2}$$

and the slope of n is

$$\frac{2+7}{6-9} = \frac{9}{-3} = -3.$$

Therefore, the slopes of the perpendicular bisectors $l_\perp$ and $n_\perp$ are 2 and $\frac{1}{3}$, respectively. The equations of these lines therefore are

$$l_\perp: \quad y + 4 = 2(x - 3) \quad \text{or} \quad 2x - y = 10;$$
$$n_\perp: \quad y + \tfrac{5}{2} = \tfrac{1}{3}(x - \tfrac{15}{2}) \quad \text{or} \quad x - 3y = 15.$$

Solving these two simultaneous equations we obtain $x = 3$ and $y = -4$. Hence the center of the circle is $(3, -4)$. (Note that since this is a right triangle, the center is also the midpoint of the hypotenuse.) The radius is $r = \sqrt{[3 - (-3)]^2 + [-4 - (-1)]^2} = \sqrt{45} = 3\sqrt{5}$. An equation of the circle is $(x - 3)^2 + (y + 4)^2 = 45$ or $x^2 + y^2 - 6x + 8y = 20$.

Problems

1. Find equations of the circles with the given centers and radii.

   (a) $(-1, 2), \quad r = \sqrt{2}$ (b) $(-\sqrt{2}, -2), \quad r = \sqrt{6}$

   (c) $(-\pi, 3), \quad r = 3$ (d) $(10, -10), \quad r = \tfrac{1}{2}$

   (e) $(0, 0), \quad r = a$

2. Find centers and radii of the circles with the following equations. Graph each circle.

   (a) $x^2 + y^2 = 6x - 6y$ (b) $x^2 + y^2 - 2x + 8y + 16 = 0$

   (c) $x^2 + y^2 - 3x + 4y - 5 = 0$ (d) $2x^2 + 2y^2 + 10x - 5 = 0$

   (e) $3x^2 + 3y^2 - 2x - 6y = 2$ (f) $x^2 + y^2 - 5x - 7y + 20 = 0$

3. What is the graph of the sentence,

   $$\text{``}x^2 + y^2 + 4x - 2y = 4, \quad x \geq 0, \quad \text{and} \quad y \geq 0\text{''?}$$

4. Find centers and radii of the following circles, and sketch each figure. Use Method I in part (a) and Method II in part (b).

   (a) The circle through $(-8, -4)$, $(8, 8)$, $(5, 9)$

   (b) The circle through $(-4, -2)$, $(0, 6)$, $(3, -3)$

   (c) The circle through $(3, 1)$ and touching the x-axis at $(0, 0)$

   (d) The circle with center on the line $x + 3y = 4$ and passing through $(-2, 2)$ and $(6, 6)$

   (e) The circle with center on the line $y = -x$, has radius 4, and passes through the origin

   (f) The circle touching the lines $x = 2$ and $x = 12$ and passing through $(4, 0)$

5. Find an equation of the line tangent at $(4, -1)$ to the circle whose equation is $x^2 + y^2 + 4x - 4y = 37$.

6. Find and sketch the points of intersection of the circles $x^2 + y^2 + 6x - 2y = 6$ and $x^2 + y^2 - 2x - 6y + 6 = 0$.

7. Show that the circle $x^2 + y^2 + 2x + 4y = 0$ is tangent to the line $2x + y = 1$ by showing that the line and circle meet in one point.

8. Determine k such that the line $x - 2y = k$ will be tangent to the circle $x^2 + y^2 - 4x - 2y + 1 = 0$. [*Hint:* Apply the discriminant condition for equal roots of a quadratic equation.] Then sketch the graph as a check on your computation. Finally, do the problem in another way.

9. Show that the set of points whose distance from $(0, 0)$ is twice their distance from $(12, 0)$ is a circle. Find its center and radius.

10. Show that the line $x + y = 1$ passes through the points of intersection of the circles

$$x^2 + y^2 - 6x + 4 = 0 \quad \text{and} \quad x^2 + y^2 - 3x + 3y + 1 = 0.$$

11. Find the length of the line segment from the point $(10, 2)$ to a point of tangency of a line from $(10, 2)$ to the circle $x^2 + y^2 - 6x + 2y - 12 = 0$.

*12. Show that if the distinct circles

$$x^2 + y^2 + ax + by + c = 0 \quad \text{and} \quad x^2 + y^2 + Ax + By + C = 0$$

intersect at P_1 and $P_2 \neq P_1$, then an equation of the line through P_1 and P_2 is $(a - A)x + (b - B)y + (c - C) = 0$.

*13. If (x', y') is exterior to the circle $(x - h)^2 + (y - k)^2 = r^2$, and if (x_1, y_1) is a point on the circle such that the line through (x_1, y_1) and (x', y') is tangent to the circle, show that the distance, L, from (x_1, y_1) to (x', y') is given by $L^2 = (x' - h)^2 + (y' - k)^2 - r^2$.

*14. Show that equations of the two lines with slope m which are tangent to the circle of radius r with center at the origin are $y = mx \pm r\sqrt{1 + m^2}$.

5-3. CYLINDERS

The graph of all points in a plane, with coordinates (x, y), satisfying the equation

$$(x - h)^2 + (y - k)^2 = r^2 \tag{1}$$

is a circle.

Let us now consider the same equation but ask a question:

What is the set of all points in space whose coordinates (x, y, z) satisfy equation (1)?

The question may at first seem strange because z does not occur in equation (1). But it is this fact which makes the graphing problem in space particularly simple. *If x and y satisfy* (1) *then x, y, and z satisfy* (1) *regardless of what z is.*

122

Part of the graph in space of equation (1) is shown in Fig. 5–4. The xy-plane consists of all points whose z-coordinate is zero. If $(x, y, 0)$ is on the circle given by (1), then (x, y, z) is on the right circular cylinder which has this circle as a base or cross section.

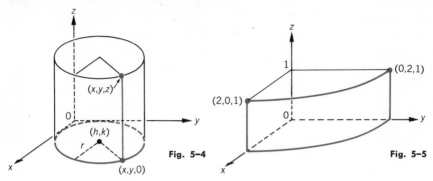

Fig. 5–4   Fig. 5–5

EXAMPLE 1

Graph the portion of the cylinder $x^2 + y^2 = 4$ which is in the first octant and between the planes $z = 0$ and $z = 1$.

In the xy-plane we have a circle of radius 2 and center at the origin. The graph in space is a right circular cylinder erected on this circle as base. The desired portion is shown in Fig. 5–5.

From this example it may be expected that cylinders, in general, will have simpler equations than many other surfaces—but what is a cylinder?

DEFINITION 5–1

Suppose that C is a curve† in space, and let l be a line through a point of C. Consider the set of all points on all lines which are parallel to l and contain a point of C. This set of points is called a cylinder with directrix C. The line l and the lines parallel to l on the cylinder are called *generators* of the cylinder (Fig. 5–6).

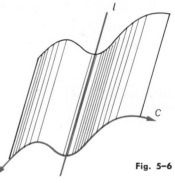

Fig. 5–6

It should be noted that the curve C need not be a circle, neither need the curve C lie on a plane, nor, if it does, need the line be perpendicular to the plane. However, if the directrix is in a coordinate plane and the generators are perpendicular to that plane, then the cylinder has an equation which is particularly simple.

---

† We shall return to curves in Chapter 14 and give there a precise description. At present, we assume that you know intuitively what a curve is.

123

EXAMPLES

2. Find an equation of the cylinder whose directrix is the circle in the xz-plane with center at $(1, 0, 2)$ and radius $\sqrt{5}$, and whose generators are parallel to the y-axis. Sketch the portion of the cylinder between the planes $y = 0$ and $y = 4$ (Fig. 5-7).

The directrix circle in the xz-plane has an equation

$$(x - 1)^2 + (z - 2)^2 = 5.$$

The same equation is an equation of the cylinder.

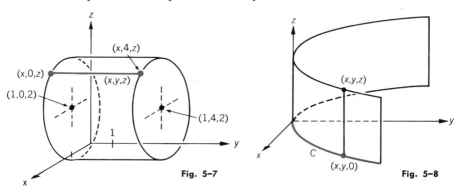

Fig. 5-7   Fig. 5-8

3. Sketch the set of all points (x, y, z) whose coordinates satisfy the equation $x^2 = y$. Show that this set is a cylinder.

The graph of $x^2 = y$, in the xy-plane, is the curve C of Fig. 5-8. If $(x, y, 0)$ is on C, then (x, y, z) satisfies the same equation. In other words, all points on a line through $(x, y, 0)$ and parallel to the z-axis are also in the set. Therefore, the graph is a cylinder. It is called a *parabolic* cylinder because a parabola is a directrix.

Problems

1. Sketch the portions of the cylinders as described.
   (a) $x^2 + y^2 - 4x = 0$, $y \geq 0$, $0 \leq z \leq 1$
   (b) $y^2 + z^2 = 9$, $y \geq 0$, $z \geq 0$, $0 \leq x \leq 2$
   (c) $x^2 = 4 - z$, $x \geq 0$, $z \geq 0$, $0 \leq y \leq 3$
   (d) $(x - 3)^2 + (y - 3)^2 = 4$, $0 \leq z \leq 1$
   (e) $xy = 1$, $0 \leq x \leq 2$, $0 \leq z \leq 2$
   (f) $3x + 4y = 12$, $x \geq 0$, $0 \leq z \leq 2$

*2. Sketch the cylinder whose equation is $|x| + |y| = 1$.

3. Sketch the part of the curve of intersection which is in the first octant of the pairs of cylinders
   (a) $2x = y$, $x^2 + z^2 = 4$ (b) $x + y = 7$, $x^2 + y^2 = 25$
   *(c) $x^2 + y^2 = 9$, $x^2 + z^2 = 4$ *(d) $x^2 = 4y$, $y^2 + z^2 = 1$

124

5–4. SPHERES

The space analog of a circle is a sphere. It is the set of all points P in space at a fixed distance from a point called the center of the sphere. Theorems analogous to Theorems 5–1 and 5–2 can be proved for spheres, and in much the same way.

Problem

State and prove the two theorems for spheres analogous to Theorems 5–1 and 5–2.

A remark needs to be made concerning the problem of sketching a sphere. It is usually convenient to sketch one or two of the great circles of the sphere which are intersections of the sphere with planes parallel to coordinate planes. Furthermore, because of the symmetry of the sphere it often suffices to sketch only one-eighth of the sphere.

EXAMPLES

1. Find an equation of the sphere with center at (1, 2, 1) and radius 2.
The point (x, y, z) is on the sphere if and only if $(x - 1)^2 + (y - 2)^2 + (z - 1)^2 = 4$ or, equivalently, if and only if $x^2 + y^2 + z^2 - 2x - 4y - 2z + 2 = 0$.
A sketch of one-eighth of the sphere is shown in Fig. 5–9.

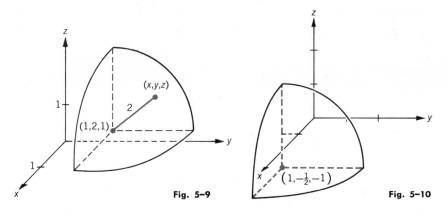

Fig. 5–9　　　**Fig. 5–10**

2. Find center and radius and sketch the sphere which has an equation $4x^2 + 4y^2 + 4z^2 - 8x + 4y + 8z = 27$. This equation is equivalent to $x^2 + y^2 + z^2 - 2x + y + 2z = \frac{27}{4}$, which, in turn, is equivalent to $(x - 1)^2 + (y + \frac{1}{2})^2 + (z + 1)^2 = 9$. This last equation is that of a sphere with center at $(1, -\frac{1}{2}, -1)$ and radius 3, as shown in Fig. 5–10.

125

Problems

1. Find equations of the following spheres and sketch one-eighth of each sphere.

   (a) Center $(2, 1, 0)$, radius 2   (b) Center $(1, 1, -1)$, radius $\frac{1}{2}$

   (c) Center at $(-1, 2, -2)$ and passing through $(0, 0, 0)$

   (d) Center $(0, 0, 0)$, radius a

2. Find center and radius and sketch a portion of each of the following spheres.

   (a) $x^2 + y^2 + z^2 - x - y - z = \frac{9}{4}$

   (b) $2x^2 + 2y^2 + 2z^2 - 9z = 1$

   (c) $x^2 + y^2 + z^2 - 20x - 20y - 201 = 0$

   (d) $x^2 + y^2 + z^2 - 2ay = 0$ if $a > 0$.   Sketch the portion for which $x > 0$ and $z > 0$.

3. Show that the point $(-2, -3, 2)$ is on the sphere whose equation is $x^2 + y^2 + z^2 = 17$. What are the direction cosines of the ray from the origin through $(-2, -3, 2)$? Write parametric equations of the line through $(-2, -3, 2)$ and the origin.

4. A ray has direction cosines $\frac{1}{2}$, $-\frac{1}{2}$, and $-1/\sqrt{2}$ and emanates from the center of the sphere with an equation $x^2 + y^2 + z^2 - 2x + 2y = 6$. Find the point where the ray intersects the sphere.

5. The plane $y = 2$ intersects the sphere $x^2 + y^2 + z^2 + 2y - 2z = 14$ in a circle. Find an equation of the cylinder which has this circle as directrix and whose generators are parallel to the y-axis. Sketch the figure.

SUMMARY

In this chapter we have used analytic geometry to study some familiar geometric figures. You should be able to recognize circles, cylinders with axes parallel to the coordinate axes, and spheres from their equations, and sketch the graphs of these figures.

1. $(x - h)^2 + (y - k)^2 = r^2$ is an equation of a circle in the xy-plane with center at (h, k) and radius r.

2. The set of all points (x, y, z) in space satisfying equation (1) is a right circular cylinder having as a directrix the circle $(x - h)^2 + (y - k)^2 = r^2$.

3. $(x - h)^2 + (y - k)^2 + (z - p)^2 = r^2$ is an equation of a sphere with center at (h, k, p) and radius r.

Review Problems

1. State the conditions for which the graph of $x^2 + y^2 + ax + by + c = 0$ will be one of the following.

   (a) a circle   (b) a point   (c) an imaginary circle

2. Determine the center and radius of the following circles.

   (a) $x^2 + y^2 - 7x + 8y = \frac{9}{2}$ (b) $x^2 + y^2 + x - y - 2 = 0$

   (c) $x^2 + y^2 - 6x = 0$

3. Write an equation of the circle which contains the points $(3, 1)$, $(-2, 4)$, and $(0, -4)$.

4. A circle has radius 5 and is tangent to the positive x- and y-axes. What is an equation of the circle?

5. A circle is tangent to the x-axis at $(5, 0)$ and is also tangent to the line $y = x$. Find the center, radius, and an equation of the circle.

6. Find the points of intersection of the pair of circles $x^2 + y^2 = 16$ and $x^2 + y^2 - 6x - 4y = 12$.

7. Describe geometrically the set of points in a plane satisfying $\alpha(x^2 + y^2 - 16) + \beta(x^2 + y^2 - 6x - 4y - 12) = 0$ given that:

   (a) $\alpha = 0$ (b) $\beta = 0$ (c) $\alpha = -\beta \neq 0$ (d) $\beta = 2\alpha$

8. Sketch pictures of the following cylinders.

   (a) $x^2 + y^2 - 2x - 3 = 0$, $\quad 0 \leq z \leq 3$

   (b) $y^2 + z^2 = 16$, $\quad z \geq 0$, $\quad 0 \leq x \leq 4$

   (c) $y^2 + z^2 - 4y - 4z + 4 = 0$, $\quad 0 \leq x \leq 5$

9. The directrix of a cylinder is $x^2 + y^2 - 6x - 6y + 9 = 0$. A generator of the cylinder is the line $y = z + 3$ in the yz-plane. Sketch that portion of the cylinder between the planes $z = 0$ and $z = 4$.

10. Sketch a picture of the set of points in the first octant satisfying $y^2 + z^2 \geq 9$ and $y^2 + z^2 \leq 16$ and $x \leq 4$.

11. Determine the center and radius of the following spheres and sketch one-eighth of the sphere.

    (a) $x^2 + y^2 + z^2 + 8x + 2y = 8$

    (b) $x^2 + y^2 + z^2 - 3x + 4y - 6z = 1$

12. The plane $z = 2$ intersects the sphere $x^2 + y^2 + z^2 - 2x - 4y - 6z + 5 = 0$ in a circle. Determine the radius of the circle.

13. A ray directed from the center of the sphere $x^2 + y^2 + z^2 - x + 3y - 4z = \frac{5}{2}$ has direction cosines $c_1 = \frac{1}{3}$, $c_2 = \frac{2}{3}$, and $c_3 = -\frac{2}{3}$. Find the coordinates of the point of intersection of the ray and the sphere.

*14. The points $(3, -1, 3)$, $(4, -4, -1)$, $(0, -1, 0)$, and $(1, -5, -1)$ are points on a sphere. What is the center and radius of the sphere? [*Hint:* Each point must satisfy an equation of the form $x^2 + y^2 + z^2 + ax + by + cz + d = 0$.]

*15. Graph the following cylinders.

    (a) $xy = 12$, $\quad x > 0$, $\quad y > 0$, $\quad 0 \leq z \leq 3$

    (b) $x^2 = 2y - 1$, $\quad x \geq 0$, $\quad 0 \leq z \leq 4$

*16. Sketch the part of the curve of intersection which is in the first octant of the pair of cylinders $x^2 + z^2 = 9$ and $x^2 + y^2 - 6y = 0$.

127

ELEMENTARY FUNCTION

6

ND THEIR GRAPHS

6–1. INTRODUCTION

You have already studied some of the elementary functions in your previous work in mathematics. The word "elementary" has no deep significance, but merely refers to certain functions which are of such common occurrence that everyone who does any mathematics at all must become familiar with them.

Most of the functions that we shall study in this chapter will not be new to you. In Chapter 7 a new set of functions, called the trigonometric functions, will be studied. Our task in this chapter is that of recalling to your mind the definition of a function and the properties of some of the elementary functions. Some of these properties are best illustrated by the graphs of the functions.

We shall discuss briefly:

1. functions: definitions, notation, language, the algebra of functions;
2. polynomial functions;
3. rational functions;
4. algebraic functions;
5. exponential functions;
6. logarithmic functions;
7. composition of functions.

6–2. FUNCTIONS

The concept of a function should be somewhat familiar to you.

Functions can be defined in several equivalent ways, each of which has its own advantages. We shall give two definitions in this section. For each definition we must have

(a) a set called the *domain;*
(b) a set called the *range;*
(c) a *correspondence* or *association* between the elements of the two sets so that each element of the domain is paired with a *unique* element of the range.

DEFINITION 6–1

Let X and Y be any two sets. A *function F on X into Y* is a set of ordered pairs (x, y), where x is an element of X and y is an element of Y, such that for *each x* in X there is *exactly one* ordered pair (x, y) in F.

DEFINITION 6–2

Let X and Y be any two sets. A function is determined if for each x in X there is associated a *unique y* in Y, called the *value of F at x.*

130

The set X in the definitions above is called the *domain* of the function F. Each element x of the domain is an *argument* of the function. The *range* of F is the set of all elements y for pairs (x, y) in F. If F is a function on X into Y, then the range is a subset of Y but need not be all of Y. If (x, y) is in F, then y is called the *value of F at x*, and is denoted by $F(x)$. We say that y is the *image* of x under the function F.

Definition 6–1 is closely related to the idea of a graph. Indeed, if X and Y are subsets of the set of real numbers, R, then the function can be identified with its graph (Fig. 6–1).

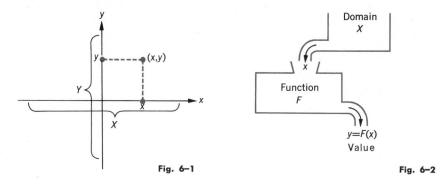

Fig. 6–1   Fig. 6–2

Definition 6–2 is the "machine" or "formula" point of view. A function may be regarded as a kind of machine which takes the elements of the domain X, processes them, and produces elements of the range (Fig. 6–2).

EXAMPLES

1. Let $X = \{1, 2, 3, 4\}$ and $Y = \{a, b, c\}$. Let G be the set of ordered pairs $\{(1, a), (2, b), (3, a), (4, b)\}$. Then, by Definition 6–1, G is a function on X into Y. Note that the range of G is the set $\{a, b\}$, which is a proper subset of Y.

2. Let X and Y be the sets of Example 1. Let h be the set of ordered pairs $\{(1, c), (2, a), (3, b), (1, a), (4, b)\}$. Then h is *not* a function, because two different elements of Y are paired with the element 1 of X.

3. Let $X = Y = R$, and let f be the set of all (x, y) such that $y = 2x - 1$. Then f is a function. The graph of f is shown in Fig. 6–3.

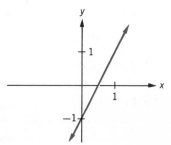

Fig. 6–3

131

Problems

1. The figures below are graphs of relations between real numbers. Which are graphs of functions? Which are graphs of functions with domain $X = R$? Which have range $Y = R$?

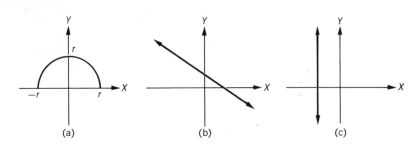

(a) (b) (c)

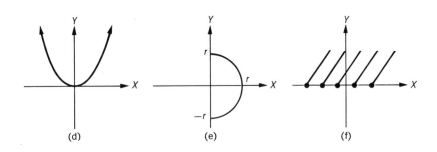

(d) (e) (f)

2. In the following, $X = \{1, 2, 3, 4, 5\}$ and $Y = \{-2, -1, 0, 1, 2\}$. Which sets of ordered pairs are functions on X into Y?

(a) $f = \{(1, 0), (2, -1), (3, 1), (4, -2), (5, 2)\}$

(b) $g = \{(1, 1), (2, 1), (3, 1), (4, 1), (5, 1)\}$

(c) $h = \{(1, 1), (2, 2), (3, 0), (4, 0), (5, 0)\}$

(d) $F = \{(0, 1), (1, 2), (-1, 3), (2, 4), (-2, 5)\}$

(e) $G = \{(1, -2), (2, -1), (3, 0), (1, 1), (2, 2)\}$

(f) $H = \{(1, 2), (3, 0), (5, 2)\}$

(g) $k = \{(1, -2), (2, 2), (4, 0), (5, 1), (6, -1)\}$

(h) $p = \{(5, -2), (4, -1), (1, 0), (3, 1), (2, -1)\}$

3. Let $X = Y = R$, and let f be the set of all (x, y) such that $y = 3x - 4$. Thus f is a function. What is the value of the function at 1? at 5? at -4? at 0?

4. (a) Explain how the students in your mathematics class and the grades they receive on a mathematics test define a function.

(b) Explain how thermometer readings can define a function.

132

5. The figure below illustrates a function on X into Y. What is the domain of the function? What is the range of the function? What is the image of -2? What is the image of 2?

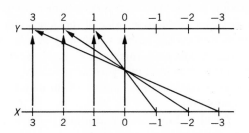

6. Assigning coordinates to a line is a function. What are the domain and the range of this function? Note that there are two answers for domain and range.

7. Let E be a function whose domain is the set of nonnegative integers, whose value is 1 at the odd integers, and whose value is 0 at the even integers. What is the value of the function at (1000)? at (999)? at $(2k + 1)$, where k is a nonnegative integer? What is the range of E?

8. Let $X = Y = R$, and let f be the function defined by the equation $f(x) = |x| + x$. Find $f(x)$ when x has the following values:

  (a) 2   (b) -2 (c) $\frac{3}{2}$ (d) $-\frac{3}{2}$ (e) a where $a < 0$

9. Let $X = Y = R$. Which of the following define a function on X into Y? Which define a function on Y into X? Which do not define a function?

  (a) $x + 4y = 5$ (b) $y = x^2$ (c) $x = y^2$ (d) $x^2 + y^2 = 4$

*10. Let X be a set of statements and Y be the set of the two words "True" and "False." Define a function G on X into Y. If α is a true statement, what is $G(\alpha)$? If "not α" denotes the negation of α, what is $G(\text{not }\alpha)$?

6-3. MAPPINGS AND FORMULAS: NOTATION AND LANGUAGE

There is a wide variety of notation and language for functions with which you should become familiar.

A function f is often called a *mapping* or *transformation* because f "maps" or "transforms" x into y or $f(x)$, as indicated in Fig. 6-4. The mapping is symbolized in various ways:

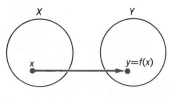

Fig. 6-4

$$f: X \to Y, \qquad f: x \to y,$$
$$X \xrightarrow{f} Y, \qquad x \xrightarrow{f} y, \qquad x \to f(x).$$

133

If f is a function mapping X into Y, and x is a variable representing elements of the domain, then x is called the *independent variable*. A variable y representing elements in the range of f is called the *dependent variable*. Sometimes a function is described as a process which assigns to each value of the independent variable a unique value of the dependent variable.

There is no restriction on the letters which may be used for functions or variables. Thus, one might have functions F, g, H, ϕ, etc., and variables u, s, t, r, ... Often the letter used in a particular context is suggested by the physical significance of the variable. Thus t might denote time, W weight, C circumference, and so on.

Two functions, f and g, are *equal* or *identical* if f and g have the same domain X and for each x in X, $f(x) = g(x)$.

EXAMPLE 1

Suppose f and g are defined as follows (see Fig. 6–5):

$$f(x) = |x|, \quad \text{for all real } x,$$
$$g(x) = x, \quad \text{for all } x \geq 0.$$

Then f and g are distinct functions, even though their graphs are identical over the common *part* of their domains. Thus we can say that $f(x) = g(x)$ for $x \geq 0$.

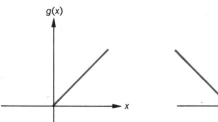
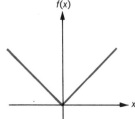

Fig. 6–5

In the following definition, we describe two special kinds of functions or mappings.

DEFINITION 6–3

If F is a function which maps X into Y, and every element y of Y is equal to $f(x)$ for at least one x in X, then F maps X *onto* Y.

If F is an *onto mapping*, that is, F maps X onto Y, and if it is true that when x_1 and x_2 are distinct elements of X, $F(x_1) \neq F(x_2)$, then F is a *one-to-one mapping* of X onto Y.

In a one-to-one mapping, every element y of Y is equal to $f(x)$ for exactly one x in X.

134

Figure 6-6 represents a function *h* which is an onto mapping but not a one-to-one mapping. Figure 6-7 shows a function *g* which is a one-to-one function.

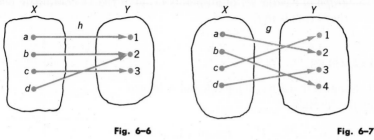

Fig. 6-6   Fig. 6-7

A function *F* is a *constant function* if the range of *F* consists of a single object. That is, there is one element *k* in *Y* such that $F(x) = k$ for all *x* in *X*.

A function is an *identity function* (Id) if for all *x* in *X*, Id $(x) = x$.

If we think of the identity function as a machine, then it is a "do-nothing" machine. It simply turns out the same objects that are placed in it (Fig. 6-8).

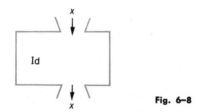

Fig. 6-8

Descriptions of some functions are extremely complicated. Our immediate aim is to study some simple functions whose values are easy to describe. Because a function *f* is determined as soon as $f(x)$ is known for each *x* in the domain, we shall study functions which are given by simple *formulas*. You should think of a formula as a rule for calculating $f(x)$ when *x* is known. Of course, if a function is to be determined by a formula, the domain of the function must be explicitly stated. In the examples and problems of this text, unless otherwise stated, the domain will be a subset of *R*, perhaps indicated by an inequality such as $x \geq 0$.

Consider the function defined by the formula

$$f(x) = 2x + 1$$

for all *x* in *R*. The value of this function, *f*, for $x = 2$ is 5. We denote this by $f(2) = 5$.

If a function has domain and range which are subsets of *R*, then the function has a graph which is a subset of the coordinate plane.

135

DEFINITION 6-4

If f has domain X, where $X \subset R$,† and range Y, where $Y \subset R$, then the *graph of f* is the set of all points (x, y) of the *xy*-coordinate plane such that (x, y) is in f.

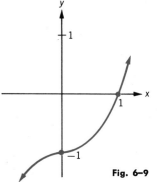

EXAMPLES

2. Suppose that F has domain R and is defined by the formula

$$F(x) = x^3 - 1, \quad \text{for all } x \text{ in } R.$$

Then $F(0) = -1$, $F(1) = 0$, $F(10) = 999$, and $F(-10) = -1001$.

A portion of the graph of F of Example 2 is shown in Fig. 6-9.

Fig. 6-9

3. G is a function which maps R into R according to the formula

$$G(t) = 1 \quad \text{if } 2k \leq t < 2k + 1, \text{ where } k \text{ is an integer}.$$
$$G(t) = 0 \quad \text{otherwise}.$$

A portion of the graph of G is shown in Figure 6-10.

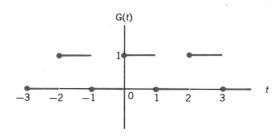

Fig. 6-10

Remark

Note that in Examples 2 and 3 *portions* of the graphs are shown. If the domain of a function is "large," say the set of all real numbers, then obviously we cannot picture all the points on the graph. We must be content to show only a portion of the graph. The portion sketched depends upon our interests and the application of the function in question.

When we say, in the future, "*the graph is shown,*" we shall mean that *a portion of the graph is shown—the interesting portion.*

When we say, "*sketch the graph,*" we shall mean *sketch enough of the graph to see how the rest goes.*

---

† Read $X \subset R$ in Definition 6-4 as "X is a subset of R."

136

Problems

1. If $f(x) = 3x - 1$ where $X = Y = R$, then determine the following:
   (a) $f(2)$ (b) $3f(2)$ (c) $f(a)$ (d) $f(a + 2)$

2. Let A be a function whose domain is the set of students in your mathematics class and whose value at any student is that student's age in years. Is A a constant function? Can you determine the range of A?

3. G is a one-to-one function mapping X onto Y, and the domain X contains exactly ten elements. What can you conclude about the set Y?

4. Sketch the graph of the identity function, Id $(x) = x$ for all real numbers x. Show that Id is a one-to-one function on R onto R.

5. In the following problems, functions are given by formulas with each domain indicated. Compute the values of the functions at the given arguments.
   (a) $f(x) = 2x^2 - x + 7$. Domain $= R$. Find $f(-3)$; $f(\frac{1}{2})$.
   (b) $F(x) = \dfrac{2x - 1}{x}$. Domain $=$ set of all real numbers greater than 1 and less than 3. Find $F(\frac{3}{2})$; $F(5)$.
   (c) $G(t) = 2|t|$. Domain $= R$. Find $G(0)$; $G(-10)$.
   (d) g has domain R. The value of g at x is the greatest integer which is less than or equal to x. Find $g(2.5)$; $g(2)$; $g(-2)$; $g(-1.3)$; $g(\pi)$; $g(-\sqrt{2})$.

6. Sketch the graphs of the following functions. Each domain is indicated.
   (a) $x \xrightarrow{f} x^2$, for all real $x \geq 0$
   (b) $t \xrightarrow{F} \frac{1}{2}t$, for $0 \leq t \leq 2$
   (c) G has domain R. $G(x) = x^3$ if $|x^3| \leq 1$; otherwise $G(x) = 1$
   (d) $H(s) = s^2 - 1$ for all s in R
   (e) $K(s) = 1 - s^2$ for all s in R
   (f) G has domain in R. $G(s) = H(s)$ if $H(s) \geq K(s)$; $G(s) = K(s)$ if $K(s) > H(s)$. H and K are the functions of parts (d) and (e)

7. (a) If f is a function mapping X onto Y, does f map X into Y?
   (b) If f maps X into Y, then does X necessarily map X onto Y?

8. The function f maps X into Y. The range of f is a set B, where B is a subset of Y. Prove that f maps X onto B.

9. The distance which a body falls from rest (in a vacuum) is a function of the time of fall. Choose a notation for the function and the dependent and independent variables. What are the domain and the range? Do you know the value of the function at some particular time?

10. Sketch the graph of the function ψ given by $\psi(x) = (x - 10^{10})^2 + 1$.

11. The function F maps X onto Y and for all x_1 and x_2 in X, if $F(x_1) = F(x_2)$, then $x_1 = x_2$. Prove that F is a one-to-one function.

137

6–4. THE ALGEBRA OF FUNCTIONS

For certain functions it is possible to define operations called addition, multiplication, subtraction, and division. In fact, these definitions are possible whenever the domains are identical and the range of the functions is in some field. In this chapter we shall be concerned with functions whose domains and ranges are subsets of the real number field. Such functions are called *real* functions.

We first consider an example of addition of two functions.

EXAMPLE 1

If f and g are functions with domain R and

$$f(x) = x^2 - 2$$

and

$$g(x) = -\tfrac{1}{2}x + 1$$

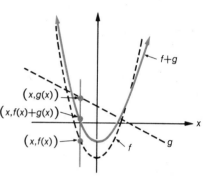

Fig. 6–11

for all x in R, then their graphs are shown by the dashed curves in Fig. 6–11. The graph of $y = f(x) + g(x)$ is shown as the solid curve in the figure. The mapping

$$x \to \big(f(x) + g(x)\big)$$

is also a function which we call the *sum* of f and g and denote by $f + g$. Hence $(f + g)(x) = f(x) + g(x)$. We may easily obtain the graph of $f + g$ by graphical addition from the separate graphs of f and g.

Note that for $f(x) + g(x)$ to make sense two requirements must be met. The element x must be in the domains of both functions f and g, and the image elements $f(x)$ and $g(x)$ must be things that can be *added*. For example, if f is the function that matches each student in the senior class with the amount of money he is carrying and g matches each student in the sophomore class with the amount of money he has, then we would not speak of adding the functions f and g because $f(x)$ and $g(x)$ are not *both* defined for any x in your school. No senior could also be a sophomore.

If f matches each person in your class with his age in years and g matches each person in your class with the name of his mother, then we would not speak of adding f to g. Certainly, for each x in your class, $f(x)$ and $g(x)$ would both be defined, but $f(x) + g(x)$ would not make sense. Note also that when we write

$$(f + g)(x) = f(x) + g(x),$$

138

the sign $+$ on the left stands for the operation *addition of functions*, and the sign $+$ on the right side stands for *addition of the numbers* $f(x)$ and $g(x)$.

DEFINITION 6-5

If f and g are real functions with domains X_1 and X_2 such that

$$X_1 \cap X_2 = X,$$

where X is not the empty set, then $f + g$ is a function with domain X given by

$$(f + g)(x) = f(x) + g(x).$$

EXAMPLE 2

If f and g are given by

$$f(x) = \sqrt{x^2 - 1}, \quad \text{for } |x| \geq 1,$$
$$g(x) = \sqrt{4 - x^2}, \quad \text{for } |x| \leq 2,$$

then the domain of $f + g$ is the union of the two intervals

$$-2 \leq x \leq -1 \quad \text{and} \quad 1 \leq x \leq 2.$$

The graphs of f, g, and $f + g$ are shown in Fig. 6–12.

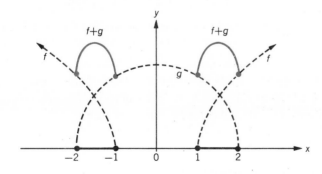

Fig. 6–12

Subtraction of functions can be similarly defined, and the graph of the difference of two functions can be constructed graphically from the separate graphs of the functions.

It should be clear how the *product* of two functions, $f \cdot g$, is defined. The construction of the graph of $f \cdot g$ from the separate graphs of f and g requires a little more thought than it does in the case of addition or subtraction.

In defining division of functions we must be careful not to divide by zero. You will be asked to state these definitions in the problems that follow.

139

Problems

1. Graph the following pairs of real functions, then construct the graph of the sum of the functions by graphical addition. Obtain a formula for the sum of the two functions. What is the domain of the sum?

   (a) $f(x) = 2x$ and $g(x) = 1 - x$ for all x in R

   (b) $A(x) = x$ and $B(x) = 1 - x^2$ for all x in R

   (c) $f(x) = x^2$ for $-2 \le x \le 2$ and $g(x) = 1$ for $x \ge 0$

2. Define $f - g$, the difference of two functions f and g.

3. Graph the pair of functions given by

$$t(x) = x^3 \quad \text{and} \quad r(x) = -x \text{ for all } x \text{ in } R.$$

   Graph the function $t - r$.

4. Define $f \cdot g$, where f and g are functions.

5. If $R(x) = 1/x$ for all $x \ne 0$ and Id $(x) = x$ for all x, obtain a formula for $R \cdot$ Id and construct its graph. What is the domain of the product function, $R \cdot$ Id?

6. f, g, and h are functions, with domain R, given by the formulas

$$f(x) = 2x, \quad g(x) = x, \quad \text{and} \quad h(x) = -3.$$

   Obtain a formula for $(f \cdot g + h)$ and sketch the graph.

7. f has as its domain the set of rational numbers and $f(x) = 1$ for all x in its domain. g has as its domain the set of irrational numbers and $g(x) = -1$ for all x in its domain. Are both $f(x)$ and $g(x)$ defined? Is $f + g$ defined?

8. Define the quotient f/g of two functions f and g.

9. If $f(x) = x + 1$ and $g(x) = x - 2$ for all real x, obtain a formula for f/g and sketch the graph. What is the domain of f/g?

6–5. POLYNOMIAL FUNCTIONS

We now consider a special class of functions which can be generated by restricting our attention to the real constant functions, $f(x) = a$, the identity function, $g(x) = x$ for all x in R, and the operations of addition and multiplication of functions. For example, if we have the functions $f(x) = 2$, $g(x) = x$, and $h(x) = -1$, each with domain R, then we may generate a new function, $f \cdot g + h$, given by

$$(f \cdot g + h)(x) = 2x - 1, \quad \text{for all } x \text{ in } R.$$

Similarly, if

$$g(x) = x, \qquad f(x) = \tfrac{3}{4}, \qquad h(x) = \sqrt{3}, \qquad \text{and} \qquad s(x) = 17$$

for all x in R, then $f \cdot (g \cdot g) + h \cdot g + s$ is a function given by

$$(f \cdot (g \cdot g) + h \cdot g + s)(x) = \tfrac{3}{4}x^2 + \sqrt{3}\, x + 17, \qquad \text{for all } x \text{ in } R.$$

The functions that can be constructed in this manner are called *polynomial functions*. With the restrictions we have imposed on the functions and operations, we *cannot* generate functions such as

$$F(x) = \frac{1}{x}, \qquad G(x) = \sqrt{x - 1},$$

$$R(x) = 5^x, \qquad \text{or} \qquad Q(x) = \frac{x + 2}{x - 1}.$$

DEFINITION 6-6

A polynomial function P over the real field is a function given by

$$P(x) = a_0 x^n + a_1 x^{n-1} + \cdots + a_{n-1}x + a_n,$$

where $a_0, a_1, \ldots, a_n$, the *coefficients* of P, are real numbers, $a_0 \neq 0$, and n is a positive integer or zero.

Remarks

1. The *degree* of a polynomial is n if $a_0 \neq 0$ and $n \geq 1$. The *constant polynomials*, of the form $P(x) = a$, *have degree zero if $a \neq 0$*. The special constant polynomial, $P(x) = 0$, called the *zero* polynomial, is not assigned a degree.

2. Accurate graphs of polynomial functions of high degree may, of course, be very difficult to construct. About all we can do is calculate a number of points on the graph and connect these points by a smooth curve. If you go on to study calculus, you will study additional methods for graphing polynomial functions.

3. The *zeros* of a function f are those numbers x in the domain of f for which $f(x) = 0$.

When we speak of a polynomial function *over* the real field, the coefficients of the function are real numbers. However, we may consider polynomials in which the coefficients are restricted to be rational numbers or are permitted to be any complex numbers. Such polynomial functions are respectively called *polynomial functions over the rational field* and *polynomials over the complex field*.

141

There are four main problems that concern us in working with polynomial functions:

1. Given a polynomial function P and x a number in the domain of P, find $P(x)$.
2. Given a polynomial function P and a number y in the range of P, determine the set of all numbers x in the domain of P such that $P(x) = y$.
3. Given a polynomial function P, determine all the zeros, if any, of the polynomial.
4. Given a polynomial function P, construct its graph.

Of the four problems, the first is usually the easiest. Problem 3 is a special case of Problem 2 and has considerable historical interest. At this point in your study of mathematics, you can solve problems of types 2 and 3 for first- and second-degree polynomial functions and for a few polynomials of higher degree. We have already pointed out that Problem 4, constructing the graphs of polynomials, is not necessarily easy, but we shall see that for some polynomial functions the graphs may be readily constructed.

There exists a considerable body of theory concerning polynomials, some of which you have studied in your previous algebra courses. We shall not attempt to review what you have learned or introduce much new theory here. Rather, we shall state a few useful theorems concerning polynomial functions that will aid us in the solution of the problems stated above.

THEOREM 6–1 (The Division Algorithm)

If P and D are polynomials and $D \neq 0$, then there are unique polynomials Q and R such that either $R = 0$ or the degree of R is less than the degree of D and

$$P = D \cdot Q + R.$$

The polynomial P is called the *dividend*, D is called the *divisor*, Q is the *quotient*, and R is the *remainder*.

Remark

It should be emphasized that the equality $P = D \cdot Q + R$ states that *for all real or complex numbers x,*

$$P(x) = D(x) \cdot Q(x) + R(x).$$

This includes numbers x for which $D(x) = 0$.

EXAMPLE **1**

If $P(x) = x^3 + 3x - 1$ and $D(x) = x + 2$, then $Q(x) = x^2 - 2x + 7$ and $R(x) = -15$, since

$$x^3 + 3x - 1 = (x + 2)(x^2 - 2x + 7) - 15.$$

THEOREM 6–2 (The Remainder Theorem)

Let P be any polynomial with complex coefficients and a any complex number. Let $P(x)$ be divided by $x - a$ so that

$$P(x) = (x - a)(Q(x)) + R,$$

where R is a complex number. Then the value of P at a is R; that is, $P(a) = R$.

EXAMPLE 2

If $P(x) = x^3 - 2x^2 + 1$ is divided by $(x - 2)$, then the remainder $R = P(2) = 1$.

THEOREM 6–3 (The Factor Theorem)

The polynomial P is divisible by the polynomial $x - a$ if and only if $P(a) = 0$.

EXAMPLE 3

The polynomial P, where $P(x) = x^3 + 1$, is divisible by $(x + 1)$ since $P(-1) = 0$.

THEOREM 6–4 (The Fundamental Theorem of Algebra)

If P is any polynomial function of degree $n > 0$ with complex coefficients, then P has a zero which is a complex number.

The German mathematician, Karl Friedrich Gauss (1777–1855), was the first to prove the theorem above. Because its proof is difficult, we shall not prove it here. We will, however, use this theorem to show that no polynomial function of degree $n > 0$ can have more than n zeros.

For example, suppose P is a fourth-degree polynomial function with complex coefficients. Then by Theorem 6–4 there is a complex number, c_1, such that $P(c_1) = 0$. Hence by the Factor Theorem, $P = (x - c_1)P_1$, where P_1 is a polynomial of degree 3. By Theorem 6–4, P_1 has a complex zero, say c_2, so that $P = (x - c_1)(x - c_2)P_2$ and P_2 is a polynomial of degree 2. It should be clear that by continuing the argument, we have

$$P(x) = a_0(x - c_1)(x - c_2)(x - c_3)(x - c_4), \qquad \text{where} \quad a_0 \neq 0.$$

Now, if x is any number different from all the numbers c_1, c_2, c_3, and c_4, then $P(x) \neq 0$, and so P does not have more than four zeros. Of course, not all the numbers c_1, c_2, c_3, and c_4 need be distinct. But it is convenient to say, even in this case, that P has four zeros. With this agreement on the use of language, we can say that each polynomial function of degree $n > 0$ has exactly n zeros.

If the coefficients of P are real, then the complex (nonreal) zeros of P must occur in pairs, as the next theorem states.

THEOREM 6–5

If the polynomial P has real coefficients and $P(a + bi) = 0$, with $b \neq 0$, then $P(a - bi) = 0$.

Proof. Given $P(x) = a_0 x^n + a_1 x^{n-1} + \cdots + a_n$, with the a_i real numbers, consider $P(\bar{x})$, where $\bar{x}$ is the complex conjugate of x. Then

$$P(\bar{x}) = a_0 \bar{x}^n + a_1 \bar{x}^{n-1} + \cdots + a_n,$$
$$= \overline{(a_0 x^n + a_1 x^{n-1} + \cdots + a_n)}, \tag{1}$$
$$= \overline{P(x)}$$

because the sum (and product) of the conjugates of complex numbers is the conjugate of their sum (and product).

Now suppose that $x = a + bi$ and $P(a + bi) = 0$. Then from (1),

$$P(a - bi) = P(\overline{a + bi}) = \overline{P(a + bi)} = \bar{0} = 0.$$

EXAMPLE 4

The polynomial $P(x) = x^3 - 2x + 4$ has one zero equal to $1 + i$, that is $P(1 + i) = 0$, as may be easily verified. Since the coefficients of P are real, $1 - i$ must also be a zero: $P(1 - i) = 0$.

Corollary

If P has real coefficients and $P(a + bi) = 0$, with $b \neq 0$, then

$$P(x) = (x^2 - 2ax + a^2 + b^2)Q(x),$$

where $Q(x)$ is a polynomial of degree 2 less than that of P, and with real coefficients.

Proof. From Theorem 6–5 and the Factor Theorem,

$$P(x) = (x - (a + bi))Q_1(x)$$
$$= (x - (a + bi))(x - (a - bi))Q(x)$$
$$= (x^2 - 2ax + a^2 + b^2)Q(x).$$

The polynomial Q must have real coefficients, for if it did not, then P would not have real coefficients.

144

It follows that any polynomial with real coefficients can be factored into the product of real linear, or real quadratic, factors.

Problems

1. The zeros of a polynomial function P are 1, 2, and -3.
   (a) Give three linear factors of the polynomial.
   (b) Give a quadratic factor of the polynomial.
   (c) Give the polynomial if $P(3) = 60$.

2. What is the remainder if $P(x) = 2x^2 - x + 3$ is divided by $x - 3$?

3. Prove Theorem 6-2.

4. Prove Theorem 6-3.

5. Is the sum of two polynomial functions a polynomial function?

6. Give an example of two third-degree polynomials whose sum is a polynomial of degree 1.

7. What is the product of the polynomial functions P and Q where $P(x) = x^3 - x + 2$ and $Q(x) = x^2 + 1$? What is the degree of the product?

8. One zero of a second-degree polynomial with real coefficients is $3 + 4i$. What are the coefficients of the polynomial if $P(0) = 25$?

9. Show that if $P(x) = x^2 + 2x + 2$, then $P(x) > 0$ for every real number x.

10. The polynomial function Q where $Q(x) = x^3 - 2x^2 + x - 2$ has i as one of its zeros. Express Q as a product of a real quadratic factor and a real linear factor.

*11. Prove that if P is a polynomial of degree n, and P has distinct zeros $b_1, b_2, \ldots, b_n$, then $P(x) \neq 0$ if $x \neq b_i$, $i = 1, 2, \ldots, n$.

6-6. GRAPHS OF POLYNOMIAL FUNCTIONS

We now turn to the problem of constructing graphs of polynomial functions over the real numbers and consider techniques that can be used to obtain the graphs of certain polynomials.

If a polynomial is completely factored into real *linear* factors, the graph is quite easy to sketch.

EXAMPLE 1

Sketch the graph of

$$P(x) = \tfrac{1}{2}(x + 1)(x)(x - 1)(x - 3).$$

145

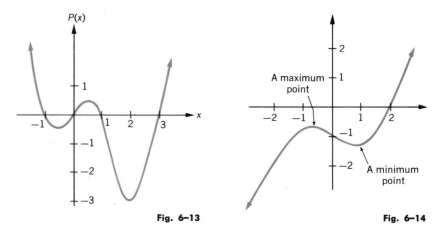

Fig. 6–13   Fig. 6–14

The zeros of P are $-1, 0, 1$, and 3. For other values of x it is easy to determine whether the factors in x are positive or negative and hence whether $P(x) > 0$ or $P(x) < 0$. Thus

$$
\begin{aligned}
P(x) &> 0 &&\text{if}\ \ x < -1,\\
P(x) &< 0 &&\text{if}\ \ -1 < x < 0,\\
P(x) &> 0 &&\text{if}\ \ 0 < x < 1,\\
P(x) &< 0 &&\text{if}\ \ 1 < x < 3,\\
P(x) &> 0 &&\text{if}\ \ x > 3.
\end{aligned}
$$

x	$-\frac{3}{2}$	$-\frac{1}{2}$	$\frac{1}{2}$	2	$\frac{7}{2}$
$P(x)$	4.2	-0.65	0.5	-3	9.8

Therefore all that remains to be done is to obtain additional points on the graph in order to sketch it. Some of these are given in the table above. The completed graph of P is shown in Fig. 6–13.

If a polynomial f, with real coefficients, is factored as completely as possible into *real* factors which are not all linear, then the graph is less easy to sketch.

EXAMPLE 2

Sketch the graph of

$$f(x) = \tfrac{1}{4}(x^2 + 2x + 2)(x - 2).$$

Because $x^2 + 2x + 2 > 0$ for all real numbers x,† the only zero of f is 2. Therefore $f(x) > 0$ if $x > 2$ and $f(x) < 0$ for $x < 2$.

---

† The sentence $x^2 + 2x + 2 > 0$ is equivalent to the sentence $(x + 1)^2 + 1 > 0$, which is a true statement for all real numbers x.

146

In this problem, to draw the curve reasonably well, we must compute the coordinates of enough points on the graph of f.

x	0	1	-1	3	-2	-0.5	0.5	1.5
$f(x)$	-1	-1.25	-0.75	-4.25	-2	-0.7	-1.2	-0.9

Remarks

1. In graphing a polynomial function, it would be a great boon if one could locate the "maximum" and "minimum" points on its graph (see Fig. 6–14). It is possible to do this with a bit of calculus, but even without calculus we can attack this problem. We shall return to this question later in the book.

2. If we cannot factor a polynomial, then the principal means at our disposal for sketching the graph is that of plotting many points. However, in some cases, the method of adding ordinates graphically will permit one to sketch a graph quickly. For example, if $f(x) = x^3 - x^2 - x - 1$, let $g(x) = x^3$ and $h(x) = -x^2 - x - 1$. Then $f = g + h$, and both g and h have graphs that are easily sketched.

Problems

1. Sketch the graphs of the polynomial functions given below.

   (a) $f(x) = (x + 1)x(x - 1)$
   (b) $P(x) = x(x - 1)(x - 2)$
   (c) $g(x) = (x - 1)(x - 2)(x - 3)$
   (d) $G(t) = t(t - 1)(t - 2)(t - 3)$
   (e) $T(x) = \frac{1}{10}(x + 2)(x + 1)(x - 1)x(x - 2)$
   *(f) $R(s) = \frac{1}{3}(s^2 + s + 1)(s + 1)$

2. Sketch the graph of the polynomial $x^3 - x + 1$ and from the graph find, approximately, the real zeros of the polynomial.

3. Sketch the graph of $P(x) = (x + 1)^2(x - 1)(x - 3) + 1$ and obtain the real zeros of P from the graph.

4. Use the Factor Theorem to argue that none of the real numbers -1, 1, or 3 are zeros of the polynomial P in Problem 3.

5. Prove that if $0 < x_1 < x_2$, then $0 < x_1^3 < x_2^3$.

6. Sketch the graphs of the polynomial functions given below.

   (a) $H(t) = t^2(t - 1)(t - 2)$ (b) $Q(s) = (s - 1)^2(s + 1)^2$
   (c) $f(s) = s^2(s - 1)^3$ (d) $P(s) = \frac{1}{4}(s^2 + 1)(s^2 - 1)$
   (e) $S(x) = \frac{1}{4}(x^2 + 4)(x^2 + 1)$ (f) $f(x) = -\frac{1}{4}x^2(x^2 - 1)$

147

6–7. GENERAL PROPERTIES OF FUNCTIONS

Functions may have a bewildering variety of properties, many of which you will encounter as you continue your study of mathematics. At this time we call attention to three of these. These properties are concerned with *boundedness*, whether a function is *increasing* or *decreasing*, and *continuity*. Each property has a simple geometric interpretation.

For a discussion of these properties, one needs to have some terminology and symbolism. The definitions given below provide us with this information.

DEFINITION 6–7

The set of all real numbers x such that $a < x < b$ is called the *open interval* determined by the real numbers a and b, or the *open interval* bounded by *endpoints* a and b. It is denoted by $\langle a, b \rangle$.

If just one of the endpoints is included in the set, then the interval is called *half-open* and is denoted by $[a, b\rangle$ or $\langle a, b]$.

If both endpoints are included in the set, the interval is called a *closed interval* and is denoted by $[a, b]$.

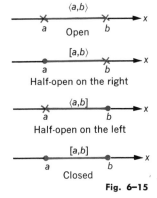

Fig. 6–15

We say that a function is *defined on an interval* if each number in the interval is in the domain of the function.

DEFINITION 6–8

A function f defined on an interval is said to be *increasing on that interval* if whenever x_1 and x_2 are in that interval and $x_1 < x_2$, then $f(x_1) < f(x_2)$. A function g, defined on an interval, is said to be *decreasing on that interval* if whenever x_1 and x_2 are in that interval and $x_1 < x_2$, then $g(x_1) > g(x_2)$.

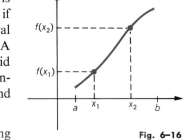

Fig. 6–16

See Fig. 6–16 for the graph of an increasing function.

DEFINITION 6–9

A real function f defined on an interval with endpoints a and b is said to be *bounded above in that interval* if there is a number M such that $f(x) \leq M$ for all x in the interval.

148

The function f is *bounded below in that interval* if there is a number m such that $m \leq f(x)$ for all x in that interval.

If f is both bounded above and bounded below, then f is *bounded in that interval* (see Fig. 6–17).

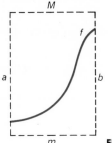

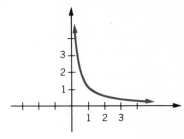

Fig. 6–17   Fig. 6–18

EXAMPLE

Suppose that f is defined by

$$f(x) = \frac{1}{x} \quad \text{for } x > 0.$$

The graph is shown in Fig. 6–18.

We see that f is not bounded above on the interval $\langle 0, 1]$. However, f is bounded below because $0 < f(x)$ for all x in the interval.

On the interval $[1, 2]$ the function is bounded. In fact, f is bounded on any closed interval $[a, b]$ if $a > 0$.

Problems

1. Picture the set of points on the real number line that are in the following intervals.

(a) $\langle -3, 2 \rangle$ (b) $[0, 1 \rangle$ (c) $\langle -1, 0]$ (d) $[2, \pi]$

(e) $\langle a - e, a + e \rangle$ (f) $\langle -2, 3]$ and $[-1, 5 \rangle$

2. Which of the following functions are bounded above?   bounded below?   bounded?

(a) $f(x) = 5$ for all x

(b) $f(x) = x$ for all x

(c) $g(x) = \begin{cases} 1 \text{ if } x \geq 0 \\ 0 \text{ if } x < 0 \end{cases}$

(d) $h(x) = \begin{cases} 1/x \text{ if } x \neq 0 \\ 2 \text{ if } x = 0 \end{cases}$

(e) $H(x) = 1/x$ for $1 \leq x \leq 5000$

(f) $Q(t) = \sqrt{t^2 - 1}$ for $t \geq 1$

(g) $F(x) = \begin{cases} 1 \text{ if } x \text{ is rational} \\ 0 \text{ if } x \text{ is irrational} \end{cases}$

(h) $P(x) = x^{16} + x^{12} + x^{10} + x^8 + x^2 + 1$ for all x

149

3. Prove that the function f with domain R given by $f(x) = 2x - 5$ is an increasing function.

4. Prove that a linear function, $F(x) = y = mx + b$, where m is the slope, is increasing if and only if $m > 0$.

5. Graph the function given by $x \to 1/x$ where $x > 0$. Prove that this function is decreasing for all $x > 0$.

6. Prove that if $0 < x_1 < x_2$, then $x_1^2 < x_2^2$. Hence prove that the function s, given by $s(x) = x^2$, is increasing for $x > 0$.

7. Prove that if g is an increasing function and $g(1) = 3$, then $g(2) \neq 0$.

6-8. CONTINUITY

The last of the three properties that we shall consider is continuity. This is a concept that you will meet again and again if you continue to study mathematics. Although continuity has a strong appeal to the intuition, its precise definition is surprisingly troublesome, and proofs of continuity are hard to manage unless the meaning of the definition is discussed in depth. For these reasons we shall confine ourselves here to a description of the idea, since the intuitive understanding of the concept is of first importance. For a more complete discussion, see Appendix C.

There are two aspects to the notion of continuity—a local one and a global one. There is *continuity at a point* and *continuity in an interval*.

DEFINITION 6-10

Let f be a function defined on $\langle a, b \rangle$ and let c be a point of the interval, that is, $a < c < b$. Then f is *continuous at c* if "for x very close to c, $f(x)$ is very close to $f(c)$" (Fig. 6–19).

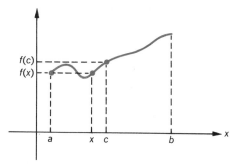

Fig. 6–19

Another way of stating this is to say that f is continuous at c if "the difference $|f(x) - f(c)|$ can be made as small as one likes by choosing x sufficiently close to c." That is, the closer we choose x to c the smaller the difference $|f(x) - f(c)|$.

150

DEFINITION 6–11

If f is defined on an interval, then f is *continuous on that interval* provided that f is continuous at each point of the interval.

Remarks

1. It is natural to ask how one goes about proving that a particular function is continuous at a point. Ultimately all such proofs rest upon the definition of continuity at a point, but we need a definition more precise than the one given here. We shall see in a moment that continuity in an interval implies that the graph has a certain property. In our problems *we shall rely upon the graph to decide upon the continuity of the function.*

But observe that we are really cheating! We cannot be *sure* of the graph of a function until we know about the continuity of the function—yet we intend to infer continuity from the graph! However, things are really not so bad as they may seem, for you *have* had some experience in drawing graphs. In other words, for simple functions the graph was easy to draw, because we intuitively knew they were continuous.

2. It can be proved that the graph of a function *continuous on an interval* has no "breaks." The graph comes in "one piece."

Furthermore, one can prove that each polynomial function is continuous. Therefore, we were essentially correct, in drawing the graph of a polynomial, when we connected the points we had found by a continuous curve.

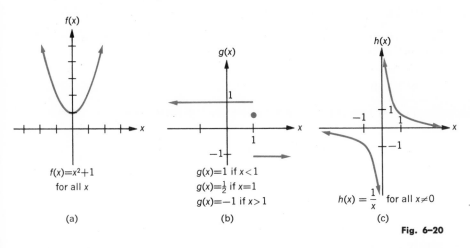

$f(x)=x^2+1$
for all x

$g(x)=1$ if $x<1$
$g(x)=\frac{1}{2}$ if $x=1$
$g(x)=-1$ if $x>1$

$h(x) = \frac{1}{x}$ for all $x \neq 0$

(a)   (b)   (c)

Fig. 6–20

Figure 6–20(a) shows the graph of a function f which is continuous at every point in its domain. The graph of the function g in Fig. 6–20(b) shows that g is *discontinuous* at 1. The function is not continuous on any closed interval that contains 1. As "x gets close to 1, $g(x)$ does not get close to $g(1)$."

The graph of the function h in Fig. 6–20(c) must be considered carefully. We note that this function is not defined at 0, and so it does not make sense to discuss continuity at this point. However, on any interval that does not contain 0, the function is continuous.

Continuous functions possess an important property which we shall use later. This is the *intermediate-value* property.

INTERMEDIATE-VALUE THEOREM (IVT)

Suppose that f is continuous on the closed interval $[a, b]$ and $f(a) \neq f(b)$, and suppose that d is a number between $f(a)$ and $f(b)$; then there is at least one number c such that $a < c < b$ and $d = f(c)$.

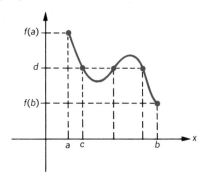

Fig. 6–21

The theorem is illustrated in Fig. 6–21, where for this particular number d, there are three possible values for the number c. The proof requires a more intensive study of continuity, and we shall assume its truth here. See Appendix C for a sketch of the proof.

EXAMPLE

The polynomial $f(x) = \frac{1}{8}(x^3 - 3x^2 - 9x + 2)$ takes on the values given in the table below.

x	0	1	2	3	4	5	-1	-2	-3
$f(x)$	0.25	-1.1	-2.5	-3.1	-2.2	0.9	0.9	0	-3.1

At 0 the function is positive, while at 1 it is negative. By the IVT the function must have the value 0 somewhere in the interval $\langle 0, 1 \rangle$. According to the graph in Fig. 6–22, this value appears to be approximately $x = 0.2$.

Because $f(-3) = -3.1$ and $f(5) = 0.9$, there must be at least one x in $\langle -3, 5 \rangle$ for which $f(x) = -2$. We see from the graph in Fig. 6–22 that there are, in fact, three such numbers, namely $x = -2.7, 1.7, 4.2$, approximately.

We note that the graph of the polynomial function f of the example is continuous. Observe also that the polynomial is bounded on each closed interval. Of course there is no one number that is an upper bound for the range of the entire polynomial and so we say that the polynomial is unbounded on the whole set of real numbers.

152

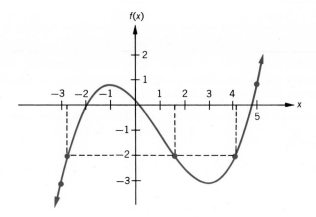

Fig. 6-22

From the graph we see that for $x > 3$ the function is increasing. Between -1 and 3 it is decreasing, and for $x < -1$ the function is again increasing.

Problems

1. Sketch the graph of the function f defined by

$$f(x) = x^3 - \tfrac{1}{2}x^2 - \tfrac{9}{4}x + \tfrac{9}{8}, \quad \text{with domain } R.$$

Show that f has a zero in each of the intervals $\langle -2, -1 \rangle$, $\langle 0, 1 \rangle$, and $\langle 1, 2 \rangle$. Can you determine any of the zeros exactly?

2. Sketch the graph of a continuous function whose domain is R, which is increasing, and is unbounded.

3. Sketch the graph of $p(x) = x(x - 1)(x + 2)$ for x in the interval $[-2, 1]$. Is p continuous in this interval? Is p bounded on this interval? Find an upper bound of the function. Find a lower bound of the function.

4. If a function is continuous on some closed interval $[a, b]$, will it be bounded on that interval?

5. If a function is bounded on some closed interval, will it necessarily be continuous on that interval?

6. The graph of a function F is shown in the figure at the right. Is F bounded? In what interval is the function increasing? decreasing? continuous everywhere? not everywhere continuous? not continuous everywhere?

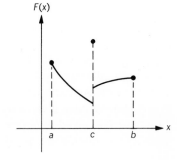

7. Sketch the graph of a function which is defined on $[0, 1]$, is bounded, and is continuous everywhere, except at $\frac{1}{2}$. Sketch another function with domain $[0, 1]$ which is unbounded and continuous except at $\frac{1}{2}$.

8. Sketch the graph of $f(x) = x^2$ for $x \geq 0$. Assuming continuity on any closed interval in the domain of this function, show that there is a positive real number whose square is 2; that is, show that $\sqrt{2}$ exists.

9. Sketch a graph of a function which will illustrate that *without* the requirement of continuity on an interval, the conclusion of the Intermediate-Value Theorem will not be valid.

10. Show, algebraically, that $\sqrt{x}$, $x \geq 0$, is an unbounded increasing function.

HISTORICAL NOTE

By 1700 calculus had been invented, by Newton and Leibnitz (see the historical notes of chapter 15), and a host of followers were using the new method to attack problems heretofore inaccessible. The first reaction to calculus was exultation in newly found power. Yet, all the while, there were no satisfactory proofs that the processes of calculus were valid! Gradually, this lack of an adequate foundation became more and more worrisome, and although there were numerous attempts to put the processes of calculus on a firm basis, real progress was slow. Eventually it became clear that the difficulties were threefold:

(1) The structure of the *real number* system needed clarification.

(2) The concept of *function*, and continuity of functions, needed precise formulation.

(3) The concept of *limit* needed a rigorous definition.

A sound, although not complete, treatment of the real numbers is today part of the mathematics curriculum in secondary schools (see Appendix C). In this text, we have given a modern definition of function. Continuity and limits are discussed in Appendix C. Thus a student today can meet these ideas in a mathematically adequate way from the very beginning.

154

Augustin-Louis Cauchy (1789–1857). One of the great pioneers in mathematical precision and rigor.

But in 1700 there was much confusion. There was no general definition of function. The reader had to know intuitively what was meant. Furthermore, mathematicians were overly concerned with functions as "nice formulas." They did not understand how vast even the class of continuous functions actually is. A few of the landmarks in the gradual evolution of the function concept are associated with the following men.

Leonhard Euler (1707–1783) was a great calculator, a great manipulator of formulas. To him we are indebted for the notation $f(x)$ for functions. (Observe that today we refer to the *function f* and reserve $f(x)$ for "the *value* of *f* at *x*.")

Augustin-Louis Cauchy (1789–1857) is the first to have approached a modern treatment of calculus, limits, and continuity. The publication of his lectures at the Ecole Polytechnique in 1821 set a definite pattern of exposition which is still used in the books of today.

Peter G. Lejeune Dirichlet (1805–1859) gave the first definition (in 1837) of a real function as a correspondence between two sets of real numbers.

Georg Cantor (1845–1918) during the 1870's initiated abstract set theory—a bold step which has profoundly affected the direction of mathematical development. Cantor's work led to the general concept of function as a mapping from sets to sets, a concept which is discussed in this book.

155

6–9. RATIONAL FUNCTIONS

So far in this chapter, we have systematically studied only polynomials. As we know from algebra, and from Section 6–4, the sum and product of polynomials is again a polynomial, and hence addition and multiplication do not lead to new functions. For division the situation is different. In the first place, we shall have to be careful not to divide by zero. But, because a polynomial, not the zero polynomial, can have only a finite set of zeros, we need to watch the behavior of a quotient function only at a finite set of numbers.

DEFINITION 6–12

If f and g are polynomials with no common nonconstant factors, then the *quotient of f divided by g*, denoted by f/g, is the function defined by

$$\frac{f}{g}(x) = \frac{f(x)}{g(x)}, \qquad \text{for all } x \text{ for which } g(x) \neq 0.$$

The function f/g, a quotient of polynomials, is called a *rational function*.

Observe the similarity between the terminology used for functions and that used for numbers. Rational numbers are quotients of integers. Rational functions are quotients of polynomials. For this reason, polynomials are often called *rational integral functions*.

One other remark about rational functions should be made. The domain of a rational function does not contain the zeros of the polynomial in the denominator. Further, if $g(a) = 0$, and $f(a) \neq 0$, then, because of continuity, $g(x)$ must be very small for x near a, and hence $|f(x)/g(x)|$ must be large near a. In other words, near a zero of the denominator, the rational function f/g must be unbounded.

EXAMPLES

1. Graph the rational function F defined by $F(x) = x/(x + 1)$. The domain of F consists of all real numbers except -1.

Several points on the graph of F are computed in the table below.

x	-3	-2	-1.5	-0.5	0	1	2
$F(x)$	1.5	2	3	-1	0	0.5	0.7

To sketch the graph of F, we must recognize that F is continuous everywhere in its domain, but is not defined at -1. Moreover, we must recognize that $|F(x)|$ is large for x near -1. Indeed F is unbounded in any open interval having -1 for an endpoint. If $x < -1$, then $F(x) > 1$. If $-1 < x < 0$, then $F(x) < 0$.

156

We also note that

$$\frac{x}{x+1} = \frac{x+1-1}{x+1} = 1 - \frac{1}{x+1}.$$

From this we see that if x is a very large positive number, then $F(x)$ is near 1 but less than 1. However, if x is negative and $|x|$ is large, then $F(x)$ is also near 1, but is greater than 1. The graph is shown in Fig. 6–23.

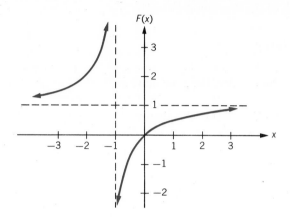

Fig. 6–23

2. Graph the rational function G given by $G(x) = x^2/(1 - x^2)$. The domain consists of all real numbers except 1 and -1.

$$\text{If } |x| < 1, \quad \text{then } G(x) \geq 0.$$
$$\text{If } |x| > 1, \quad \text{then } G(x) < -1.$$

This last example illustrates several properties of graphs. From Fig. 6–24 we see that the graph has *symmetry*. The left half is a mirror image of the

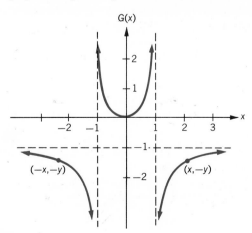

Fig. 6–24

157

right half. We say that the graph is symmetric with respect to the y-axis. Symmetry with respect to the y-axis can easily be determined from the formula for a function. A graph has this symmetry if and only if for each point (x, y) on the graph, the point $(-x, y)$ is also on the graph. In other words, we must have $F(x) = F(-x)$ for every x in the domain of F. A function with this property is called an *even* function.

We can also have symmetry with respect to a point.

3. The graph of the function g given by

$$g(x) = \frac{-1}{x},$$

is shown in Fig. 6–25. Here we have symmetry with respect to the origin 0. If (x, y) is a point on the graph, then so is $(-x, -y)$. The function g has the property

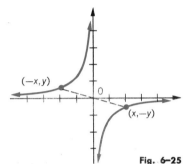

Fig. 6–25

$$g(-x) = -g(x).$$

A function with this property is called an *odd* function. All functions are not necessarily odd or even; that is, many functions are neither odd nor even.

Figures 6–23, 6–24, and 6–25 are pictures of graphs having *asymptotes*. In Fig. 6–23 we observe from the graph that when $|x|$ is large, $F(x)$ is very near to 1. We say that the line $y = 1$ is a *horizontal asymptote* of F. Also, in the same figure, when x is near -1, $F(x)$ is unbounded. The line $x = -1$ is a *vertical asymptote* of F.

In Fig. 6–24, we observe that

$$G(x) = \frac{x^2}{1 - x^2} = \frac{1}{(1/x^2) - 1},$$

so that when $|x|$ is large, $G(x)$ is near -1. Thus the line $y = -1$ is a horizontal asymptote. Also, when $|x|$ is near 1, $G(x)$ is unbounded. Hence the lines $x = \pm 1$ are vertical asymptotes.

In Fig. 6–25, we observe that the x- and y-axes are asymptotes.

In these examples the asymptotes were either horizontal or vertical lines. One might ask whether a rational function could have an asymptote not parallel to either axis. The following example shows that this can occur.

EXAMPLE 4

The function f given by

$$f(x) = \frac{x^2 + 1}{x} = x + \frac{1}{x}$$

has the graph shown in Fig. 6–26.

158

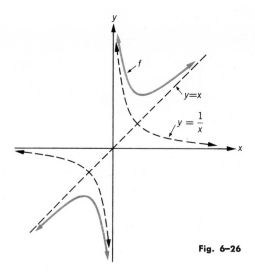

Fig. 6–26

When $|x|$ is large, $f(x)$ is very near x. Therefore the line $y = x$ is an asymptote. The curve was drawn by graphical addition of the graphs of $y = x$ and $y = 1/x$.

It will be convenient, for graphing and for later uses, to introduce the symbols $+\infty$ and $-\infty$, called "infinity" and "minus-infinity." *These symbols do not represent numbers.* Whenever one of the symbols $\pm\infty$ is used, stop and remember that some kind of *shorthand* is involved, that is, a short phrase has been used for a long, more complicated one. We collect some of these phrases in the following definition.

DEFINITION 6–13

(a) "x approaches $+\infty$" or "x becomes positively infinite" means that we are considering arbitrarily large numbers x. In other words, for any number B, we shall consider numbers larger than B.

(b) "x approaches $-\infty$" means that for any number B, we shall consider numbers less than B.

(c) $[a, +\infty\rangle$ is the interval that includes all real numbers x such that $x \geq a$. Similarly, $\langle -\infty, +\infty\rangle = R$.

(d) "If x approaches a, then $F(x)$ approaches $+\infty$," which is expressed symbolically by "If $x \to a$, then $F(x) \to +\infty$," means that given any number B, if x is close enough to a, then $F(x) > B$.

We can now better describe horizontal and vertical asymptotes of the graph of a function f.

159

DEFINITION 6-14

A vertical line, $x = a$, is a *vertical asymptote* if as x approaches a from one side or the other, then $f(x) \to +\infty$ or $f(x) \to -\infty$.

A horizontal line, $y = b$, is a *horizontal asymptote* if $f(x) \to b$ as either $x \to +\infty$, or $x \to -\infty$.

We shall not define other asymptotes at this time.

Problems

1. Sketch the graphs of the following rational functions. Determine their symmetries. Find all horizontal and vertical asymptotes. What is the domain of each function?

(a) $f(x) = \dfrac{x}{x^2 + 1}$

(b) $W(x) = \dfrac{x^2}{x^2 + 1}$

(c) $h(x) = \dfrac{x^2 - 1}{x^2 + 1}$

(d) $F(x) = \dfrac{x^2 + 1}{x^2 - 1}$

(e) $G(x) = \dfrac{1}{(x^2 - 1)^2}$

(f) $T(x) = \dfrac{3x^2}{x^2 - 4}$

(g) $g(x) = \dfrac{x - 1}{x^2(x - 2)}$

(h) $S(x) = \dfrac{x}{2x - 1}$

(i) $U(x) = \dfrac{x^2 - 1}{(x - 2)^2}$

(j) $V(x) = \dfrac{x^2 - 1}{x - 1}$

2. Show that the graph of the equation

$$x^3 y + 2x^2 y + 4xy + y + x^2 + x + 1 = 0$$

is the graph of a rational function.

3. Show that the rational function

$$f(x) = \frac{x^{10}}{x^{12} + 17}$$

has a horizontal asymptote.

4. If $f(x) = \dfrac{-1}{x - 1}$ and if y is in the interval $\langle -\infty, 0 \rangle$, show that there is a unique x in the interval $\langle 1, \infty \rangle$ such that $f(x) = y$.

5. Show that every rational function satisfies an equation of the form

$$P_0(x)F(x) + P_1(x) = 0,$$

where P_0 and P_1 are polynomials with no common nonconstant polynomial factors.

6. Given $F(x) = \dfrac{x}{x^2 - 1}$, show that for each real number r there is a unique real number a in the interval $\langle -1, 1 \rangle$ such that $F(a) = r$.

6–10. ALGEBRAIC FUNCTIONS

We are considering more and more complicated functions. With rational functions we have exhausted the possible functions which can be defined directly in terms of the rational operations, addition, multiplication, subtraction, and division. To get more functions we must introduce a new operation, namely that of solving algebraic equations. This will introduce the larger class of algebraic functions. First we consider three examples.

EXAMPLES

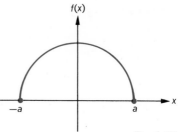

1. Consider the function f given by

$$f(x) = \sqrt{a^2 - x^2}\,,$$

where the domain is the interval $[-a, a]$.

If we set $y = f(x)$, then

$$y^2 = a^2 - x^2 \quad \text{or} \quad x^2 + y^2 = a^2,$$

Fig. 6–27

and we see that the graph of f is the upper half of the circle of radius a with center at the origin (Fig. 6–27).

We obtain the formula for f by solving the equation $x^2 + y^2 = a^2$ for y. Let us note, however, that solving this equation also gives the formula for a function g other than f, namely $g(x) = -\sqrt{a^2 - x^2}$. Of course, the graph of g is the bottom half of the circle.

2. Consider F given by

$$F(x) = -1 + \frac{1}{\sqrt{x}},$$

where the domain is $\langle 0, +\infty \rangle$. The graph is shown in Fig. 6–28.

If $y = F(x)$, then

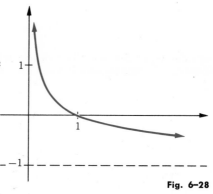

$$y = -1 + \frac{1}{\sqrt{x}}$$

and

$$\sqrt{x}\,(y + 1) = 1$$

or

$$xy^2 + 2xy + x - 1 = 0. \quad (1)$$

Fig. 6–28

We find that we obtain the formula for F by solving equation (1) for y. What formula for a function other than F is obtained by solving (1) for y?

In both of these examples functions are obtained by solving an equation. Both equations solved were quadratic equations, and therefore rather simple. But we can consider much more complicated equations.

161

EXAMPLE 3

Consider the equation

$$(x^4 - 3x^2 + 5)y^{12} + (x^{10} + 1)y^7 + (x - 2)y^3 - y - 7 = 0 \quad (2)$$

and suppose that it has been solved. By this we mean that for each real number x, the roots of equation (2) are known. In general, there will be 12 values of y for each x, so that equation (2) will define not one function but 12! Each of these functions is an algebraic function.

DEFINITION 6–15

If f is a continuous function and if $y = f(x)$ and x and y satisfy an algebraic equation,

$$P_0(x)y^n + P_1(x)y^{n-1} + \cdots + P_n(x) = 0, \quad (3)$$

where $P_0, P_1, \ldots, P_n$ are polynomials in x, then f is called an *algebraic function*.

Remark

In general, because of our limited algebraic skills, we will be unable to handle equation (3) if $n > 2$. However, some special equations of higher degree can be considered. For example, if

$$(x^2 + 1)y^3 - (x - 1) = 0, \quad (4)$$

then the algebraic function

$$f(x) = y = \sqrt[3]{\frac{x - 1}{x^2 + 1}}$$

satisfies equation (4). The other two functions that satisfy this equation involve complex numbers.

Problems

1. Graph the following algebraic functions. In each case prove that the function is algebraic by showing that $y = f(x)$ satisfies an equation of the form (3).

   (a) $f(x) = 2 - \sqrt{1 - (x - 1)^2}$ (b) $f(x) = 1 - 2\sqrt{x + 2}$

   (c) $f(x) = \frac{2}{3}\sqrt{9 - x^2}$ (d) $f(x) = \frac{2}{3}\sqrt{x^2 - 9}$

   (e) $f(x) = \dfrac{1 - x + \sqrt{x^2 + 4}}{2x}$ (f) $f(x) = 1 + \sqrt[3]{x}$

   (g) $f(x) = \sqrt[3]{x^2}$ (h) $f(x) = \sqrt{x(x^2 - 1)}$

   (i) $f(x) = \sqrt[3]{\dfrac{x}{x^2 + 1}}$ (j) $f(x) = x - \sqrt[3]{x^3 + 27}$

162

2. Prove that rational functions are algebraic functions.

3. Given that $f(x) = \sqrt{x} + \dfrac{1}{\sqrt{x}} + 1$, show that f is an algebraic function.

*4. If n is the smallest positive integer for which x and y satisfy an equation of the form (3), then f is said to be an algebraic function of degree n. Give an example of an algebraic function of degree 4.

*5. Show that if F is a rational function and $f(x) = \sqrt{F(x)}$, then f is an algebraic function.

6–11. EXPONENTIAL FUNCTIONS

There are many functions other than algebraic functions. Functions which are not algebraic are called *transcendental functions*. Some nonalgebraic functions occur so frequently that they are referred to as the *elementary transcendental functions*. The first transcendental functions we will study are the *exponential* functions. It will be convenient to recall the properties of exponents. For integral exponents:

(a) $a^0 = 1$ if $a \neq 0$ (0^0 is *not* defined).

(b) $a^1 = a$.

(c) $a^n = a \cdot a \cdot \ldots \cdot a$ to n factors if n is an integer > 1.

(d) $a^{-n} = 1/a^n$ if n is a positive integer.

The following laws for integral exponents are valid.

$$a^n \cdot a^m = a^{n+m},$$

$$\frac{a^n}{a^m} = a^{n-m} = \frac{1}{a^{m-n}},$$

$$(a^n)^m = a^{nm}.$$

The next step is to extend the definition to exponents which are rational numbers.

If p is a positive integer and $a \geq 0$, then† $a^{1/p} = \sqrt[p]{a}$ is that unique non-negative number y such that $y^p = a$.

We then define, if q is a positive integer, and q/p is in lowest terms,

$$a^{q/p} = (a^{1/p})^q$$

and

$$a^{-q/p} = (a^{1/p})^{-q}$$

---

† The restriction to $a \geq 0$ is necessary if p is even because negative numbers do not have real even roots. For example, $\sqrt{-4} = 2i$, which is complex.

163

and find that the same laws of exponents are valid. That is if r_1 and r_2 are any rational numbers, then

$$a^{r_1} \cdot a^{r_2} = a^{r_1 + r_2},$$

$$\frac{a^{r_1}}{a^{r_2}} = a^{r_1 - r_2} = \frac{1}{a^{r_2 - r_1}},$$

$$(a^{r_1})^{r_2} = a^{r_1 r_2}.$$

The final step is to extend the domain of exponents to the set R of real numbers in such a way that the laws of exponents remain valid. To make this extension it is convenient to consider the cases $a > 1$ and $a < 1$ separately.

Let us suppose that $a > 1$ and consider the function defined by

$$f(x) = a^x, \qquad \text{for all rational numbers } x.$$

The graph of this function is shown in Fig. 6–29, where the red graph is dotted to emphasize that the domain of the function is the set of rational numbers and not the set of all real numbers.

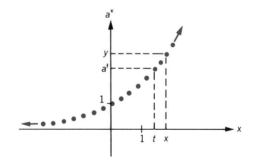

Fig. 6–29

Several items are clear from the graph, namely that the function is increasing, is unbounded, is always positive, and assumes arbitrarily small positive values as $x \to -\infty$.

Now let us suppose that x is any real number and consider the set of all numbers a^t, for all *rational* numbers $t < x$. As may be seen from the graph, these numbers a^t comprise a set S which is bounded above and which therefore has a least upper bound† y. We *define*

$$a^x = y = \text{least upper bound of } S.$$

---

† That is, y is an upper bound of S: $s \leq y$ for all s in S, and y is the smallest such number. See also Appendix C, p. 481.

164

The following important theorem can now be proved, although the proof of each assertion is not at all easy. We shall assume that this theorem is valid.

THEOREM 6–6

The function $x \xrightarrow{f} a^x$, where x is a real number and $a > 1$

(1) is increasing,
(2) is continuous,
(3) is a one-to-one mapping of the real numbers onto the positive real numbers,
(4) obeys the laws of exponents,

$$a^u \cdot a^v = a^{u+v},$$

$$\frac{a^u}{a^v} = a^{u-v} = \frac{1}{a^{v-u}},$$

$$(a^u)^v = a^{uv}.$$

If $0 < a < 1$, a similar definition can be made for a^x. Then, in defining the set S, we choose rational numbers $t > x$. The definition of a^x is the same as before. The function a^x, with $0 < a < 1$, is *decreasing* but has the other properties (2), (3), and (4) of Theorem 6.

Because a^x is continuous and increasing if $a > 1$, it is easy to sketch the graph.

EXAMPLE 1

Sketch the graph of $f(x) = 2^x$.

We compute the values given in the table below,

x	0	1	2	3	-1	-2	-3
2^x	1	2	4	8	$\frac{1}{2}$	$\frac{1}{4}$	$\frac{1}{8}$

and connect these points by a smooth curve to represent an increasing continuous function (Fig. 6–30).

From the graph we can compute, approximately, other powers of 2. Thus if $x = 1.5$, we get $2^{1.5} = 2.8$, approximately. If $x = \sqrt{2}$, then $2^{\sqrt{2}} = 2^{1.41\ldots} = 2.7$, approximately.

When you study calculus you will find that there is a particularly convenient choice for a base. This choice is the number represented by e which is given approximately by $e = 2.71828 \ldots$ We cannot explain here how this rather strange irrational number is defined or why it makes our work easier.

165

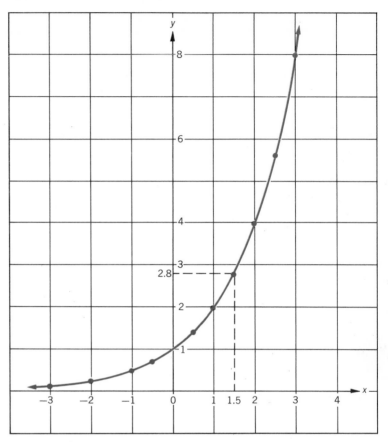

Fig. 6–30

In the problems in this book we shall use more familiar bases. In particular, 10 is an important base because of its relation to common logarithms.

Exponential functions occur in many applications, most importantly as a means of expressing the law of growth or decay in mathematical terms.

2. Bacteria in a pure nutrient solution tend to increase according to the law

$$N = N_0 2^{kt},$$

where t is time measured in some units; k is a positive constant depending on the unit of time, the kind of bacteria, and the nutrient; and N_0 is the number of bacteria present at time $t = 0$.

Suppose that initially 10^4 bacteria are present in the solution, and $k = 1$ when time is measured in hours. Then at time t the number of bacteria present would be $N = 10^4 \cdot 2^t$. Hence at the end of $\frac{5}{2}$ hours,

$$N = 10^4 \cdot 2^{2.5} = 10^4(5.7) = 57{,}000, \text{ approximately.}$$

166

3. Radioactive substances tend to decay according to the law

$$S = S_0 2^{-kt},$$

where t is time measured in some units, k is a positive constant depending upon the substance, and S_0 is the quantity of the substance present at time $t = 0$.

The element actinium decays according to the law $A = A_0 2^{-0.05t}$, where t is measured in years. Then at the end of 10 years, the quantity left would be $A = A_0 2^{-0.5} = A_0(0.707)$.

In discussing radioactive decay, one customarily works with the *half-life*, which is the time required to reduce A to $A_0/2$, instead of using the constant k. In this example, if T is the half-life, then

$$\frac{A_0}{2} = A_0 2^{-0.05T}; \qquad 2^{-1} = 2^{-0.05T},$$

whence $2 = 2^{0.05T}$, and $0.05T = 1$ or $T = 20$ years. Some radioactive substances decay very slowly, having half-lives of thousands of years. Others decay almost as fast as they are formed, having half-lives of much less than one second.

Problems

1. Graph each of the following functions. Obtain the value of each at $x = 1.5$ and $x = -1.5$ from the graph.

(a) 3^x (b) $(\frac{1}{2})^x$ (c) 2^{-x} (d) 4^x

(e) 4^{-x} (f) $(\frac{1}{3})^x$ (g) $3 \cdot 2^x$ (h) $2^x - 2$

(i) e^x, where $e = 2.718\ldots$ (j) e^{-x}, where $e = 2.718\ldots$

2. There are other functions involving exponential functions, some of which are given below. The one in part (a) is of great importance in the theory of probability. Graph each of these functions.

(a) $f(x) = 2^{-x^2}$ (b) $f(x) = 2^{x^2}$

(c) $f(x) = 2^{1/x}, \quad x \neq 0$ (d) $f(x) = 2^{-1/x^2}, \quad x \neq 0$

(e) $f(x) = 2^x + 2^{-x}$ (f) $f(x) = 2^x - 2^{-x}$

3. Bacteria in a nutrient solution double at the end of two hours. How many are present after $3\frac{1}{2}$ hours?

4. The half-life of a certain radioactive substance is 1000 years. Obtain a formula for the amount present at the end of t years.

5. On coordinate paper sketch the graph of $f(x) = 10^x$, for $-1 \le x \le 1$, as accurately as you can. Then from the graph, find x such that $f(x) = 0.2, 0.3, 0.8, 2, 3, 8$.

*6. Define a^x for $0 < a < 1$.

6–12. LOGARITHM FUNCTIONS

The logarithm functions are easily defined in terms of exponential functions. They are simply *inverses* of exponential functions. Because the concept of an inverse function is of great importance, we first discuss that topic.

EXAMPLES

1. Consider the linear function f,

$$y = f(x) = 2x - 1, \tag{1}$$

which maps the real numbers *one-to-one* on the real numbers (Fig. 6–31a).
  The inverse function is obtained by solving (1) for x:

$$x = \tfrac{1}{2}(y + 1) = g(y).$$

In this case the inverse function is also a linear function (Fig. 6–31b).

2. Consider the function f,

$$y = f(x) = x^2, \qquad x \geq 0, \tag{2}$$

which maps the nonnegative real numbers *one-to-one* on the nonnegative real numbers (Fig. 6–32a).

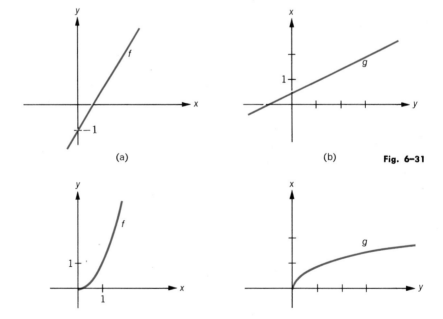

(a) (b) **Fig. 6–31**

(a) (b) **Fig. 6–32**

The inverse function is obtained by solving (2) for x:

$$x = \sqrt{y} = g(y).$$

In this case, the inverse function *defines* what we mean by the square-root function (Fig. 6–32 b).

DEFINITION 6–16

If X and Y are any sets and if f is a function that is a one-to-one mapping of X onto Y, then for each y in Y there is a unique x in X such that $f(x) = y$ (Fig. 6–33). We define a function g with domain Y and range X by agreeing that $g(y) = x$ if and only if $f(x) = y$. This function g is called *the inverse of* f, and is often denoted† by f^{-1}.

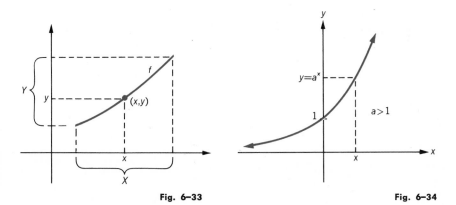

Fig. 6–33   Fig. 6–34

Remark

If X and Y are subsets of R, and if the function f is increasing (or decreasing), then the mapping f is always one-to-one and the inverse function exists. We apply this notion to define the logarithm functions.

Let us consider the mapping $x \xrightarrow{f} y = a^x$, $a > 1$. The domain is R, and the function maps R one-to-one onto the set of positive real numbers. Therefore the function $x \xrightarrow{f} a^x$ has an inverse (Fig. 6–34).

DEFINITION 6–17

The inverse of the function f defined by $f(x) = a^x$ is called the *logarithm function with base a* and is denoted by $\log_a$.

---

† Do not mistake the -1 in f^{-1} for an exponent, although there is a similarity in behavior, for $f^{-1}(f(x)) = x$ for all x in X. In other words, $f^{-1}(f)$ is the identity function on X.

169

The value of this function at N is that unique number n such that

$$N = a^n,$$

that is, $\log_a N = n$. We read this as "the logarithm of N to the base a is n." We repeat:

$\log_a N = n$ if and only if $a^n = N$.

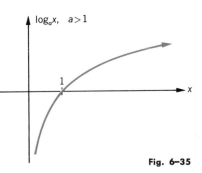

Fig. 6–35

The graph of the logarithm function with base $a > 1$ is shown in Fig. 6–35. Observe that the logarithm function is increasing, unbounded, and continuous, and is defined for x in $\langle 0, +\infty \rangle$. Also note that as $x \to 0$, then $\log_a x \to -\infty$ if $a > 1$.

Because logarithm functions are inverses of exponential functions and because exponential functions obey the laws of exponents, it is natural to suppose that these laws of exponents have a formulation in terms of logarithms. This is indeed the case. We have the following.

THE LAWS OF EXPONENTS AND LAWS OF LOGARITHMS

$$a^x \cdot a^y = a^{x+y} \qquad \text{and} \qquad \log_a uv = \log_a u + \log_a v,$$

$$\frac{a^x}{a^y} = a^{x-y} \qquad \text{and} \qquad \log_a \frac{u}{v} = \log_a u - \log_a v,$$

$$(a^x)^y = a^{xy} \qquad \text{and} \qquad \log_a u^z = z \log_a u.$$

The proofs of the laws of logarithms are left as an exercise. All we need to do is use the laws of exponents and the definitions of the logarithm functions.

Problems

1. Sketch the graphs of the functions:

(a) $f(x) = \log_2 x$

(b) $f(x) = \log_3 x$

(c) $f(x) = \log_{1/2} x$

(d) $f(x) = \log_2 1/x$

(e) $f(x) = \log_2 2x$

(f) $f(x) = \log_2 \sqrt{x}$

(g) $f(x) = \log_2 (-x)$

(h) $f(x) = (\log_2 x)^2$

(i) $f(x) = \log_2 (x + 1)$

2. Prove that $\log_a u + \log_a v = \log_a uv$.

3. Prove that $\log_a u/v = \log_a u - \log_a v$.

4. Prove that $\log_a u^z = z \log_a u$.

5. What is $\log_a a$? $\log_a a^t$? $a^{\log_a x}$? Give your explanations in terms of the definition.

6. Graph $f(x) = x \log_2 x$.

7. Sketch as accurately as you can the graph of $x = 10^y$ for y in the interval $[-1, 1]$. Use this graph to draw the graph of $\log_{10} x$ for x in the interval $[\frac{1}{10}, 10]$. From your graph, read the values of $\log_{10}$ of

    (a) 0.2   (b) 2   (c) 0.3   (d) 3   (e) 0.8   (f) 8

8. Show that if $1 \le x < 10$, then $0 \le \log_{10} x < 1$.

9. Show that $\log_a N = \log_b N \cdot \log_a b$.

10. Show that $\log_a 1/N = -\log_a N$.

11. Explain why the function f, $f(x) = \sqrt{a^2 - x^2}$, $-a \le x \le a$, does not have an inverse. How could one restrict the domain of f so that the restricted function would have an inverse?

12. Show that each of the following real functions has an inverse. Sketch the graph of each and find a formula for the inverse function. What is its domain?

    (a) $f(x) = x^3$

    (b) $f(x) = \sqrt{3(x + 1)} + 1$

    (c) $f(x) = \begin{cases} x \text{ if } x \ge 0 \\ \frac{1}{2}x \text{ if } x < 0 \end{cases}$

    (d) $f(x) = x^4 + x^2$

6-13. TABLES AND COMPUTATION

As you know from algebra, logarithms to the base 10, called *common* logarithms, can be used to expedite numerical computation. That base 10 is convenient is due to the fact that our system of numeration has 10 as its base. Although logarithms are still a useful computational tool, particularly as applied in slide rules, the advent of mechanical and electronic computing machines has made this aspect much less important than it once was. Nevertheless, *understanding logarithms is as important as ever!* Logarithm functions occur in most fields of mathematics, and it is important to know *the properties of these functions*. In calculus you will find that the most convenient base is not 10, but the number $e = 2.718 \ldots$ Logarithms to the base e are called *natural* logarithms. There exist tables of natural logarithms just as there are tables of common logarithms. Both tables are computed by methods of the calculus. According to Problem 9 of Section 6-12, the two sets of logarithms are related by

$$\log_{10} N = \log_{10} e \log_e N = (0.4303) \log_e N.$$

We shall assume that computation with common logarithms is familiar to you and make only a few remarks in review. The integral part of the logarithm is called the *characteristic* and the fractional part, the *mantissa*. If

$\log_{10} 2 = 0.3010$, then $\log_{10} 2000 = 3.3010$ because $2000 = 10^3 \cdot 2$ and

$$\log_{10} 10^3 + \log_{10} 2 = 3 + 0.3010.$$

If the characteristic is less than zero, we introduce special notation so that the mantissa will always appear in a form which allows it to be greater than zero. For example,

$$\log_{10} 0.002 = \log_{10} 10^{-3} + \log_{10} 2 = (-3) + 0.3010$$
$$= (7 - 10) + 0.3010 = 7.3010 - 10.$$

We now make some remarks on *interpolation*. These remarks are related to the shape of the graph of $\log_{10} x$.

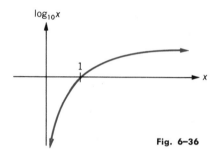

Fig. 6–36

In the first place, the process of interpolation involves replacing a short arc of the graph by a straight line segment. Since the graph of $\log_{10} x$ is "concave down," as is seen in Fig. 6–36, the approximating straight line segment lies *under* the graph of the function, albeit very slightly. Thus, in interpolation, when we are faced with a question of "rounding," that is, when we have to decide whether to throw away a "5" in the extra decimal place or to make the digit preceding the "5" one larger, then we proceed as follows: *in looking up logarithms* (mantissas), we increase the next to last digit by one. When finding a number whose logarithm is given, the situation is reversed, and hence we reject the extra digit.

EXAMPLE

To determine $\log_{10} 2.747$ we find from the table that

$$0.4378 < \log_{10} 2.747 < 0.4393.$$

The slope of the approximating segment is

$$m = \frac{0.0015}{0.01} = 0.15.$$

172

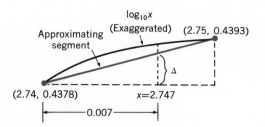

Fig. 6–37

Hence, if $\triangle$ is the desired difference, shown in Fig. 6–37, we have

$$m = 0.15 = \frac{\triangle}{0.007} \quad \text{and} \quad \triangle = 0.00105.$$

Then, according to our discussion concerning the downward concavity of the graph of $\log_{10} x$, we should choose

$$\triangle = 0.0011,$$

and we obtain, to four decimal places,

$$\log_{10} 2.747 = 0.4378 + 0.0011 = 0.4389.$$

Problems

1. Find the common logarithms of the following numbers.
   (a) 45.6   (b) 0.389   (c) 1.642   (d) 0.7444
   (e) 0.00345 (f) 366,500   (g) 2.718   (h) 0.0005936

2. Find the numbers with the following logarithms.
   (a) 0.9571   (b) 1.6542   (c) 9.4116–10 (d) 2.5660
   (e) 8.7731–10 (f) 0.9807   (g) 7.6228–10 (h) 3.0424

3. Use logarithms to find approximate decimal representation of the following numbers.
   (a) (24.3)(5.78)   (b) (1771)(0.687)
   (c) $\dfrac{7.48}{0.0553}$ (d) $(3.14)^7$
   (e) $\sqrt{2793}$ (f) $\sqrt[3]{89.5}$

HISTORICAL NOTE

John Napier (1550–1617)

Logarithms are the invention of John Napier (1550–1617), the eighth Laird of Merchiston. The publication in 1614 of his *Mirifici Logarithmorum Canonis Descriptio*, aroused immediate interest because the use of logarithms greatly facilitated astronomical calculations. Soon attention focused on the construction of tables, and until his death, Napier worked on tables of logarithms with Henry Briggs, who pointed out the use of 10 as a base. The interest in the calculation of tables of logarithms is a thing of the past, for once done there is no point in repeating the calculations. The tables we use today have been computed by means of infinite series which are derived in elementary calculus books—a method which cannot be pursued here. However, it may be of interest to indicate briefly how, from our perspective on functions but with no other special techniques, one *can* calculate tables of mantissas.

First we note that

$$2^{10} = 1024 = (10^3) \times (1.024) = 1000, \text{ approximately.}$$

Therefore $10 \log 2 = 3$, approximately, and $\log 2 = 0.3$, approximately. Further, we observe that if we knew the logarithm of 1.024, we would be able to calculate log 2 exactly. This directs our attention to logarithms of numbers "near 1." Figure 6–38(a) shows the graph of $y = \log x$, with a small portion near $x = 1$ encircled. Figure 6–38(b) shows the encircled portion greatly magnified.

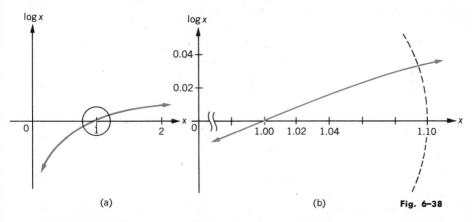

(a) (b) **Fig. 6–38**

As can be seen from the figure, the graph is nearly straight and so a straight-line approximation to the logarithm function should be quite accurate near $x = 1$. If we knew the slope of the line, we could compute logarithms quickly, for if m is the slope of the line, then the line has equation $y = m(x - 1)$. Can we find m? Yes! Because we can compute square roots! After some labor we can obtain the following table.

Square roots		Logarithms
$\sqrt{10} = 10^{1/2}$	$= 3.1622...$	$\log 3.1622... = 0.5$
$\sqrt{\sqrt{10}} = 10^{1/4}$	$= 1.7782...$	$\log 1.7782... = 0.25$
$\sqrt{\sqrt{\sqrt{10}}} = 10^{1/8}$	$= 1.3335...$	$\log 1.3335... = 0.125$
.	$10^{1/16} = 1.1555...$	$\log 1.1555... = 0.0625$
.	$10^{1/32} = 1.0749...$	$\log 1.0749... = 0.03125$
.	$10^{1/64} = 1.0367...$	$\log 1.0367... = 0.015625$
.	$10^{1/128} = 1.0182...$	$\log 1.0182... = 0.0078125$

175

If we use the last three lines of this table to compute approximations to the slope m, we obtain:

$$0.03125 \ = m(0.0749) \quad \text{and} \quad m \doteq 0.419,$$
$$0.015625 \ = m(0.0367) \quad \text{and} \quad m \doteq 0.427,$$
$$0.0078125 = m(0.0182...) \quad \text{and} \quad m \doteq 0.429.$$

Further calculation would change m but slightly. It appears that m is about 0.43 with an error of less than 0.01. Therefore, if x is near 1 (say within 0.05), then
$$\log x = 0.43(x - 1). \tag{1}$$

Now let us return to the logarithm of 2.

$$\log 2^{10} = 10 \log 2 = \log 1024 = \log (10^3 \times 1.024)$$
$$= 3 + \log 1.024.$$

But, using our straight-line approximation to logarithms of numbers near 1, we have
$$\log 1.024 = (0.43)(0.024) = 0.0103.$$
Therefore,
$$10 \log 2 = 3 + 0.0103 = 3.0103,$$
$$\log 2 = 0.30103,$$

and we have obtained the exact five-place value!

Once we have $\log 2$, we get $\log 5 = \log 10 - \log 2 = 0.69897$. The logarithm of 3 can be obtained in various ways. One is to compute $\log 6$ first, using the fact that

$$6^9 = 10077696 = 10^7 \times 1.00777.$$
Then

$$9 \log 6 = 7 + \log 1.00777 = 7 + (0.43)(0.00777) = 7.00334,$$
$$\log 6 = 0.77815.$$

Since $\log 6 = \log 3 + \log 2$, one can get $\log 3$. We can find other logarithms, using (1). For example,

$$\log 6.01 = \log (6 \times 1.00166)$$
$$= \log 6 + \log 1.00166$$
$$= 0.77815 + (0.43)(0.00166)$$
$$= 0.77887.$$

As an exercise, note that to compute $\log 3$, one might use the fact that

$$3^{13} = 1594323 = 2^4 \times 10^5, \text{ approximately.}$$

176

6-14. COMBINATIONS OF FUNCTIONS

At this point in our study of functions, we have considered polynomial, rational, algebraic, and two classes of transcendental functions, namely, exponential functions and logarithm functions. Others can be obtained by combinations of these functions. We are already familiar with addition, multiplication, and division of functions. When our task is to add functions, it is often easiest to sketch the curve by *graphical addition*.

EXAMPLE 1

Sketch the graph of
$$f(x) = 2^x + 2^{-x}.$$

We first sketch the graphs of $y = 2^x$ and $y = 2^{-x}$. Then we add graphically to obtain the points and the solid curve shown in Fig. 6-39.

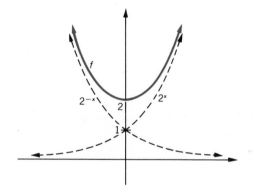

Fig. 6-39

Besides combining functions by the rational operations of addition, multiplication, subtraction, and division, one can also form the *composition* of two functions.

DEFINITION 6-18

If g is a function with domain X and range Y and if f is a function with a domain containing Y and range Z, then the *composition of f and g*, denoted by $f \circ g$, or by $f(g)$, is defined on the domain X, and

$$[f \circ g](x) = f(g(x)) \quad \text{or} \quad f(g)(x) = f(g(x)).$$

Diagramatically, we have

$$X \xrightarrow{g} Y \xrightarrow{f} Z$$

$$X \xrightarrow{f \circ g} Z$$

177

EXAMPLES

2. If $F(x) = \sqrt{a^x}$ then F is the composition of the two functions $g(x) = a^x$ and $f(y) = \sqrt{y}$. We have $F = f \circ g$, because $F(x) = \sqrt{y}$, where $y = a^x$. Note also that

$$F(x) = f(g(x)) = f(a^x) = \sqrt{a^x}.$$

3. If $H(x) = \log_2 (x^2 + 1)$, then H is the composition of f and g, where g is the polynomial function $g(x) = x^2 + 1$, and $f(y) = \log_2 y$. Since $f(g(x)) = f(x^2 + 1) = \log_2 (x^2 + 1)$, it follows that $H = f(g) = f \circ g$.

In each example the range of g is contained in the domain of f; hence the composition of f and g is possible.

Remark

Graphing these composite functions might present some problems. At the moment this does not concern us. We are interested solely in the way in which complicated functions are made up from simpler ones by composition of functions.

Problems

1. All functions in this problem set are real functions. Explain how each of the following functions is the composition of two functions.

   (a) $f(x) = 3^{x^2+1}$ (b) $F(x) = \log_2 \sqrt{x}$

   (c) $H(x) = 2^{2x} + (3 \cdot 2^x) - 3$

   (d) $L(x) = \log_2 (\log_2 x)$; what is the domain?

   (e) $E(x) = 10^{10^x}$

   (f) $T(x) = \log_e (3x^3 + x^2 + 7)$

2. The following functions are obtained from simpler ones in a variety of ways. Explain.

   (a) $f(x) = \sqrt{x} + x$ (b) $f(x) = x + e^{-x^2}$

   (c) $f(x) = (x \cdot 10^x) + \log_{10} (1 + 10^x)$ (d) $f(x) = xe^x - xe^{-x}$

3. Graph the following functions by graphical addition.

   (a) $f(x) = x^2 + (1 - x)$ (b) $f(x) = (\log_2 x) - x, \quad x > 0$.

   (c) $f(x) = 2^x - 2^{-x}$ (d) $f(x) = 7 - \sqrt{4 - x^2}$

   (e) $f(x) = \dfrac{1}{x} + x$ (f) $f(x) = \dfrac{x}{10} + \dfrac{2x}{x^2 + 1}$

4. Given: p and q are polynomial functions and $p(x) = (x^2 + 1)$ and $q(x) = x - 1$. Show that $p \circ q$ is a polynomial.

5. Give an example to show that the composition of two functions f and g is noncommutative; that is, find functions f and g such that $f \circ g \neq g \circ f$.

178

6. If $p(x) = 2x + 1$ and $q(x) = \dfrac{x - 1}{2}$

for all x, what is a formula for $p \circ q$? for $q \circ p$?

7. If Id is the identity function given by Id $(x) = x$ for all x, show that $(\text{Id} \circ f)(x) = f(x)$ for every function f; that $(f \circ \text{Id})(x) = f(x)$.

8. S and R are rational functions given by the formulas

$$S(x) = \frac{x + 1}{x} \qquad \text{for all } x \neq 0,$$

and

$$R(x) = \frac{x}{x^2 + 1} \qquad \text{for all } x.$$

Find a formula for $R \circ S$ and show that the composition is also a rational function. What is the domain of $R \circ S$?

SUMMARY

In this chapter we have reviewed the definition of a function and have studied some of the elementary functions, their properties, and their graphs.

Because of the wide variety of functions that occur in mathematics, it is helpful to classify them as shown, for example, in the diagram below, which illustrates how some of the elementary functions are related to one another.

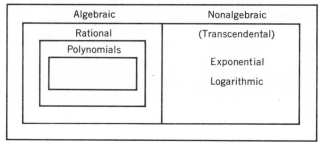

All functions

Algebraic	Nonalgebraic
Rational	(Transcendental)
Polynomials	Exponential
	Logarithmic

It is important to understand the following ideas related to functions.

(a) Intervals
(b) Bounds
(c) Continuity
(d) Increasing and decreasing functions
(e) Horizontal and vertical asymptotes
(f) Symmetry: odd and even functions
(g) Composition of functions

In the next chapter we shall study another class of nonalgebraic functions, called the *trigonometric* functions.

Review Problems

1. Sketch the graphs of the functions given. The domain is indicated in each case.

   (a) $A(x) = |x|$, for all x

   (b) $g(x) = -x$, if $x < 0$
   $g(x) = x^2$, if $0 \le x \le 2$
   $g(x) = 4$, if $x > 2$

   (c) $f(x) = 1$, if $x > 0$
   $f(0) = 0$
   $f(x) = -1$, if $x < 0$

   (d) $h(x) = \sqrt{16 - x^2}$, if $-4 \le x \le 4$
   $h(x) = x - 4$, if $x > 4$
   $h(x) = -x - 4$, if $x < -4$

   (e) $f(x) = 1$, if x is rational
   $f(x) = -1$,
   if x is irrational

   (f) $k(x) = |x| - x$, for all x

2. Which functions of Problem 1 are continuous throughout their domains.

3. Show that $r(x) = 1/x$ is decreasing in $\langle -\infty, 0 \rangle$.

4. Draw the graph of

$$G(x) = \frac{2x}{x^2 + 1}, \qquad \text{for all } x.$$

Discuss the bounds (if any), continuity, and asymptotes of G.

5. The figure on the right shows part of the graph of a function. Sketch the remaining part, given that the function has domain R except for 0 and is

   (a) odd.   (b) even.

6. Can a function on X into Y, other than the zero function [$f(x) = 0$ for all x], have a graph which is symmetric to the x-axis?

7. Find a function f such that for all x in the domain of f,

$$f(x) = -\left[f\left(\frac{1}{x}\right)\right].$$

8. A certain radioactive material tends to decay according to the law

$$A = A_0 2^{-.04t},$$

where A_0 is the quantity present at the time t_0 given in years. What is the half-life of the substance?

180

9. Sketch the graph of a function W defined as follows: the domain of W is the set of real numbers in $[-a, a]$.

$W(0) = 0$,

$W(x) = 1$, for x in $\langle 0, a/2 \rangle$,

$W(a/2) = \frac{1}{2}$,

$W(x) = 0$ for x in $\langle a/2, a \rangle$,

W is an odd function.

10. Find two algebraic functions defined by

$$y^2 - 4xy + 4x^2 - x = 0.$$

11. The functions F and G have the real numbers as their domains, and

$$G(x) = \frac{x + 1}{3} \quad \text{and} \quad F(y) = 9y^2 - 2.$$

Write a rule for determining $F(G(x))$.

12. Graph the function $f(x) = -(2^{-\frac{1}{2}x})$, which has the real numbers as its domain. Discuss the range, bounds, continuity, and asymptotes of f.

13. Graph and discuss $\log_2 (\log_2 x)$.

14. Prove that if f is an increasing function and f has an inverse f^{-1}, then f^{-1} is also increasing.

15. Prove that if g is a linear function with slope $m \neq 0$, then g^{-1} has slope $1/m$. [*Hint:* $g(x) = mx + b$.]

THE CIRCULAR

7

FUNCTIONS

7-1. INTRODUCTION

In this chapter we shall study six functions called the *circular functions* or *trigonometric functions*. We shall define these functions and study some of their properties. In later chapters we shall consider further properties and some applications of these functions.

Before introducing these new functions, we briefly review some ideas of angle measurement.

7-2. ANGLE MEASUREMENT

In geometry an angle is defined as the set of points on two rays originating from a single point. The rays may be identical, or they may have opposite directions on one line, or they may lie on distinct lines (Fig. 7-1).

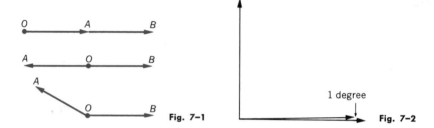

Fig. 7-1   Fig. 7-2

Associated with each angle is a real number called the *measure of the angle*. This number depends upon the choice of a *unit angle*. The unit angle most often used in elementary mathematics is the *degree*. To visualize an angle of 1 degree, imagine a right angle divided into 90 congruent angles. Each of the small angles has a measure of 1 degree (Fig. 7-2).

In your study of mathematics in this course and in later courses, the unit angle will often be the *radian*. Radian measure of angles is based upon the concept of *length of circular arc*. We shall not attempt to make this concept precise, but will assume that the idea of the length of a circular arc is intuitively clear.

If $\angle AOB$ is a central angle of a circle with radius r, then there is a unique positive real number L, the length of the arc subtended by $\angle AOB$ (Fig. 7-3). Note that L is a part of the circumference. If $\angle AOB$ is not a straight angle, then $0 < L < \pi r$. A straight angle may be considered as subtending a semicircle so that $L = \pi r$. Conversely, in a circle with center O and radius r let A be a point on the circle (Fig. 7-3). Then, if L is a real number such that $0 < L < \pi r$, there are exactly two points, B and B', on the circle and on opposite sides of the line through A and O, such that the lengths of the arcs subtended by $\angle AOB$ and $\angle AOB'$ are both equal to L.

184

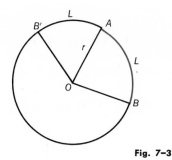

Fig. 7-3

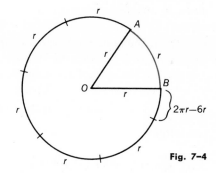

Fig. 7-4

DEFINITION 7-1

If $\angle AOB$ is a central angle of a circle with radius r and if $\angle AOB$ subtends an arc of length r, then the measure of $\angle AOB$ is one *radian* (Fig. 7-4). The phrase "the measure of $\angle AOB$" will be denoted symbolically by $m(\angle AOB)$.

DEFINITION 7-2

If $\angle AOB$ is a central angle of a circle with radius r (Fig. 7-3), and if L is the length of the arc subtended by $\angle AOB$, then $m(\angle AOB) = L/r$ (radians).

Remarks

1. Angle measurement is independent of the radius, r, because on different circles, congruent central angles subtend arcs of length proportional to the radii. Thus, if $\angle A \cong \angle A'$ and these angles subtend arcs of L and L' on circles of radii r and r', respectively, then

$$\frac{L}{r} = \frac{L'}{r'}.$$

Hence, the number L/r depends only upon the angle and not upon the circle chosen.

2. A right angle subtends an arc of length $\pi r/2$ and therefore has measure equal to $\pi/2$. A straight angle has measure equal to π. It is customary to say that "there are 2π radians in a circle."

3. We found it convenient to introduce the idea of directed length to combine the concepts, *length of segment* and *direction along a line*. In Section 7-4 we shall see that by introducing "directed angles" we may consider angles whose measures are "negative" or "greater than π." Our problem is that of explaining what we mean by such language.

You are familiar with degree measure of angles from your previous work in mathematics, and you should be able to convert degree measure to radian

185

measure, and vice versa. Because the radian measure of a straight angle is π, whereas its degree measure is 180, it follows that an angle of 1 degree is an angle of $\pi/180$ radian, or approximately 0.017 radian. An angle of 1 radian is an angle of $180/\pi$ degrees, or approximately 57.3 degrees.

If θ is the measure of any angle in radians, then its degree measure is

$$\theta \cdot \frac{180}{\pi} = 57.3 \cdot \theta, \text{ approximately.}$$

EXAMPLE

An angle of measure $\pi/3$ has degree measure of

$$\frac{\pi}{3} \cdot \frac{180}{\pi} = 60.$$

An angle whose degree measure is 36 has radian measure of

$$36 \cdot \frac{\pi}{180} = \frac{\pi}{5}.$$

Remark

We shall follow the customary practice of using real numbers, such as $\pi/3$, 0.7438, 2, etc., as measures of angles without specifically referring to the fact that we are using the radian as the unit angle. However, when we use degree measure, we shall denote this by the usual symbol; thus we shall write 23°, 45°, etc.

Problems

1. What are the radian measures of angles whose degree measures are:
   (a) 150   (b) 180   (c) 30   (d) 45   (e) 60   (f) 120
   (g) 80   (h) 72   (i) 135   (j) 67.5   (k) $22\frac{1}{2}$ (l) 15

2. Find the degree measures of the angles whose radian measures are given below.

   (a) $\frac{5\pi}{9}$ (b) $\frac{1}{2}$ (c) $\frac{7\pi}{12}$ (d) $\frac{11\pi}{14}$

   (e) 1.2   (f) $\frac{\pi}{36}$ (g) $\frac{5\pi}{6}$ (h) $\frac{2\pi}{3}$

   (i) $\frac{7\pi}{18}$ (j) $\frac{\pi}{15}$ (k) $\frac{3\pi}{10}$ (l) 3

3. A 60° central angle of a circle subtends an arc of length $4\pi/3$ units. What is the radius of the circle?

4. A central angle of a circle with radius 10 has measure of $3\pi/4$. What is the length of the arc subtended by this angle?

5. $\angle AOB$ is a central angle of a circle. $\overline{AC}$ is a diameter of the circle. If $m(\angle ACB) = \pi/8$, what is $m(\angle AOB)$?

186

6. A wheel rotates at 700 revolutions per minute (rpm). Through how many radians does a spoke of the wheel rotate in one second?

7. A three-speed record player can be set so that the turntable will rotate at $33\frac{1}{3}$, 45, or 78 rpm. Through how many radians will a point on the turntable move in one second at each of these speeds?

8. The line $y = 2$ intersects the circle $x^2 + y^2 = 16$ in points A and B. What is the length of the arc subtended by $\angle AOB$, where O is the center of the circle? What are the coordinates of points A and B? What is the length of $\overline{AB}$?

9. Construct a radian protractor.

7-3. THE WRAPPING FUNCTION, ϕ — INTUITIVE DESCRIPTION

In this section we shall describe, in an intuitive way, a new function which we shall call the "wrapping function" and denote by the symbol ϕ. This function will help us formulate precise definitions of the circular or trigonometric functions which we shall meet later in the chapter.

Suppose that a point P on a circle of radius 1 touches a coordinate line at the origin, as shown in Fig. 7–5(a). If the circle rolled along the line, each point would touch a point of the line. After it has rolled so that point Q touches the line at point x (Fig. 7–5b), the length of arc PQ is the distance from 0 to x, namely x. After one complete revolution of the circle (wheel), the point P again touches the line at the point 2π. Hence to each real number between 0 and 2π, there corresponds a unique point on the circle. Numbers greater than 2π also correspond to points on the circle, as do negative real numbers. In the latter case, correspondence is obtained by rolling the circle in the other direction.†

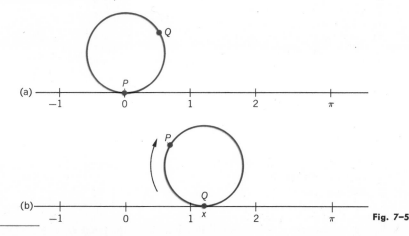

Fig. 7–5

† We are *not* interested here in the path of the point P as the circle rolls. The point P describes a curve called a cycloid.

187

The above describes the wrapping function ϕ. The domain of ϕ is the set of real numbers, and the range of ϕ is the set of points on the circle whose radius is 1.

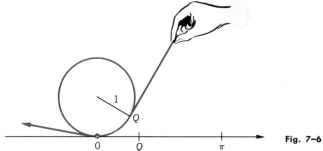

Fig. 7–6

Another way of thinking of the wrapping function ϕ is illustrated in Fig. 7–6. Imagine the real line as a flexible, but nonstretchable, string which is wrapped around the circle. Each real number is mapped (wrapped) into a unique point of the circle. Note that this is not a one-to-one mapping, because many real numbers correspond to the same point on the circle.

Problems

1. Imagine that a circle of radius 1 is tangent to the real line so that a point P of the circle touches the real line at 0. What point of the line is tangent to the circle if the circle is rolled:

   (a) 2 revolutions in the positive direction of the line?

   (b) 7 revolutions in the negative direction of the line?

   (c) $\frac{1}{2}$ revolution in the negative direction?

   (d) $\frac{1}{4}$ revolution in the positive direction?

2. Consider the unit circle with center at the origin, and the real line tangent to the circle so that 0 on the line corresponds to the point $A = (1, 0)$, as shown in the figure.

   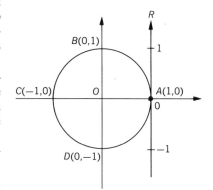

   (a) What is the smallest positive number R that will correspond to the point $B = (0, 1)$ if we imagine that the real line is wrapped around the circle?

   (b) What is the largest negative number that will correspond to B?

   (c) Develop a formula for all real numbers that map into the point B.

3. Repeat the parts (a) through (c) of Problem 2, for the point $D = (0, -1)$.

4. Repeat the parts (a) through (c) of Problem 2, for the point $C = (-1, 0)$.

188

7-4. THE DEFINITION OF ϕ

In Section 7–3 we gave an intuitive description of the function ϕ which mapped the real numbers onto a circle of radius 1. We now give a precise definition of this function.

DEFINITION 7-3

Let C_1 be the circle with radius 1 with center at the origin. The *standard map*, ϕ, is the function with domain R, which maps the real numbers onto C_1 as follows. (See Fig. 7–7.)

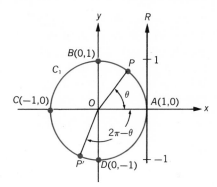

Fig. 7–7

(a) To the real number 0, there corresponds the point $A = (1, 0)$; that is, $\phi(0) = A$.

(b) To the real number π, there corresponds the point $C = (-1, 0)$; $\phi(\pi) = C$.

(c) If θ is a real number such that $0 < \theta < \pi$, then $\phi(\theta) = P$, where P is a point of C_1 on the same side of the x-axis as the point $B = (0, 1)$ and such that $m(\angle AOP) = \theta$.

(d) If $\pi < \theta < 2\pi$, then $\phi(\theta) = P'$, where P' is a point of C_1 on the side of the x-axis opposite to $B = (0, 1)$ and such that $m(\angle AOP') = 2\pi - \theta$.

(e) $\phi(2\pi) = A$.

(f) Now let θ be any real number. There is an integer k (positive, negative, or zero) such that

$$2\pi k \leq \theta < 2\pi(k + 1).$$

Then $0 \leq \theta - 2\pi k < 2\pi$ and $\phi(\theta) = \phi(\theta - 2\pi k)$.

Remarks

1. The definition first defines the wrapping function, ϕ, for $0 \leq \theta \leq 2\pi$ and the definition is extended so that ϕ is defined as a periodic function. In other words, if two real numbers differ by an integral multiple of 2π then ϕ maps each number into the same point of C_1. The positive reals map on C_1 by "wrapping counterclockwise," whereas the negative reals map onto C_1 by "wrapping clockwise."

189

2. Sometimes it is helpful to think of the position vector of $P = \phi(\theta)$ as obtained by rotating $\overrightarrow{OA}$ through an angle of measure θ. Positive numbers θ correspond to counterclockwise rotation and negative numbers θ to clockwise rotation. For simplicity, we often speak of "the angle θ" instead of using the more lengthy expression, "the angle AOP, where $P = \phi(\theta)$."

3. We can now clarify the remark made earlier concerning "negative angles." As an example, let us show that $\phi(3\pi/4) = \phi(-5\pi/4)$. Since $0 < 3\pi/4 < \pi$, then by part (c) of Definition 7–3, $\phi(3\pi/4) = P$, where P is a point of C_1 in the upper half-plane such that the measure $\angle AOP = 3\pi/4$ (see Fig. 7–8). We now consider the real number $-5\pi/4$ and observe that by part (f) of Definition 7–3 and letting $k = -1$,

$$-2\pi < \frac{-5\pi}{4} < 0$$

so that

$$0 < \frac{-5\pi}{4} - (-2\pi) < 2\pi.$$

Hence

$$\phi\left(\frac{-5\pi}{4}\right) = \phi\left(\frac{-5\pi}{4} - (-2\pi)\right)$$

$$= \phi\left(\frac{3\pi}{4}\right) = P.$$

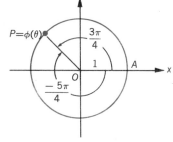

Fig. 7–8

While we may use language such as "the negative angle, $-5\pi/4$," we wish to emphasize that this is mathematical slang and that we really mean $\angle AOP$, where $\phi(-5\pi/4) = P$. The measure of $\angle AOP$ is $3\pi/4$, a number between 0 and π. Similar remarks hold for "angles greater than π."

EXAMPLE

The points $\phi(\theta)$ for various θ are shown in Fig. 7–9.

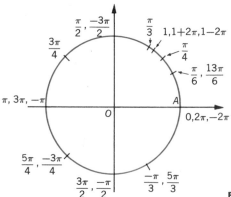

Fig. 7–9

190

Problems

1. Graph $\phi(\theta)$ for $\theta = 2\pi$, $-\pi/6$, $7\pi/6$, $-5\pi/6$, $5\pi/12$, 1, -1, 2, -2, 3, 0.5, -2.5, $-\pi/4$, $-5\pi/4$, $21\pi/4$, $15\pi/2$, 17π.

2. What integer is k in part (f) of Definition 7–3 if $\theta = 20$? $11\pi/3$? $-15\pi/6$?

3. Show that $\phi(11\pi/4) = \phi(-5\pi/4)$.

4. Given that $\phi(\pi/4) = P$, determine the coordinates (x, y) of P.

5. Determine the coordinates of Q, where $\phi(\pi/3) = Q$.

6. What are the coordinates of $\phi(-\pi/3)$?

7. If $\phi(\theta) = P$, where is $\phi(-\theta)$ on C_1?

8. Part (f) of Definition 7–3 asserts that for any real number θ there is an integer k such that
$$2\pi k \leq \theta < 2\pi(k + 1).$$

What property of the real numbers assures the existence of such an integer k?

*9. Show that for any real number θ, there is a unique real number θ_1 such that $0 \leq \theta_1 < 2\pi$ and $\phi(\theta) = \phi(\theta_1)$.

*10. Show that $\phi(\theta + 2\pi) = \phi(\theta)$. More generally, show that if k is an integer, then $\phi(\theta + 2\pi k) = \phi(\theta)$.

7-5. THE SINE AND COSINE FUNCTIONS

We now have the preliminaries out of the way and are able to define the principal *circular functions*. These functions are called the *sine* and *cosine*† and are abbreviated as *sin* and *cos*.

DEFINITION 7–4

If θ is a real number and

$$\phi(\theta) = P = (x, y),$$

then

$$\sin(\theta) = \sin\theta = y,$$
$$\cos(\theta) = \cos\theta = x.$$

(See Fig. 7–10.)

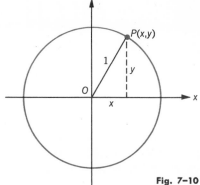

Fig. 7–10

---

† The word "sine" comes from the Latin "sinus" meaning a bend, or fold. Originally the sine was taken to be twice as large, that is, it was considered to correspond to a full chord of the circle. The significance of the "co" in cosine will be discussed later.

These functions, sin and cos, are of fundamental importance in all branches of mathematics. At present we are concerned only with their relations to the circle and to direction cosines, which we defined in Chapter 1.

THEOREM 7–1

If $\phi(\theta) = P$, then the x-direction cosine of $\overrightarrow{OP}$ is $\cos \theta$, and the y-direction cosine of $\overrightarrow{OP}$ is $\sin \theta$.

Proof. The distance between $0 = (0, 0)$ and $P = (x, y)$ is 1. The direction cosines of a ray are defined as the horizontal (or vertical) change divided by distance. Therefore

$$c_1 = x\text{-direction cosine of } \overrightarrow{OP} = \frac{x - 0}{1} = x = \cos \theta,$$

$$c_2 = y\text{-direction cosine of } \overrightarrow{OP} = \frac{y - 0}{1} = y = \sin \theta.$$

As a corollary to this theorem, we obtain parametric equations of a circle of radius r with center at $(0, 0)$. For each real number θ, the equations

$$\begin{cases} x = r \cos \theta, \\ y = r \sin \theta \end{cases} \tag{1}$$

give a point (x, y) on the circle, because of the similar triangles shown in Fig. 7–11.

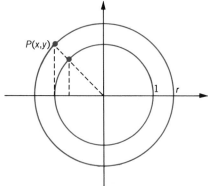

Fig. 7–11

Conversely, if $P(x, y)$ is a point on the circle, it corresponds to some θ (and indeed infinitely many θ). Hence every point given by (1) is on the circle, and every point on the circle is given by (1).

Remark 1

If $\pi/2 < \theta < \pi$, then $\phi(\theta) = P(x, y)$ is in the second quadrant; hence $x < 0$ and $y > 0$.

192

EXAMPLE

If $\theta = 3\pi/4$, then

$$\cos \theta = x = -\frac{\sqrt{2}}{2} = -0.707, \text{ approximately,}$$

$$\sin \theta = y = \frac{\sqrt{2}}{2} = 0.707, \text{ approximately.}$$

Remarks

2. Similarly, if $\pi < \theta < 3\pi/2$, then $\phi(\theta) = P(x, y)$ is in the third quadrant, and both $x < 0$ and $y < 0$. If $3\pi/2 < \theta < 2\pi$, then $x > 0$ and $y < 0$.

3. The signs of the circular functions can be determined for any θ by locating the quadrant of which $\phi(\theta) = P(x, y)$ is a member.

THEOREM 7-2

$$\sin^2 \theta + \cos^2 \theta = 1.$$

The proof of this important theorem is left as an exercise. We usually write $(\sin \theta)^2$ as $\sin^2 \theta$.

Problems

1. Compute from Definition 7–4:

(a) $\sin 0$ (b) $\cos 0$ (c) $\sin \frac{\pi}{2}$ (d) $\cos \frac{\pi}{2}$

(e) $\sin \frac{\pi}{4}$ (f) $\cos \frac{\pi}{4}$ (g) $\sin \pi$ (h) $\cos \pi$

(i) $\sin 2\pi$ (j) $\cos -4\pi$ (k) $\sin 15\pi$ (l) $\sin \frac{15\pi}{2}$

(m) $\sin \frac{3\pi}{4}$ (n) $\cos \frac{3\pi}{4}$ (o) $\sin \frac{\pi}{6}$ (p) $\cos \frac{\pi}{6}$

(q) $\sin \frac{\pi}{3}$ (r) $\cos \frac{\pi}{3}$ (s) $\sin \frac{5\pi}{6}$ (t) $\cos \frac{-5\pi}{6}$

(u) $\cos \frac{-\pi}{6}$ (v) $\sin \frac{-\pi}{6}$

2. Show that for all real numbers θ, $\cos^2 \theta + \sin^2 \theta = 1$. *Note:* $\cos^2 \theta = (\cos \theta)^2$.

3. Imagine that θ increases from 0 as time passes. Then $\phi(\theta)$ will move on C_1. How will $\sin \theta$ and $\cos \theta$ change?

4. Are there real numbers θ such that $\sin \theta = 2$?

*5. Show that if $0 < \theta < \pi/2$, then $\sin (\pi/2 - \theta) = \cos \theta$.

*6. Construct graphs of $y = \sin \theta$ and $x = \cos \theta$.

193

7-6. OTHER CIRCULAR FUNCTIONS

There are six trigonometric functions. So far, we have defined only the sine and cosine functions. We now give definitions of all six functions.

DEFINITION 7-5

If ϕ is the standard map of the real numbers on the circle of radius 1 with center at the origin, and if $\phi(\theta) = P(x, y)$ (Fig. 7–12), then

$$\text{sine of } \theta = \sin \theta = y,$$
$$\text{cosine of } \theta = \cos \theta = x,$$
$$\text{tangent of } \theta = \tan \theta = y/x \quad \text{if } x \neq 0,$$
$$\text{cotangent of } \theta = \cot \theta = x/y \quad \text{if } y \neq 0,$$
$$\text{secant of } \theta = \sec \theta = 1/x \quad \text{if } x \neq 0,$$
$$\text{cosecant of } \theta = \csc \theta = 1/y \quad \text{if } y \neq 0.$$

There are several immediate and important consequences of the definitions.

1. The domains of the sine and cosine functions are both R, that is, the set of real numbers.

2. The tangent and the secant are not defined if $x = 0$. We have $x = 0$ when $\phi(\theta) = P$ is a point on the y-axis and this occurs when θ is an odd multiple of $\pi/2$.

3. The cotangent and cosecant are not defined if $y = 0$. We have $y = 0$ when $\phi(\theta) = P$ is a point on the x-axis and this occurs when θ is any multiple of π.

4. When $\phi(\theta) = P$ is a point in the first quadrant, then all the circular functions have positive values at the real number θ. For θ corresponding to points in the other quadrants, some of the circular functions will have

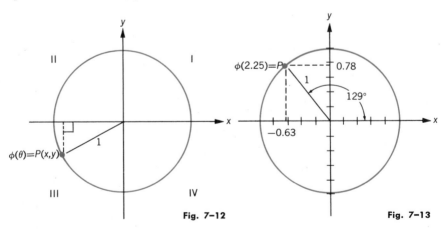

Fig. 7-12   Fig. 7-13

positive values, and others will have negative values. For example, in quadrant III only the tangent and the cotangent functions have positive values because both x and y are negative in this quadrant.

EXAMPLE

One can estimate the values of the functions for any given real number θ by drawing a reasonably accurate figure. For example, if

$$\theta = \tfrac{9}{4} = 2.25,$$

then $m(\angle AOP)$ in degrees is approximately 129°. The angle can be drawn with a protractor to obtain Figure 7–13. Using the figure we can estimate the values of each function at 2.25. Thus

$$\sin 2.25 = 0.78, \qquad\qquad \sec 2.25 = \frac{1}{-0.63} = -1.59,$$

$$\cos 2.25 = -0.63, \qquad\qquad \cot 2.25 = \frac{-0.63}{0.78} = -0.81,$$

$$\tan 2.25 = \frac{0.78}{-0.63} = -1.23, \qquad \csc 2.25 = \frac{1}{0.78} = 1.28.$$

Problems

1. Construct a circle of radius 1 on graph paper and obtain approximate values of the trigonometric functions of θ, given that:

   (a) $\theta = 1$ (b) $\theta = 0.5$ (c) $\theta = -7$
   (d) $\theta = \pi$ (e) $\theta = \pi/2$ (f) $\theta = -\pi/2$
   (g) $\theta = -0.1$ (h) $\theta = \pi + 0.3$ (i) $\theta = 2$
   (j) $\theta = -2$ (k) $\theta = 20$ (l) $\theta = -20$

2. Which trigonometric functions have positive values in

   (a) quadrant I?   (b) quadrant II?
   (c) quadrant III?   (d) quadrant IV?

3. By referring to the standard map, ϕ, and the definitions of sine and cosine, determine whether the functions are increasing or decreasing in the intervals given below.

Interval	sine	cosine
$\langle 0, \pi/2 \rangle$		
$\langle \pi/2, \pi \rangle$		
$\langle \pi, 3\pi/2 \rangle$		
$\langle 3\pi/2, 2\pi \rangle$		

4. Draw an angle with measure θ so that $\phi(\theta)$ is in quadrant I and $\sin\theta = 0.25$.

5. Draw an angle in the second quadrant so that $\sin\theta = 0.25$. Is there an angle in the third quadrant whose sine is 0.25?

6. Draw an angle in the second quadrant whose cosine is $-\frac{2}{3}$. What is the value of the secant of this angle?

7. If
$$\sin\theta = -\tfrac{2}{3}, \quad \text{and} \quad \phi(\theta) = P$$
is in the third quadrant, what are $\tan\theta$ and $\sec\theta$?

8. If
$$\cos\theta = -\tfrac{1}{4}, \quad \text{and} \quad P = \phi(\theta)$$
is in the second quadrant, what are the values of the other functions of θ?

9. What is $\sin\theta/\cos\theta$ if θ is not an odd multiple of $\pi/2$?

10. What is $\cos\theta/\sin\theta$ if θ is not a multiple of π?

11. What is $1/\sin\theta$ if θ is not a multiple of π?

12. What is $1/\cos\theta$ if θ is not an odd multiple of $\pi/2$?

7-7. SPECIAL ANGLES

For certain angles, the exact coordinates of $P(x, y) = \phi(\theta)$ can be found from our knowledge of elementary geometry. These angles are the multiples of $\pi/6$ or 30° and $\pi/4$ or 45°. In order to obtain the exact coordinates of $\phi(\theta)$ in these cases, we need a clear mental picture of the right triangles shown in Figs. 7-14 and 7-15.

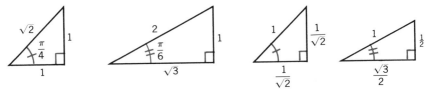

Fig. 7-14   Fig. 7-15

EXAMPLES

1. Find the six trigonometric functions of $2\pi/3$. The angle $2\pi/3$ is one of 120°. Thus we have $\phi(2\pi/3)$ in the second quadrant and

$$\phi\left(\frac{2\pi}{3}\right) = \left(-\frac{1}{2}, \frac{\sqrt{3}}{2}\right),$$

196

as shown in Fig. 7–16. Therefore

$$\sin \frac{2\pi}{3} = \frac{\sqrt{3}}{2} = 0.866, \qquad \sec \frac{2\pi}{3} = -2,$$

$$\cos \frac{2\pi}{3} = -\frac{1}{2} = -0.5, \qquad \csc \frac{2\pi}{3} = \frac{2}{\sqrt{3}} = \frac{2\sqrt{3}}{3} = 1.155,$$

$$\tan \frac{2\pi}{3} = -\sqrt{3} = -1.732, \qquad \cot \frac{2\pi}{3} = -\frac{1}{\sqrt{3}} = \frac{-\sqrt{3}}{3} = -0.577.$$

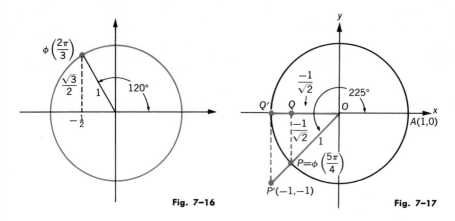

Fig. 7–16   Fig. 7–17

2. Find the six trigonometric functions of $5\pi/4$. The angle has degree measure equal to

$$\frac{5\pi}{4} \cdot \frac{180}{\pi} = 225°,$$

and is in the third quadrant.

One can read off the values of the functions from either the coordinates of the point

$$P = \phi\left(\frac{5\pi}{4}\right)$$

in Fig. 7–17, or from the coordinates of the point $P' = (-1, -1)$, because triangles OPQ and $OP'Q'$ are similar. Thus we have

$$\sin \frac{5\pi}{4} = \frac{-1}{\sqrt{2}}, \qquad \sec \frac{5\pi}{4} = -\sqrt{2},$$

$$\cos \frac{5\pi}{4} = -\frac{1}{\sqrt{2}}, \qquad \csc \frac{5\pi}{4} = -\sqrt{2},$$

$$\tan \frac{5\pi}{4} = 1, \qquad \cot \frac{5\pi}{4} = 1.$$

197

3. Find the trigonometric functions of $-5\pi/2$. The standard map (Fig. 7–18) has

$$\phi\left(\frac{-5\pi}{2}\right) = (0, -1).$$

Then

$$\sin \frac{-5\pi}{2} = \frac{-1}{1} = -1, \qquad\qquad \sec \frac{-5\pi}{2} \text{ is undefined,}$$

$$\cos \frac{-5\pi}{2} = \frac{0}{1} = 0, \qquad\qquad\quad \csc \frac{-5\pi}{2} = -1,$$

$$\tan \frac{-5\pi}{2} \text{ is undefined,} \qquad \cot \frac{-5\pi}{2} = \frac{0}{-1} = 0.$$

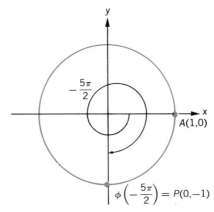

$$\phi\left(-\frac{5\pi}{2}\right) = P(0,-1)$$

Fig. 7–18

Problems

1. Find the following values of trigonometric functions. In each case convert radian measure to degree measure.

(a) $\sin -\dfrac{\pi}{6}$ (b) $\cos -\dfrac{\pi}{3}$ (c) $\tan -9\pi$ (d) $\tan \dfrac{5\pi}{2}$

(e) $\sec \dfrac{5\pi}{2}$ (f) $\sin 13\pi$ (g) $\sin \dfrac{-5\pi}{4}$ (h) $\cos \dfrac{-7\pi}{4}$

(i) $\sin \dfrac{5\pi}{6}$ (j) $\sin \dfrac{7\pi}{6}$ (k) $\tan \dfrac{-3\pi}{4}$ (l) $\sec \dfrac{-3\pi}{4}$

(m) $\sin \dfrac{11\pi}{6}$ (n) $\sin \dfrac{2\pi}{3}$ (o) $\sin \dfrac{4\pi}{3}$ (p) $\sin \dfrac{7\pi}{3}$

(q) $\cos \dfrac{2\pi}{3}$ (r) $\cos \dfrac{4\pi}{3}$ (s) $\cos \pi$ (t) $\cos \dfrac{5\pi}{3}$

(u) $\cos \dfrac{3\pi}{2}$ (v) $\cot -\dfrac{\pi}{2}$ (w) $\tan -\dfrac{\pi}{3}$ (x) $\tan -\dfrac{2\pi}{3}$

(y) $\tan -\pi$ (z) $\tan -\dfrac{4\pi}{3}$

198

(a') $\tan \dfrac{-5\pi}{3}$ (b') $\csc \dfrac{5\pi}{6}$ (c') $\csc \dfrac{7\pi}{6}$ (d') $\sec -\dfrac{\pi}{4}$

2. Find all $\theta, 0 \le \theta < 2\pi$, such that

(a) $\sin \theta = \frac{1}{2}$
(b) $\sin \theta = 0$
(c) $\sin \theta = 1$

(d) $\sin \theta = \dfrac{\sqrt{3}}{2}$
(e) $\sin \theta = -1$
(f) $\cos \theta = -\dfrac{1}{\sqrt{2}}$

(g) $\cos \theta = -\dfrac{\sqrt{3}}{2}$
(h) $\cos \theta = -1$
(i) $\tan \theta = 0$

(j) $\tan \theta = \dfrac{1}{\sqrt{3}}$
(k) $\tan \theta = 1$
(l) $\tan \theta = \sqrt{3}$

(m) $\sin \theta = -\frac{1}{2}$
(n) $\sin \theta = \dfrac{-\sqrt{3}}{2}$
(o) $\sin \theta = \dfrac{1}{\sqrt{2}}$

(p) $\sin \theta = \dfrac{-1}{\sqrt{2}}$
(q) $\cos \theta = 0$
(r) $\tan \theta =$ undefined

(s) $\cot \theta = 0$
(t) $\cot \theta = \dfrac{1}{\sqrt{3}}$
(u) $\cot \theta = 1$

(v) $\cot \theta = \sqrt{3}$
(w) $\cot \theta =$ undefined
(x) $\tan \theta = \dfrac{-1}{\sqrt{3}}$

(y) $\cos \theta = \frac{1}{2}$
(z) $\cos \theta = \dfrac{1}{\sqrt{2}}$
(a') $\cos \theta = \dfrac{\sqrt{3}}{2}$

(b') $\cos \theta = 1$
(c') $\cos \theta = -\frac{1}{2}$
(d') $\tan \theta = -1$

(e') $\tan \theta = -\sqrt{3}$
(f') $\cot \theta = -\dfrac{1}{\sqrt{3}}$
(g') $\cot \theta = -1$

(h') $\cot \theta = -\sqrt{3}$
(i') $\sec \theta = 0$
(j') $\sec \theta = \dfrac{2}{\sqrt{3}}$

(k') $\sec \theta = \sqrt{2}$
(l') $\sec \theta = 2$
(m') $\sec \theta = \dfrac{-2}{\sqrt{3}}$

(n') $\sec \theta = -\sqrt{2}$
(o') $\sec \theta = -2$
(p') $\csc \theta = \dfrac{-2}{\sqrt{3}}$

(q') $\csc \theta = \sqrt{2}$
(r') $\csc \theta = -2$
(s') $\csc \theta =$ undefined

(t') $\csc \theta = -\sqrt{2}$

3. Prove that $\sin(\theta + 2\pi) = \sin \theta$ for all θ in R.

4. Prove that $\cos(\theta + n2\pi) = \cos \theta$ for all integers n and all θ in R.

5. Prove that $\cos[(2n + 1)\pi] = -1$ for all integers n.

6. Prove that $\tan(k\pi - \pi/4) = -1$ if k is an odd integer.

199

7–8. GRAPHS

Since a clear mental picture of the graphs of each of the six circular functions and the ability to sketch these graphs quickly are of vital importance in our work, we shall discuss both aspects in some detail. Our method in sketching the graphs will be to plot a few points, make some observations about those intervals in the domain where the functions are increasing or decreasing, and then draw the graph, remembering that for each circular function f,

$$f(\theta + 2n\pi) = f(\theta)$$

if n is an integer.

The sine function is 0 at $n\pi$, is 1 at $\pi/2 + 2n\pi$, and is -1 at $-\pi/2 + 2n\pi$, where n is any integer. The function is increasing in the interval $[0, \pi/2]$ and decreasing in the interval $[\pi/2, \pi]$. The graph is shown in Fig. 7–19.

The cosine function takes on the same values as the sine function but at different values of θ. The cosine function is decreasing in the interval $[0, \pi]$. Its graph is shown in Fig. 7–20.

The tangent function is not defined at odd multiples of $\pi/2$, and its graph has vertical asymptotes at these points. It is increasing in the interval $\langle -\pi/2, \pi/2 \rangle$. The graph is shown in Fig. 7–21.

The graphs of the other three circular functions are left as exercises.

As is evident from the graphs, the sine and cosine functions are continuous. Because the tangent is not defined at $\pm\pi/2, \pm 3/2\pi, \ldots$, it does not make sense to speak of continuity at these values of θ, but the tangent is continuous on any interval on which it is defined.

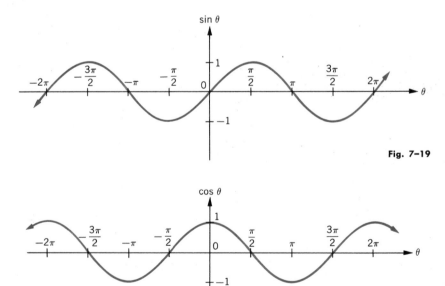

Fig. 7–19

Fig. 7–20

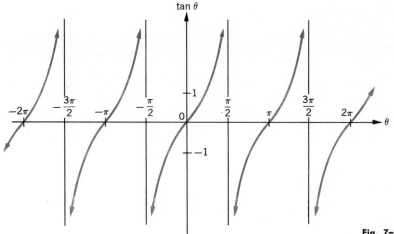

Fig. 7-21

In Section 6–11 we defined *transcendental functions* to be nonalgebraic functions. The trigonometric functions are six of those functions, known as the *elementary* transcendental functions. A proof that these functions are not algebraic, and are therefore transcendental, requires more mathematics than we have had to date. But it is easy to see that they are not polynomials. Note that the sine function has zeros at $\pm\pi, \pm 2\pi, \pm 3\pi, \ldots$ On the other hand a polynomial P of degree n has at most n real zeros; that is, the equation

$$P(x) = a_0 x^n + a_1 x^{n-1} + \cdots + a_n = 0$$

is satisfied by at most n real numbers x. Since $\sin x = 0$ is satisfied for $x = k\pi$, where k is any integer, the sine function cannot be a polynomial. Furthermore, one can prove that the sine function cannot be a rational function, and, with somewhat more effort, that the sine function is not an algebraic function.

Problems

1. Graph on coordinate paper the sine function in the interval $[0, \pi/2]$. Plot those points for which the sine is known exactly and using the definition, plot a few other points.

2. Repeat Exercise 1 for the cosine function.

3. Draw the graph of the cotangent function. What is its domain? its range?

4. Draw the graph of the secant function. What is its domain? Can it assume all real values?

5. Draw the graph of the cosecant function. What is its domain? Can it assume all real values?

201

6. If f is any one of the trigonometric functions, show that $f(\theta \pm 2\pi) = f(\theta)$. What does this indicate about its graph?

7. From the graph of the tangent function, prove that for any real number y, there is exactly one real number x, $-\pi/2 < x < \pi/2$, such that $y = \tan x$.

8. From the graph of the sine function, prove that if $-1 \leq y \leq 1$, then there is exactly one real number x, $-\pi/2 \leq x \leq \pi/2$, such that $y = \sin x$.

9. From the graph of the cosine function, prove that if $-1 \leq y \leq 1$, then there is exactly one real number x, $0 \leq x \leq \pi$, such that $y = \cos x$.

7-9. OTHER GRAPHS

There are certain other functions which are simply related to the trigonometric functions. These are compositions of linear and trigonometric functions.

EXAMPLES

1. Sketch the graph of the equation

$$y = 3 \sin 2x. \tag{1}$$

Equation (1) defines a mapping, $x \xrightarrow{F} 3 \sin 2x$. This mapping is the composition of three functions, $F = f \circ (g \circ h)$, where $h(x) = 2x$, $g(x) = \sin x$ and $f(x) = 3x$. Thus

$$[f \circ (g \circ h)](x) = f(g(h))(x) = f(g(2x)) = f(\sin 2x) = 3 \sin 2x.$$

x	0	$\pi/8$	$\pi/4$	$\pi/12$	$\pi/6$	$3\pi/8$	$\pi/2$
$2x$	0	$\pi/4$	$\pi/2$	$\pi/6$	$\pi/3$	$3\pi/4$	π
y	0	$3/\sqrt{2}$	3	$3/2$	$\frac{3}{2}\sqrt{3}$	$3/\sqrt{2}$	0

One method for obtaining the graph of this composite function is that of plotting points. When the points in the table are plotted, a pattern emerges, and the graph is easy to draw. It is shown in Fig. 7–22.

Note that if x increases from 0 to π, then in the interval $[0, \pi)$, $\phi(2x) = P$ takes all possible positions on the unit circle. Hence in this interval, $\sin 2x$ must complete a full cycle of values. There must be "one wave" between $x = 0$ and $x = \pi$. But the wave must be of "height" or "amplitude" 3 because of the factor 3 in $y = 3 \sin 2x$. Thus we see that it would have been possible to sketch the graph of $y = 3 \sin 2x$ without making a table of values.

202

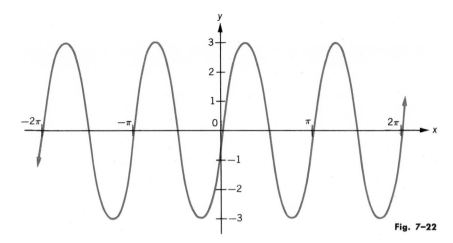

Fig. 7-22

All that would have been necessary would have been the observation of the "length" and amplitude of the wave.

2. Sketch the graph of $y = 2 \cos \dfrac{x}{2}$.

Although we could make a table of values, we shall, instead, use the short-cut method described above. Recall the general shape of the graph of the cosine function in Fig. 7-20.

In our problem, we observe that x must increase from 0 to 4π in order that $x/2$ increase from 0 to 2π. Therefore, the wavelength will be 4π. Because of the factor 2 in $2 \cos \dfrac{x}{2}$, the wave height will be 2. We therefore only need to sketch a cosine wave of the appropriate length and height, as shown in Fig. 7-23.

Similar considerations apply to graphs of $y = A \tan \alpha x$, as well as to graphs involving compositions of the other functions. Note that the tangent function is repetitive but repeats in intervals of length π rather than 2π as is the case for the sine and cosine functions.

In many cases, it will be convenient to use different scales on the two axes to fit the graph better to the coordinate paper.

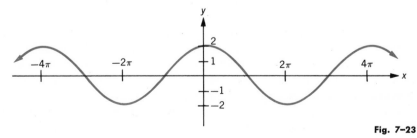

Fig. 7-23

203

Problems

1. Functions are defined by the formulas below. In each case, determine the least positive number p such that the graph in the interval $\langle 0, p \rangle$ will be repeated in each interval of length p.

(a) $f(x) = \sin 3x$ (b) $F(x) = \sin (x/3)$

(c) $g(x) = \sin \pi x$ (d) $T(x) = \tan (x/3)$

(e) $C(x) = \cot (x/3)$ (f) $S(x) = \sec (\pi x/3)$

(g) $E(t) = \sin (\pi t/2)$ (h) $H(s) = \cos 2s$

(i) $h(v) = \cos (v/2)$ (j) $m(x) = \csc (\pi x/2)$

(k) $r(t) = \tan 2t$ (l) $w(t) = \sin (2\pi t/p), \quad p > 0$

2. Sketch the graphs of the following equations. In each case, and *before* drawing the graph, determine the least interval of the independent variable which will give a full cycle of values of the function.

(a) $y = 2(\sin 3x)$ (b) $y = 2 \sin \pi x$

(c) $y = \frac{1}{2} \cos (x/2)$ (d) $I = 5 \cos (\pi x/2)$

(e) $E = \sqrt{2} \sin 2\pi x$ (f) $L = -\sqrt{3} \cos (\pi x/3)$

(g) $y = \tan (\pi x/2)$ (h) $y = 2 \tan 2x$

(i) $y = 2 \sec (x/3)$ (j) $y = 3 \csc (x/2)$

(k) $F = 2 \cot \pi x$

7-10. PERIODIC FUNCTIONS

From the graphs we see that the circular functions repeat themselves again and again. Functions with this repetitive property are called *periodic functions*.

DEFINITION 7-6

If f is a function with domain R and there is a number $p > 0$ such that

$$f(x + p) = f(x)$$

for all x in R, then f is said to be *periodic*. If p is the smallest positive number with this property, then we call p *the period* of f.

Examples of periodic functions are shown in Fig. 7-24. The function f in part (a) is continuous. The function F of part (b) is not. There is an infinite variety of periodic functions, and such functions occur again and again in applications of mathematics.

You are already familiar with some periodic functions, namely the circular functions. The period of the sine function, for example, is 2π. To prove this,

204

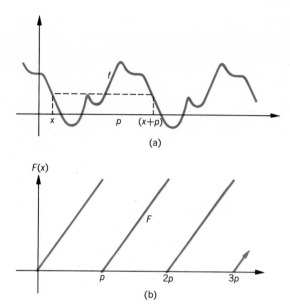

Fig. 7-24

we observe that for every real number θ, $\sin(\theta + 2\pi) = \sin \theta$ since $P(x, y) = \phi(\theta) = \phi(\theta + 2\pi)$ and $y = \sin \theta$ by definition. (See Problem 10, p. 191.) The sine, therefore, is periodic and 2π is a period of the sine function. To show that 2π is the smallest positive period of the sine function, suppose that there is a real number p, $0 < p < 2\pi$, and $\sin(\theta + p) = \sin \theta$ for all real numbers θ. Then for $\theta = 0$, we have $\sin p = \sin 0 = 0$. There is exactly one real number p, $0 < p < 2\pi$, such that $\sin p = 0$, namely π. But π is not a period of the sine function, for if it were, then $\sin(\theta + \pi) = \sin \theta$ for every real number θ. But for $\theta = \pi/2$, we have

$$\sin \theta = \sin \frac{\pi}{2} = 1,$$

whereas

$$\sin(\theta + \pi) = \sin\left(\frac{\pi}{2} + \pi\right) = \sin \frac{3\pi}{2} = -1.$$

Hence the period of the sine function is 2π. The proofs of periodicity of the other circular functions are left as exercises.

Problems

1. Prove that if a function is periodic with period $p > 0$, then $2p$ is also a period of the function.

2. Prove that the cosine, secant, and cosecant all have period 2π.

3. Prove that the tangent and cotangent have period π.

205

4. The graphs of some functions are shown below. Which are graphs of periodic functions? Determine, by inspection, the periods of those functions that are periodic.

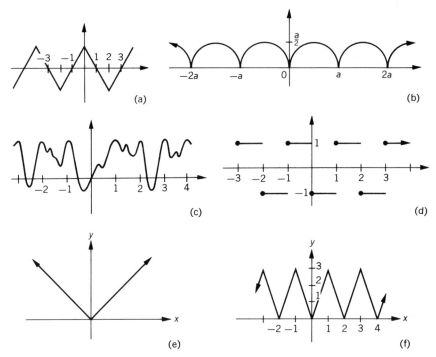

(a)

(b)

(c)

(d)

(e)

(f)

5. Is the standard map, ϕ, a periodic function? If so, what is the period?

6. Show that if f is periodic with period p, then $1/f$ is periodic with period p.

7. Consider the constant function $f: x \rightarrow c$ for all real numbers x. Is f periodic? Does it have a unique period? Is it correct to speak of *the* period of f?

*8. (a) Graph the function f with domain R defined by

$$f(x) = 1, \quad \text{if } x \text{ is rational,}$$
$$f(x) = -1, \quad \text{if } x \text{ is irrational.}$$

(b) Prove that every positive rational number is a period of f.

(c) Prove that no irrational number is a period of f.

(d) Why does it not make sense to speak of *the* period of f?

7-11. SUMS OF PERIODIC FUNCTIONS

We have seen that from the circular functions one can obtain periodic functions with periods different from 2π. We shall now see how to get other periodic functions from the circular functions.

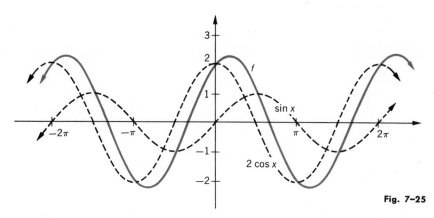

Fig. 7–25

EXAMPLES

1. We can show that the sum of two periodic functions with the same period is a periodic function with that period. (See Problem 4, p. 209). Consider the function f defined by

$$f(x) = \sin x + 2 \cos x.$$

To obtain the graph of f we could, of course, prepare a table of values of f and plot points. It is easier, and quicker, to sketch the graph of f by graphical addition. The graphs of

$$y = \sin x$$

and

$$y = 2 \cos x$$

are drawn dashed in Fig. 7–25. The graph of f, which is the red curve, clearly shows that f has period 2π. It appears to be a "sine wave" somewhat shifted sideways, and with height slightly more than 2. Such is indeed the case, and in Chapter 8 we shall prove it.

2. We now add two functions, the period of one being twice the period of the other. Consider f given by

$$f(x) = \sin x + 2 \cos 2x.$$

As in the previous example, we graph

$$y = \sin x \qquad \text{(period } 2\pi\text{)},$$
$$y = 2 \cos 2x \quad \text{(period } \pi\text{)},$$

and obtain Fig. 7–26. The figure shows that f has period 2π but is not a pure sine wave.

207

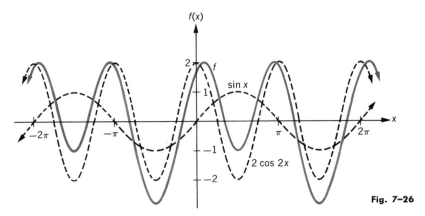

Fig. 7-26

3. In this example we graph a function which is a pure sine wave with altered period and height, and which has been "shifted along the horizontal." Consider

$$f(x) = 2 \sin \left(2x + \frac{\pi}{3}\right).$$

To graph this function one could prepare a table and plot points, but this is too laborious. We first observe that the "angle" $(2x + \pi/3)$ is 0 when $x = -\pi/6$. Therefore the graph of f must "start" at $-\pi/6$. Next we determine the "endpoint" of f. Since the period of the sine function is 2π, we must have, for some x, $(2x + \pi/3) = 2\pi$. Hence $x = 5\pi/6$. Thus in the interval $[-\pi/6, 5\pi/6]$, $f(x)$ has a full cycle of its values, and the period of f must be

$$\left(\frac{5}{6}\pi\right) - \left(-\frac{\pi}{6}\right) = \pi.$$

Clearly, the height, or amplitude, of the wave is 2. A sketch of one period of this function is shown in Fig. 7-27.

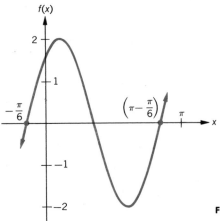

Fig. 7-27

This last example illustrates the behavior of functions given by

$$f(x) = A \sin (kx + \alpha), \qquad g(x) = A \cos (kx + \alpha).$$

The periods of both f and g are $2\pi/|k|$ and both have height, or *amplitude*, equal to $|A|$. The graphs are sine or cosine waves starting where $kx + \alpha = 0$ or at $x = -\alpha/k$. Therefore the graphs of f and g can usually be sketched very quickly.

Problems

1. Find the period and amplitude of the following functions and then sketch the graphs. Check your graph by evaluating the functions at one or two values of the independent variable.

(a) $F(x) = \sqrt{2} \sin 2\pi x$

(b) $F(x) = 2 \cos \dfrac{\pi x}{3}$

(c) $y(t) = 3 \sin \dfrac{t}{2}$

(d) $E(t) = -\frac{1}{2} \sin 3t$

(e) $I(t) = 10 \cos \dfrac{\pi t}{1000}$ (use different t-, I-scales)

(f) $V(t) = 110 \sin 120 \pi t$ (use different t-, V-scales)

(g) $g(x) = 1.5 \cos 6x$

(h) $A(t) = A_0 \sin kt, \quad k > 0$

2. Determine the period, amplitude, and starting point, and then sketch the graphs by drawing a suitable wave.

(a) $y(x) = 2 \sin \left(\pi x - \dfrac{\pi}{4} \right)$

(b) $f(x) = 3 \sin (2x - \frac{1}{2})$

(c) $F(x) = 4 \sin \left(\dfrac{x}{2} - 2 \right)$

(d) $G(x) = 8 \cos \left(\dfrac{x}{3} + 1 \right)$

(e) $E(t) = 110 \sin \left(120 \pi t + \dfrac{2\pi}{3} \right)$ (use different t-, E-scales)

(f) $H(t) = 3 \sin (t - 1)$

(g) $R(t) = 2 \cos \dfrac{t - 1}{3}$

3. Sketch the graphs of the following functions by graphical addition. What is the period of each?

(a) $y(x) = \sin x + \cos x$

(b) $y(x) = \sin x - \cos x$

(c) $f(x) = 2 \sin x - \cos x$

(d) $F(x) = \frac{1}{2} \sin x - \cos 3x$

(e) $g(x) = \sin x - \frac{1}{8} \sin 4x$

(f) $E(t) = \sin t + \sin 2t + \sin 3t$

(g) $K(t) = 1.5 \cos \frac{1}{2}t - 2 \sin 2t$

4. Let f and g be periodic functions with the same period. Prove that $(f + g)$ is periodic with the same period.

5. Give an argument similar to the one of Example 3, above, to show that $f(x) = A \sin (kx + \alpha)$ has period $2\pi|k|$ and amplitude $|A|$.

209

SUMMARY

In this chapter we have defined the six trigonometric functions, studied the graphs of these functions, and considered a few of their properties. We shall study relations between the functions and further properties of the functions in Chapters 8 and 10.

The ideas in this chapter form the basis for our study of trigonometry. The following concepts presented in this chapter are important.

    (a) Radian measure.

    (b) The standard map, ϕ, of the real numbers onto the points of the unit circle with center at the origin.

    (c) The definitions of the six circular functions.

    (d) Values of the functions at the special real numbers $\pi/3$, $\pi/4$, $\pi/6$, and integral multiples of these numbers.

    (e) The graphs of the circular functions.

    (f) Periodic functions.

    (g) The graphs of $y = A \sin (kx + \alpha)$ and $y = B \cos (kx + \alpha)$.

    (h) $\sin^2 \theta + \cos^2 \theta = 1$.

Review Problems

1. If $m(\angle A) = 72°$, what is the measure of the angle in radians?

2. The measure of an angle in radians is 1.7. What is the approximate degree measure of the angle?

3. A central angle of a circle of radius 6.25 has a measure of 1.5 radians. What is the length of the arc subtended by the central angle?

4. Prove that

$$\phi\left(\frac{-21\pi}{4}\right) = \phi\left(\frac{3\pi}{4}\right),$$

where ϕ is the standard map.

5. Is the standard map ϕ a periodic function? If so, what is the period of the function?

6. Which of the trigonometric functions are even functions?

7. Which of the trigonometric functions are odd functions?

8. If both θ_1 and θ_2 are in $\langle \pi/2, 3\pi/2 \rangle$, and $\theta_1 < \theta_2$, compare $\sin \theta_1$ and $\sin \theta_2$.

9. Which is the larger number, $\cos 2$ or $\cos 3$?

10. Without graphing, determine the period and amplitude of each of the following functions.

    (a) $f(x) = 3 \sin 4\pi x$ (b) $g(t) = -10 \cos (2t + \pi/2)$

    (c) $F(x) = 5 \cos (\pi x + \pi/4)$ (d) $f(\theta) = 3 \sin (5\theta + 2\pi/3)$

11. Sketch the graph of $y = \frac{1}{2} \cos 2x$.

12. Sketch by graphical addition: $y = 2 \cos \theta + \sin \frac{\theta}{2}$, $0 \le \theta \le 4\pi$.

13. Prove that

$$\begin{cases} x = a + r \cos \theta, \\ y = b + r \sin \theta \end{cases}$$

are parametric equations of a circle with center at (a, b) and radius r. The *parameter*, or auxiliary variable, is the real number θ.

14. The point Q is a point on a circle of radius 4, with center at O; $\overrightarrow{OQ}$ has direction cosines

$$c_1 = \frac{-1}{3} \quad \text{and} \quad c_2 = \frac{2\sqrt{2}}{3}.$$

What are the coordinates of Q?

15. Sketch one full cycle of $f(x) = 2 \sin (2x - \frac{1}{2})$.

16. Which circular functions are bounded functions?

17. Determine a real number t in $\langle \pi/2, \pi \rangle$ such that $\sqrt{3} \cos t + 3 \sin t = 0$.

18. Identify the function whose graph is shown in the figure.

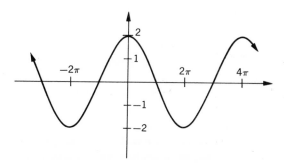

19. Prove that if x is a real number and $0 < x \le 1$, then $1/x \ge 1$. Also, if $-1 \le x < 0$, then $1/x \le -1$. Use the results of this problem to explain the range of the secant and cosecant functions.

*20. Sketch the graph of the relation given by the parametric equations

$$\begin{cases} x = \sin 2\pi t, \\ y = \cos \pi t, \end{cases}$$

where t is a parameter with domain R.

211

HISTORICAL NOTE

François Viète (1540–1603)

In the ancient world, astronomy was the principal science and the only one that made much use of mathematics. The world's first great astronomer was Hipparchus of Nicaea (second century B.C.), whose objective was to give a mathematical description of the motions of the planets. He apparently invented trigonometry to help him in this endeavor. As seen from the earth, the planets seem to move in an irregular way (the name planet means "wanderer") on the surface of a large sphere, the celestial sphere. Hence, to describe their positions with respect to one another and with respect to the stars, *spherical* trigonometry, the solution of triangles on the surface of a sphere, is a necessity. Consequently, one must be familiar with the trigonometric, or circular, functions. Hipparchus compiled a crude table of sines.

The historical note of Chapter 8 contains some remarks on the manner in which early writers conceived the trigonometric functions. In this note we are concerned mainly with the gradual evolution of the subject. During antiquity, and long thereafter, trigonometry was inseparable from astronomy. All books on astronomy contained a discussion of spherical trigonometry, and there were no books on trigonometry alone. It was not until the thirteenth century that the first treatise on trigonometry, independent of astronomy, appeared, written by the Arab astronomer Nasir-Eddin (1201–1274).

During the Middle Ages, the culture of the Greeks and the Hindus was preserved and enriched by the Arabs. The geographic expansion of Islam through the Mediterranean, beginning in the ninth century, coincided with an expansion of intellectual activity in which mathematics played an important part. Among the names that may be mentioned, we give only that of Mohammed Ibn Musa Al-Khowarizmi, who wrote a book (in 825 A.D.) entitled, *al-jebr w' almuquabala*, which means "restoration and reduction." From the title we derive our word "algebra" and from the author's name, the term "algorithm."

Eventually, via the Moslems in Spain, the Greek-Hindu-Arabic culture reached Europe and sparked the revival of the arts and sciences which historians call the renaissance period. Mathematics played an important part in this general intellectual upsurge. By the end of the sixteenth century, elementary, or computational, trigonometry was almost in its modern form. This reformulation of trigonometry was in large measure the work of the great François Viète (1540–1603), who by his systematic use of algebra materially simplified the exposition. He also extended the circular function tables (to 7 places for every second) begun by the German, Rhaeticus. These extensive and quite accurate tables were computed by hand, without the use of logarithms and without the use of the convenient formulas derived in the calculus. Rhaeticus was the first to define the six circular functions as the ratios of the sides of a right triangle. The word "trigonometry" appears for the first time in the sixteenth century.

OF TH

8

APPLICATIONS
CIRCULAR FUNCTIONS

8–1. INTRODUCTION

Circular functions have two essentially different types of application. One of these arises because the circular functions are periodic. Applications of this kind abound in the physics of sound, light, electricity, and mechanics. Whenever a physical motion is repetitive, or periodic, the circular functions may provide a convenient tool for describing the motion.

The second kind of application is to geometry, where the circular functions are the proper tool for solving triangles. This geometric application to triangles is sometimes called numerical trigonometry. Historically, it is this application which aroused interest in the subject. (The word *trigonometry* means "three-angle-measurement.") We shall see in Chapter 11 how the circular functions are applicable to calculations with vectors. Here, too, there is an application to physics, for we can resolve forces into components by use of the sine and cosine functions.

8–2. SIMPLE HARMONIC MOTION

Many motions in physics are periodic. Examples include the oscillations of a pendulum, the vibrations of a tuning fork, and the pressure pulsations in a sound wave. Periodic motions which have mathematical models that are pure sine or cosine waves are given the special name *simple harmonic motions*.

DEFINITION 8–1

If d is any displacement in distance, pressure, or voltage such that

$$d = A \sin \omega t, \quad \text{or} \quad d = A \cos \omega t, \tag{1}$$

where A and ω are real constants and t is the time, then the displacement is said to be a simple harmonic motion of *amplitude* $|A|$.

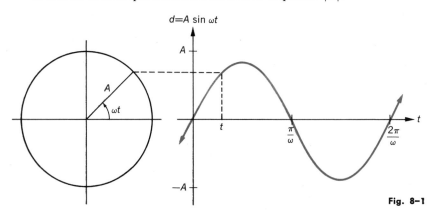

Fig. 8–1

Remark

Displacements given by $d = A \sin [\omega(t - \alpha)]$ or $d = A \cos [\omega(t - \beta)]$, where α and β are constants, are also simple harmonic motions. The cycle simply "begins" at $t = \alpha$ or $t = \beta$.

A simple construction of the graph of (1) is shown in Fig. 8–1.

EXAMPLES

1. Figure 8–1 is closely related to the simple harmonic voltage variations in an alternating current generator. Figure 8–2 represents an idealized generator. The armature is a rectangular loop of wire which rotates about its axis at a speed of ω radians per second. It is suspended between the poles of a magnet. As the armature rotates, the wires pass through the magnetic field and generate an electromotive force, or voltage, E. If the armature is vertical (as shown) at time $t = 0$, then the voltage is proportional to $\sin \omega t$: $E = E_0 \sin \omega t$, where E_0 is a constant related to the strength of the magnet. If the armature were inclined to the vertical at angle α when $t = 0$, then the voltage variation would be given by $E = E_0 \sin (\omega t + \alpha)$.

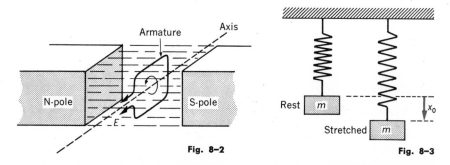

Fig. 8–2

Fig. 8–3

2. Consider a mass m suspended from a weightless spring (Fig. 8–3). Let x measure the displacement of the mass from its position at rest, where x is positive if the displacement is downward.

Suppose that the mass is pulled down a short distance x_0 and then released. The mass will oscillate on either side of the rest position. Neglecting air resistance and friction in the spring, one shows in physics that the mass will execute the simple harmonic motion given by

$$x(t) = x_0 \cos \sqrt{\frac{k}{m}}\, t,$$

where k is a constant associated with the spring. The period of the motion is seen to be $2\pi/\sqrt{k/m}$. Thus heavier masses on the same spring will oscillate more slowly than lighter ones, because the period is larger for the heavier mass.

217

In Chapter 7 we defined the period, p, of a periodic function. If the independent variable measures time, the period is the time for one full cycle, or oscillation. Definitions follow for two other terms often encountered.

DEFINITION 8–2

If F is a periodic function with period p [so that $F(t + p) = F(t)$ for all t, and p is the least positive number with this property], then

(a) the *frequency* of $F = 1/p = \nu$,
(b) the *circular frequency* of $F = 2\pi\nu = \omega$.

The number ν is *the number of cycles per unit time*. The number ω is the *number of radians per unit time* and is the same ω that appeared in equation (1).

Problems

1. In Example 1 on p. 217, suppose that the armature makes n revolutions per second. What is the speed of the armature in radians per second? What is the frequency of the alternating voltage? What is its period?

2. In Example 2, what is the frequency of the oscillations?

3. What is the period of the simple harmonic motion $d = A \sin \omega t$? What is its frequency? its circular frequency?

4. A simple harmonic motion has frequency equal to 3 cycles per second and amplitude 4. Write a formula for such a displacement and sketch its graph.

5. Show that the circular frequency of a simple harmonic motion of period p is $2\pi/p$.

6. The frequency of a periodic function is 2 cycles per second. What is the period of the function?

7. What are the period, frequency, circular frequency, and amplitude of a simple harmonic motion given by $d = 20 \sin 4\pi t$?

8. The position of a pendulum determined by the angle θ describes, very nearly, a simple harmonic motion (see figure). Given that at $t = 0$, the pendulum hangs vertically downward, the period of the pendulum is 2 seconds, and the maximum angular displacement is $\frac{1}{10}$ radian, write a formula giving θ as a function of time t, in seconds.

9. A particle moves in simple harmonic motion between two points on a line that are 10 inches apart (see figure). How far will the particle move during the first 1/8 period after passing the midpoint? during the first 1/6 period? during the first 1/4 period?

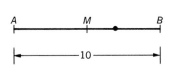

218

8-3. HARMONIC ANALYSIS

In Section 7–11 we saw that the sum of two periodic functions *with the same period* is another periodic function.

If, however, the two functions have different periods, then their sum may not be periodic at all. For example, the function f given by

$$f(x) = \sin x + \sin \pi x$$

is not periodic, for the two summands never quite repeat together. In general, if f_1 and f_2 are periodic with periods p_1 and p_2, respectively, then $f_1 + f_2$ is not periodic if the ratio p_1/p_2 is irrational.

In Fig. 8–4, parts (a), (b), and (c) illustrate simple harmonic motions with periods 4π, 2π, and π, respectively. Motion (b) has twice the frequency of (a), and (c) has twice the frequency of (b). Thus each motion repeats itself every 4π units of time. The sum of these three functions is shown in Fig. 8–4(d) and is seen to have period 4π. It is not a simple harmonic motion even though it is the sum of such motions, yet it is a periodic motion.

A natural question now arises: Given some "nonsimple" periodic function, such as F in Fig. 8–5, is it a sum of simple harmonic functions? In other words, can we resolve any periodic function into simple harmonic compo-

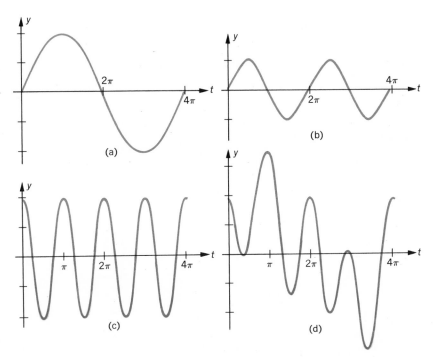

Fig. 8–4

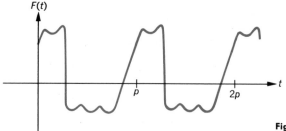

Fig. 8–5

nents? Surprisingly, the answer to this question is *yes*. This fact is the celebrated theorem of the French mathematician and physicist J. B. J. Fourier (1768–1830). This theorem, stated below, has innumerable ramifications in both mathematics and the physical sciences. A complete statement and proof of the theorem requires calculus, but the intuitive content should be clear and the applications to physics meaningful.

FOURIER'S THEOREM

If F is any smooth† continuous periodic function of frequency ν, then $F(t)$ can be approximated as closely as one desires by a sum of simple harmonic functions of frequencies that are whole-number multiples of ν:

$$a_0 + a_1 \cos 2\pi\nu t + b_1 \sin 2\pi\nu t$$
$$+ a_2 \cos 4\pi\nu t + b_2 \sin 4\pi\nu t + \cdots$$
$$+ a_n \cos 2\pi n\nu t + b_n \sin 2\pi n\nu t.$$

The calculation of the numbers $a_0,\ a_1,\ b_1,\ a_2,\ b_2,\ \ldots$, which are called *Fourier coefficients*, is called *harmonic analysis*.

EXAMPLE

Sound is pressure pulsation in the air. A *pure tone* is a simple harmonic variation from the normal pressure P_0. If $P(t)$ is the pressure at time t of a pure tone of frequency ν, then $P(t)$ can be expressed by

$$P(t) = P_0 + A \sin 2\pi\nu t.$$

A tuning fork, Fig. 8–6, emits a tone which is very nearly pure. For example, the tone of middle C has a frequency $\nu = 256$ vibrations per second.

Fig. 8–6

† The adjective "smooth" means that the tangent line to the graph of F turns continuously.

220

Hence the pressure variation for a pure tone of middle C would be given by

$$P(t) = P_0 + A \sin 512\pi t.$$

Loud tones correspond to large values of A.

Other musical tones are combinations, that is, sums, of pure tones. For a given note, most musical instruments produce, besides the ground tone, or *fundamental*, some of the *higher harmonics*. For example, middle C on a violin might consist not only of the fundamental at 256 vibrations per second, but may also comprise tones at double (512) and triple (768) the frequency:

$$P(t) = P_0 + A_1 \sin 512\pi t + A_2 \sin 1024\pi t + A_3 \sin 1536\pi t.$$

The higher harmonics, in different intensities, give a musical note its particular character, or timbre, and enable one to distinguish between the same note played on different instruments.

The human ear-brain combination is a harmonic analyzer, because it can recognize subtle differences in the character of the sound, that is, the presence, or absence, of higher harmonics.

Noise is a sum of random pure sounds of different intensities and frequencies.

8–4. RADIO

Two different methods are used today to transmit sound (and pictures) by means of electromagnetic waves. In this section, we *sketch* the *mathematical aspects* of these two systems, called *amplitude modulation* (AM) and *frequency modulation* (FM).

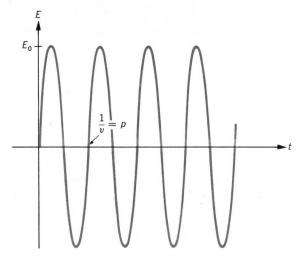

Fig. 8–7

221

In either system, the voltage variation E of the *carrier wave* is a pure sine wave (Fig. 8–7),

$$E(t) = E_0 \sin 2\pi\nu t,$$

where ν is the frequency of the transmitter. The carrier wave produces no sound in a receiver.

In *amplitude modulation* (AM) radio, the amplitude E_0 of the carrier wave is a function of time. For a pure tone, E_0 would be a simple sine variation from a constant,

$$E_0(t) = A_0 + A_1 \sin 2\pi n t \qquad (1)$$

where n is the frequency of the tone. In practice, the frequency of the carrier wave is at least 1000 times as large as that of the tone, $\nu > 1000n$. The modulated carrier wave appears as in Fig. 8–8. Note that the amplitude, A, of the carrier wave is modulated; that is, the amplitude of the sound wave is added to, or subtracted from, the amplitude of the carrier wave. The antenna voltage $E(t)$ is then given by

$$E(t) = (A_0 + A_1 \sin 2\pi n t) \sin 2\pi\nu t.$$

Thus we can say that the carrier wave has been *modulated* by equation 1.

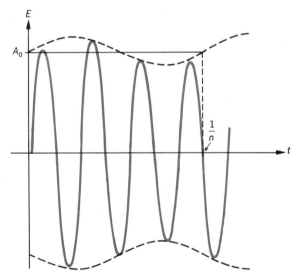

Fig. 8–8

A radio receiver receives from the station a *signal* like that shown in Fig. 8–8 but much diminished in strength. The receiver then amplifies the signal and changes it into a pulsating voltage $V(t)$ of frequency n (Fig. 8–9). The loudspeaker responds to the final output signal, $V(t)$. The information (sound) of the modulation (1) has then been recovered.

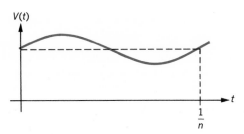

Fig. 8-9

In *frequency modulation* radio (FM), the alteration (modulation) of the carrier wave is obtained by a change in the frequency of the carrier wave, $E(t) = E_0 \sin 2\pi\nu t$. In this case, E_0 is constant, and ν is no longer constant but varies. For a pure tone, ν would vary sinusoidally (in the form of a sine wave),

$$\nu(t) = \nu_0 + \nu_1 \sin 2\pi n t, \tag{2}$$

where n is the frequency of the tone. Then

$$E(t) = E_0 \sin 2\pi(\nu_0 + \nu_1 \sin 2\pi n t)t.$$

A graph of $E(t)$ for this case is shown in Fig. 8-10. The graph gives the appearance of being squeezed together in places and stretched out in others, in an accordionlike fashion.

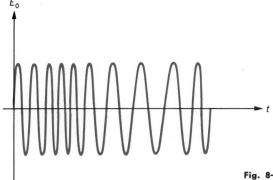

Fig. 8-10

The FM receiver is able to take a signal such as the one shown in Fig. 8-10, recover a copy of the pure tone, $\nu_1 \sin 2\pi n t$, and impart to the loudspeaker a signal like that graphed in Fig. 8-9.

Problems

1. Ordinary electric light circuits supply an alternating voltage of frequency $\nu = 60$ cycles per second and about 110 volts. The number 110 refers to an equivalent direct current of the same power. The true amplitude V_0 is $100\sqrt{2}$. Write a formula for the instantaneous voltage V of ordinary electric light circuits.

2. Sketch the graphs of $y = 3 + 2 \sin \pi t$ and $y = 2 \cos (\pi t + \pi/2)$ on the same axes and find their sum by graphical addition.

3. Draw a graph of a carrier wave of frequency 8 cycles per second. Draw a graph of the same wave with its amplitude modulated by a pure tone of frequency 1 cycle per second. Write a formula for the modulated wave.

4. Consider the functions f and g where

$$f(x) = \sin 3x \quad \text{and} \quad g(x) = \sin \frac{8x}{3}.$$

What are the periods of these functions? Now consider the sum of f and g. Is $f + g$ periodic? If $f + g$ is periodic, what is its period?

5. Is the function F given by $F(x) = \cos 3x + \cos \pi x$ periodic?

6. Concert pitch A has a frequency of 440 vibrations per second. If A, as produced by a flute, has first and second harmonics that are $\frac{1}{4}$ and $\frac{1}{8}$ the amplitude of the fundamental, what is a formula for the pressure variation in terms of t in seconds?

8–5. TABLES

For numerical applications one must be able to find, or compute, the values of the trigonometric functions for any value of the independent variable. Because of their importance, values of these functions have been computed (using calculus methods) once and for all and collected in tables. At first glance the problem appears monumental, because each function has for its domain the set of all real numbers. But it turns out that the tables can be condensed.

In the first place, it is easy to see that

$$\sec \theta = \frac{1}{\cos \theta} \quad \text{and} \quad \csc \theta = \frac{1}{\sin \theta},$$

so that one can obtain secant and cosecant when cosine and sine are known. Usually small tables do not contain the values of secant and cosecant.

The next simplification arises from the periodicity of the functions. Each is periodic with period 2π so that it is necessary to tabulate the functions at most between 0 and 2π.

We next observe that the value of a trigonometric function, for θ in any quadrant, differs at most in sign from the value of the same function for a number r, where $0 \le r \le \pi/2$. The angle whose measure is r is a first-quadrant angle, called the *reference angle*. For example, Fig. 8–11 shows the various positions of $P = (x, y) = \phi(\theta)$, in each quadrant, having the same reference angle AOP_1. In every case we have

$$\text{circular function } (\theta) = \pm \text{ same circular function } (r).$$

224

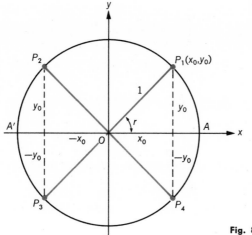

Fig. 8–11

In Fig. 8–11, we have

$$P_1(x_0, y_0) = \phi(\theta_1), \qquad P_2(-x_0, y_0) = \phi(\theta_2), \qquad P_3(-x_0, y_0) = \phi(\theta_3),$$

and

$$P_4(x_0, -y_0) = \phi(\theta_4)$$

all having the same reference angle AOP_1. By definition,

$$\sin \theta_1 = y_0, \qquad \cos \theta_1 = x_0,$$
$$\sin \theta_2 = y_0, \qquad \cos \theta_2 = -x_0,$$
$$\sin \theta_3 = -y_0, \qquad \cos \theta_3 = -x_0,$$
$$\sin \theta_4 = -y_0, \qquad \cos \theta_4 = x_0.$$

Therefore

$$|\sin \theta_1| = |\sin \theta_2| = |\sin \theta_3| = |\sin \theta_4|$$

and

$$|\cos \theta_1| = |\cos \theta_2| = |\cos \theta_3| = |\cos \theta_4|.$$

That is, except for their signs the sines and the cosines of θ_1, θ_2, θ_3, and θ_4 are the same. Note that

$$m(\angle AOP_1) = m(\angle A'OP_2) = m(\angle A'OP_3) = m(\angle AOP_4).$$

This fact helps in determining the reference angles of any $P(x, y) = \phi(\theta)$.

Since a similar argument can be made for tangent and cotangent, it follows that only the functions on the part of the domain between 0 and $\pi/2$ must be tabulated.

225

EXAMPLES

1. In Fig. 8–11, if $r = \pi/6$, what are the values of θ_2, θ_3, and θ_4?

$$\theta_2 = \pi - m(\angle A'OP_2) = \pi - r = \frac{5\pi}{6},$$

$$\theta_3 = \pi + m(\angle A'OP_3) = \pi + r = \frac{7\pi}{6},$$

$$\theta_4 = 2\pi - m(\angle AOP_4) = 2\pi - r = \frac{11\pi}{6}.$$

2. Determine the values of the sine and cosine functions for θ_1, θ_2, θ_3, and θ_4 of Example 1.

$$\sin \theta_1 = \sin \frac{\pi}{6} = \frac{1}{2}, \qquad \cos \theta_1 = \cos \frac{\pi}{6} = \frac{\sqrt{3}}{2},$$

$$\sin \theta_2 = \sin \frac{\pi}{6} = \frac{1}{2}, \qquad \cos \theta_2 = -\cos \frac{\pi}{6} = -\frac{\sqrt{3}}{2},$$

$$\sin \theta_3 = -\sin \frac{\pi}{6} = -\frac{1}{2}, \qquad \cos \theta_3 = -\cos \frac{\pi}{6} = -\frac{\sqrt{3}}{2},$$

$$\sin \theta_4 = -\sin \frac{\pi}{6} = -\frac{1}{2}, \qquad \cos \theta_4 = \cos \frac{\pi}{6} = \frac{\sqrt{3}}{2}.$$

3. $\sin 3 = \sin (\pi - 3)$, because the reference angle is $\pi - 3$ (Fig. 8–12).

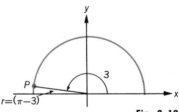

Fig. 8–12

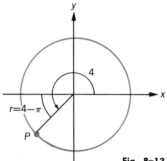

4. $\cos 4 = -\cos (4 - \pi)$, because the reference angle is $4 - \pi$ and the cosine is negative in the third quadrant (Fig. 8–13).

Fig. 8–13

5.

$$\tan \frac{2\pi}{3} = -\tan \left(\pi - \frac{2\pi}{3} \right)$$

$$= -\tan \frac{\pi}{3},$$

because the reference angle is $\pi - 2\pi/3 = \pi/3$ and the tangent is negative in the second quadrant (Fig. 8–14).

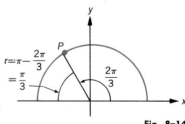

Fig. 8–14

226

So, what has been shown so far is that we need only tables between 0 and $\pi/2$. There is yet another relation which will permit the tables to be just half this large.

Let us look at the names of the functions. There are functions and *co*-functions:

sine and *co*-sine

tangent and *co*-tangent.

We shall agree that the *co*-cosine is the sine, and the *co*-cotangent is the tangent. We shall now prove that for $0 < \theta < \pi/2$,

$$\text{function of } \theta = \text{co-function of } \left(\frac{\pi}{2} - \theta\right) \cdot \dagger \tag{1}$$

Consider Fig. 8–15. Triangle $\triangle PQO$ is a right triangle with right angle PQO;

$$m(\angle PQO) = \pi/2,$$
$$m(\angle POQ) = \theta,$$
$$m(\angle OPQ) = \pi/2 - \theta,$$
$$OQ = x_0, \quad \text{and} \quad PQ = y_0.$$

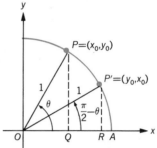

Fig. 8–15

We now choose P' with coordinates (y_0, x_0), that is, $x = y_0$ and $y = x_0$. We immediately see that $\triangle PQO \cong \triangle ORP'$, and since this is true for any $P(x_0, y_0)$ and $P'(y_0, x_0)$, we can make the following general statement.

If $P = (x, y) = \phi(\theta)$, then

$$P' = (y, x) = \phi\left(\frac{\pi}{2} - \theta\right) \cdot$$

So directly from the definition of the functions, we have

$$\sin \theta = y = \cos\left(\frac{\pi}{2} - \theta\right), \qquad \tan \theta = \frac{y}{x} = \cot\left(\frac{\pi}{2} - \theta\right),$$
$$\cos \theta = x = \sin\left(\frac{\pi}{2} - \theta\right), \qquad \cot \theta = \frac{x}{y} = \tan\left(\frac{\pi}{2} - \theta\right).$$

Therefore tables need give the circular functions of θ only for $0 \le \theta \le \pi/4$.

---

† The relation (1) is actually correct for all θ, as will be shown in Chapter 9. At the moment, we need the relation only for the restricted values of $\theta : 0 < \theta < \pi/2$.

Problems

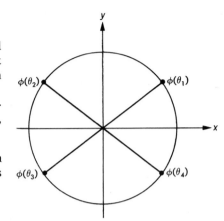

1. $\phi(\theta_1)$, $\phi(\theta_2)$, $\phi(\theta_3)$, and $\phi(\theta_4)$ all have the same reference angle but are in different quadrants, as shown in the figure. If $\phi(\theta_3) = Q_3 = (a, b)$, then determine the rectangular coordinates of points Q_1, Q_2, and Q_4.

2. In Problem 1, if $\theta_1 = \pi/3$, then what are the smallest positive values of θ_2, θ_3, and θ_4?

3. $\sin(\pi/6) = \frac{1}{2}$. Determine the values for $\sin(5\pi/6)$, $\sin(7\pi/6)$, and $\sin(11\pi/6)$.

4. $\cos(7\pi/6) = -\sqrt{3}/2$. Determine the values for $\cos(11\pi/6)$, $\cos(\pi/6)$, and $\cos(5\pi/6)$.

5. Which of the following numbers are positive?

   (a) $\sin 0.5$ (b) $\sin 2$ (c) $\cos 1.4$ (d) $\sin 4$

   (e) $\tan 3.5$ (f) $\cot 5$ (g) $\csc 4$ (h) $\sec 6$

6. Find the values for $\sin\theta$, $\cos\theta$, and $\tan\theta$, if the coordinates of $P(x, y) = \phi(\theta)$ are as follows:

   (a) $\left(\dfrac{1}{3}, \dfrac{2\sqrt{2}}{3}\right)$ (b) $\left(-\dfrac{5}{13}, \dfrac{12}{13}\right)$

   (c) $\left(-\dfrac{1}{\sqrt{5}}, -\dfrac{2}{\sqrt{5}}\right)$ (d) $\left(\dfrac{40}{41}, -\dfrac{9}{41}\right)$

   (e) $(0.97, 0.24)$

8–6. TABLES *(Cont.)*

Before describing our tables, we remark that originally circular functions were primarily used to solve triangle problems and, in particular, problems which arose in physical applications, notably astronomy, where degree measure was customary. Therefore in applications it is traditional and convenient to continue the practice of using the measure of an angle in degrees:

$$\theta \cdot \frac{180}{\pi} \cdot$$

Thus in Fig. 8–16, $\angle AOP$ has radian measure $\pi/6$ and degree measure 30. Instead of writing sin $\pi/6$, we can write sin 30°. There need be no confusion about this change of notation because it will always be clear from the context what is meant. It should be noted, however, that sin 30° is a corruption of our careful notation. It can be viewed as mathematical "slang." Because, in the past, the circular functions were thought of as functions of an *angle*, the symbol "30" could be viewed as merely a symbol for the geometric angle. For our purposes, we can look at 30° as locating the point $P = \phi(\pi/6)$ on the unit circle.

Because

$$\text{function } \theta = \text{co-function} \left(\frac{\pi}{2} - \theta \right),$$

we have, in degree measure

$$\text{function } A° = \text{co-function } (90 - A)°.$$

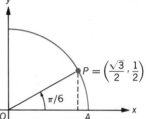

Fig. 8–16

Therefore the tables are abbreviated as in Fig. 8–17. Angles less than, or equal to, 45° ($\pi/4$ is approximately 0.7854) are listed in the left-hand column, and the name of the function appears at the top of the table. Angles greater than 45° are in the right-hand column, and the name of the function appears at the bottom of the table. Thus we find:

$$\sin 22° = 0.3746 = \sin 0.3840,$$
$$\cos 68° = 0.3746 = \cos 1.1868.$$

Reading sin 22° = 0.3746 from the table, we must realize that most of the numbers in the body of the table are approximations. Thus sin 22° = 0.3746 ± e, where $0 < e < 0.00005$. If greater accuracy is required, then more extensive tables are necessary. Mathematical tables are available which contain trigonometric tables for five- or six-place (and more) values of the functions.

Degrees	Radians	sin	tan	cot	cos		
0	0					$\pi/2$	90
22	0.3840	0.3746	0.4040	2.4751	0.9272	1.1868	68
45	0.7854					0.7854	45
		cos	cot	tan	sin	Radians	Degrees

Fig. 8–17

229

The tables of the circular functions are to be found on pp. 494–498. The reader will note that the measures of angles are given in both degrees and radians.

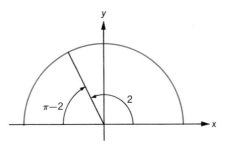

Fig. 8–18

EXAMPLES

1. To find cos 2, we observe that the reference angle is $\pi - 2 = 1.1416$, approximately (Fig. 8–18). Therefore, from the table,

$$\cos 2 = -\cos 1.1416,$$

where we have to interpolate

$$29 \left(13 \begin{pmatrix} \cos 1.1403 = 0.4173 \\ \cos 1.1416 = \ ? \\ \cos 1.1432 = 0.4147 \end{pmatrix} \right) 0.0026.$$

Thus the difference between cos 1.1403 and cos 1.1416 is $\frac{13}{29}$ $(-0.0026) = -0.0012$. (Note that the cosine is decreasing.)

$$\cos 2 = -(0.4173 - 0.0012) = -0.4161.$$

2. To find tan 56° 22′, we see from the table that

$$
\begin{array}{rl}
\tan 56°\ 20′ = & 1.5013 \\
\tan 56°\ 30′ = & 1.5108 \\
\hline
\text{Difference} = & 0.0095
\end{array}
$$

Therefore

$$\tan 56°\ 22′ = 1.5013 + \tfrac{2}{10}(0.0095) = 1.5013 + 0.0019 = 1.5032.$$

3. Find A in degrees and minutes such that $0 < A < 90$ and cos $A° = 0.2323$.

$$
\begin{array}{rl}
\cos 76°\ 30′ = & 0.2334 \\
\cos A° \quad = & 0.2323 \\
\cos 76°\ 40′ = & 0.2306
\end{array} \bigg\} 0.0011 \bigg] 0.0028
$$

Therefore

$$A° = 76°\ 30′ + \tfrac{11}{28} \cdot 10′ = 77°\ 30′ + 4′ = 76°\ 34′.$$

230

Problems

1. Write the following functions as $\pm$ the same function of a real number between 0 and $\pi/2$. That is, express each of them in terms of the reference angle. Then find the numerical value of each.

   (a) tan 2
   (b) sin 2
   (c) $\cos \dfrac{2\pi}{3}$

   (d) cot 2.5
   (e) sin 2.5
   (f) cos 2.9

   (g) tan 1.7
   (h) cot 1.83
   (i) $\cos (\pi - 0.1)$

2. Express the following functions as functions of a real number between 0 and $\pi/4$. Find the numerical value of each.

   (a) tan 2
   (b) tan 1.6
   (c) cos 1.6

   (d) cot 3
   (e) $\sin \dfrac{2\pi}{3}$
   (f) $\sin (\pi - 0.2)$

3. Find from the table each of the following.

   (a) cos 18° 20′
   (b) cos 78° 40′
   (c) tan 65° 50′

   (d) cot 37° 40′
   (e) sin 213° 20′
   (f) sin 132° 30′

   (g) cos 167° 20′
   (h) cot 107° 40′
   (i) sin 251° 10′

   (j) tan 293° 20′
   (k) cos 242° 10′
   (l) sin 312° 20′

4. Find A, $0 < A < 90$, such that:

   (a) sin $A°$ = 0.9588
   (b) cos $A°$ = 0.5807
   (c) tan $A°$ = 1.6107

   (d) cot $A°$ = 2.4545
   (e) sin $A°$ = 0.3854
   (f) cos $A°$ = 0.7753

   (g) sin $A°$ = 0.5200
   (h) cot $A°$ = 0.7177
   (i) cos $A°$ = 0.0814

   (j) sin $A°$ = 0.8004
   (k) tan $A°$ = 1.3111
   (l) cot $A°$ = 0.3939

5. Interpolate to find approximate values of the following:

   (a) cos 59° 37′
   (b) sin 28° 42′
   (c) tan 41° 45′

   (d) cot 61° 45′
   (e) sin 126° 33′
   (f) cos 99° 59′

   (g) tan 98° 32′
   (h) cot 162° 18′
   (i) sin 212° 12′

   (j) cos 261° 37′
   (k) tan 310° 24′
   (l) cot 278° 32′

6. Find A to the nearest minute such that $0 < A < 90$ and

   (a) sin $A°$ = 0.7777
   (b) cos $A°$ = 0.7444
   (c) tan $A°$ = 1.1000

   (d) cot $A°$ = 1.2000
   (e) cos $A°$ = 0.9923
   (f) sin $A°$ = 0.0400

   (g) tan $A°$ = 0.0400
   (h) cos $A°$ = 0.0200
   (i) sin $A°$ = 0.0900

   (j) cos $A°$ = 0.9000
   (k) cot $A°$ = 0.6950
   (l) tan $A°$ = 1.3000

7. Find a real number θ other than an integral multiple of $\pi/2$ such that sin θ in the table is not an approximation. Find other values of θ such that cos θ and tan θ are exact values in the tables.

231

8-7. RIGHT TRIANGLES

Geometric application of the circular functions to right triangles depends upon properties of similar triangles. Suppose that one has a right triangle, $\triangle ABC$, with the right angle at C and sides of length a, b, c opposite the corresponding angles. Let us choose the coordinate axes as in Fig. 8–19 with vertex A at the origin and C on the x-axis. Consider the right triangle, $\triangle APQ$, with the right angle at Q and $|AP| = 1$, then $\triangle APQ$ is similar to $\triangle ABC$, and

$$\left\{ \begin{array}{l} \sin A = \dfrac{a}{c} = \dfrac{\text{length of opposite side}}{\text{length of hypotenuse}}, \\[2mm] \cos A = \dfrac{b}{c} = \dfrac{\text{length of adjacent side}}{\text{length of hypotenuse}}, \\[2mm] \tan A = \dfrac{a}{b} = \dfrac{\text{length of opposite side}}{\text{length of adjacent side}}, \\[2mm] \cot A = \dfrac{b}{a} = \dfrac{\text{length of adjacent side}}{\text{length of opposite side}}. \end{array} \right. \tag{1}$$

Equations (1) are immediate consequences of the definitions of the functions. The opposite-adjacent-hypotenuse language is often used in formulating definitions of the circular functions of acute angles.

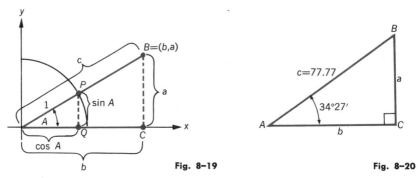

Fig. 8-19   Fig. 8-20

EXAMPLE

In a right triangle the measure of one angle is 34° 27′ and the length of the hypotenuse is 77.77 feet. Find the measure of the other angle and the lengths of the remaining sides.

Labeling the triangle as in Fig. 8–20, we have, on using the table of functions,

$$\sin A° = 0.5657 = \frac{a}{77.77}.$$

Therefore

$$a = (0.5657)(77.77) = 43.99 \quad \text{to four significant figures.}$$

And since

$$\cos A° = 0.8246 = \frac{b}{77.77},$$

$$b = (0.8246)(77.77) = 64.13 \quad \text{to four significant figures,}$$

$$m(\angle B) = 90° - 34° \, 27' = 55° \, 33'.$$

Problems

1. In the triangles below, A, B, C are the angles, with C a right angle and a, b, c the lengths of the sides opposite these angles, respectively. Find the part designated. Draw a figure in each case.

   (a) $a = 17.36$, $m(\angle B) = 67° \, 12'$. Find c.

   (b) $b = 1.832$, $m(\angle B) = 37° \, 34'$. Find c.

   (c) $a = 0.2766$, $m(\angle A) = 48° \, 15'$. Find b.

   (d) $a = 21.32$, $b = 14.72$. Find $m(\angle B)$.

   (e) $c = 4.321$, $b = 3.456$. Find $m(\angle A)$.

2. A student finds the height of a tree in the following manner (see figure). Using a steel tape, he finds that $|OA| = 50$ feet. He estimates that $m(\angle BAO) = 50°$. Using the tables, he computes $|OB|$, the height of the tree, as

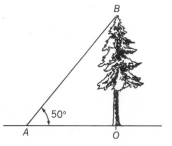

$$|OB| = 50 \tan 50° = 50 \, (1.1918)$$

$$= 59.5900 \text{ feet.}$$

Comment on the accuracy of the solution.

3. The side of a regular pentagon is approximately 11.83 units. Find the radii of the inscribed and circumscribed circles.

4. A 24-foot ladder leans against a wall with the foot of the ladder $8\frac{1}{2}$ feet from the wall. What angle does the ladder make with the wall? Note that your answer should be precise only to the nearest half degree.

5. The base angles of an isosceles trapezoid have measures of $39° \, 14'$. The top and bottom edges have lengths of 8.62 and 18.53 centimeters. What is the altitude of the trapezoid?

8–8. LOGARITHMS OF THE CIRCULAR FUNCTIONS

From the last set of problems, it is clear that using common logarithms would expedite the computation because only multiplications and divisions need be performed. One could, of course, find the trigonometric functions in a table and then look up their logarithms in a table of logarithms, but these two operations can be combined into one, since tables of logarithms of the

233

circular functions have been compiled. A remark may be in order before we proceed to examples. Both sine and cosine are between 0 and 1 for angles of measure between 0° and 90°. Therefore log sin A and log cos A will have negative characteristics. The tangent and cotangent, on the other hand, can be either greater or less than one and so may have logarithms with positive, zero, or negative characteristics. In the tables, 10 is to be subtracted from each logarithm except those for the tangents of angles between 45° and 90°, and the cotangents of angles between 0° and 45°.

EXAMPLES

1. Find log sin 53° 28'.
From the table, we have

$$\begin{array}{r} \log \sin 53° \ 20' = 9.9042 - 10 \\ \log \sin 53° \ 30' = 9.9052 - 10 \\ \hline \text{Difference} = 0.0010 \end{array}$$

Therefore

$$\log \sin 53° \ 28' = 9.9042 - 10 + \tfrac{8}{10}(0.0010) = 9.9050 - 10.$$

2. Find A if log tan $A = 0.0792$.
From the table,

$$\begin{array}{l} \log \tan 50° \ 10' = 0.0788 \\ \log \tan A \qquad = 0.0792 \\ \log \tan 50° \ 20' = 0.0813 \end{array} \left. \begin{array}{l} \\ \end{array} \right\} 0.0004 \left. \begin{array}{l} \\ \\ \end{array} \right\} 0.0025$$

Therefore
$$A = 50° \ 10' + \tfrac{4}{25}(10') = 50° \ 10' + 2' = 50° \ 12'.$$

3. An airplane is directly over an airport hangar. At a point 6000 yards distant from the hangar the angle of elevation is 18° 25' (Fig. 8–21). Find the height of the plane.
If h is the height in yards, we have

$$\tan 18° \ 25' = \frac{h}{6000}.$$

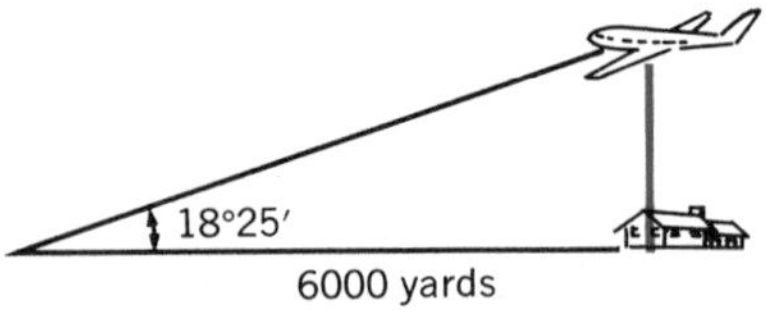

18°25'

6000 yards

Hence

$$h = 6000 \tan 18° \ 25'$$

Fig. 8–21

$$\begin{array}{r} \log 6000 = 3.7782 \\ \log \tan 18° \ 25' = 9.5224 - 10 \\ \hline \log h = 3.3006 \\ h = 1998. \end{array}$$

Therefore the height of the plane is about 2000 yards.

234

4. From a point along a straight shore, a boat is sighted at an angle of 44° from the shore. From a point 400 yards farther along the shore, the boat is sighted at an angle of 25° from the shore (Fig. 8–22). How far is the boat from the shore?

From Fig. 8–22, we have

$$x = (400 + y) \tan 25°,$$
$$y = x \cot 44°.$$

Therefore

$$x = (400 + x \cot 44°) \tan 25°,$$

and solving for x, we obtain

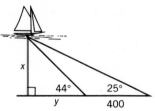

Fig. 8–22

$$x = \frac{400 \tan 25°}{(1 - \cot 44° \tan 25°)}$$

log tan 25° =	9.6687 − 10
log cot 44° =	0.0152
log product =	9.6839 − 10
product =	0.4830
1 − cot 44° tan 25° =	0.5170
log 400 =	2.6021
log tan 25° =	9.6687 − 10
log product =	12.2708 − 10
log 0.5170 =	9.7135 − 10
log x =	2.5573

$$x = 360.8, \text{ or approximately 360 yards.}$$

Problems

1. Find the following logarithms of circular functions.

   (a) log cos 48° 14′   (b) log tan 16° 38′   (c) log sin 62° 17′

   (d) log cot 71° 19′   (e) log cos 5° 5′   (f) log sin 3° 13′

   (g) log tan 67° 24′   (h) log sin 79° 18′   (i) log cos 31° 31′

2. Find the measure of the acute angle A in degrees, given that:

   (a) log sin A = 9.7777 − 10   (b) log tan A = 0.0327

   (c) log cos A = 9.8000 − 10   (d) log cot A = 9.4552 − 10

   (e) log sin A = 8.1500 − 10   (f) log cos A = 8.8800 − 10

   (g) log tan A = 9.4567 − 10   (h) log sin A = 9.8902 − 10

   (i) log cos A = 9.7000 − 10

3. From the top of a tower 152.5 feet high, an object is sighted on the ground. If the measure of the angle of depression is 13° 25′, how far is it from the object to the foot of the tower? How far is it from the top of the tower to the object?

235

4. Points P and Q are directly opposite each other on the bank of a straight river. At a point R 300 yards along the river from Q, the angle PRQ is found to be 53° 10′. How wide is the river?

5. In a right triangle, the two legs have lengths 12.73 and 21.82. Find the measures of the angles of the triangles.

6. In a right triangle, one leg is 1.375 inches long, and the hypotenuse is 2.483 inches long. Find the measures of the angles of the triangle and the length of other leg.

7. In a right triangle, one leg is 3 times as long as the other. Find the measures of the angles.

8. From a point on a level road the angle of elevation of a mountain peak is found to be 6° 27′. From a point on the road 4 miles closer to the mountain, the elevation is 8° 48′. Find the height of the mountain.

9. The hypotenuse and one leg of a right triangle have lengths 372.5 and 237.4, respectively. Find the length of the other side (a) by the Pythagorean Theorem, (b) by trigonometry.

10. From the top of a building the angles of depression of two stakes are 25° 10′ and 35° 20′. The stakes are 100 feet apart and in a line with the observer. How high is the building?

11. A triangle has sides of lengths 12.73 and 14.86 inches. The included angle has measure 63° 21′. What is the area of the triangle?

12. A force in the xy-plane of 125.2 pounds makes an angle of 125° 24′ with the positive x-axis. What are the components of the force?

13. A force has horizontal and vertical components of 8.76 and 10.93 pounds, respectively. What angle does the force make with the horizontal?

14. What angles does the ray from $(0, 0)$ to $(8.30, 6.42)$ make with the positive x- and y-axes? What are the cosines of these angles? What are the direction cosines of the ray?

*15. Two radar stations are 8 miles apart on an east-west line. Station A sights a plane at 20° north at the same time that station B sights the plane at 30° north. How far from station A is the plane?

8-9. OBLIQUE TRIANGLES: LAWS OF SINES AND COSINES

In applying the circular functions to triangles other than right triangles, one can proceed in several ways. One can subdivide the given triangles into right triangles or one can use new formulas relating the sides and angles of any triangle. It turns out that these new formulas have applications in other situations and so are important in their own right. We shall now consider these formulas.

Let us recall from geometry that a triangle is uniquely determined if either

(1) angle-side-angle are given (ASA);
(2) side-angle-side are given (SAS);
(3) side-side-side are given (SSS).

Our problem is that of devising formulas to find the other three parts of the given triangle for these cases. The desired formulas are called the *Law of Sines* and the *Law of Cosines* and are derived below.

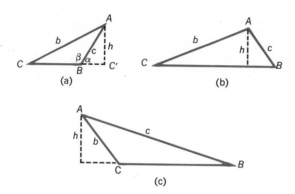

(a)   (b)

(c)   **Fig. 8-23**

Consider $\triangle ABC$ as in Fig. 8-23, where we have two cases depending on whether C is acute or obtuse. In all three cases, we have

$$h = c \sin B = b \sin C.$$

$$\frac{c}{\sin C} = \frac{b}{\sin B}.$$

Note that in the case shown in Fig. 8-23(a), $\sin \beta = \sin \alpha$, because $m\angle CBA < 180°$ or π, and the reference angle for $\angle CBA$ has a measure equal to $m\angle C'BA$. If the perpendicular of length h had been dropped to side b, we would have obtained

$$\frac{c}{\sin C} = \frac{a}{\sin A}.$$

Combining these equations, we have a theorem called the Law of Sines.

LAW OF SINES

In every triangle with angles A, B, C and opposite sides of lengths a, b, c, respectively,

$$\frac{a}{\sin A} = \frac{b}{\sin B} = \frac{c}{\sin C}.$$

Clearly, knowing two angles and a side will enable us to compute the other sides. Hence the Law of Sines solves case (1) for us.

237

EXAMPLE 1

In $\triangle ABC$ (Fig. 8–24), $a = 63.88$ feet, $m\angle B = 64°\ 22'$, and $m\angle C = 59°\ 36'$. Find side c.

Solving for $m\angle A$ first, we have

$$m\angle A = 180° - (64°\ 22' + 59°\ 36') = 56°\ 2'.$$

Then adapting the formula to solve for side c, we obtain

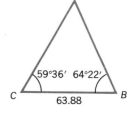

$$c = \sin C \cdot \frac{a}{\sin A}$$

$\log \sin C =$	$9.9358 - 10$
$\log a =$	1.8054
Sum $=$	$11.7412 - 10$
$\log \sin A =$	$9.9188 - 10$
$\log c =$	1.8224
$c =$	66.43 feet.

Fig. 8–24

The Law of Sines can also be used when two sides and the angle opposite one of them are given. For example, suppose that a, b and angle A are given, as in Fig. 8–25. This is the so-called ambiguous case (see Problem 5 below) which has

no solution	if	$a < b \sin A$,
one solution	if	$a = b \sin A$,
two solutions	if	$b \sin A < a < b$,
one solution	if	$a \geq b$.

We now turn to the Law of Cosines and for its derivation apply a little of our knowledge of analytic geometry. Given $\triangle ABC$, suppose that the axes are chosen so that C is at the origin, A on the positive x-axis, and B above the x-axis, as in Fig. 8–26. Then the coordinates of B are ($a \cos C$, $a \sin C$), and the coordinates of A are $(b, 0)$. Note that by $\angle C$ we mean $\angle BCA$, and further that

$$\cos C = \cos \alpha = -\cos \beta$$

in the case shown in Fig. 8–26. In general, if C is greater than 90°, then the cosine for that angle will be a negative number.

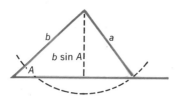

Fig. 8–25

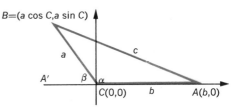

Fig. 8–26

The distance formula gives us

$$c^2 = (a \cos C - b)^2 + (a \sin C - 0)^2$$
$$= a^2(\cos^2 C + \sin^2 C) + b^2 - 2ab \cos C.$$

We have shown that for all angles θ, $\sin^2 \theta + \cos^2 \theta = 1$. Therefore we get

$$c^2 = a^2 + b^2 - 2ab \cos C.$$

Clearly, similar formulas must hold for a^2 and b^2. We have thus obtained the Generalized Pythagorean Theorem, or a theorem called the Law of Cosines.

LAW OF COSINES

In every triangle, with angles A, B, C and opposite sides of lengths, a, b, c, respectively,

$$a^2 = b^2 + c^2 - 2bc \cos A,$$
$$b^2 = c^2 + a^2 - 2ca \cos B,$$
$$c^2 = a^2 + b^2 - 2ab \cos C.$$

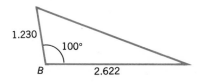

Fig. 8–27

EXAMPLE **2**

In $\triangle ABC$, $a = 1.230$, $c = 2.622$, $m(\angle B) = 100°$ (Fig. 8–27). Find side b.

$$\cos 100° = -\cos (180 - 100)° = -\cos 80°.$$

The law of cosines is not well adapted to logarithms.

$\log a = 0.0899$	$\log c = 0.4186$	$\log a = \quad 0.0899$
$\log a^2 = 0.1798$	$\log c^2 = 0.8372$	$\log c = \quad 0.4186$
$a^2 = 1.513$	$c^2 = 6.873$	$\log 2 = \quad 0.3010$

$$\log \cos (180° - B) = \quad \log \cos 80° = \quad 9.2397 - 10$$
$$\log 2ac \cos 80° = \quad 10.0492 - 10$$
$$2ac \cos B = \quad -1.120$$

$$b^2 = a^2 + c^2 - 2ac \cos B = 1.513 + 6.873 + 1.120$$
$$= 9.506$$
$$\log b^2 = 0.9780$$
$$\log b = 0.4890$$
$$b = 3.083$$

239

Problems

1. Two sides of a triangle are 10 and 12 inches long. The included angle is 60°. Find the remaining parts.

2. A triangle has sides of 8, 10, and 14 inches. Find the measure of the largest angle.

3. Two angles of a triangle have measures 117° 21′ and 32° 14′. The length of the side opposite the largest angle of the triangle is 12.43 feet long. Find the length of the side opposite the smallest angle of the triangle.

4. Find the remaining part of $\triangle ABC$, given that:
   (a) $m(\angle A) = 17° 31′$, $a = 42.00$, $b = 62.00$
   (b) $m(\angle A) = 17° 31′$, $c = 42.00$, $b = 62.00$
   (c) $m(\angle C) = 130° 0′$, $a = 5.000$, $b = 10.000$
   (d) $m(\angle B) = 71° 13′$, $m(\angle C) = 12° 12′$, $a = 14.21$
   (e) $m(\angle A) = 67° 10′$, $m(\angle C) = 29° 13′$, $b = 41.32$
   (f) $m(\angle B) = 53° 5′$, $m(\angle C) = 21° 32′$, $b = 14.27$
   (g) $m(\angle C) = 125° 34′$, $a = 12.76$, $c = 20.73$
   (h) $m(\angle A) = 35° 44′$, $c = 17.37$, $a = 7.77$
   (i) $a = 5.432$, $b = 2.716$, $c = 6.007$
   (j) $a = 0.05163$, $b = 0.08442$, $c = 0.10760$
   (k) $a = 1.596 \times 10^5$, $b = 2.473 \times 10^5$, $c = 1.938 \times 10^5$
   (l) $a = 9.83 \times 10^{-4}$, $b = 8.774 \times 10^{-4}$, $c = 13.78 \times 10^{-4}$

5. The measure of one angle of a triangle is 37° 20′. The length of the side opposite this angle is 15 feet long. If a side adjacent to the given angle is 22 feet long, find the other parts of the triangle. This is the "ambiguous case." There are two solutions.

6. Show that the Pythagorean Theorem is a special case of the Law of Cosines.

7. Show that if angle C of a triangle is obtuse, then $c^2 > a^2 + b^2$.

8. Show that the area of any triangle is given by

$$\text{area} = \tfrac{1}{2}ab \sin C.$$

9. Show that if $\angle AOB$ is a central angle of a circle with center at O and radius r, and if $m(\angle AOB) = \theta$, then $|AB| = r\sqrt{2(1 - \cos \theta)}$. If $\angle AOB$ is a straight angle, what does the formula give?

10. $\overrightarrow{OP}$ and $\overrightarrow{OQ}$ have endpoints at $(2, 6)$ and $(5, 2)$, respectively. If $\overrightarrow{OR} = \overrightarrow{OP} + \overrightarrow{OQ}$, what is the measure of the angle that $\overrightarrow{OR}$ makes with the positive x-axis?

*11. Prove that if R is the radius of the circumscribed circle of $\triangle ABC$, and s is one-half its perimeter, then:

   (a) $R(\sin A + \sin B + \sin C) = s$,   (b) $2R = \dfrac{a}{\sin A} = \dfrac{b}{\sin B} = \dfrac{c}{\sin C}$.

240

SUMMARY

The significant topics of the chapter are:

1. Simple harmonic motion, amplitude, period, frequency, circular frequency
2. Periodic functions as sums of simple harmonic functions
3. Tables of the circular functions. (How were the tables condensed?) Interpolation.
4. Degree and radian measure of angles
5. Solution of right triangles   6. Logarithms of the circular functions
7. Law of Sines   8. Law of Cosines
9. Solution of oblique triangles, with the cases SAS, ASA, SSA, SSS.

Review Problems

1. Write a formula for the displacement d of a particle undergoing a simple harmonic motion which has amplitude 2 and a frequency of 4 cycles per second.

2. A simple harmonic motion has amplitude 6 and circular frequency of 100π radians per second. Write a formula for the displacement d at any time t. What is the period of the simple harmonic motion?

3. Express each of the following as a function of a real number between 0 and $\pi/4$, and find the value of each.

   (a) $\cos \dfrac{14\pi}{3}$ (b) $\sin \dfrac{-\pi}{6}$ (c) $\tan \dfrac{5\pi}{6}$

   (d) $\sin 3$ (e) $\cos 4$ (f) $\tan \dfrac{-2\pi}{3}$

4. Triangle ABC is a right triangle, and $\angle C$ is the right angle. Compute the length of the hypotenuse c, given that $m(\angle A) = 37° \, 12'$, and $a = 45.00$.

5. Compute the height h of $\triangle ABC$ shown in the left-hand figure below.

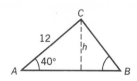 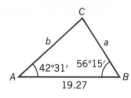

6. Find the lengths a, b, and $m(\angle C)$ in $\triangle ABC$ shown in the right-hand figure above.

7. Find the measure of the largest angle of a triangle whose sides have lengths 5, 7, and 8.

8. The lengths of two sides of a triangle are 5 and 6 units, and the measure of the included angle is $2\pi/3$. Find the length of the third side.

9. Show that in any triangle ABC, $\cos C = (a^2 + b^2 - c^2)/2ab$.

10. Find the measure of each acute angle of a 3-4-5 right triangle.

241

HISTORICAL NOTE

CI PTOLEMAEO·ALEX·   FI·

Ptolemy (Second Century A.D.).   From a drawing by Raphael.

Let us look back at the tables of the circular functions as they existed in ancient times.

Both Greeks and Hindus divided the circle into four quadrants of 90 degrees each, and each degree into 60 minutes—a procedure which they inherited from the Babylonians. For the sine, the Greeks used the whole chord, $|AC|$, subtended by twice the angle (or arc). The Hindus, on the other hand, used the half-chord, $|AB|$, subtended by double the arc. (See Fig. 8–28.) Observe that the Hindu definition would correspond to the modern one *if the radius, R, of the circle were* 1. But neither Greeks nor Hindus used $R = 1$! Various radii were used. Ptolemy (second century A.D.) used $R = 60$. Most Hindu astronomers used $R = 120$ (observe that with $R = 120$ the Hindu entries in their tables were the same as the Greek entries). One Hindu astronomer, Aryabhata (born 476 A.D.) used $R = 3468$!

The reader should keep in mind that in those days numerical work was not the easy task it is today. For most of the time (perhaps up to 600 A.D. in India and 1200 A.D. in Europe) our convenient decimal notation, based on the Hindu-Arabic numerals, was not known. Therefore, the *representation* of the length of the chord (or half-chord), even though it be a whole number, was a problem of some complexity that required special skill.

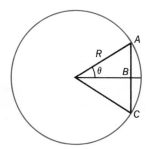

Fig. 8–28

Many of the ancient tables, for example the one computed by Ptolemy, gave the entries only for every 3° 45', and often with little accuracy. The standard method of computing tables at this time was a Hindu invention. They started with the known values for 30°, 45°, and 60° and, using the half-angle formula (see chapter 9), $\sin^2 \frac{1}{2}\theta = \frac{1}{2}(1 - \cos\theta)$, were able to compute the sines of 15°, 22° 30', and then 7° 30', 11° 15', and 3° 45'. The next step would be to find the sines of all the complementary angles, 86° 15', 82° 30', 78° 45', 75°, 67° 30', and repeat the process, determining the sines of half of these angles. Eventually, with some interpolation, they obtained tables with entries for every 3° 45'.

243

ANALYTIC

9

TRIGONOMETRY

9–1. INTRODUCTION

The trigonometric functions arise in all sorts of ways in all branches of mathematics, both pure and applied. Although the functions have their origin in a rather simple geometric situation, their uses are much broader, as might be expected from the discussion of Chapter 8 concerning harmonic analysis of periodic functions. The study of the special properties that circular functions possess as "functions" is called *analytic trigonometry*. The word "analytic" comes from *analysis* which refers to a general study of functions.

The fundamental topics of this chapter are:

(a) the elementary identities,
(b) the addition formulas,
(c) the double and half-angle formulas.

You should be able to derive all of these formulas; there are about twenty of them. You will also find it helpful to memorize most of them.

9–2. THE ELEMENTARY IDENTITIES

Identities have been encountered before this. For example:

(a) $x^2 - 1 = (x - 1)(x + 1)$ for all real, or complex, numbers x.

(b) $2x^2 - x - 1 = (2x + 1)(x - 1)$ for all real, or complex, numbers x.

(c) $\dfrac{x^3 - 1}{x - 1} = x^2 + x + 1$ for all real, or complex, numbers $x \neq 1$.

(d) $\dfrac{x^3 + x}{x^2 + 1} = x$ for all real x (and for all real, or complex, $x \neq \pm i$).

In other words, an identity states that two functions or expressions represent the same number for all values of the variable in some domain which is usually clear from context.

DEFINITION 9–1

Suppose that f and g are functions with domains which overlap on a set D, and suppose that

$$f(x) = g(x) \qquad \text{for all } x \text{ in } D. \tag{1}$$

Then we say that (1) is an *identity* in D.

(See Fig. 9–1.) In other words, an identity is a statement that two functions are identical on a certain set. It is vital to be sure what this set, or domain, is.

246

We could also denote such an identity by $f = g$ on D. In practice one does not often specifically mention what the domain D of the identity happens to be, but leaves it to the reader to see from context what it must be. We shall proceed in both ways. At first we shall be quite specific about the domain and then later relax our vigilance.

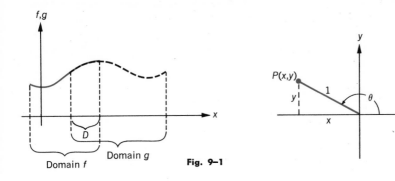

Fig. 9–1

Fig. 9–2

All the elementary identities arise directly from the definitions of the circular functions. We have (see Fig. 9–2)

$$\phi(\theta) = P = (x, y), \qquad x = \cos \theta, \qquad y = \sin \theta,$$

whence it immediately follows that

$\tan \theta = \dfrac{y}{x} = \dfrac{\sin \theta}{\cos \theta}$,	for all $\theta \neq \dfrac{\pi}{2}(2k + 1)$, k an integer;
$\cot \theta = \dfrac{x}{y} = \dfrac{\cos \theta}{\sin \theta}$,	for all $\theta \neq k\pi$, k an integer;
$\sec \theta = \dfrac{1}{x} = \dfrac{1}{\cos \theta}$,	for all $\theta \neq \dfrac{\pi}{2}(2k + 1)$, k an integer;
$\csc \theta = \dfrac{1}{y} = \dfrac{1}{\sin \theta}$,	for all $\theta \neq k\pi$, k an integer.

(2)

The above are the simplest of the elementary identities. There are three more elementary ones, called the *Pythagorean identities*. Because

$$x^2 + y^2 = 1;$$

$$1 + \frac{y^2}{x^2} = \frac{1}{x^2} \qquad \text{if } x \neq 0,$$

$$\frac{x^2}{y^2} + 1 = \frac{1}{y^2} \qquad \text{if } y \neq 0,$$

247

we have the identities

$\sin^2\theta + \cos^2\theta = 1,$	for all θ;
$1 + \tan^2\theta = \sec^2\theta,$	if $\theta \neq k\pi + \pi/2,\ k$ an integer;
$\cot^2\theta + 1 = \csc^2\theta,$	if $\theta \neq k\pi,\ k$ an integer.

(3)

The identities of (2) and (3) are the *elementary identities*, and should be memorized, since they may be used to establish other identities.

EXAMPLES

1. Establish the identity

$$\frac{1}{\cos\theta} - \cos\theta = \tan\theta \cdot \sin\theta \tag{4}$$

and determine the domain for which it is valid.
We have

$$\frac{1}{\cos\theta} - \cos\theta = \frac{1 - \cos^2\theta}{\cos\theta}, \qquad \text{where} \quad \theta \neq k\pi + \frac{\pi}{2},$$

$$= \frac{\sin^2\theta}{\cos\theta}$$

$$= \frac{\sin\theta}{\cos\theta} \cdot \sin\theta$$

$$= \tan\theta \sin\theta.$$

In this problem we have worked with *one* side of the supposed identity and, by a succession of steps, reduced it to the other. This method is, perhaps, the most elegant way of proceeding, but one can work with both sides. Thus

$$\frac{1}{\cos\theta} - \cos\theta = \frac{1 - \cos^2\theta}{\cos\theta}$$

$$= \frac{\sin^2\theta}{\cos\theta},$$

whereas

$$\tan\theta \cdot \sin\theta = \frac{\sin\theta}{\cos\theta} \cdot \sin\theta$$

$$= \frac{\sin^2\theta}{\cos\theta}.$$

248

Therefore both sides of the presumed identity (4) are equal (for all $\theta \neq k\pi + \pi/2$) to $\sin^2 \theta/\cos \theta$, and so

$$\frac{1}{\cos \theta} - \cos \theta = \tan \theta \cdot \sin \theta \qquad \text{if} \quad \theta \neq k\pi + \frac{\pi}{2}.$$

In this example we have been careful about the domain of the variable θ. But this domain can really be seen from the context. The tangent function is not defined for $\theta = k\pi + \pi/2$ and $\cos \theta = 0$ for $\theta = k\pi + \pi/2$. Therefore the functions given by the left- and right-hand sides of (4) are defined if and only if $\theta \neq k\pi + \pi/2$. From this point of view, the identity (4) is a statement that two functions are the same function, and we may delete the variable θ and write

$$\frac{1}{\cos} - \cos = \tan \cdot \sin.$$

The proof in this form is precisely the same:

$$\frac{1}{\cos} - \cos = \frac{1 - \cos^2}{\cos}$$

$$= \frac{\sin^2}{\cos} = \frac{\sin}{\cos} \cdot \sin$$

$$= \tan \cdot \sin.$$

2. Establish that

$$\frac{\sin \theta}{1 + \cos \theta} = \frac{1 - \cos \theta}{\sin \theta},$$

and determine the domain of validity.

First we observe that $\cos \theta + 1 = 0$ if θ is an *odd* multiple of π, whereas $\sin \theta = 0$ if θ is *any* multiple of π. Therefore the identity can be valid only if $\theta \neq k\pi$, where k is an integer. With this restriction on the domain of θ, we can drop the variable θ and write

$$\frac{\sin}{1 + \cos} = \frac{\sin}{1 + \cos} \frac{1 - \cos}{1 - \cos}$$

$$= \frac{\sin (1 - \cos)}{1 - \cos^2}$$

$$= \frac{\sin (1 - \cos)}{\sin^2}$$

$$= \frac{1 - \cos}{\sin}.$$

249

Notational Remark

We have been representing the variable in the circular functions by θ, where θ is a real number. However, one may use any convenient letter for the argument of the functions, even x or y. Of course, if this is done, then x and y do not refer to the coordinates of the point P which is the image of the standard map.

Problems

1. Establish the following identities, without recourse to pencil and paper. In each case state the domain on which the identity is valid.

   (a) $\sin \theta = \dfrac{1}{\csc \theta}$

   (b) $\cos x = \dfrac{1}{\sec x}$

   (c) $\tan t = \dfrac{\sec t}{\csc t}$

   (d) $\cot \theta = \dfrac{1}{\tan \theta}$

   (e) $\sin x \csc x = 1$

   (f) $\cos u \sec u = 1$

   (g) $\cot z \tan z = 1$

   (h) $\cos^2 a = 1 - \sin^2 a$

2. Express each of the functions below in terms of sine and/or cosine. In each case, give the domain on which the function is defined.

   (a) $\cot^2 \theta$

   (b) $\cot \theta + \tan \theta$

   (c) $\sec x - \tan x$

   (d) $\dfrac{1}{\sec^2 y} - \dfrac{1}{\tan^2 y}$

   (e) $(\sec u - \tan u)^2$

   (f) $(\csc t - \cot t)^2$

   (g) $\dfrac{1 - \tan^2}{1 + \tan^2}$

   (h) $\dfrac{\tan + \cot}{\sec \csc}$

   (i) $\dfrac{\cot \theta + 1}{\cot \theta - 1}$

   (j) $\dfrac{\tan}{1 - \cot} + \dfrac{\cot}{1 - \tan}$

   (k) $\dfrac{1 - \cos^2 \theta}{\sin \theta}$

   (l) $\dfrac{1 + \tan^2 a}{\sec a}$

3. Establish the following identities,† and give the domain of validity for each.

   (a) $\cot \theta + \tan \theta = \sec \theta \csc \theta$

   (b) $(1 - \sin x)(1 + \sin x) = \dfrac{1}{1 + \tan^2 x}$

   (c) $\dfrac{1}{\sec^2 x} + \dfrac{1}{\csc^2 x} = 1$

---

† When one is faced with a presumed identity, a thorough familiarity with the basic identities will usually enable him to see a convenient method of attack. When no obvious procedure is apparent, it will often help to express all the functions in terms of sines and cosines.

(d) $\sec^2 \theta - \csc^2 \theta = \tan^2 \theta - \cot^2 \theta$

(e) $\sin^2 y \cot^2 y + \cos^2 y \tan^2 y = 1$

(f) $\dfrac{\sec t}{\tan t + \cot t} = \sin t$

(g) $(\csc A - \cot A)^2 = \dfrac{1 - \cos A}{1 + \cos A}$

(h) $\dfrac{\tan x - \sec x + 1}{\tan x + \sec x - 1} = \dfrac{\cos x}{1 + \sin x}$

(i) $\dfrac{\csc^2 \theta - 1}{\csc^2 \theta} = \cos^2 \theta$

(j) $\tan u(1 - \cot^2 u) + \cot u(1 - \tan^2 u) = 0$

(k) $\sin^3 \theta \cos \theta + \cos^3 \theta \sin \theta = \sin \theta \cos \theta$

(l) $\dfrac{\sec^2 x}{1 + \sin x} = \dfrac{\sec^2 x - \sec x \tan x}{\cos^2 x}$

(m) $\dfrac{2 \sin \alpha \cos \alpha}{\cos^2 \alpha - \sin^2 \alpha} = \dfrac{2 \tan \alpha}{1 - \tan^2 \alpha}$

(n) $\dfrac{1/2}{1 - \sin v} + \dfrac{1/2}{1 + \sin v} = 1 + \tan^2 v$

(o) $(1 + \cot 2\theta - \csc 2\theta)(1 + \tan 2\theta + \sec 2\theta) = 2$

(p) $\dfrac{\sin x}{\csc x} - 1 = -\dfrac{\cos x}{\sec x}$

(q) $\sin^4 3\theta - \cos^4 3\theta = 1 - 2 \cos^2 3\theta$

(r) $2 \sin^2 \alpha - 1 = \dfrac{\tan \alpha - \cot \alpha}{\tan \alpha + \cot \alpha}$

(s) $\tan A + \cot A = \sec A \csc A$

(t) $\sec^2 x + \csc^2 x = \sec^2 x \csc^2 x$

(u) $(1 + \tan^2 z)(1 - \sin^2 z) = 1$

(v) $\sec^4 x - \tan^4 x = 1 + 2 \tan^2 x$

*(w) $\dfrac{\sin \alpha \cos \beta + \cos \alpha \sin \beta}{\cos \alpha \cos \beta - \sin \alpha \sin \beta} = \dfrac{\tan \alpha + \tan \beta}{1 - \tan \alpha \tan \beta}$

*(x) $\cos \theta \sqrt{\sec^2 \theta - 1} = \sin \theta$ if θ is in quadrants I, III

*(y) $\cos \theta \sqrt{\sec^2 \theta - 1} = -\sin \theta$ if θ is in quadrants II, IV

*(z) $\dfrac{1}{\sqrt{1 - \sin^2 \theta}} = -\sec \theta$ if θ is in quadrants II, III

251

4. Establish the following identities and give the domain of validity for each.

(a) $\sec^2 (A + \sqrt{2} B) - \sin^2 (A + \sqrt{2} B) \sec^2 (A + \sqrt{2} B) = 1$

(b) $\sin \tan = \sec - \cos$

(c) $\dfrac{\tan + \sec}{\cos - \tan - \sec} = -\csc$

(d) $\sin + \cos + \dfrac{\sin}{\cot} = \sec + \csc - \dfrac{\cos}{\tan}$

(e) $\sin \cos \tan \cot \sec \csc = 1$

(f) $\dfrac{\sin}{\csc - \cot} = 1 + \cos$

(g) $\dfrac{\tan^2 - 1}{\tan^2 + 1} = 2 \sin^2 - 1$

(h) $\dfrac{\sin + \tan}{\cot + \csc} = \sin \tan$

(i) $\dfrac{1 + \csc x}{\csc x - 1} = \dfrac{1 + \sin x}{1 - \sin x}$

(j) $\dfrac{1 + \tan^2}{\tan^2} = \csc^2$

(k) $\dfrac{2 \sin^2 - 1}{\sin \cos} = \tan - \cot$

*(l) $\sin^6 + \cos^6 = 1 - 3 \sin^2 \cos^2$

5. Express each of the other circular functions in terms of the one cited. The angle θ may be in any one of the quadrants. In each case, state what signs to use on the radicals when θ is in the different quadrants.

(a) sine   (b) cosine   (c) tangent

(d) cotangent   (e) secant   (f) cosecant

6. Express the following in terms of sine and cosine.

(a) $\dfrac{\sin x + \tan x}{1 + \sec x}$

(b) $\dfrac{\csc \theta}{\csc \theta - 1} + \dfrac{\csc \theta}{\csc \theta + 1}$

(c) $\dfrac{1 - \tan^2}{1 + \tan^2}$

(d) $(\csc + \cot)^2$

(e) $(\sec + \csc)^2 \tan$

9–3. THE ADDITION FORMULAS

Among the important identities for the circular functions are those which express functions of the sum, or difference, of two real numbers in terms of functions of each number. We will now obtain these formulas. It is important that the development of these formulas be understood. The formulas themselves should be memorized.

If α, β are real numbers and

$$P = \phi(\alpha), \qquad Q = \phi(\beta),$$

where ϕ is the standard map, then the points O, P, Q will, in general,† form a triangle, $\triangle OPQ$. (See Fig. 9–3.) The angle, $\angle POQ$, has a radian measure

---

† If $P = Q$, or if P, O, and Q form a straight angle, the formula below for $\cos (\alpha - \beta)$ is easily checked and found to be correct.

$\gamma = \pm(\alpha - \beta) + k \cdot 2\pi$, where k is some integer. We will now obtain the number $|PQ|^2$ in two ways. From analytic geometry, using the coordinates of P (cos α, sin α) and Q(cos β, sin β), we have

$$|PQ|^2 = (\cos \alpha - \cos \beta)^2 + (\sin \alpha - \sin \beta)^2 \qquad (1)$$
$$= \cos^2 \alpha - 2 \cos \alpha \cos \beta + \cos^2 \beta + \sin^2 \alpha - 2 \sin \alpha \sin \beta + \sin^2 \beta$$
$$= 2 - 2 \cos \alpha \cos \beta - 2 \sin \alpha \sin \beta.$$

By the law of cosines, we obtain

$$|PQ|^2 = 1 + 1 - 2 \cos \gamma = 2 - 2 \cos \gamma \qquad (2)$$
$$= 2 - 2 \cos [\pm(\alpha - \beta) + k \cdot 2\pi] = 2 - 2 \cos [\pm(\alpha - \beta)]$$
$$= 2 - 2 \cos (\alpha - \beta).$$

[cos $(\pm\theta) = \cos \theta$ because cosine is an *even* function†]. From (1) and (2) we have

$$2 - 2 \cos (\alpha - \beta) = 2 - 2 \cos \alpha \cos \beta - 2 \sin \alpha \sin \beta,$$

or

$$\cos (\alpha - \beta) = \cos \alpha \cos \beta + \sin \alpha \sin \beta. \qquad (3)$$

Identity (3) is the first of the new identities. We shall obtain others from this one.

Because the cosine is an *even* function and the sine is an *odd*‡ function, we have for all real numbers θ,

$$\cos (-\theta) = \cos \theta$$

and

$$\sin (-\theta) = -\sin \theta.$$

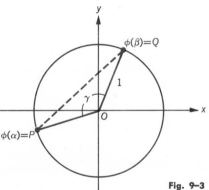

Fig. 9-3

Therefore

$$\cos (\alpha + \beta) = \cos [\alpha - (-\beta)]$$
$$= \cos \alpha \cos (-\beta) + \sin \alpha \sin (-\beta),$$

or

$$\cos (\alpha + \beta) = \cos \alpha \cos \beta - \sin \alpha \sin \beta. \qquad (4)$$

This is the second of the new identities.

---

† A function f is *even* if $f(-x) = f(x)$ for all x. The graph of an even function possesses line symmetry. The cosine is an even function because if $\phi(\theta) = (x, y)$, then $\phi(-\theta) = (x, -y)$. Therefore cos $(-\theta) = x = \cos \theta$. See Chapter 6, p. 158.

‡ A function f is *odd* if $f(-x) = -f(x)$ for all x. The graph of an odd function possesses point symmetry. The sine is an odd function because if $\phi(\theta) = (x, y)$, then $\phi(-\theta) = (x, -y)$. Therefore sin $(-\theta) = -y = -\sin \theta$. See Chapter 6, p. 158.

253

To obtain corresponding formulas for the sine function, we digress first to examine functions of the "complementary angle." You are familiar with complementary acute angles. What is new, perhaps, is our agreement to call $\pi/2 - \theta$ the *complement of θ* for any real number θ. Then from (3), we find that

$$\cos\left(\frac{\pi}{2} - \beta\right) = \cos\frac{\pi}{2}\cos\beta + \sin\frac{\pi}{2}\sin\beta$$
$$= 0 \cdot \cos\beta + 1 \cdot \sin\beta.$$

Therefore

$$\cos\left(\frac{\pi}{2} - \beta\right) = \sin\beta, \qquad \text{for all} \quad \beta. \tag{5}$$

Because β is arbitrary in (5), if we set $\beta = (\pi/2 - \theta)$, we obtain

$$\cos\left[\frac{\pi}{2} - \left(\frac{\pi}{2} - \theta\right)\right] = \sin\left(\frac{\pi}{2} - \theta\right)$$

or

$$\sin\left(\frac{\pi}{2} - \theta\right) = \cos\theta, \qquad \text{for all} \quad \theta. \tag{6}$$

Formulas analogous to (5) and (6) are valid for the tangent (see Problem 13 of this section) and cotangent, and for the secant and cosecant. Thus in every case the circular functions satisfy the formula

$$\text{function of } \theta = \text{cofunction of } \left(\frac{\pi}{2} - \theta\right).$$

We can now apply (5) and (6) to obtain addition formulas for the sine. We have

$$\sin(\alpha + \beta) = \cos\left[\frac{\pi}{2} - (\alpha + \beta)\right]$$
$$= \cos\left[\left(\frac{\pi}{2} - \alpha\right) - \beta\right]$$
$$= \cos\left(\frac{\pi}{2} - \alpha\right)\cos\beta + \sin\left(\frac{\pi}{2} - \alpha\right)\sin\beta$$
$$= \sin\alpha\cos\beta + \cos\alpha\sin\beta,$$

or

$$\sin(\alpha + \beta) = \sin\alpha\cos\beta + \cos\alpha\sin\beta. \tag{7}$$

To obtain $\sin(\alpha - \beta)$, we can either proceed in the same way or consider $\sin(\alpha - \beta) = \sin[\alpha + (-\beta)]$. The derivation is left as an exercise. The result is

$$\sin(\alpha - \beta) = \sin\alpha\cos\beta - \cos\alpha\sin\beta. \tag{8}$$

To obtain a formula for $\tan(\alpha + \beta)$, we use the elementary identities and our formulas for $\sin(\alpha + \beta)$ and $\cos(\alpha + \beta)$. That is,

$$\tan(\alpha + \beta) = \frac{\sin(\alpha + \beta)}{\cos(\alpha + \beta)} = \frac{\sin\alpha\cos\beta + \cos\alpha\sin\beta}{\cos\alpha\cos\beta - \sin\alpha\sin\beta}.$$

254

Dividing numerator and denominator of this last fraction by $\cos \alpha \cos \beta$ gives

$$\tan (\alpha + \beta) = \frac{\tan \alpha + \tan \beta}{1 - \tan \alpha \tan \beta}. \tag{9}$$

Similarly, one obtains

$$\tan (\alpha - \beta) = \frac{\tan \alpha - \tan \beta}{1 + \tan \alpha \tan \beta}. \tag{10}$$

Formulas for $\cot (\alpha + \beta)$ and $\cot (\alpha - \beta)$ can also be obtained, but they are not commonly used. One seldom sees formulas for $\sec (\alpha + \beta)$ or $\csc (\alpha + \beta)$, since they are neither elegant nor necessary. For convenient reference, we list the addition formulas below:

$$\cos (\alpha \pm \beta) = \cos \alpha \cos \beta \mp \sin \alpha \sin \beta$$
$$\sin (\alpha \pm \beta) = \sin \alpha \cos \beta \pm \cos \alpha \sin \beta$$
$$\tan (\alpha \pm \beta) = \frac{\tan \alpha \pm \tan \beta}{1 \mp \tan \alpha \tan \beta}$$

EXAMPLE

The addition formulas permit us to extend the set of numbers for which exact values of the functions are known. Thus

$$\sin \frac{\pi}{12} = \sin \left(\frac{\pi}{3} - \frac{\pi}{4}\right) = \sin \frac{\pi}{3} \cos \frac{\pi}{4} - \cos \frac{\pi}{3} \sin \frac{\pi}{4}$$
$$= \frac{\sqrt{3}}{2} \cdot \frac{\sqrt{2}}{2} - \frac{1}{2} \frac{\sqrt{2}}{2} = \frac{\sqrt{6} - \sqrt{2}}{4}.$$

Problems

1. Develop the formula for $\sin (\alpha - \beta)$ by using the formula for $\sin (\alpha + \beta)$.

2. Complete the development of the formula for $\tan (\alpha + \beta)$. For what numbers α and β is it valid?

3. Derive the formula for $\tan (\alpha - \beta)$.

4. Obtain the formula for $\cot (\alpha + \beta)$ in terms of $\cot \alpha$ and $\cot \beta$.

5. Obtain the formula for $\cot (\alpha - \beta)$ in terms of $\cot \alpha$ and $\cot \beta$.

6. Find $\cos (\pi/12)$ in two ways: $\pi/12 = \pi/3 - \pi/4 = \pi/4 - \pi/6$.

7. Find $\tan (7\pi/12)$.

8. Find $\sin (11\pi/12)$.

9. Find $\cos (5\pi/12)$.

10. Verify the remark of the footnote on p. 252. If $P = Q$, or if P, O, and Q form a straight angle, then $\cos (\alpha - \beta) = \cos \alpha \cos \beta + \sin \alpha \sin \beta$.

11. Show that

(a) $\sin (x + y) + \sin (x - y) = 2 \sin x \cos y$

(b) $\tan (x + \pi/4) - \tan (x - 3\pi/4) = 0$

(c) $\sin (x + y) \sec x \sec y = \tan x + \tan y$

(d) $\tan (\theta + \pi/4) = \dfrac{\cos \theta + \sin \theta}{\cos \theta - \sin \theta}$

(e) $\cos (\pi/3 + x) - \sin (\pi/6 - x) = 0$

(f) $\sin (\pi/4 + x) + \cos (\pi/4 - x) = 2 \sin (x + \pi/4)$

(g) $\sin (x - y) \cos y + \cos (x - y) \sin y = \sin x$

(h) $\cos (x + y) \cos y + \sin (x + y) \sin y = \cos x$

(i) $\cos \theta = \cos \left(\dfrac{\theta}{2} + \dfrac{\theta}{2}\right) = 2 \cos^2 \dfrac{\theta}{2} - 1$

12. Show that $\cos (x + y) + \cos (x - y) = 2 \cos x \cos y$. Let $x + y = A$ and $x - y = B$ to obtain

$$\cos A + \cos B = 2 \cos \frac{A + B}{2} \cos \frac{A - B}{2}.$$

Obtain similar formulas for $\cos A - \cos B$, $\sin A + \sin B$, and $\sin A - \sin B$.

13. Show that $\tan (\pi/2 - x) = \cot x$ for all x that is not an integral multiple of π.

14. Show that if $\alpha + \beta + \gamma = \pi$, then $\sin \alpha = \sin \beta \cos \gamma + \cos \beta \sin \gamma$.

15. Show that $\sin (x + y + z) = \sin x \cos y \cos z - \sin x \sin y \sin z$
$\qquad\qquad\qquad\qquad + \cos x \sin y \cos z + \cos x \cos y \sin z.$

16. Find a formula for $\cos (x - y + z)$ similar to that of Problem 15.

17. Establish the following identities:

(a) $\dfrac{\tan (x + y) - \tan x}{1 + \tan (x + y) \tan x} = \dfrac{\sin y}{\cos y}$

(b) $\sin (A + B) \sin (A - B) = \sin^2 A - \sin^2 B$

(c) $\cos (A + B) \sin (A - B) = \sin A \cos A - \sin B \cos B$

*18. Suppose that A, B, and C are the measures of the angles of a triangle. Prove

(a) $\tan A + \tan B + \tan C = \tan A \tan B \tan C$,

(b) $\cos^2 A + \cos^2 B + \cos^2 C + 2 \cos A \cos B \cos C = 1$.

*19. The Greeks were familiar with the addition formulas in the form of Ptolemy's Theorem: If $ABCD$ is any quadrilateral inscribed in a circle (see figure), then

$$|AB| \cdot |CD| + |AD| \cdot |BC| = |AC| \cdot |BD|.$$

Show that Ptolemy's theorem implies the formula for $\sin (\alpha + \beta)$. *Hint:* Select a quadrilateral so that $\overline{BD}$ is a diameter in a circle of diameter 1. Then show that $|AB| = \sin \alpha$, $|AD| = \cos \alpha$, $|BC| = \sin \beta$, $|CD| = \cos \beta$, and $|AC| = \sin (\alpha + \beta)$.

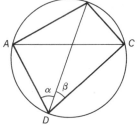

9–4. APPLICATIONS OF THE ADDITION FORMULAS

The addition formulas may be applied in a wide variety of problems. We shall consider a few examples in this section.

EXAMPLES

1. *Reduction formulas* are simple consequences of the addition formulas, for example,

$$\cos (\pi - \theta) = \cos \pi \cos \theta + \sin \pi \sin \theta$$
$$= -1 \cdot \cos \theta + 0 \cdot \sin \theta$$
$$= -\cos \theta,$$

and

$$\sin \left(\frac{3\pi}{2} + \theta\right) = \sin \frac{3\pi}{2} \cos \theta + \cos \frac{3\pi}{2} \sin \theta$$
$$= -1 \cdot \cos \theta + 0 \cdot \sin \theta$$
$$= -\cos \theta.$$

2. The problem is to find $\sin (\alpha - \beta)$ and $\cos (\alpha - \beta)$ given that $\sin \alpha = -\frac{5}{13}$ and $\cos \beta = \frac{3}{5}$, with α in the third quadrant and β in the fourth.
    We shall first find $\cos \alpha$ and $\sin \beta$. From Fig. 9–4 we see that

$$\phi(\alpha) = (-\tfrac{12}{13}, -\tfrac{5}{13}), \qquad \phi(\beta) = (\tfrac{3}{5}, -\tfrac{4}{5}),$$

therefore

$$\cos \alpha = -\tfrac{12}{13} \quad \text{and} \quad \sin \beta = -\tfrac{4}{5}.$$

Then

$$\sin (\alpha - \beta) = \sin \alpha \cos \beta - \cos \alpha \sin \beta$$
$$= (-\tfrac{5}{13})(\tfrac{3}{5}) - (-\tfrac{12}{13})(-\tfrac{4}{5})$$
$$= -\tfrac{63}{65},$$

$$\cos (\alpha - \beta) = \cos \alpha \cos \beta + \sin \alpha \sin \beta$$
$$= (-\tfrac{12}{13})(\tfrac{3}{5}) + (-\tfrac{5}{13})(-\tfrac{4}{5})$$
$$= -\tfrac{16}{65}.$$

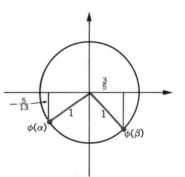

Fig. 9–4

We observe that $\sin (\alpha - \beta) < 0$ and $\cos (\alpha - \beta) < 0$, so that $\alpha - \beta$ must be in the third quadrant.

3. An important application of the addition formulas occurs in electrical circuit work. The sum of a sine and a cosine function (of the same period) is again a sine, or cosine, function with a new amplitude and graph "slid" sideways. We first consider a special numerical case. We start with the function F, given by

$$F(\theta) = 2 \sin \theta + 3 \cos \theta.$$

257

Let us multiply and divide by $\sqrt{2^2 + 3^2} = \sqrt{13}$. Then

$$F(\theta) = \sqrt{13} \left(\frac{2}{\sqrt{13}} \sin \theta + \frac{3}{\sqrt{13}} \cos \theta \right).$$

We see that the point $(2/\sqrt{13}, 3/\sqrt{13})$ is on the unit circle (Fig. 9–5), and there is a real number α, $0 < \alpha < \pi/2$, such that

$$\phi(\alpha) = \left(\frac{2}{\sqrt{13}}, \frac{3}{\sqrt{13}} \right);$$

so

$$\cos \alpha = \frac{2}{\sqrt{13}} \quad \text{and} \quad \sin \alpha = \frac{3}{\sqrt{13}}.$$

Hence

$$F(\theta) = \sqrt{13} \, (\cos \alpha \sin \theta + \sin \alpha \cos \theta)$$
$$= \sqrt{13} \sin (\theta + \alpha).$$

This is the desired result. The formula makes it easy for us to graph the function F.

We now turn to the general situation and consider

$$I(t) = A_1 \sin 2\pi f t + A_2 \cos 2\pi f t,$$

where we are thinking of t as time measured in, say, seconds. Then f is the frequency of the motion, and A_1 and A_2 are some given constants. If this is an electrical application, $I(t)$ might be the current in an electrical circuit at a given time. The numbers A_1 and A_2 will be determined by the components of the circuit. We shall suppose here that $A_1 > 0$ and $A_2 > 0$. Then

$$I(t) = \sqrt{A_1^2 + A_2^2} \left(\frac{A_1}{\sqrt{A_1^2 + A_2^2}} \sin 2\pi f t + \frac{A_2}{\sqrt{A_1^2 + A_2^2}} \cos 2\pi f t \right),$$

and there is a real number α, such that $0 < \alpha < \pi/2$ and

$$\cos \alpha = \frac{A_1}{\sqrt{A_1^2 + A_2^2}},$$

$$\sin \alpha = \frac{A_2}{\sqrt{A_1^2 + A_2^2}}.$$

(See Fig. 9–6.) Then

$$I(t) = \sqrt{A_1^2 + A_2^2} \, (\cos \alpha \sin 2\pi f t + \sin \alpha \cos 2\pi f t)$$
$$= \sqrt{A_1^2 + A_2^2} \sin (2\pi f t + \alpha),$$

where $0 < \alpha < \pi/2$.

258

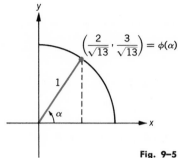

Fig. 9-5

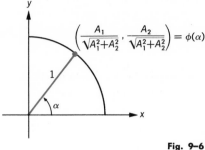

Fig. 9-6

We see that in general, *the sum of two simple harmonic motions of the same period is again a simple harmonic motion of the same period but with an amplitude which depends on the amplitudes of the summands. There is also a sideways shift, or phase shift.*

Problems

1. Establish the identities below.

(a) $\cos (\pi + \theta) = -\cos \theta$ (b) $\sin (\pi + \theta) = -\sin \theta$

(c) $\sin (3\pi/2 - \theta) = -\cos \theta$ (d) $\cos (\theta - 3\pi/2) = -\sin \theta$

(e) $\sin (\pi/2 + \theta) = \cos \theta$ (f) $\cos (\pi/2 + \theta) = -\sin \theta$

2. Given that $\sin \alpha = \frac{1}{3}$ and $\cos \beta = \frac{2}{3}$ and α and β are in quadrant I, find the following:

(a) $\sin (\alpha + \beta)$ (b) $\cos (\alpha - \beta)$

(c) $\tan (\alpha + \beta)$ (d) $\tan (\alpha - \beta)$

(e) $\sec (\alpha + \beta)$

3. Given that $\sin \alpha = u$ and $\cos \beta = v$, find the following in terms of u, v.

(a) $\sin (\alpha + \beta)$; α is in quadrant I, β in quadrant I

(b) $\tan (\alpha - \beta)$; α is in quadrant I, β in quadrant II

(c) $\tan (\alpha + \beta)$; α is in quadrant I, β in quadrant III

4. Find $\cos (\alpha + \beta)$ if $\tan \alpha = -\frac{12}{5}$ and $\sec \beta = -\frac{5}{3}$. Give all possibilities.

5. Show that $\tan (\pi/2 - \theta) = \cot \theta$.

6. Obtain a reduction formula for $\sin \left[(2k + 1)\dfrac{\pi}{2} + \theta \right]$, where k is an integer.

7. Obtain a reduction formula for $\sin (k\pi + \theta)$, where k is an integer.

8. Obtain a reduction formula for $\tan \left[(2k + 1)\dfrac{\pi}{2} - \theta \right]$, where k is an integer.

9. Express the following in terms of $\sin \theta$ and $\cos \theta$.

(a) $\sin (\pi/3 + \theta)$ (b) $\cos (\pi/4 - \theta)$

(c) $\sec (\theta - \pi/6)$ (d) $\sin (\theta - \pi/4)$

(e) $\tan (\theta - \pi/4)$

10. Express the following functions in the form $A \sin (\theta + \alpha)$. Be sure to specify α.

(a) $3 \sin \theta + 4 \cos \theta$ (b) $3 \sin \theta - 4 \cos \theta$

(c) $B \sin \theta + B \cos \theta,\ B > 0$ (d) $\sqrt{3} \sin \theta + \sqrt{7} \cos \theta$

(e) $\sqrt{3} \sin \theta - \sqrt{7} \cos \theta$ (f) $A \sin \theta + B \cos \theta;\ A, B > 0$

(g) $A \sin \theta + B \cos \theta,\ A > 0,\ B < 0$

11. Derive a formula for $\sin 2\alpha$ from $\sin (\alpha + \beta)$.

12. Derive a formula for $\cos 2\alpha$.

9–5. DOUBLE AND HALF-ANGLE FORMULAS

From the basic addition formulas we easily obtain (where $\theta = \alpha = \beta$)

$$
\begin{aligned}
\sin 2\theta &= 2 \sin \theta \cos \theta, \\
\cos 2\theta &= \cos^2 \theta - \sin^2 \theta = 1 - 2 \sin^2 \theta = 2 \cos^2 \theta - 1, \\
\tan 2\theta &= \frac{2 \tan \theta}{1 - \tan^2 \theta}.
\end{aligned}
\tag{1}
$$

From these, in turn, formulas can be derived for the functions of half an angle. Thus, setting $2\theta = x$ so that $\theta = x/2$, we have

$$\cos x = 2 \cos^2 \frac{x}{2} - 1 = 1 - 2 \sin^2 \frac{x}{2}.$$

Therefore

$$
\begin{aligned}
\cos^2 \frac{x}{2} &= \frac{1 + \cos x}{2}, \\
\sin^2 \frac{x}{2} &= \frac{1 - \cos x}{2}.
\end{aligned}
\tag{2}
$$

Taking square roots of both sides, we have

$$
\begin{aligned}
\cos \frac{x}{2} &= \pm \sqrt{\frac{1 + \cos x}{2}}, \\
\sin \frac{x}{2} &= \pm \sqrt{\frac{1 - \cos x}{2}},
\end{aligned}
\tag{3}
$$

where the sign used depends on the quadrant to which $x/2$ belongs. From

260

(3) we obtain a formula for $\tan x/2$:

$$\tan \frac{x}{2} = \pm \sqrt{\frac{1 - \cos x}{1 + \cos x}}. \tag{4}$$

However, (4) is not the best possible formula, since there is another form free from radicals and ambiguity in sign, and that is

$$\tan \frac{x}{2} = \frac{\sin \frac{x}{2}}{\cos \frac{x}{2}} = \frac{\sin \frac{x}{2} \sin \frac{x}{2}}{\cos \frac{x}{2} \sin \frac{x}{2}}$$

$$= \frac{\sin^2 \frac{x}{2}}{\frac{1}{2} \cdot 2 \sin \frac{x}{2} \cos \frac{x}{2}} = \frac{\frac{1}{2}(1 - \cos x)}{\frac{1}{2} \sin 2 \cdot \frac{x}{2}},$$

or

$$\tan \frac{x}{2} = \frac{1 - \cos x}{\sin x}. \tag{5}$$

By a similar argument, one can also obtain the following equation:

$$\tan \frac{x}{2} = \frac{\sin x}{1 + \cos x}. \tag{6}$$

Formulas (5) and (6) need not be memorized.

EXAMPLES

1. Find $\cos (\pi/12)$.
   We do this in the following manner:

$$\cos \frac{\pi}{12} = \cos \frac{1}{2} \cdot \frac{\pi}{6} = \sqrt{\frac{1 + \sqrt{3}/2}{2}} = \frac{\sqrt{2 + \sqrt{3}}}{2}.$$

The above result is perfectly satisfactory, but it may be given a different form as follows:

$$\frac{\sqrt{2 + \sqrt{3}}}{2} = \frac{\sqrt{2}\sqrt{2 + \sqrt{3}}}{\sqrt{2} \cdot 2} = \frac{\sqrt{4 + 2\sqrt{3}}}{2\sqrt{2}} = \frac{\sqrt{(1 + \sqrt{3})^2}}{2\sqrt{2}}$$

$$= \frac{1 + \sqrt{3}}{2\sqrt{2}} = \frac{\sqrt{2} + \sqrt{6}}{4}.$$

This is the answer that we would have obtained if we had used the fact that $\pi/12 = \pi/3 - \pi/4$, so that

$$\cos \frac{\pi}{12} = \cos \left(\frac{\pi}{3} - \frac{\pi}{4} \right) = \cos \frac{\pi}{3} \cos \frac{\pi}{4} + \sin \frac{\pi}{3} \sin \frac{\pi}{4}$$

$$= \frac{1}{2} \frac{\sqrt{2}}{2} + \frac{\sqrt{3}}{2} \cdot \frac{\sqrt{2}}{2} = \frac{\sqrt{2} + \sqrt{6}}{4}.$$

Most *binomial surds* (that is, of the form $a\sqrt{b} + c\sqrt{d}$, where a, b, c, d are positive integers) do not have square roots which are also binomial surds. The example is an exceptional case.

Observe that by the continued halving of an angle we could find the values of the circular functions for arbitrarily small angles and we could determine these values as accurately as we wished. From these values, using the addition formulas and some interpolation, we could, in time, construct a very accurate table of the circular functions. This is *not* the method used to construct the tables, but it does show that we are able to compute accurate tables if we so desire.

2. If $\sin \alpha = -\frac{3}{5}$ and α is in quadrant III, what is $\sin 2\alpha$? Also find $\sin \alpha/2$ if $\pi < \alpha < 3\pi/2$.

We have $\cos \alpha = -4/5$ and

$$\sin 2\alpha = 2 \cdot \frac{-3}{5} \cdot \frac{-4}{5} = \frac{24}{25}.$$

Then

$$\sin \frac{\alpha}{2} = +\sqrt{\frac{1 - (-4/5)}{2}} = \frac{3}{\sqrt{10}},$$

where the positive root is taken because $\pi/2 < \alpha/2 < 3\pi/4 < \pi$.

Problems

1. Find $\sin 2x$, $\cos 2x$, and $\tan 2x$ given the following:

  (a) $\cos x = -\frac{5}{13}$

  (b) $\sin x = -\frac{9}{41}$ and x in quadrant IV

  (c) $\csc x = \frac{3}{2}$ and x in quadrant II

  (d) $\cot x = 2$ (e) $\tan x = 1/\sqrt{2}$

  (f) $\cos x = -\frac{3}{5}$ (g) $\sin x = a$ and x in quadrant III

2. Find $\tan \pi/12$ using two different formulas.

3. Derive the formula for $\sin 2\theta$, for $\cos 2\theta$, for $\tan 2\theta$.

4. Derive the formula $\cos 2\theta = \cos^2 \theta - \sin^2 \theta$ for $\cos^2 \frac{x}{2}$, for $\sin^2 \frac{x}{2}$.

5. Derive the formula

$$\tan \frac{x}{2} = \frac{\sin x}{1 + \cos x}.$$

6. Show that $\cos 3x = 4\cos^3 x - 3\cos x$.

7. Obtain a formula for $\sin 3x$ in terms of $\sin x$.

262

8. Show that the following are identities.

(a) $2 - 2 \tan x \cot 2x = \sec^2 x$

(b) $\dfrac{1 - \cos 2\alpha}{1 + \cos 2\alpha} = \tan^2 \alpha$

(c) $\tan \left(\dfrac{\pi}{4} + \theta \right) = \dfrac{1 + \sin 2\theta}{\cos 2\theta}$

(d) $\dfrac{\sin^3 x + \cos^3 x}{\sin x + \cos x} = 1 - \dfrac{1}{2} \sin 2x$

(e) $\tan 3x - \tan x = 2 \sin x \sec 3x$

(f) $\cos 2x = \cos^4 x - \sin^4 x$

(g) $\dfrac{1 + \sin 2\theta}{1 + \cos 2\theta} = \frac{1}{2}(1 + \tan \theta)^2$

(h) $\dfrac{2 \tan x}{1 + \tan^2 x} = \sin 2x$

(i) $\dfrac{2 \cot x}{1 + \cot^2 x} = \sin 2x$

(j) $\dfrac{\cot \frac{1}{2}x - \tan \frac{1}{2}x}{\cot \frac{1}{2}x + \tan \frac{1}{2}x} = \cos x$

(k) $\dfrac{\sin 2\alpha}{\sin \alpha} - \dfrac{\cos 2\alpha}{\cos \alpha} = \sec \alpha$

(l) $\dfrac{\sin 2\alpha}{\sin \alpha} + \dfrac{\cos 2\alpha}{\cos \alpha} = \dfrac{2 \sin 3\alpha}{\sin 2\alpha}$

(m) $\csc 2\theta - \cot 2\theta = \tan \theta$

(n) $\csc 2\theta + \cot 2\theta = \cot \theta$

(o) $\cot \frac{1}{2}\theta = \dfrac{1}{\csc \theta - \cot \theta}$

(p) $\tan \frac{1}{2}\theta = \dfrac{1}{\csc \theta + \cot \theta}$

9. Determine $\sin (\pi/8)$, using a half-angle formula.

10. Find all the functions of $x/2$ given that $\sin x = \frac{3}{4}$ and x is in quadrant II.

*11. If $A + B + C = \pi$, show that the following is true.

(a) $\sin A + \sin B + \sin C = 4 \cos (A/2) \cos (B/2) \cos (C/2)$

(b) $\sin A + \sin B - \sin C = 4 \sin (A/2) \sin (B/2) \cos (C/2)$

[*Hint*: $\frac{1}{2}A = \frac{1}{2}\pi - \frac{1}{2}(B + C)$; and work with the right-hand side.]

9-6. COMPLEX NUMBERS

In this section we use the addition formulas to obtain a graphical interpretation of the product of two complex numbers. Recall that addition of complex numbers had a simple geometric representation in terms of the parallelogram law.

Our first step in obtaining an interpretation of the product will be to define the *polar form of a complex number.*

Suppose that

$$z = x + iy,$$

where x and y are real, is any complex number different from 0. We will let P be the point representing z in the complex plane (Fig. 9–7), and P_1 be the intersection of the ray $\overrightarrow{OP}$ with the unit circle. Then there is a real number θ (in fact, infinitely many of them) such that $\phi(\theta) = P_1$. Let $r = \sqrt{x^2 + y^2}$. Observe that $r = |OP|$.

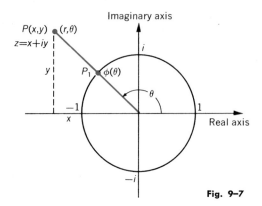

Fig. 9–7

DEFINITION 9–2

> With the notation as above, the numbers r and θ are *polar coordinates*†
> of $P(x, y)$, and are written as the ordered pair (r, θ). If $|OP| = 0$, then its
> polar coordinates are $(0, \theta)$, where θ is arbitrary.

Remark

Because θ (for $r \neq 0$) is determined only to a multiple of 2π, each point has
infinitely many polar coordinates, $\theta + 2\pi k$, where k is an integer.

For the complex number $x + iy$, we have

$$x = r \cos \theta, \qquad y = r \sin \theta$$

and

$$x + iy = r(\cos \theta + i \sin \theta). \tag{1}$$

DEFINITION 9–3

> With notation as above, the *polar form* of the complex number
> $z = x + iy$ is given by‡

$$z = x + iy = r(\cos \theta + i \sin \theta).$$

---

† See Chapter 13 for a full discussion of polar coordinates.

‡ In reading other books you may encounter the shorthand form "cis θ" which stands for

$$\cos \theta + i \sin \theta.$$

In more advanced mathematics it is shown that the exponential function, e^z, where
$e = 2.7182\ldots$, which we have defined only for real z, can have its domain extended to
all complex numbers. When this extension is made, we find that

$$e^{i\theta} = \cos \theta + i \sin \theta.$$

This astonishing result (known as Euler's formula) implies, for example, that

$$e^{i\pi} = \cos \pi + i \sin \pi = -1.$$

264

The absolute value of a complex number, $z = x + yi$, is the number

$$|x + yi| = \sqrt{x^2 + y^2}.$$

Since for any $P(x, y)$, the number $r = \sqrt{x^2 + y^2}$, we can conclude that $|x + yi| = r$. The number r is called the *absolute value*, or *modulus*, of z. The number θ (not unique) is called an *amplitude*, or *argument*, of z.

EXAMPLE 1

To put $-2 + 2\sqrt{3}\,i$ in polar form, we first compute the modulus

$$r = |(-2 + 2\sqrt{3}\,i)| = \sqrt{4 + 12} = 4.$$

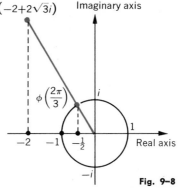

Then

$$-2 + 2\sqrt{3}\,i = 4\left(-\frac{1}{2} + \frac{\sqrt{3}}{2}i\right),$$

and from Fig. 9–8 we observe that

$$\phi\left(\frac{2\pi}{3}\right) = \left(-\frac{1}{2}, \frac{\sqrt{3}}{2}\right),$$

therefore

$$-2 + 2\sqrt{3}\,i = 4\left(\cos\frac{2\pi}{3} + i\sin\frac{2\pi}{3}\right).$$

Fig. 9–8

   Let us now use the polar form to consider the product of two complex numbers,

$$z_1 = r_1(\cos\theta_1 + i\sin\theta_1)$$

and

$$z_2 = r_2(\cos\theta_2 + i\sin\theta_2).$$

Then

$$\begin{aligned}
z_1 z_2 &= r_1 r_2(\cos\theta_1 + i\sin\theta_1)(\cos\theta_2 + i\sin\theta_2) \\
&= r_1 r_2[(\cos\theta_1\cos\theta_2 - \sin\theta_1\sin\theta_2) \\
&\qquad + i(\sin\theta_1\cos\theta_2 + \cos\theta_1\sin\theta_2)] \\
&= r_1 r_2[\cos(\theta_1 + \theta_2) + i\sin(\theta_1 + \theta_2)].
\end{aligned}$$

We state this important result as Theorem 9–1.

THEOREM 9–1

   The absolute value of the product of two complex numbers is the product of their absolute values. An amplitude of their product is the sum of their amplitudes.

265

Corollary

The absolute value of the quotient of two complex numbers is the quotient of their absolute values. An amplitude of their quotient is the difference of their amplitudes:

$$\frac{r_1(\cos \theta_1 + i \sin \theta_1)}{r_2(\cos \theta_2 + i \sin \theta_2)} = \frac{r_1}{r_2}[\cos (\theta_1 - \theta_2) + i \sin (\theta_1 - \theta_2)].$$

If we let the quotient be $r(\cos \theta + i \sin \theta)$, then

$$r_1(\cos \theta_1 + i \sin \theta_1) = [r(\cos \theta + i \sin \theta)][r_2(\cos \theta_2 + i \sin \theta_2)],$$

and Theorem 9–1 applies. The details are left to the reader.

Observe the following special case:

$$\frac{1}{r(\cos \theta + i \sin \theta)} = \frac{1}{r}(\cos \theta - i \sin \theta).$$

EXAMPLE 2

Compute the product $(-1 + \sqrt{3}\,i)(2\sqrt{3} + 2i)$ using both rectangular and polar forms; then compare the results.

In rectangular form we have

$$(-1 + \sqrt{3}\,i)(2\sqrt{3} + 2i) = -2\sqrt{3} - 2i + 6i - 2\sqrt{3} = -4\sqrt{3} + 4i.$$

Since

$$-1 + \sqrt{3}\,i = 2\left(-\frac{1}{2} + \frac{\sqrt{3}}{2}i\right) = 2\left(\cos\frac{2\pi}{3} + i \sin\frac{2\pi}{3}\right),$$

and

$$2\sqrt{3} + 2i = 4\left(\frac{\sqrt{3}}{2} + \frac{1}{2}i\right) = 4\left(\cos\frac{\pi}{6} + i \sin\frac{\pi}{6}\right),$$

we have, in polar form,

$$(-1 + \sqrt{3}\,i)(2\sqrt{3} + 2i) = 2\left(\cos\frac{2\pi}{3} + i \sin\frac{2\pi}{3}\right) \cdot 4\left(\cos\frac{\pi}{6} + i \sin\frac{\pi}{6}\right)$$

$$= 8\left[\cos\left(\frac{4\pi}{6} + \frac{\pi}{6}\right) + i \sin\left(\frac{4\pi}{6} + \frac{\pi}{6}\right)\right]$$

$$= 8\left(\cos\frac{5\pi}{6} + i \sin\frac{5\pi}{6}\right) = 8\left(-\frac{\sqrt{3}}{2} + \frac{1}{2}i\right)$$

$$= -4\sqrt{3} + 4i.$$

Theorem 9–1 is of particular interest when the factors are equal. We have

$$[r(\cos \theta + i \sin \theta)]^2 = r^2(\cos 2\theta + i \sin 2\theta),$$

266

and, by an inductive argument,† we get, for any positive integer n,

$$[r(\cos \theta + i \sin \theta)]^n = r^n(\cos n\theta + i \sin n\theta). \tag{2}$$

Formula (2) is known as de Moivre's Theorem.‡ The main application of this theorem is its use "in reverse" to find roots of complex numbers. Suppose that $z = r(\cos \theta + i \sin \theta)$ is any given complex number, and n is a positive integer. We seek a complex number $R(\cos \varphi + i \sin \varphi)$ such that

$$[R(\cos \varphi + i \sin \varphi)]^n = r(\cos \theta + i \sin \theta).$$

Clearly there will be such a number if and only if $R^n = r$ and $n\varphi = \theta + 2\pi k$, where k is any integer.

In other words, we must have

$$R = \sqrt[n]{r} \quad \text{and} \quad \varphi = \frac{\theta + 2\pi k}{n}. \tag{3}$$

Observe that we get distinct complex numbers $R(\cos \varphi + i \sin \varphi)$ if $k = 0, 1, 2, \ldots, n - 1$. For larger integral values of k, the numbers recur. Observe also that by the fundamental theorem of algebra, a complex number A can have, at most, n roots; these roots are the solutions of the equation $z^n - A = 0$ which is of nth degree. Since formula (3) gives n different roots, it must give all of them. We state these results as Theorem 9-2.

THEOREM 9-2

The complex number $r(\cos \theta + i \sin \theta)$, $r > 0$, has n nth roots given by

$$\sqrt[n]{r}\left(\cos \frac{\theta + 2\pi k}{n} + i \sin \frac{\theta + 2\pi k}{n}\right), \qquad k = 0, 1, \ldots, n - 1.$$

EXAMPLES

3. Find the cube roots of -1. We have

$$-1 = 1(\cos \pi + i \sin \pi);$$

hence the cube roots are

$$\sqrt[3]{1}\left(\cos \frac{\pi}{3} + i \sin \frac{\pi}{3}\right) = 1\left(\frac{1}{2} + \frac{i\sqrt{3}}{2}\right) = \frac{1 + i\sqrt{3}}{2},$$

$$\sqrt[3]{1}\left(\cos \frac{\pi + 2\pi}{3} + i \sin \frac{\pi + 2\pi}{3}\right) = 1(-1 + 0) = -1,$$

$$\sqrt[3]{1}\left(\cos \frac{\pi + 4\pi}{3} + i \sin \frac{\pi + 4\pi}{3}\right) = 1\left(\frac{1}{2} + i\frac{-\sqrt{3}}{2}\right) = \frac{1 - i\sqrt{3}}{2}.$$

† For a discussion of induction see Appendix B.
‡ Abraham de Moivre (1667–1754) was an English mathematician of French extraction.

267

4. Find the square roots of i.

We have

$$i = 1\left(\cos\frac{\pi}{2} + i\sin\frac{\pi}{2}\right),$$

and the square roots of i are

$$\sqrt{1}\left(\cos\frac{\pi}{4} + i\sin\frac{\pi}{4}\right) = \frac{1}{\sqrt{2}} + i\frac{1}{\sqrt{2}} = \frac{1+i}{\sqrt{2}},$$

$$\sqrt{1}\left(\cos\frac{5\pi}{4} + i\sin\frac{5\pi}{4}\right) = \frac{-1}{\sqrt{2}} + i\frac{-1}{\sqrt{2}} = \frac{-1-i}{\sqrt{2}}.$$

Problems

1. Find the polar forms of the following complex numbers. Graph each to check.

   (a) 3

   (b) $-2i$

   (c) $-\sqrt{3} - i$

   (d) $\sqrt{2} - \sqrt{2}\,i$

   (e) $-1 - i$

   (f) $\frac{-1}{2} + \frac{\sqrt{3}}{2}\,i$

2. Express the following in the form $x + yi$ by evaluating the circular functions.

   (a) $2\left(\cos\frac{3\pi}{4} + i\sin\frac{3\pi}{4}\right)$

   (b) $2\left(\cos\frac{11\pi}{4} + i\sin\frac{11\pi}{4}\right)$

   (c) $4\left(\cos\frac{4\pi}{3} + i\sin\frac{4\pi}{3}\right)$

   (d) $2\left(\cos\frac{3\pi}{2} + i\sin\frac{3\pi}{2}\right)$

   (e) $1\left(\cos\frac{5\pi}{6} + i\sin\frac{5\pi}{6}\right)$

   (f) $8(\cos\pi + i\sin\pi)$

3. Plot the following pairs of complex numbers and find each product. Put them in polar form and obtain the product using Theorem 9-1. Plot the product and check graphically.

   (a) $(1 + i)i$

   (b) $(-\sqrt{3} + i)(2 - 2\sqrt{3}\,i)$

   (c) $(-\sqrt{3} + i)(-\sqrt{3} - i)$

   (d) $(2 + 2i)(-2 + 2i)$

   (e) $(-1 + \sqrt{3}\,i)^2$

4. Give, in polar form, a complex number which when multiplied by

$$2[\cos(\pi/3) + i\sin(\pi/3)]$$

gives a product equal to 1.

5. What is the formula for

$$\frac{r_1(\cos\theta_1 - i\sin\theta_1)}{r_2(\cos\theta_2 - i\sin\theta_2)}?$$

Prove your assertion.

268

6. Obtain the following powers:

(a) $\left[2\left(\cos\frac{\pi}{8} + i\sin\frac{\pi}{8} \right) \right]^4$

(b) $\left[2\left(\cos\frac{\pi}{12} + i\sin\frac{\pi}{12} \right) \right]^6$

(c) $\left[1\left(\cos\frac{2\pi}{3} + i\sin\frac{2\pi}{3} \right) \right]^3$

(d) $\left[\sqrt{2}\left(\cos\frac{\pi}{4} + i\sin\frac{\pi}{4} \right) \right]^4$

7. Find the two square roots of the following: (a) $-4i$ (b) $1 + \sqrt{3}\,i$

8. Find the three cube roots of the following: (a) 1 (b) -8

9. If $|z| = 1$ and the complex number z with its three cube roots are plotted, what is the geometric relation between z and its three roots? Between z and its n nth roots?

10. Solve these equations:
    (a) $z^3 + i = 0$ (b) $z^6 + 8 = 0$ (c) $z^2 + 1 + i = 0$

SUMMARY

The principal identities and formulas are listed, for reference, below. You should be able to derive all of them.

A. Elementary identities

$$\tan\theta = \frac{\sin\theta}{\cos\theta} = \frac{1}{\cot\theta}, \qquad \cot\theta = \frac{\cos\theta}{\sin\theta} = \frac{1}{\tan\theta},$$

$$\sec\theta = \frac{1}{\cos\theta}, \qquad \csc\theta = \frac{1}{\sin\theta},$$

$$\sin^2\theta + \cos^2\theta = 1, \qquad 1 + \tan^2\theta = \sec^2\theta, \qquad 1 + \cot^2\theta = \csc^2\theta.$$

B. The addition formulas

$$\sin(\alpha \pm \beta) = \sin\alpha\cos\beta \pm \cos\alpha\sin\beta,$$

$$\cos(\alpha \pm \beta) = \cos\alpha\cos\beta \mp \sin\alpha\sin\beta,$$

$$\tan(\alpha \pm \beta) = \frac{\tan\alpha \pm \tan\beta}{1 \mp \tan\alpha\tan\beta}.$$

C. Double and half-angle formulas

$$\sin 2\theta = 2\sin\theta\cos\theta,$$

$$\cos 2\theta = \cos^2\theta - \sin^2\theta = 2\cos^2\theta - 1 = 1 - 2\sin^2\theta,$$

$$\tan 2\theta = \frac{2\tan\theta}{1 - \tan^2\theta},$$

$$\sin\frac{\theta}{2} = \pm\sqrt{\frac{1 - \cos\theta}{2}}, \qquad \cos\frac{\theta}{2} = \pm\sqrt{\frac{1 + \cos\theta}{2}},$$

$$\tan\frac{\theta}{2} = \pm\sqrt{\frac{1 - \cos\theta}{1 + \cos\theta}} = \frac{1 - \cos\theta}{\sin\theta} = \frac{\sin\theta}{1 + \cos\theta}.$$

These identities and formulas were used in the chapter in the following ways:

1. To establish new identities from the elementary ones.
2. To find exact values of the circular functions at points other than 0, $\pi/6$, $\pi/4$, $\pi/3$, $\pi/2$, for example at $\pi/12$.
3. To obtain reduction formulas, for example $\sin(\pi + \theta) = -\sin\theta$.
4. To obtain functions of 2θ and $\theta/2$ when a function of θ is known.
5. To add two simple harmonic motions of the same period and obtain a simple harmonic motion.
6. To find powers and roots of complex numbers using de Moivre's theorem.

Review Problems

1. Establish the following identities and determine the domain of validity.

(a) $\dfrac{\csc^2\theta}{\csc^2\theta - 1} = \sec^2\theta$

(b) $\dfrac{1 + \tan x}{1 + \cot x} = \tan x$

(c) $\dfrac{1 - \cos 2\theta}{\sin 2\theta} = \tan\theta$

(d) $\dfrac{\sin 2x}{\sin x} - \dfrac{\cos 2x}{\cos x} = \sec x$

(e) $\sin\theta\left(\dfrac{\cot\theta}{\sec\theta} + \csc\theta\right) = \cos^2\theta + 1$

(f) $\sin^3 y \cos y - \sin^5 y \cos y = \sin^3 y \cos^3 y$

2. Give another, possibly simpler, form for each of the following:

(a) $1 + \cot^2\theta$ (b) $2\sin x \cos x$ (c) $\cos\left(\dfrac{\pi}{2} + \theta\right)$

(d) $\sin(\pi - \theta)$ (e) $\cos^2 x - \sin^2 x$ (f) $\dfrac{1 - \cos x}{\sin x}$

3. Given that $\sin\alpha = \frac{1}{3}$, with α in quadrant I, and $\cos\beta = -\frac{2}{3}$, with β in quadrant II, find $\cos(\alpha + \beta)$ and $\sin(\alpha + \beta)$.

4. Given that $\sin\alpha = \frac{3}{5}$, with α in quadrant II, and $\cos\beta = \frac{1}{2}$, with β in quadrant IV, find $\cos(\alpha - \beta)$ and $\tan(\alpha + \beta)$.

5. What relation does one get from the addition formula for $\cos(\alpha - \beta)$ if $\alpha = \beta$?

6. Determine $\tan(\pi/8)$ using a half-angle formula.

7. Prove that $\csc\theta \neq \cot\theta$ for any real number for which the functions are defined.

8. If $\sin\theta = \sqrt{5}/3$, and θ is in quadrant I, find all the functions of 2θ.

9. What is $\cos(\alpha - \beta)$ if α is the complement of β?

10. Express each function below in the form $A[\sin(\theta + \alpha)]$, where A is a real number and $-\pi/2 < \alpha < \pi/2$.

(a) $f(\theta) = 2\sin\theta + 2\cos\theta$ (b) $g(\theta) = 3\sin\theta + 4\cos\theta$
(c) $T(\theta) = 3\sin\theta - 4\cos\theta$

11. Determine the amplitude and period of a function f, where

$$f(\theta) = \sin \theta + \sqrt{3} \cos \theta.$$

Sketch a graph of f over an interval of one full period.

12. Establish the following identities:

(a) $\dfrac{1}{1 + \sin^2 2\theta} = \dfrac{\csc^2 2\theta}{2 + \cot^2 2\theta}$

(b) $\dfrac{\cos (\alpha + \beta)}{\cos (\alpha - \beta)} = \dfrac{1 - \tan \alpha \tan \beta}{1 + \tan \alpha \tan \beta}$

(c) $\dfrac{\sin 3\theta}{\sec 2\theta} - \dfrac{\cos 3\theta}{\csc 2\theta} = \sin \theta$

(d) $(\sin x + \sec x)^2 + (\cos x + \csc x)^2 = (1 + \sec x \csc x)^2$

(e) $\sin 4\theta = 2 \sin 2\theta - 8 \sin^3 \theta \cos \theta$

(f) $\cos^2 \theta + \cos^2 (\tfrac{2}{3}\pi + \theta) + \cos^2 (\tfrac{2}{3}\pi - \theta) = \tfrac{3}{2}$

(g) $\tan (\theta + \pi/3) \tan (\theta - \pi/3) + \tan \theta \tan (\theta + \pi/3)$
$\qquad + \tan (\theta - \pi/3) \tan \theta = -3$

(h) $(\cos \theta + \sin \theta)^4 + (\cos \theta - \sin \theta)^4 = 3 - \cos 4\theta$

13. The right triangle ABC is inscribed in a semicircle of radius a. Show that the sides shown in the figure have the lengths indicated, and then derive the formula for $\sin 2\alpha$.

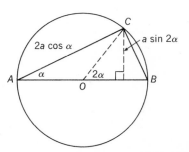

14. Write each complex number below in polar form.

(a) $2 - 2i$ (b) $\sqrt{3} + i$ (c) 4 (d) $-5i$

15. The polar coordinates of a complex number z are $(3, 3\pi/4)$.

(a) Write z in polar form.

(b) Write z in the form $a + bi$, where a and b are real.

(c) What is the absolute value of z?

(d) What are some other polar coordinates of z?

16. Find the product of the complex numbers z_1 and z_2, given that

$$z_1 = 3 \left(\cos \frac{\pi}{2} + i \sin \frac{\pi}{2} \right) \quad \text{and} \quad z_2 = 5 \left(\cos \frac{\pi}{6} + i \sin \frac{\pi}{6} \right).$$

271

17. Write the following in the form $a + bi$.

(a) $10\left(\cos\dfrac{\pi}{4} + i\sin\dfrac{\pi}{4}\right)$

(b) $7\left(\cos\dfrac{3\pi}{2} + i\sin\dfrac{3\pi}{2}\right)$

(c) $2\left(\cos\dfrac{5\pi}{6} + i\sin\dfrac{5\pi}{6}\right)$

(d) $23(\cos 2\pi + i\sin 2\pi)$

18. Find the 4 fourth roots of $16i$.

19. Determine the complex number z such that

$$z\left(\cos\frac{5\pi}{4} + i\sin\frac{5\pi}{4}\right) = 1.$$

*20. Given that $A + B + C = \pi$ show that

$$\cos A + \cos B + \cos C = 1 + 4\sin\frac{A}{2}\sin\frac{B}{2}\sin\frac{C}{2}.$$

*21. Triangle ABC, with angles of measures α, β, γ, is inscribed in a circle of radius r with center O. (See figure.) Show that

$$c = a\cos\beta + b\cos\alpha.$$

Use this result and $\sin\gamma = \sin(\alpha + \beta)$ to derive the addition formula for $\sin(\alpha + \beta)$. [*Hint:* Express a, b, and c in terms of r and α, β, and γ.]

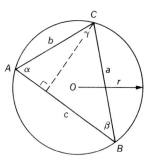

HISTORICAL NOTE

Leonard Euler (1707–1783)
(Courtesy British Museum)

Today spherical trigonometry (see the Historical Note of Chapter 7) is a specialized subject seldom studied in schools. Once one has mastered the properties of the circular functions, their application to spherical trigonometry can be learned when needed. It has turned out that these *functions*, considered simply as functions and without regard for their use in the solution of triangles, have become indispensable. With the rise of science as a major discipline, beginning in the seventeenth century, and the application of calculus to the solution of physical and mathematical problems, the universality of the circular functions gradually became apparent. It is a matter for wonder that these few functions have so many uses. The key to this universality is the fact that they are, in some sense, the simplest periodic functions, and that every periodic function can be represented in terms of them by means of Fourier's theorem.

The analytical theory of the circular functions began during the period of the development of calculus and received a strong impetus from the work of Leonhard Euler (1707–1783), who showed that the elementary functions, including the circular functions, can be extended to have domains which include complex numbers. Thus it can be shown that it makes sense to speak of the exponential functions, e^z, with *complex exponents z*. In particular, one has Euler's beautiful formula, $e^{i\theta} = \cos \theta + i \sin \theta$, where $i^2 = -1$ and θ is a real number.

273

CIRCULAR
AND TRIGONOMETRIC

10

INVERSE FUNCTIONS EQUATIONS

10-1. INTRODUCTION

The concept of an inverse function has been discussed in Chapter 6. For example, the function $\log_a$ is the inverse of the exponential function with base a.

Another example is supplied by the square-root function. Consider first the squaring function f, with domain R, given by

$$f(x) = x^2.$$

The range of f is the interval $[0, \infty)$. Since for each real number $b > 0$ there are two real numbers a such that $a^2 = b$, it is necessary to restrict attention to *one* of them in order to get a unique inverse function. We then select the *principal value*, that is, the *positive* number whose square is b. See Fig. 10–1(a).

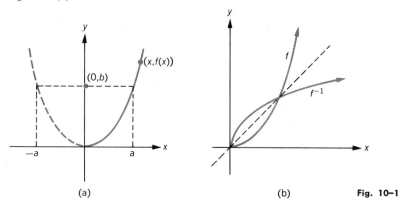

(a)   (b)   **Fig. 10–1**

When we restrict the domain of f to the interval $[0, \infty)$, then the inverse function is the square-root function

$$f^{-1}(x) = \sqrt{x}.\dagger$$

The graphs of f and f^{-1} are shown in Fig. 10–1(b). Observe that the graph of the inverse function is obtained by "reflecting" the graph of f in the line $y = x$.

Let us recall the definition of inverse functions in general. Suppose that (Fig. 10–2) X and Y are sets and $X \xrightarrow{f} Y$ is a *one-to-one* mapping of X *onto* Y. Then for each y in Y there is a unique x in X such that $y = f(x)$. This defines the inverse function, f^{-1}, that is

$$x = f^{-1}(y).$$

_____

† Do not confuse the "-1" in f^{-1} with an exponent. The notation f^{-1} stands for the whole function. In some ways, however, it acts like an exponent. For example, $f(f^{-1}(y)) = y$ and $f^{-1}(f(x)) = x$.

276

In this chapter we shall consider the possibility of inverses to the circular functions sine, cosine, and tangent. (We shall not define the inverses of secant, cosecant, and cotangent, although it is possible to do so.) Then we shall make a brief application to the solution of equations involving the circular functions.

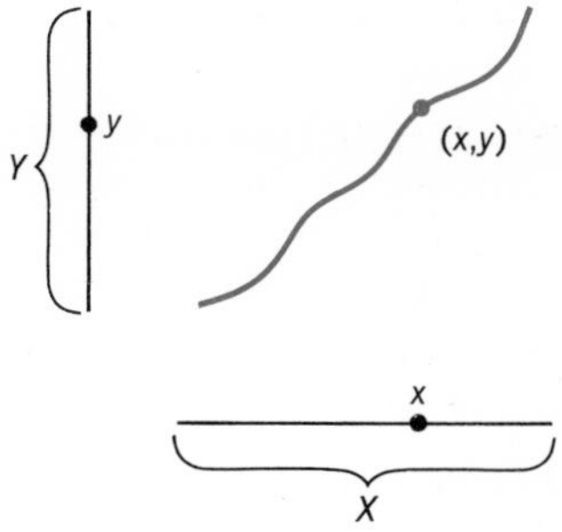

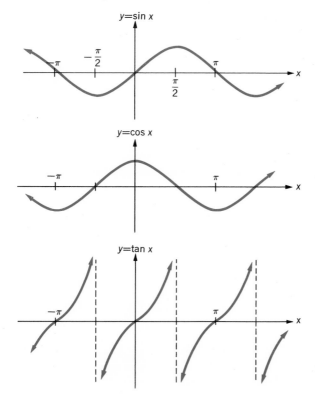

Fig. 10-2

10-2. THE INVERSE CIRCULAR FUNCTIONS

Recall that the graphs of sine, cosine, and tangent appear as in Fig. 10-3. It should be clear from the graphs of the functions that none of the functions are one-to-one mappings. In order to discuss the inverses of the circular functions, we must restrict the domain of the functions so that in the restricted domain the functions will be one-to-one mappings. In the case of the sine function, we note that in the interval $[-\pi/2, \pi/2]$ the mapping is one-to-one and the sine has its full range of values on this restricted domain.

Fig. 10-3

For convenience, we make the following definitions.

DEFINITION 10-1

The *Sine function* (capital S is used to distinguish it from the ordinary sine function) is the function Sin defined by

$$\text{Sin } \theta = \sin \theta \qquad \text{for} \qquad -\frac{\pi}{2} \le \theta \le \frac{\pi}{2}.$$

DEFINITION 10-2

The inverse of the Sine function is called the *Arcsine* function and is abbreviated to Arcsin (or Sin^{-1}).† If $y = \text{Sin } \theta$, then $\theta = \text{Arcsin } y$ (or $\theta = \text{Sin}^{-1} y$).

The graphs of $y = \text{Sin } \theta$ and $\theta = \text{Sin}^{-1} y$ are shown in Fig. 10–4 (a) and (b).

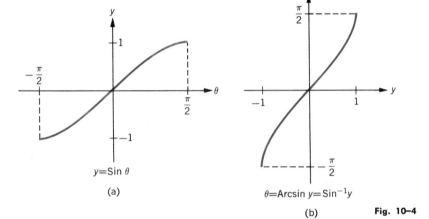

y=Sin θ

(a)

θ=Arcsin y=Sin⁻¹y

(b)

Fig. 10–4

Arcsin y is often interpreted as "the number (or arc) whose sine is y." On the other hand, if *any* number whose sine is y is intended, one often sees "arcsin y" rather than "Arcsin y."

In a similar manner, we get a unique inverse to $y = \cos \theta$ if we restrict θ to the interval $0 \le \theta \le \pi$.

DEFINITION 10-3

The Cosine function is the function Cos defined by

$$\text{Cos } \theta = \cos \theta \qquad \text{for} \qquad 0 \le \theta \le \pi.$$

---

† Both notations, *Arcsin* and *Sin*⁻¹, are used by mathematicians and so we shall use both in this text. However, the Arc-notation is less likely to lead to confusion.

The inverse of Cos is the Arccos function (also denoted by Cos^{-1}). If $y = \text{Cos}\,\theta$, then

$$\theta = \text{Arccos}\,y = \text{Cos}^{-1}\,y.$$

The graphs of $y = \text{Cos}\,\theta$ and $\theta = \text{Cos}^{-1}\,y$ are shown in Fig. 10–5.

The mapping is one-to-one from $[0, \pi]$ to $[-1, 1]$. We have

$$0 \leq \text{Arccos}\,y \leq \pi$$

or

$$0 \leq \text{Cos}^{-1}\,y \leq \pi.$$

Similarly, by restricting the domain of the tangent function, we get a unique inverse to the tangent function.

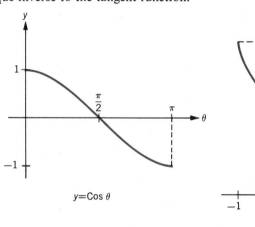

$y = \text{Cos}\,\theta$

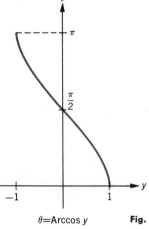

$\theta = \text{Arccos}\,y$ **Fig. 10–5**

DEFINITION 10–4

The Tangent function is the function Tan defined by

$$\text{Tan}\,\theta = \tan\theta \quad \text{for} \quad -\frac{\pi}{2} < \theta < \frac{\pi}{2}.$$

The inverse of Tan is the function Arctan (also denoted by Tan^{-1}). Then if $y = \text{Tan}\,\theta$, $\theta = \text{Arctan}\,y = \text{Tan}^{-1}\,y$.

The graphs of $y = \text{Tan}\,\theta$ and $\theta = \text{Arctan}\,y$ are shown in Fig. 10–6.

In the same manner, one *can* define inverses of the other circular functions, but it is not actually necessary to do so. For example, one might define the inverse cosecant as follows. Set

$$\text{Csc}\,\theta = \csc\theta = t, \quad \text{for} \quad -\frac{\pi}{2} \leq \theta < \frac{\pi}{2}, \quad \theta \neq 0;$$

then

$$\text{Sin}\,\theta = \frac{1}{t}, \quad \text{and} \quad \theta = \text{Arccsc}\,t = \text{Arcsin}\frac{1}{t}.$$

279

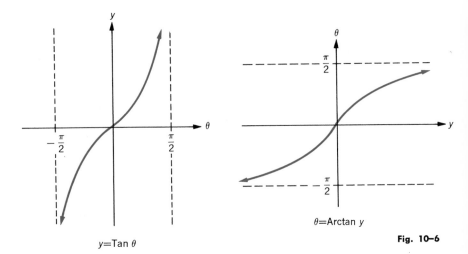

$y=\text{Tan }\theta$

$\theta=\text{Arctan }y$

Fig. 10-6

Thus it is not necessary to define the other inverse functions. The inverses of the sine, cosine, and tangent will suffice. Furthermore, not all mathematicians agree on the definitions for Csc^{-1} and Sec^{-1}. For Cot^{-1} there is a natural choice. See Problem 8 below.

Remark

In many situations, one wishes to discuss all possible values for inverse relations of the circular functions, not necessarily just the ones above which are the principal values. When this is the case, the capital letter is not used and one simply writes arcsin, arccos, and arctan. Then, for example, one would have

$$\arcsin \frac{1}{2} = \frac{\pi}{6}, \quad \frac{5\pi}{6}, \quad \frac{\pi}{6} \pm 2\pi, \quad \frac{5\pi}{6} \pm 2\pi, \quad \text{etc.,}$$

$$\arccos\left(-\frac{1}{2}\right) = \frac{2\pi}{3}, \quad \frac{4\pi}{3}, \quad \frac{2\pi}{3} \pm 2\pi, \quad \frac{4\pi}{3} \pm 2\pi, \quad \text{etc.,}$$

$$\arctan(-1) = \frac{3\pi}{4} \pm \pi, \quad \frac{3\pi}{4} \pm 2\pi, \quad \text{etc.}$$

The numbers Arcsin θ, Arccos θ, and Arctan θ are just the selected *principal values* of the relations arcsin θ, arccos θ, and arctan θ.

EXAMPLES

$$\text{Arcsin } \frac{1}{2} = \text{Sin}^{-1}\frac{1}{2} = \frac{\pi}{6},$$

$$\text{Arcsin } \frac{1}{-2} = \text{Sin}^{-1}\frac{-1}{2} = -\frac{\pi}{6},$$

$$\text{Arctan } 1 = \text{Tan}^{-1} 1 = \frac{\pi}{4},$$

$$\text{Arccos}\left(-\frac{1}{2}\right) = \text{Cos}^{-1}\frac{-1}{2} = \frac{2\pi}{3}.$$

Problems

1. Compute the following:
   - (a) $\text{Sin}^{-1} 1$
   - (b) $\text{Cos}^{-1} 1$
   - (c) $\text{Arcsin} (\sqrt{3}/2)$
   - (d) $\text{Arccos} (-\sqrt{3}/2)$
   - (e) $\text{Tan}^{-1} (-1)$
   - (f) $\text{Tan}^{-1} (-\sqrt{3})$
   - (g) $\text{Cos}^{-1} (-1/\sqrt{2})$
   - (h) $\text{Sin}^{-1} (-1/\sqrt{2})$
   - (i) $\text{Sin}^{-1} (0.4820)$
   - (j) $\text{Arccos} (0.8888)$
   - (k) $\text{Arctan} (1.5)$
   - (l) $\text{Tan}^{-1} (0.5)$
   - (m) $\text{Tan}^{-1} (-2)$
   - (n) $\text{Arccos} (-1)$
   - (o) $\text{Arcsin} (-\sqrt{3}/2)$
   - (p) $\text{Tan}^{-1} (-1/\sqrt{3})$

2. Give all possible values of the following:
   - (a) $\arcsin - 1$
   - (b) $\arctan \sqrt{3}$
   - (c) $\arccos (-\sqrt{3}/2)$
   - (d) $\arccos 1/\sqrt{2}$
   - (e) $\arcsin (-0.1234)$
   - (f) $\arctan (-2)$

3. What are the following?
   - (a) $\text{Arcsin} \left(\sin \dfrac{5\pi}{4} \right)$
   - (b) $\text{Arccos} \left(\cos \dfrac{\pi}{3} \right)$
   - (c) $\text{Arctan} \left(\tan \dfrac{2\pi}{3} \right)$
   - (d) $\text{Arccos} \left(\sin \dfrac{-5\pi}{6} \right)$

4. Which statements below are true and which are false?
   - (a) $\text{Sin}^{-1} 1 + \text{Sin}^{-1} (-1) = 0$
   - (b) $\text{Cos}^{-1} 1 + \text{Cos}^{-1} (-1) = 0$
   - (c) $\text{Sin}^{-1} x = -\text{Sin}^{-1} (-x)$ for all x in the domain of Sin^{-1}
   - (d) $\text{Arccos} x = \text{Arccos} (-x)$ for all x in the domain of Arccos

5. Why would we not want to define $\text{Cos}^{-1} z$ such that
$$-\frac{\pi}{2} \leq \text{Cos}^{-1} z \leq \frac{\pi}{2} ?$$

6. If $\theta = \text{Arccos} t$, express t as a function of θ. What is the domain of the function you have written?

7. If $r = \frac{1}{2} \text{Sin}^{-1} u$, express u as a function of r. What is the domain of u as a function of r?

8. Define $\text{Cot}^{-1} y$.

9. Solve
$$3y = 4 - 2 \text{Cos}^{-1} x$$
   for x in terms of y. What is the domain of the function of y?

10. Solve
$$a^2 = b^2 + c^2 - 2bc \text{Cos} A$$
    for A.

11. For what real number x is $\text{Arcsin} (2x^2 - 2x) = -\pi/6$?

10-3. APPLICATIONS OF THE INVERSE FUNCTIONS

We consider some examples.

EXAMPLES

1. The law of cosines states that in a triangle, with the usual notation,

$$a^2 = b^2 + c^2 - 2bc \cos A.$$

Because in any triangle $m(\angle A)$ is a number in $\langle 0, \pi \rangle$, we have

$$\cos A = \frac{b^2 + c^2 - a^2}{2bc},$$

and by definition,

$$A = \text{Arccos} \frac{b^2 + c^2 - a^2}{2bc}.$$

2. Find sin (Arcsin u).

Evidently the answer is u, for u is the sine of any number (or angle) whose sine is u: sin (Arcsin u) = u.

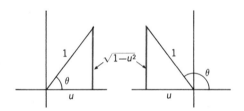

Fig. 10-7

However, if we try to find sin (Arccos u), the problem is more difficult. Suppose $y = \sin (\text{Arccos } u)$. Let $\theta = \text{Arccos } u$. Then $u = \text{Cos } \theta$ and $y = \sin \theta$. By the definition of Cos, θ must be in $[0, \pi]$, so the two graphs in Fig. 10-7 apply to the problem. If $u \geq 0$, then $0 \leq \theta \leq \pi/2$ and $\sin \theta = \sqrt{1 - u^2}$. If $u < 0$, then $\pi/2 < \theta \leq \pi$ and $\sin \theta = \sqrt{1 - u^2}$. Thus in all cases, sin (Arccos u) = $\sqrt{1 - u^2}$.

Problems

1. Find $\cos (\text{Sin}^{-1} t)$ in terms of t.

2. Show that

$$\sin (\text{Cos}^{-1} x + \text{Sin}^{-1} y) = \sqrt{1 - x^2}\sqrt{1 - y^2} + xy.$$

3. Show that

$$\sin (\text{Arcsin } x + \text{Arcsin } y) = x\sqrt{1 - y^2} + y\sqrt{1 - x^2}.$$

282

4. Show that

$$\text{Arctan}\,\frac{1}{2} + \text{Arctan}\,\frac{1}{3} = \frac{\pi}{4}.$$

5. Show that

$$2\,\text{Arctan}\,\frac{1}{3} + \text{Arctan}\,\frac{1}{7} = \frac{\pi}{4}.$$

6. Show that

$$4\,\text{Tan}^{-1}\,\frac{1}{5} - \text{Tan}^{-1}\,\frac{1}{239} = \frac{\pi}{4}.$$

(Problems 4, 5, and 6 can be used with a calculus formula for Tan^{-1}, to compute $\pi/4$, and hence π.)

7. Show that $2\,\text{Arctan}\,\frac{2}{3} = \text{Arctan}\,\frac{12}{5}$.

8. Compute the following:
   (a) $\cos\,(\frac{1}{2}\,\text{Sin}^{-1}\,\frac{4}{5})$
   (b) $\cos\,(2\,\text{Tan}^{-1}\,\frac{3}{4})$
   (c) $\tan\,[2\,\text{Cos}^{-1}\,(-\frac{3}{5})]$
   (d) $\sin\,(\text{Sin}^{-1}\,\frac{63}{65} + 2\,\text{Tan}^{-1}\,\frac{1}{5})$
   (e) $\tan\,[\text{Tan}^{-1}\,(2 + \sqrt{3}) - \text{Tan}^{-1}\,(2 - \sqrt{3})]$
   (f) $\cos\,[\text{Sin}^{-1}\,(-\frac{1}{2}) + \text{Cos}^{-1}\,(-\frac{1}{2})]$

9. Find $\tan\,(\text{Arctan}\,x + \text{Arctan}\,y)$ in terms of x and y.

10. Show that
$$\text{Arcsin}\,x + \text{Arccos}\,x = \pi/2.$$

11. Find $\tan\,[\text{Arcsin}\,(-\frac{8}{17}) + \text{Arccos}\,\frac{4}{5}]$.

12. Sketch the graphs of the following functions.
   (a) $f(x) = \text{Arctan}\,(\cot x)$
   (b) $g(x) = \text{Arcsin}\,(\cos x)$
   (c) $h(x) = \text{Arccos}\,(\cos x)$

10-4. TRIGONOMETRIC EQUATIONS

Equations involving the trigonometric functions, or their inverses, occur in applications with considerable frequency. Solutions of such equations can be either quite trivial, or quite difficult. There are no general rules, so we shall examine a few equations.

EXAMPLES

1. Solve $\sin \theta = 1/\sqrt{2}$ for θ.
   Clearly,

$$\theta = \frac{\pi}{4} + 2\pi n, \quad \text{or} \quad \theta = \frac{3\pi}{4} + 2\pi n \ldots,$$

where n is an integer.

2. Solve $\tan x + \cot x = -2$.

We have

$$\tan x + \frac{1}{\tan x} = -2,$$

which is equivalent to the *quadratic* equation

$$\tan^2 x + 2 \tan x + 1 = 0 = (\tan x + 1)^2.$$

Then

$$\tan x = -1,$$

$$x = -\frac{\pi}{4} + n\pi,$$

where $n = 0, \pm 1, \pm 1, \pm 2, \pm 3 \ldots$

3. Solve $\tan x + x = \pi/4$.

This innocent-appearing problem is much more troublesome to handle than the previous problem. Let us write the equation in the equivalent form

$$\tan x = \frac{\pi}{4} - x,$$

and let us graph the two functions

$$y = \tan x, \qquad y = \frac{\pi}{4} - x.$$

Their graphs are the red and dashed curves, respectively, in Fig. 10–8.

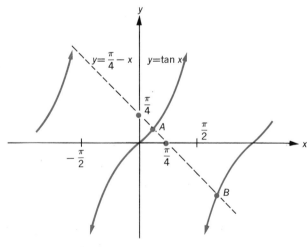

Fig. 10-8

From the graphs we see that there are crossings at A, B, and infinitely many other points.

284

Let us try to locate A with some accuracy. From a table we find that

$$\tan \frac{\pi}{8} = 0.4142,$$

whereas

$$\frac{\pi}{4} - \frac{\pi}{8} = \frac{\pi}{8} = 0.3927.$$

Therefore the solution is somewhat less than $\pi/8$. A process of successive trial and error with use of the tables would enable us to find the x-coordinate of A as accurately as desired. But there is no direct method giving an exact decimal answer. The best one can hope for is a sequence of consecutively better approximations. In calculus, there are quick methods which will give excellent approximations to the roots of such equations.

Problems

1. Find all θ, $0 < \theta < 2\pi$, such that:
   (a) $\sin \theta = -\sqrt{3}/2$
   (b) $\sin \theta = -0.3762$
   (c) $\cos \theta = -0.8880$
   (d) $\tan \theta = -1$
   (e) $\tan \theta = -2.1200$
   (f) $\cot \theta = 1.2000$
   (g) $\cos \theta = -0.4999$
   (h) $\cos \theta = -1$

2. Solve for θ, $0 \le \theta < 2\pi$.
   (a) $4 \sin^2 \theta + 1 = 8 \cos \theta$
   (b) $\sin^2 \theta + \sin \theta - 1 = 0$
   (c) $2 \cos^2 \theta - 3 \sin \theta = 0$
   (d) $4 = 2 \sin^2 \theta + 5 \cos \theta$
   (e) $3 \cot \theta = \tan \theta$
   (f) $\sin^2 \theta + 3 \cos^2 \theta = 2$
   (g) $4 \cot \theta - \tan \theta = 3$
   (h) $2 \sin^2 \theta + \cos \theta = 1$
   (i) $2 \sin \theta + \csc \theta = 3$
   (j) $\sin 2\theta = \frac{1}{2}$
   (k) $\tan 3\theta = 1$
   (l) $\sin 2\theta = -\frac{1}{3}$

3. Solve for θ.
   (a) $\cos 2\theta + 3 \cos \theta - 1 = 0$
   (b) $\cos \theta + \cos 2\theta = 0$
   (c) $\cos \theta + \cos 2\theta + 2 \sin^2 \theta = 0$
   (d) $\cos 3\theta + \cos \theta = 0$
   (e) $\sin 2\theta = \sin \theta$
   (f) $\cos 2\theta = \cos^2 \theta$
   (g) $\sin 4\theta - \sin 2\theta = \cos 3\theta$
   (h) $\sin 2\theta = 2 \cos \theta$
   *(i) $\cos 5\theta + \cos 3\theta = 0$

4. Find the θ such that $|\theta|$ is as small as possible, given that:
   (a) $2 \sin \theta - \theta = 0$
   (b) $\cos \theta = \theta$
   (c) $\cos \theta = \theta^2$
   (d) $\tan \theta = 1 + \theta$

INVERSE CIRCULAR FUNCTIONS AND TRIGONOMETRIC EQUATIONS

SUMMARY

1. In order to define *functions* inverse to the circular functions, it was necessary to restrict the domains of the circular functions. Thus, the Sin, Cos, and Tan functions were defined by

$$\text{Sin } \theta = \sin \theta, \qquad -\frac{\pi}{2} \le \theta \le \frac{\pi}{2};$$

$$\text{Cos } \theta = \cos \theta, \qquad 0 \le \theta \le \pi;$$

$$\text{Tan } \theta = \tan \theta, \qquad -\frac{\pi}{2} < \theta < \frac{\pi}{2}.$$

The inverses to these functions are

$$\text{Arcsin } x = \text{Sin}^{-1} x, \qquad -1 \le x \le 1;$$

$$\text{Arccos } x = \text{Cos}^{-1} x, \qquad -1 \le x \le 1;$$

$$\text{Arctan } x = \text{Tan}^{-1} x, \qquad -\infty < x < \infty.$$

In addition to the definitions, you should also know the graphs of these functions.

2. Trigonometric equations are easy to solve if they can be reduced to the form

$$\text{a circular function of } \theta = \text{a number.}$$

Then one can obtain θ from tables of the functions. However, not all equations can be reduced to this simple form.

Review Problems

1. Give the range and domain of the following:
   (a) Arcsine (b) Arccosine (c) Arctangent

2. Why is the following statement false?

$$\text{Cos}^{-1}\left(-\frac{1}{2}\right) = \text{Sin}^{-1}\frac{\sqrt{3}}{2}$$

3. Compute
   (a) $\sin [\text{Tan}^{-1}(-1)]$ (b) $\cos\left(\text{Cos}^{-1}\frac{12}{13}\right)$
   (c) $\sin\left(2\,\text{Tan}^{-1}\frac{1}{\sqrt{3}}\right)$ (d) $\text{Tan}^{-1}\left(\tan\frac{\pi}{7}\right)$

4. What is the relation between $\text{Cos}^{-1} x$ and $\text{Cos}^{-1}(-x)$?

5. Prove that $\text{Sin}^{-1} x + \text{Cos}^{-1} x = \pi/2$.

6. Compute
   (a) $\sin\left(2\,\text{Sin}^{-1}\frac{4}{5} + \text{Cos}^{-1}\frac{1}{5}\right)$ (b) $\cos\left(2\,\text{Sin}^{-1}\frac{4}{5} + \text{Cos}^{-1}\frac{1}{5}\right)$

286

7. Given $4 \cos \theta - 4 \sin^2 \theta + 5 = 0$. Find all θ such that $0 \leq \theta \leq 2\pi$.

8. Show that the *only* real numbers in $[0, \pi]$ satisfying $\sin \theta + \cos \theta = 1$ are 0 and $\pi/2$.

9. Find all real numbers θ in $[0, 2\pi]$ such that

$$\sin^2 \theta - \cos^2 \theta - \cos \theta = 1.$$

10. Solve $2 \cos \theta = \theta - \pi/3$ for θ by graphing. Use tables to estimate θ as accurately as you can.

ANGLES, LINES, AN

11

11–1. INTRODUCTION

In our study of coordinate geometry, we did not discuss the measure of angles between lines or planes nor did we find distances from points to lines or from points to planes. However, now that we have studied the circular functions, we may use these functions to help us solve such problems.

The basic formula in this chapter concerns the angle between two rays or two vectors. Other formulas are simple consequences of this formula. We shall also define two new operations for vectors. Both operations are kinds of "multiplication," but one operation combines two vectors to produce a real number while the other operation combines two vectors to give another vector. These new operations have numerous physical applications and will help us deal efficiently with angles, lines, and planes.

11–2. THE ANGLE BETWEEN RAYS

Let us suppose that we have two rays or vectors from a common point P, as shown in Fig. 11–1. Then, if P_1, P, and P_2 are not collinear, the three points lie in a unique plane and the rays from P through P_1 and P_2 form an angle whose measure is a real number θ in the open interval $\langle 0, \pi \rangle$.

If $\overrightarrow{PP_1}$ and $\overrightarrow{PP_2}$ have the same direction, we say that the measure of the angle is zero; if $\overrightarrow{PP_1}$ and $\overrightarrow{PP_2}$ are oppositely directed, the angle is a straight angle and has measure π. Thus the angle between two rays, or vectors, needs no special comment if the rays have a common endpoint.

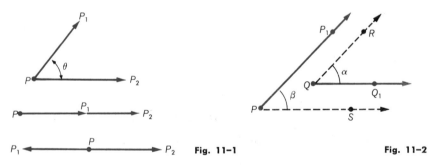

Fig. 11–1   Fig. 11–2

Let us suppose that we have rays from points P and Q, not necessarily in the same plane, as shown in Fig. 11–2. We wish to define "the measure of the angle between these rays." To do this, we will let R be a point such that the ray from Q through R is parallel to the ray from P through P_1. Then $\overrightarrow{QR}$ and $\overrightarrow{QQ_1}$ form an angle whose measure is some real number α. On the other hand, if S is a point such that the ray from P through S is parallel to the ray from Q through Q_1, then $\overrightarrow{PP_1}$ and $\overrightarrow{PS}$ form an angle of measure β.

It is an exercise in geometry (see Theorem 3–16) to show that $\angle P_1 PS \cong \angle RQQ_1$ so that

$$\alpha = \beta.$$

DEFINITION 11–1

The *measure of the angle between two nonzero vectors* $\overrightarrow{PP_1}$ and $\overrightarrow{QQ_1}$ is the real number α described above. It is the measure of the angle between the rays determined by the vectors.

DEFINITION 11–2

Let $\overrightarrow{OP}$ be any vector and X, Y, and Z be points on the *positive x-*, *y-*, and *z*-axes, respectively. (See Fig. 11–3.) The angles, $\angle XOP$, $\angle YOP$, and $\angle ZOP$, are called the *direction angles* of $\overrightarrow{OP}$. We shall denote the measures of these direction angles by α, β, and γ, respectively.

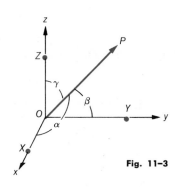

Fig. 11–3

We shall see, in the following theorem, that the direction cosines of $\overrightarrow{OP}$ are simply the cosines of the direction angles of $\overrightarrow{OP}$.

THEOREM 11–1

If l, m, and n are the *x-*, *y-*, and *z*-direction cosines, respectively, of $\overrightarrow{OP}$ (see Fig. 11–4), and α, β, γ are the measures of the direction angles of $\overrightarrow{OP}$, then

$$l = \cos \alpha,$$
$$m = \cos \beta,$$
$$n = \cos \gamma.$$

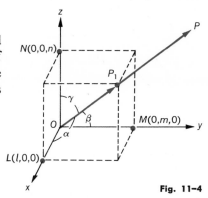

Fig. 11–4

Proof. We choose P_1 on the ray determined by $\overrightarrow{OP}$ so that $|\overrightarrow{OP_1}| = 1$. Then P_1 has coordinates (l, m, n). Planes through P_1 perpendicular to the coordinate axes will meet the axes in the points

$$L = (l, 0, 0), \qquad M = (0, m, 0), \qquad \text{and} \qquad N = (0, 0, n).$$

291

In the plane of P_1, O, L we have the situation shown in Fig. 11–5. From the definition of the cosine function,

$$\cos \alpha = l.$$

In the same manner, by considering planes through the points P_1, O, and M and the points P_1, O, and N, we obtain

$$\cos \beta = m \qquad \text{and} \qquad \cos \gamma = n.$$

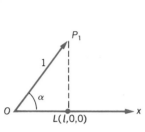

Fig. 11–5

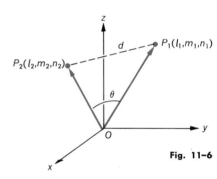

Fig. 11–6

THEOREM 11–2

If $\overrightarrow{OP_1}$ and $\overrightarrow{OP_2}$ are vectors of unit length with direction cosines (l_1, m_1, n_1) and (l_2, m_2, n_2), respectively, and if θ is the angle between them (see Fig. 11–6), then

$$\cos \theta = l_1 l_2 + m_1 m_2 + n_1 n_2.$$

Proof. The coordinates of P_1 and P_2 are (l_1, m_1, n_1) and (l_2, m_2, n_2). The law of cosines and the distance formula provide two different expressions for the distance d between P_1 and P_2:

$$d^2 = 1 + 1 - 2 \cos \theta \quad \text{(by the law of cosines)},$$
$$d^2 = (l_1 - l_2)^2 + (m_1 - m_2)^2 + (n_1 - n_2)^2 \quad \text{(by the distance formula)}.$$

Therefore

$$2 - 2 \cos \theta = l_1^2 - 2l_1 l_2 + l_2^2 + m_1^2 - 2m_1 m_2 + m_2^2 + n_1^2 - 2n_1 n_2 + n_2^2$$
$$= (l_1^2 + m_1^2 + n_1^2) + (l_2^2 + m_2^2 + n_2^2) - 2(l_1 l_2 + m_1 m_2 + n_1 n_2)$$
$$= 1 + 1 - 2(l_1 l_2 + m_1 m_2 + n_1 n_2),$$

so that

$$\cos \theta = l_1 l_2 + m_1 m_2 + n_1 n_2.$$

Corollary 1

If P_1, P_2 lie in the xy-plane, then $\cos \theta = l_1 l_2 + m_1 m_2$.

292

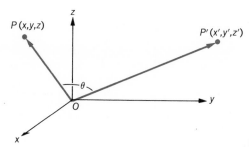

Fig. 11-7

Corollary 2

If the points P, P' are different from the origin O and have coordinates (x, y, z) and (x', y', z'), respectively (see Fig. 11-7), and θ is the angle between $\overrightarrow{OP}$ and $\overrightarrow{OP'}$, then

$$\cos \theta = \frac{xx' + yy' + zz'}{\sqrt{x^2 + y^2 + z^2}\sqrt{x'^2 + y'^2 + z'^2}}.$$

Corollary 3

If the vectors $\mathbf{v} = v_1\mathbf{i} + v_2\mathbf{j} + v_3\mathbf{k}$ and $\mathbf{u} = u_1\mathbf{i} + u_2\mathbf{j} + u_3\mathbf{k}$ are not zero vectors, then the angle θ between them is given by

$$\cos \theta = \frac{u_1v_1 + u_2v_2 + u_3v_3}{|\mathbf{u}| \cdot |\mathbf{v}|}.$$

EXAMPLES

1. Find the measures of the direction angles of $\overrightarrow{OP}$ where $P = P(1, -2, 3)$. (See Fig. 11-8.)

We have $|\overrightarrow{OP}| = \sqrt{1 + 4 + 9} = \sqrt{14}$ whence

$$\cos \alpha = \frac{1}{\sqrt{14}}, \qquad \cos \beta = \frac{-2}{\sqrt{14}}, \qquad \cos \gamma = \frac{3}{\sqrt{14}},$$

and

$$\alpha = \text{Arccos}\frac{1}{\sqrt{14}} = 1.3003,$$

or 74° 30′,

$$\beta = \text{Arccos}\frac{-2}{\sqrt{14}} = 2.1348,$$

or 122° 19′,

$$\gamma = \text{Arccos}\frac{3}{\sqrt{14}} = 0.6405,$$

or 36° 42′.

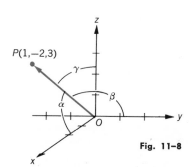

Fig. 11-8

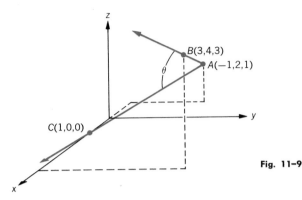

Fig. 11-9

2. Find the measure of $\angle BAC$ where $A = P(-1, 2, 1)$, $B = P(3, 4, 3)$, and $C = P(1, 0, 0)$. (See Fig. 11-9.) We have

$$\overrightarrow{AB} = 4\mathbf{i} + 2\mathbf{j} + 2\mathbf{k},$$
$$\overrightarrow{AC} = 2\mathbf{i} - 2\mathbf{j} - \mathbf{k}.$$

If $m(\angle BAC) = \theta$, then by Corollary 3,

$$\cos \theta = \frac{4 \cdot 2 + 2(-2) + 2(-1)}{\sqrt{16 + 4 + 4} \sqrt{4 + 4 + 1}} = \frac{2}{2\sqrt{6} \cdot 3} = \frac{1}{3\sqrt{6}} = \frac{\sqrt{6}}{18},$$

$$\theta = \text{Arccos} \frac{\sqrt{6}}{18} = \text{Arccos } 0.1361 = 1.4344 \ (82° \ 11').$$

Problems

1. Find the direction cosines of the position vector to each of the following points. Sketch each vector and estimate the measures of the direction angles. Then compute the measures of the direction angles in degrees.

   (a) $(4, -2, 4)$ (b) $(-4, 0, 3)$ (c) $(0, 0, -7)$

   (d) $(-4, 8, -1)$ (e) $(\frac{2}{3}, -\frac{2}{3}, \frac{1}{3})$ (f) $(2, 2, 2)$

2. Find the direction cosines of the vector $\overrightarrow{P_1 P_2}$ if P_1 and P_2 have the following coordinates:

   (a) $(2, 3, 4), (-4, 1, 4)$ (b) $(1, -1, 0), (-3, -5, 0)$

   (c) $(5, 4, -7), (-2, -1, -8)$ (d) $(2, 3, -3), (-4, 0, -1)$

3. Show that a vector $\overrightarrow{OP}$ cannot have direction angles such that

$$\alpha = \beta = \pi/6.$$

4. The direction angles of a vector $\overrightarrow{OP}$ are such that $\alpha = \pi/4$ and $\beta = \pi/3$. Find γ and draw a figure.

5. A vector has $\cos \alpha = \cos \beta = -1/\sqrt{2}$. Find γ.

294

6. Are the numbers $1/\sqrt{5}$, $-2/\sqrt{5}$, 0 direction cosines of some directed line? are the numbers $1/\sqrt{3}$, $-1/\sqrt{2}$, $1/2$?

7. What are the direction cosines of $\overrightarrow{OP} = 2\mathbf{i} + 3\mathbf{j} + 6\mathbf{k}$? What are the direction cosines of $\overrightarrow{OQ} = \frac{2}{7}\mathbf{i} + \frac{3}{7}\mathbf{j} + \frac{6}{7}\mathbf{k}$? Sketch the vectors.

8. Find a set of direction cosines of a vector which are proportional to the numbers 2, 3, and 4. [*Hint:* Consider $\overrightarrow{OP}$, where $P = P(2, 3, 4)$.]

9. If a, b, and c are real numbers, not all zero, find a set of direction cosines proportional to these numbers.

10. Find the cosine of the angle between the vectors $\overrightarrow{P_1P_2}$ and $\overrightarrow{P_3P_4}$ if P_1, P_2, P_3, and P_4 are, in order, the following points:

   (a) $(0, -1, 3)$, $(-2, 1, 2)$, $(-10, -2, -1)$, $(10, 3, 3)$
   (b) $(-2, -3, 1)$, $(0, 1, 2)$, $(-5, -2, 1)$, $(-2, 2, 3)$

11. Show that the line through $(1, 3, 5)$ and $(3, 0, 1)$ is perpendicular to the line through $(1, 11, -1)$ and $(-5, 3, 2)$.

12. A triangle has vertices $(-1, -1, 2)$, $(3, 2, -1)$, and $(0, 4, 3)$. Find the measure of the angle whose vertex is $(-1, -1, 2)$.

13. Prove that the vectors $\mathbf{a} = a_1\mathbf{i} + a_2\mathbf{j} + a_3\mathbf{k}$ and $\mathbf{b} = b_1\mathbf{i} + b_2\mathbf{j} + b_3\mathbf{k}$, neither of which is the null vector, are perpendicular if and only if $a_1b_1 + a_2b_2 + a_3b_3 = 0$.

14. A directed line has direction cosines $1/2$, $\dfrac{-\sqrt{3}}{2}$, 0. Find direction cosines of a directed line in the xy-plane perpendicular to the given line.

*15. A directed line parallel to the xy-plane has direction cosines l, m, and 0. Show that a directed line perpendicular to the given line and also parallel to the xy-plane has direction cosines $\pm m$, $\mp l$, 0.

*16. Show that the distinct points (x_1, y_1, z_1), (x_2, y_2, z_2), (x_3, y_3, z_3) are vertices of a right triangle with the right angle at (x_1, y_1, z_1) if and only if

$$(x_2 - x_1)(x_3 - x_1) + (y_2 - y_1)(y_3 - y_1) + (z_2 - z_1)(z_3 - z_1) = 0.$$

11–3. THE SCALAR PRODUCT OF VECTORS

An important function defined on pairs of vectors is the *scalar product*. Actually the term "product" is a misnomer because *this* "product" of two vectors is not a vector, but a real number, or scalar. Nevertheless, the name is not unreasonable because, as we shall see, this "product" does obey some of the same laws that ordinary multiplication does. The scalar product of two vectors is also called the *dot product* because of the "·" used to indicate this kind of multiplication. Sometimes it is also called the *inner product*.

DEFINITION 11-3

> If **u** and **v** are vectors, neither the null vector, and θ is the angle between them, then the *scalar product* of **u** and **v**, denoted by $\mathbf{u} \cdot \mathbf{v}$, is the real number
>
> $$|\mathbf{u}|\, |\mathbf{v}| \cos \theta.$$
>
> If either **u** or **v** is the null vector, then $\mathbf{u} \cdot \mathbf{v} = 0$.

Because vectors are ordinarily given in terms of their components, it will be desirable to be able to compute the scalar product of two vectors in terms of their components. The next theorem gives the method for accomplishing this.

THEOREM 11-3

> If $\mathbf{u} = u_1\mathbf{i} + u_2\mathbf{j} + u_3\mathbf{k}$ and $\mathbf{v} = v_1\mathbf{i} + v_2\mathbf{j} + v_3\mathbf{k}$, then
>
> $$\mathbf{u} \cdot \mathbf{v} = u_1v_1 + u_2v_2 + u_3v_3.$$

Proof. Apply Corollary 3 of Theorem 11-2.

EXAMPLES

Applications of Scalar Products to Geometry

1. If $\mathbf{u} = u_1\mathbf{i} + u_2\mathbf{j} + u_3\mathbf{k}$, then from the definitions of inner product and direction cosines

$$\mathbf{u} \cdot \mathbf{i} = |\mathbf{u}| \cos \alpha = u_1,$$
$$\mathbf{u} \cdot \mathbf{j} = |\mathbf{u}| \cos \beta = u_2,$$
$$\mathbf{u} \cdot \mathbf{k} = |\mathbf{u}| \cos \gamma = u_3.$$

This result also follows directly from Theorem 11-3 because

$$\mathbf{i} = 1\mathbf{i} + 0\mathbf{j} + 0\mathbf{k} \qquad \text{so that} \qquad \mathbf{u} \cdot \mathbf{i} = u_1 \cdot 1 + u_2 \cdot 0 + u_3 \cdot 0 = u_1.$$

2. If **n** is any unit vector, then $\mathbf{u} \cdot \mathbf{n} = |\mathbf{u}| \cos \theta$, where θ is the angle between **u** and **n**. This number is the length of the projection of **u** on **n**, as shown in Fig. 11-10. Note that $\mathbf{u} \cdot \mathbf{n}$ will be positive if $0 \le \theta < \pi/2$, and negative if $\pi/2 < \theta \le \pi$.

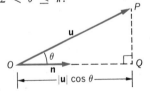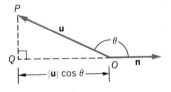

Fig. 11-10

Later in this chapter we shall see how to use the scalar product of vectors to study lines perpendicular to planes, or lines perpendicular to lines in a plane.

296

Applications of Scalar Products to Physics

3. Work. Let us suppose that F is a force, say measured in pounds. Then $\mathbf{F}$ is a vector, since it has both magnitude and direction. Let us assume that the force $\mathbf{F}$ acts through a distance given by a vector $\mathbf{d}$ whose magnitude is measured in feet. (See Fig. 11–11.) Let F_1 be the component of $\mathbf{F}$ along $\mathbf{d}$, and F_2 the component of $\mathbf{F}$ which is perpendicular to $\mathbf{d}$. By definition, the *work* performed by $\mathbf{F}$ acting through the distance $|\mathbf{d}|$ is $F_1|\mathbf{d}|$. But $F_1 = |\mathbf{F}| \cos \theta$, where θ is the measure of the angle between $\mathbf{F}$ and $\mathbf{d}$. Hence

$$\text{work (in ft-lb)} = |\mathbf{F}|\,|\mathbf{d}| \cos \theta = \mathbf{F} \cdot \mathbf{d}.$$

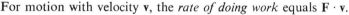

Fig. 11–11

Because there is no motion perpendicular to $\mathbf{d}$, the component F_2 does no work.

For motion with velocity $\mathbf{v}$, the *rate of doing work* equals $\mathbf{F} \cdot \mathbf{v}$.

Usually forces and displacements are resolved into components along three mutually perpendicular directions which one selects as directions of the x-, y-, and z-axes. If $\mathbf{F} = F_1\mathbf{i} + F_2\mathbf{j} + F_3\mathbf{k}$ and $\mathbf{d} = d_1\mathbf{i} + d_2\mathbf{j} + d_3\mathbf{k}$, then

$$\mathbf{F} \cdot \mathbf{d} = F_1 d_1 + F_2 d_2 + F_3 d_3.$$

4. Gravitational fields. For many purposes the earth may be considered as flat with the acceleration due to gravity, $\mathbf{g}$, constant in the downward direction. (See Fig. 11–12.) Then a mass m is pulled by a force

$$\mathbf{F} = m\mathbf{g}.$$

If there is a vertical displacement $\mathbf{d}$, then the work done will be

$$\mathbf{F} \cdot \mathbf{d} = m\mathbf{g} \cdot \mathbf{d}.$$

A horizontal displacement $\mathbf{d}$ gives

$$\mathbf{F} \cdot \mathbf{d} = m\mathbf{g} \cdot \mathbf{d} = 0.$$

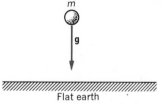

Flat earth

Fig. 11–12

For a round earth, the gravitational force is exerted toward the center of the earth and is not constant. In fact (see Fig. 11–13),

$$|\mathbf{g}| = \frac{k}{r^2},$$

where k is the *gravitational constant* and r is the distance from the center of the earth. But in this case there is no work done if the

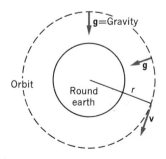

Fig. 11–13

297

motion is at a fixed distance r from the center of the earth. Thus a satellite in a circular orbit does no work, and so loses no energy because of the gravitational field, since $\mathbf{F} \cdot \mathbf{v} = 0$.

Algebraic considerations. We have called $\mathbf{u} \cdot \mathbf{v}$ a "product," and hence it is natural to expect that some properties of multiplication are valid. All that may be said is given by the following theorem.

THEOREM 11–4

For all vectors $\mathbf{u}$, $\mathbf{v}$, and $\mathbf{w}$,

$$\mathbf{u} \cdot \mathbf{v} = \mathbf{v} \cdot \mathbf{u} \quad \text{(commutativity),}$$

and

$$\mathbf{u} \cdot (\mathbf{v} + \mathbf{w}) = (\mathbf{u} \cdot \mathbf{v}) + (\mathbf{u} \cdot \mathbf{w}) \quad \text{(distributivity).}$$

The theorem is an easy consequence of Theorem 11–3, and its proof is left to the student. Observe that there is no vector which acts as a multiplicative identity for scalar products as the number 1 does for ordinary multiplication. Furthermore, there is no associative law for scalar products.

Problems

1. If $\mathbf{u} = \mathbf{i} + (-2)\mathbf{j} + 2\mathbf{k}$, what is $\mathbf{u} \cdot \mathbf{i}$? $\mathbf{u} \cdot \mathbf{j}$? $\mathbf{u} \cdot \mathbf{k}$?

2. Prove that for every vector $\mathbf{u}$, $\mathbf{u} \cdot \mathbf{u} = |\mathbf{u}|^2$.

3. Compute the scalar product of the following pairs of vectors.
   (a) $2\mathbf{i} + 3\mathbf{j} + 4\mathbf{k}$, $\mathbf{i} - \mathbf{j} - \mathbf{k}$ (b) $\mathbf{i} + 2\mathbf{j} - 5\mathbf{k}$, $2\mathbf{i} + 4\mathbf{j} + 2\mathbf{k}$
   (c) $3\mathbf{i} + \mathbf{j} - \mathbf{k}$, $-3\mathbf{i} - \mathbf{j} + \mathbf{k}$ (d) $6\mathbf{i} - 9\mathbf{j} + 3\mathbf{k}$, $\frac{2}{3}\mathbf{i} + \frac{2}{3}\mathbf{j} + \frac{1}{3}\mathbf{k}$
   (e) $2\mathbf{i} + \mathbf{j} - 4\mathbf{k}$, $2\mathbf{i} + \mathbf{j} - 4\mathbf{k}$

4. Let $\mathbf{n}$ be a unit vector and $\mathbf{u} = -6\mathbf{i} + 3\mathbf{j} + 6\mathbf{k}$. What is the length of the projection of $\mathbf{u}$ on $\mathbf{n}$ if the measure of the angle between the two vectors is:
   (a) 0   (b) $\pi/6$ (c) $\pi/4$ (d) $\pi/3$
   (e) $\pi/2$ (f) $2\pi/3$ (g) π

5. Prove that $\mathbf{u}$ is perpendicular to $\mathbf{v}$ (neither a zero vector) if and only if $\mathbf{u} \cdot \mathbf{v} = 0$.

6. Prove that the commutative law holds for scalar products.

7. Prove that the distributive law holds for scalar products; that is, prove that if $\mathbf{a}$, $\mathbf{b}$, and $\mathbf{c}$ are any vectors, then

$$\mathbf{a} \cdot (\mathbf{b} + \mathbf{c}) = \mathbf{a} \cdot \mathbf{b} + \mathbf{a} \cdot \mathbf{c}.$$

8. In the statement of the distributive law for scalar products, do the "+" symbols refer to the same operation on the same kind of objects in each case? Explain.

9. Show that there is no vector which behaves for the scalar product as 1 does for ordinary multiplication.

10. Show that there is no associative law for scalar products.

11. Interpret the distributive law for scalar products in terms of work. Refer to the accompanying figure.

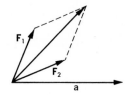

12. Show that if $\mathbf{u} \cdot \mathbf{v} = \pm|\mathbf{u}|\,|\mathbf{v}|$, then the vectors are either in the same or opposite direction.

13. The unit vector $\mathbf{n} = \frac{3}{7}\mathbf{i} + (-\frac{6}{7}\mathbf{j}) + \frac{2}{7}\mathbf{k}$ is perpendicular to a plane, π. If the point $P = P(3, 1, 4)$ is a point in the plane π (see figure), what is the perpendicular distance from the origin to the plane?

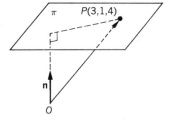

14. A force of 80 lb moves an object along a line which forms an angle whose measure is 30° with the direction of the force. What is the component of the force along the line? What is the component perpendicular to the line? What is the work done if the object is moved 10 ft along the line?

15. A boy weighing 150 lb climbs a flight of stairs which rise 10 ft vertically. How much work does he do in climbing the stairs?

16. A plane flies southwest and the wind is from the south at 60 mph. What is the component of the wind velocity in the direction of the flight? in a direction perpendicular to flight path?

17. Scalar products can be thought of as a function. What is the domain and range of this function?

*18. Prove that $\mathbf{u} = \mathbf{v}$ if and only if $\mathbf{u} \cdot \mathbf{w} = \mathbf{v} \cdot \mathbf{w}$ for every vector $\mathbf{w}$.

11–4. NORMALS TO LINES IN A PLANE

A line is said to be *normal* to another line if the two lines are perpendicular to each other. The word "orthogonal"† is also used in reference to perpendicular lines. We shall also speak of vectors which are normal or orthogonal to lines or to other vectors.

---

† From *ortho* meaning right and *gonal* meaning angular.

299

If l is a line in the xy-plane, it should be evident that there are exactly two vectors of unit length in the plane which are normal to the line l. It is convenient to designate one of these vectors as the *positive unit normal* to the line. For the present, let us agree that the positive unit normal to a line is that unit vector whose position vector points from the origin to the line. Thus $\mathbf{n}$ in Fig. 11–14 represents the positive unit normal to the line l. If the line contains the origin, either unit normal may be chosen as the positive unit normal.

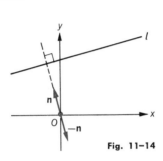

Fig. 11–14

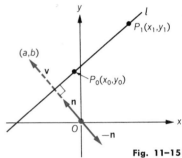

Fig. 11–15

THEOREM 11-5

If a line l has an equation $ax + by + c = 0$, then the two unit normals to l are

$$\frac{a}{\sqrt{a^2 + b^2}}\mathbf{i} + \frac{b}{\sqrt{a^2 + b^2}}\mathbf{j} \quad \text{and} \quad \frac{-a}{\sqrt{a^2 + b^2}}\mathbf{i} + \frac{-b}{\sqrt{a^2 + b^2}}\mathbf{j}.$$

Proof. If $P_0 = P(x_0, y_0)$ and $P_1 = P(x_1, y_1)$ are two points on the line $ax + by + c = 0$, as in Fig. 11–15, then

$$ax_0 + by_0 + c = 0 \tag{1}$$

and

$$ax_1 + by_1 + c = 0. \tag{2}$$

Subtracting equation (1) from equation (2), we obtain

$$a(x_1 - x_0) + b(y_1 - y_0) = 0. \tag{3}$$

Now, $\overrightarrow{P_0P_1} = (x_1 - x_0)\mathbf{i} + (y_1 - y_0)\mathbf{j}$, and if we let $\mathbf{v} = a\mathbf{i} + b\mathbf{j}$, then

$$\mathbf{v} \cdot \overrightarrow{P_0P_1} = a(x_1 - x_0) + b(y_1 - y_0) = 0 \tag{4}$$

from statement (3) above. Statement (4) asserts that $\mathbf{v}$ must be a vector normal to the line through P_0 and P_1 because $\mathbf{v} \cdot \overrightarrow{P_0P_1} = |\mathbf{v}| \cdot |\overrightarrow{P_0P_1}| \cos \theta$. Since neither $\mathbf{v}$ nor $\overrightarrow{P_0P_1}$ is null, $\cos \theta = 0$, which implies that $\theta = \pi/2$. The direction cosines of $\mathbf{v}$ are

$$\frac{a}{\sqrt{a^2 + b^2}} \quad \text{and} \quad \frac{b}{\sqrt{a^2 + b^2}}.$$

300

The vector $-\mathbf{v}$ is also normal to the line l and has direction cosines

$$\frac{-a}{\sqrt{a^2 + b^2}} \quad \text{and} \quad \frac{-b}{\sqrt{a^2 + b^2}}.$$

Hence the two unit normals to l are

$$\frac{a}{\sqrt{a^2 + b^2}}\mathbf{i} + \frac{b}{\sqrt{a^2 + b^2}}\mathbf{j} \quad \text{and} \quad \frac{-a}{\sqrt{a^2 + b^2}}\mathbf{i} + \frac{-b}{\sqrt{a^2 + b^2}}\mathbf{j}.$$

EXAMPLE

The two unit normals to the line $2x - 3y + 6 = 0$ are

$$\mathbf{n}_1 = \frac{2}{\sqrt{13}}\mathbf{i} + \frac{-3}{\sqrt{13}}\mathbf{j} \quad \text{and} \quad \mathbf{n}_2 = \frac{-2}{\sqrt{13}}\mathbf{i} + \frac{3}{\sqrt{13}}\mathbf{j}.$$

The line and the unit vectors are shown in Fig. 11–16. Observe that $\mathbf{n}_2$ appears to be the *positive* unit normal.

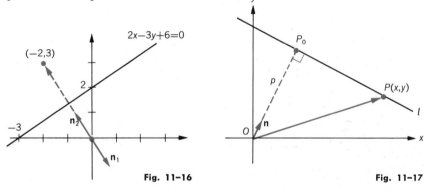

Fig. 11–16   Fig. 11–17

We can now develop a formula for computing the perpendicular distance from the origin to a line. First, if a line is parallel to one of the coordinate axes, no special formula is needed. (Why?) Second, if a line contains the origin, then its distance from the origin must be 0. A line with equation $ax + by + c = 0$ will contain the origin if and only if $c = 0$. (Why?)

Let l be a line with an equation

$$ax + by + c = 0,$$

and P_0 be the foot of the perpendicular from the origin 0 to l as in Fig. 11–17. Then $|\overrightarrow{OP_0}| = p$ is the distance from the origin to the line. If $P = P(x, y)$ is any other point on the line and $\mathbf{n}$ is the *positive* unit normal to the line, then

$$p = \overrightarrow{OP} \cdot \mathbf{n}. \quad \text{(Why?)}$$

301

We have seen that there are two unit normals to a line, namely,

$$\mathbf{n} = \frac{a\mathbf{i}}{\pm\sqrt{a^2 + b^2}} + \frac{b\mathbf{j}}{\pm\sqrt{a^2 + b^2}},$$

and our problem is to decide which of the two is to be the positive unit normal. Let us examine the scalar products of $\overrightarrow{OP}$ and the unit normals.

$$p = \overrightarrow{OP} \cdot \mathbf{n} = (x\mathbf{i} + y\mathbf{j}) \cdot \left(\frac{a\mathbf{i}}{\pm\sqrt{a^2 + b^2}} + \frac{b\mathbf{j}}{\pm\sqrt{a^2 + b^2}} \right)$$

$$= \frac{ax + by}{\pm\sqrt{a^2 + b^2}}.$$

The sign of the radical must be chosen so that the scalar product, p, is positive. But $ax + by = -c$ so that

$$p = \frac{-c}{\pm\sqrt{a^2 + b^2}},$$

and the sign of the radical must be chosen opposite to that of c. We have therefore proved the following theorem.

THEOREM 11-6

The positive unit normal to the line $ax + by + c = 0$ which does not contain the origin is

$$\frac{a}{\sqrt{a^2 + b^2}}\mathbf{i} + \frac{b}{\sqrt{a^2 + b^2}}\mathbf{j} \qquad \text{if} \qquad c < 0,$$

or

$$\frac{a}{-\sqrt{a^2 + b^2}}\mathbf{i} + \frac{b}{-\sqrt{a^2 + b^2}}\mathbf{j} \qquad \text{if} \qquad c > 0.$$

The distance from the origin O to the line is

$$p = \frac{|c|}{\sqrt{a^2 + b^2}}.$$

EXAMPLE

The positive unit normal to the line $3x - 4y + 7 = 0$ is

$$\mathbf{n} = -\tfrac{3}{5}\mathbf{i} + \tfrac{4}{5}\mathbf{j}.$$

The distance from the origin to the line is

$$p = \tfrac{7}{5}.$$

Problems

1. Find the distance from the origin to the lines whose equations are given below. Sketch each line.

   (a) $x - 3y + 10 = 0$ (b) $5x + 12y - 30 = 0$

   (c) $x + y + 8 = 0$ (d) $3x + 5y - 8 = 0$

   (e) $\sqrt{5}\,x - 7 = 0$ (f) $8y + 17 = 0$

   (g) $5x + 6y = 0$ (h) $\sqrt{2}\,x + \sqrt{3}\,y + \sqrt{5} = 0$

2. Find and sketch the positive unit normal to each line of Problem 1.

3. Find the distance from the origin to the line through $(-4, 0)$ and $(12, 6)$.

4. A line has parametric equations

$$\begin{cases} x = 4 + \dfrac{3}{\sqrt{10}}\,d, \\[2mm] y = 2 + \dfrac{-1}{\sqrt{10}}\,d. \end{cases}$$

   What is the distance from the origin to the line?

5. The positive unit normal to a line is

$$\mathbf{n} = \frac{1}{\sqrt{5}}\mathbf{i} + \frac{2}{\sqrt{5}}\mathbf{j}.$$

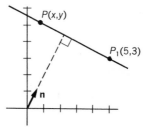

   If the point $P_1 = P(5, 3)$ is a point on the line, as in the figure, what is a rectangular equation of the line? [*Hint:* A point $P = P(x, y)$ is on the line if and only if $\mathbf{n} \cdot \overrightarrow{P_1P} = 0$.]

6. A line has a positive unit normal

$$n = \frac{2}{3}i - \frac{\sqrt{5}}{3}j,$$

   and the distance from the origin to the line is 3 units. Find a rectangular equation of the line.

11-5. THE DISTANCE FROM A POINT TO A LINE

We can now use Theorem 11–6 to derive a formula for the distance from a point $P_1 = P(x_1, y_1)$ to the line $ax + by + c = 0$.

Referring to Fig. 11–18, we see that

$$d_1 = \mathbf{n} \cdot \overrightarrow{OP_1} = \frac{ax_1 + by_1}{\pm\sqrt{a^2 + b^2}}$$

303

is the length of $\overline{OR}$, the projection of $\overrightarrow{OP_1}$ on the positive unit normal to the line l. The distance d_1 may be positive, as is the case for the point P_1 in the figure, or negative, as is the case for the point P_1', but in each case the distance d is

$$d = |\mathbf{n} \cdot \overrightarrow{OP_1} - p|$$
$$= \left| \frac{ax_1 + by_1}{\pm\sqrt{a^2 + b^2}} - \frac{-c}{\pm\sqrt{a^2 + b^2}} \right|$$
$$= \frac{|ax_1 + by_1 + c|}{\sqrt{a^2 + b^2}}.$$

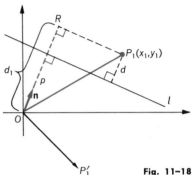

Fig. 11-18

This proves the following theorem.

THEOREM 11-7

The distance d from the point $P_1 = P(x_1, y_1)$ to the line

$$ax + by + c = 0$$

is

$$d = \frac{|ax_1 + by_1 + c|}{\sqrt{a^2 + b^2}}.$$

Remark

We can get a little more mileage out of this theorem if we interpret the expression

$$\frac{ax_1 + by_1 + c}{\sqrt{a^2 + b^2}}. \tag{1}$$

The numerator of this expression will be positive, negative, or zero depending upon the relative positions of the point P_1, the line, and the origin. If $P_1 = P(x_1, y_1)$ is any point, and

$$\frac{ax_1 + by_1 + c}{\sqrt{a^2 + b^2}}$$

has the same sign as

$$\frac{c}{\sqrt{a^2 + b^2}},$$

then P_1 and the origin are on the same side of the line. If the signs are different, then P_1 is on the opposite side of the line from the origin. For $P_1 = P(0, 0)$, we get the directed distance from the origin to the line, which may be positive, negative, or zero.

EXAMPLE

The distance from the point $(-3, 2)$ to the line

$$2x - y + 4 = 0$$

is

$$d = \frac{|2(-3) - 2 + 4|}{\sqrt{5}} = \frac{|-4|}{\sqrt{5}} = \frac{4}{\sqrt{5}}.$$

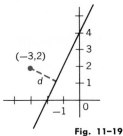

Fig. 11-19

Because $2 \cdot 0 - 0 + 4 > 0$, whereas $2(-3) - 2 + 4 < 0$, the point $(-3, 2)$ and the origin $(0, 0)$ are on opposite sides of the line $2x - y + 4 = 0$, as may be seen from Fig. 11-19.

Finally, we can use the scalar products of normals to lines to develop a formula for the cosines of the angles between two lines.

It is not difficult to show that the angles between two lines are congruent to the angles between the normals to the lines. Applying Theorem 11-2, we obtain the following theorem.

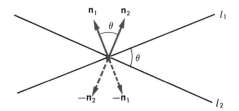

Fig. 11-20

THEOREM 11-8

The cosines of the angles between the lines $l_1: a_1x + b_1y + c_1 = 0$ and $l_2: a_2x + b_2y + c_2 = 0$ are (see Fig. 11-20)

$$\cos \theta = \frac{a_1a_2 + b_1b_2}{\pm \sqrt{a_1^2 + b_1^2} \sqrt{a_2^2 + b_2^2}}.$$

The proof of Theorem 11-8 is left to the student.

Problems

1. Find the distance to the line $3x - 2y + 12 = 0$ from each of the following points. Draw the line and plot each point.

   (a) $(1, 3)$ (b) $(-1, 7)$ (c) $(0, 0)$ (d) $(-2, 3)$

   (e) $(2, -2)$ (f) $(-3, -2)$ (g) $(2, 9)$ (h) $(-4, 4)$

2. Find the distance from the point $(-2, 3)$ to the line $3x - 2y + 1 = 0$. Is $(-2, 3)$ on the same side of the line as the origin, or is it on the opposite side?

305

3. A rectangular equation of a line is $4x - 3y + 12 = 0$. Find the coordinates of the point P_0 which is the foot of the perpendicular from the origin to the line. [*Hint:* $\overrightarrow{OP_0} = p \cdot \mathbf{n}$.]

4. Write equations of the two lines parallel to the line through $(1, 2)$ and $(4, 6)$ which are 3 units distant from the given line. Draw a figure.

5. A triangle has its base vertices at the points $(-5, 6)$ and $(-1, 3)$. The area of the triangle is 10 square units. Find an equation satisfied by those points and only those points that could be the third vertex of the triangle.

6. Prove that the equation $bx - ay = k$, where k is arbitrary, represents a line normal to the line $ax + by + c = 0$.

7. Use the result of Problem 6 to find the two unit vectors directed *along* the line $ax + by + c = 0$.

8. Determine the measures of the angles between the pairs of lines below. Draw figures in each case.

   (a) $y = x$ and $x = 3$
   (b) $3x - 2y = 0$ and $2x + 3y = 6$
   (c) $x - 3y - 5 = 0$ and $x + y - 1 = 0$
   (d) $2x + 5y = 10$ and $y = 2$

9. Find the cosines of the angles between the lines $3x + 4y + 4 = 0$ and $4x - 3y - 10 = 0$. Draw a figure.

10. Prove Theorem 11–8.

11. Find the cosines of the angles between $x + 3y - 6 = 0$ and $4x - y + 8 = 0$.

12. Show from angle considerations that the lines $7x - 4y + 3 = 0$, $3x + 2y + 5 = 0$, and $x - 8y + 45 = 0$ intersect in the vertices of an isosceles triangle.

*13. Find equations and draw figures of the two lines which bisect the angles formed by the lines $3x - 4y + 3 = 0$ and $12x + 5y - 5 = 0$. [*Hint:* A point (x, y) is on a bisector if and only if it is equidistant from each line.]

*14. Find an equation of the line bisecting the smaller angle between the lines $x + 3y - 10 = 0$ and $3x + y - 14 = 0$.

11-6. NORMALS TO PLANES

We now pursue the same ideas that were presented in Section 11–4, except that in this section, we shall apply them to space.

In our study of space in Chapter 3, we assumed that every plane has a linear equation of the form

$$Ax + By + Cz + D = 0, \tag{1}$$

where not all the real numbers A, B, and C are zero. We shall prove this theorem now.

306

As was the case for lines in the xy-plane, every plane has two unit vectors which are normal to the plane. The unit vector which has a position vector pointing toward the plane is called the *positive unit normal* to the plane.

Let us suppose that we have a plane π with a positive unit normal $\mathbf{n} = l_1\mathbf{i} + l_2\mathbf{j} + l_3\mathbf{k}$, where l_1, l_2, and l_3 are the direction cosines of $\mathbf{n}$. (See Fig. 11–21.) Let $P_0 = P(x_0, y_0, z_0)$ be the foot of the perpendicular from the origin O to the plane π. Then a point $P = P(x, y, z)$ is a point in the plane if and only if

$$\mathbf{n} \cdot \overrightarrow{P_0P} = 0.$$

Since $\overrightarrow{P_0P} = (x - x_0)\mathbf{i} + (y - y_0)\mathbf{j} + (z - z_0)\mathbf{k}$,

$$\mathbf{n} \cdot \overrightarrow{P_0P} = l_1(x - x_0) + l_2(y - y_0) + l_3(z - z_0) = 0, \qquad (2)$$

or equivalently,

$$l_1x + l_2y + l_3z - (l_1x_0 + l_2y_0 + l_3z_0) = 0. \qquad (3)$$

In equation (3), we see that

$$l_1x_0 + l_2y_0 + l_3z_0 = \mathbf{n} \cdot \overrightarrow{OP_0} = p,$$

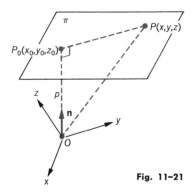

Fig. 11–21

where p is the perpendicular distance from the origin to the plane π. Therefore an equation of the plane is

$$l_1x + l_2y + l_3z - p = 0. \qquad (4)$$

Clearly, if $k \neq 0$, an equivalent equation is

$$kl_1x + kl_2y + kl_3z - kp = 0. \qquad (5)$$

We have shown in equations (4) and (5) that the plane π has an equation of the form of equation (1):

$$Ax + By + Cz + D = 0.$$

Conversely, let us suppose that equation (1) is given with not all A, B, and C zero. There are exactly two unit vectors with direction cosines proportional to the numbers A, B, and C. (See Problem 9, Section 11–2.) These vectors are

$$\mathbf{n} = \frac{A\mathbf{i}}{\pm\sqrt{A^2 + B^2 + C^2}} + \frac{B\mathbf{j}}{\pm\sqrt{A^2 + B^2 + C^2}} + \frac{C\mathbf{k}}{\pm\sqrt{A^2 + B^2 + C^2}}.$$

Dividing each term of equation (1) by $\pm\sqrt{A^2 + B^2 + C^2}$, we obtain

$$\frac{Ax}{\sigma} + \frac{By}{\sigma} + \frac{Cy}{\sigma} + \frac{D}{\sigma} = 0, \qquad (6)$$

where

$$\sigma = \pm\sqrt{A^2 + B^2 + C^2}.$$

307

Comparing, we see that equation (6) has the same form as equation (4) except that we must choose the sign of the radical so that the coefficients of x, y, and z will be the components of the *positive unit normal* to the plane we seek. We also observe that we must have

$$p = \frac{-D}{\pm\sqrt{A^2 + B^2 + C^2}},$$

and since p must be ≥ 0, this will be the case if we choose the sign of the radical opposite to that of D. Hence we have proved that equation (1) is equivalent to equation (4) which is an equation of a plane π.

The following theorem gives a resume of what has been proved.

THEOREM 11-9

(a) The set of all points (x, y, z) satisfying an equation $Ax + By + Cz + D = 0$, where not all of A, B, and C are zero, is a plane; conversely, every plane has an equation of this form.

(b) The plane $Ax + By + Cz + D = 0$ has a positive unit normal

$$\mathbf{n} = \frac{A\mathbf{i}}{\pm\sigma} + \frac{B\mathbf{j}}{\pm\sigma} + \frac{C\mathbf{k}}{\pm\sigma},$$

where $\sigma = \sqrt{A^2 + B^2 + C^2}$, and the sign of σ is chosen opposite to that of D.

(c) The distance from the origin to the plane $Ax + By + Cz + D = 0$ is

$$p = \frac{|D|}{\sqrt{A^2 + B^2 + C^2}}.$$

(d) If a plane has a positive unit normal

$$\mathbf{n} = l_1\mathbf{i} + l_2\mathbf{j} + l_3\mathbf{k}$$

and is at a distance p from the origin, then an equation of the plane is

$$l_1x + l_2y + l_3z - p = 0.$$

EXAMPLES

1. The positive unit normal to the plane $x - 2y + 2z - 6 = 0$ is

$$\mathbf{n} = \tfrac{1}{3}\mathbf{i} + (-\tfrac{2}{3})\mathbf{j} + \tfrac{2}{3}\mathbf{k}.$$

The distance from the origin to the plane is

$$p = \frac{|-6|}{3} = 2.$$

308

2. Find an equation of a plane which has a positive unit normal

$$\mathbf{n} = -\tfrac{6}{7}\mathbf{i} + \tfrac{2}{7}\mathbf{j} + (-\tfrac{3}{7})\mathbf{k},$$

and which is 4 units from the origin. From Theorem 11–9(d) we have for an equation of the plane

$$-\tfrac{6}{7}x + \tfrac{2}{7}y + (-\tfrac{3}{7})z - 4 = 0$$

or equivalently,

$$6x - 2y + 3z + 28 = 0.$$

Using the ideas developed in Theorem 11–9, we can now derive a formula for the distance from a point to a plane which will be quite analogous to the corresponding formula developed for the distance from a point to a line.

THEOREM 11-10

The distance from a point $P_1 = P(x_1, y_1, z_1)$ to the plane $Ax + By + Cz + D = O$ is

$$d = \frac{|Ax_1 + By_1 + Cz_1 + D|}{\sqrt{A^2 + B^2 + C^2}}.$$

Proof. Let $\mathbf{n}$ be the positive unit normal to the plane and

$$d_1 = \mathbf{n} \cdot \overrightarrow{OP_1}$$

be the length of the projection of $\overrightarrow{OP_1}$ on $\mathbf{n}$. Then d_1 can be positive, as for the point P_1 in Fig. 11–22, or zero, or negative as for the point P_1' in the same figure. If d is the distance from P_1 to the plane, then in every case we have

$$d = |d_1 - p|,$$

where p is the distance from the origin to the plane. Now,

$$d_1 = \frac{Ax_1 + By_1 + Cz_1}{\pm\sqrt{A^2 + B^2 + C^2}}$$

and

$$p = \frac{-D}{\pm\sqrt{A^2 + B^2 + C^2}},$$

where the sign of the radical is chosen opposite to that of D. Hence

$$d = \frac{|Ax_1 + By_1 + Cz_1 + D|}{\sqrt{A^2 + B^2 + C^2}}.$$

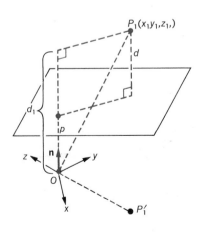

Fig. 11–22

309

We observe that for $P_1 = P(0, 0, 0)$, we have the formula for the distance from the origin to the plane,

$$d = p = \frac{|D|}{\sqrt{A^2 + B^2 + C^2}}.$$

If $P_2 = P(x_2, y_2, z_2)$ is any other point and $Ax_2 + By_2 + Cz_2 + D$ has the same sign as D, then P_2 is on the same side of the plane as the origin, whereas if they are opposite in sign, P_2 is on the opposite side of the plane from the origin.

EXAMPLE 3

The distance from the point whose coordinates are $(2, 3, 4)$ to the plane $3x + 3y + 4z - 12 = 0$ is

$$d = \frac{|3 \cdot 2 + 3 \cdot 3 + 4 \cdot 4 - 12|}{\sqrt{34}} = \frac{|19|}{\sqrt{34}} = \frac{19}{\sqrt{34}}.$$

The distance from the origin to the plane is

$$p = \frac{|-12|}{\sqrt{34}} = \frac{12}{\sqrt{34}}.$$

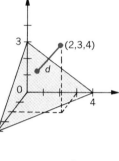

Fig. 11–23

Since 19 and -12 are opposite in sign, we conclude that the point $(2, 3, 4)$ is on the opposite side of the plane from the origin. A sketch of a portion of the plane and the points in Fig. 11–23 substantiates, approximately, these results.

Problems

1. Find the distance from the origin to each of the following planes. Sketch a portion of the planes.

(a) $x + y - z + 3 = 0$ (b) $20x - 5y - 4z + 63 = 0$

(c) $\sqrt{3}\, x + 9y - \sqrt{21} = 0$ (d) $13x + 16 = 0$

(e) $-6x - \dfrac{1}{\sqrt{2}} y - 2z + 18 = 0$ (f) $\dfrac{1}{\sqrt{3}} x - \dfrac{1}{\sqrt{3}} y + \dfrac{1}{\sqrt{3}} z - 7 = 0$

2. What are the direction cosines of the positive unit normal to the plane $2x - y - z + a = 0$ if $a > 0$? if $a < 0$?

3. A plane has a positive unit normal

$$\mathbf{n} = \tfrac{1}{3}\mathbf{i} - \tfrac{2}{3}\mathbf{j} + \tfrac{2}{3}\mathbf{k}$$

and is 3 units from the origin. What is a rectangular equation of the plane?

4. A line has direction cosines

$$-\frac{1}{\sqrt{2}}, \quad -\frac{1}{\sqrt{3}}, \quad \frac{1}{\sqrt{6}}$$

and lies in a plane. If $P = P(2, 3, 4)$, is $\overrightarrow{OP}$ perpendicular to that plane?

5. A rectangular equation of a plane is $3x - 2y - 4z - 12 = 0$. Find the coordinates of the point P_0 in the plane which is the foot of the perpendicular from the origin to the plane.

6. Find equations and sketch a picture of the two planes which are parallel to the plane $x - 2y + 2z - 6 = 0$, and which are 4 units from the given plane.

7. A plane has a positive unit normal

$$\mathbf{n} = \frac{1}{\sqrt{14}}\mathbf{i} - \frac{2}{\sqrt{14}}\mathbf{j} + \frac{3}{\sqrt{14}}\mathbf{k},$$

and the point $P = P(-2, 4, 5)$ lies in the plane. What is a rectangular equation of the plane?

8. Show that the planes $4x - 3y + z - 7 = 0$,
$$4x - 3y + z + 6 = 0$$

are parallel planes and find the distance between them.

9. Show that the planes $3x - 2y + z + 5 = 0$,
$$-9x + 6y - 3z + 14 = 0$$

are parallel planes and find the distance between them.

10. Show that a plane parallel to the plane

$$Ax + By + Cz + D = 0$$

and containing the point $P_0 = P(x_0, y_0, z_0)$ has an equation $A(x - x_0) + B(y - y_0) + C(z - z_0) = 0$.

11. Find the distance from each of the following points to the plane $x - 4y - 8z + 16 = 0$. Sketch.

(a) $(2, 3, 4)$ (b) $(0, 0, 1)$ (c) $(-4, 1, 1)$

(d) $(1, 5, 0)$ (e) $(-10, \frac{1}{2}, \frac{1}{2})$ (f) $(0, 0, 10^m)$.

12. Find the distance from each of the given points to the planes and determine whether the point is on the same side of the plane as the origin or on the opposite side.

(a) $(1, 1, 2)$ and $x + y + 2z - 4 = 0$

(b) $(3, 0, -2)$ and $2x - 3y + z - 3 = 0$

(c) $(-1, 2, 1)$ and $4x + 4y + 2z + 7 = 0$

(d) $(-2, 3, 0)$ and $5x + 2y - 10 = 0$

(e) $(2, 2, 2)$ and $3x + 4z - 12 = 0$

311

13. Angles between two planes are defined as the angles between normals to the planes. What are the cosines of the angles between the planes whose equations are

$$2x + 3y - z + 5 = 0 \quad \text{and} \quad -x + y + z + 1 = 0?$$

14. What are the measures of the dihedral angles formed by the plane $x + y - 2z = 0$ and the xy-coordinate plane?

15. The point $P = P(x, y, z)$ is equidistant from the planes $2x - y - z + 6 = 0$ and $x + 2y - 7z + 12 = 0$. Write an equation satisfied by the coordinates (x, y, z). Prove that the set of all such points lie on two planes. What are these planes geometrically?

16. A plane is parallel to the plane $x - y + 3z = 1$ and is at a distance of 3 units from the point $P = P(2, -1, 1)$. Find an equation of the plane. (There are two correct answers.)

*17. Show that the plane $3x - y - 3 = 0$ is tangent to the sphere

$$x^2 + y^2 + z^2 + 4x - 2y - 4z = 1.$$

Sketch the plane and the sphere.

*18. What are the coordinates of the point of tangency of the plane and the sphere of Problem 17?

*19. A ray from the center of the sphere $x^2 + y^2 + z^2 + 2x - 6y + 1 = 0$ passes through the point $P = P(2, 0, 3)$. Find an equation of the plane tangent to the sphere at the point where the ray pierces the sphere.

20. Show that the planes $-2x + 5y - 3z + 8 = 0$ and $7x + 4y + 2z + 1 = 0$ are perpendicular planes.

11–7. VECTOR MULTIPLICATION

In Section 11–3 the scalar product of two vectors was defined to be a real number. In this section we define a new operation on vectors which will combine two 3-space vectors to produce another 3-space vector. We call this new operation *vector multiplication* and describe it in an intuitive manner.

Suppose $\mathbf{a} = \overrightarrow{OA}$ and $\mathbf{b} = \overrightarrow{OB}$ are vectors, and θ is the measure of the angle between them, $0 < \theta < \pi$. Consider the parallelogram $OAPB$ determined by these vectors. (See Fig. 11–24.) We define the *vector product* of $\mathbf{a}$ and $\mathbf{b}$, denoted by $\mathbf{a} \times \mathbf{b}$, to be a vector $\mathbf{c}$ which is perpendicular to the plane of $\mathbf{a}$ and $\mathbf{b}$. The magnitude of $\mathbf{c}$ is the real number which is the measure of the area of the parallelogram determined by $\mathbf{a}$ and $\mathbf{b}$. Of course, there are two vectors perpendicular to the plane of $\mathbf{a}$ and $\mathbf{b}$, and so we must decide (if we wish $\mathbf{c}$ to be unique) which of these two vectors shall be the vector product of $\mathbf{a}$ and $\mathbf{b}$.

312

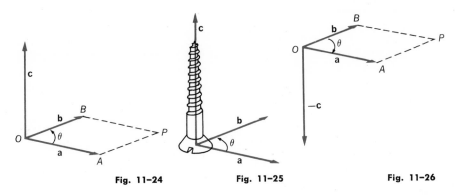

Fig. 11–24   Fig. 11–25   Fig. 11–26

It is convenient to choose vector **c** as pointing in the same direction as is an advancing right-threaded screw when its head is turned, or rotated, from **a** to **b** through angle θ. (See Fig. 11–25.)

If we consider **b** $\times$ **a**, then **b** $\times$ **a** would be a vector which is opposite in direction to **c**. (See Fig. 11–26.) Thus

$$\mathbf{a} \times \mathbf{b} = \mathbf{c} \quad \text{and} \quad \mathbf{b} \times \mathbf{a} = -\mathbf{c}.$$

EXAMPLES

1. Find **i** $\times$ **j**. Vectors **i** and **j** determine a parallelogram whose area is 1. (See Fig. 11–27.) Using the "right-hand" rule, we find that

$$\mathbf{i} \times \mathbf{j} = 1 \cdot \mathbf{k} = \mathbf{k}.$$

2. From Fig. 11–28, we see that

$$\mathbf{k} \times \mathbf{j} = -\mathbf{i}.$$

3. If **a** and **b** are vectors and θ is the measure of the angle between them, then the area of the parallelogram determined by **a** and **b** is

$$|\mathbf{a}| \cdot (|\mathbf{b}| \sin \theta).$$

(See Fig. 11–29.) Hence

$$|\mathbf{a} \times \mathbf{b}| = |\mathbf{a}| \cdot |\mathbf{b}| \sin \theta.$$

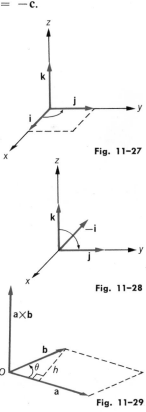

Fig. 11–27

Fig. 11–28

Fig. 11–29

313

DEFINITION 11-4

> If **a** and **b** are nonzero vectors, then the *vector product* of **a** and **b**, denoted by **a** × **b**, is the vector **c** which is perpendicular to the plane determined by **a** and **b** and whose direction is chosen as described above. The magnitude of **a** × **b** is $|\mathbf{a}| \cdot |\mathbf{b}| \sin \theta$, where θ is the measure of the angle between **a** and **b**.

Remark

Note that $\mathbf{c} = (|\mathbf{a}| \cdot |\mathbf{b}| \sin \theta) \mathbf{n}$, where **n** is the unit vector in the direction of **c**.

The vector product of two vectors is also called the *cross product*, or *outer product*, of the vectors, to distinguish it from the inner, or scalar, product. (See the historical note at the end of this chapter.)

Problems

1. Find the vector which is described as the vector product indicated. Sketch a picture of the vector in each case.

   (a) **i** × **k**   (b) **j** × **k**   (c) **i** × **i**

   (d) **k** × **i**   (e) $2\mathbf{i} \times 3\mathbf{j}$ (f) $-2\mathbf{i} \times -3\mathbf{j}$

   (g) $2\mathbf{i} \times -3\mathbf{j}$ (h) **j** × 4**k**   (i) (**i** × **j**) × **k**

   (j) **i** × (**j** × **k**)

2. Show that if **a** and **b** are nonzero vectors with the same direction, then **a** × **b** = **0**.

3. Prove that if **a** and **b** are nonzero vectors and **a** × **b** = **0**, then **a** and **b** have the same or opposite directions.

4. Show that for any nonzero vector **v**, **v** × **v** = **0**.

5. Is vector multiplication commutative?

6. Is vector multiplication associative?

7. Is $(\mathbf{i} \times 2\mathbf{j}) \times 3\mathbf{i} = \mathbf{i} \times (2\mathbf{j} \times 3\mathbf{i})$? Is $(\mathbf{i} \times \mathbf{i}) \times \mathbf{j} = \mathbf{i} \times (\mathbf{i} \times \mathbf{j})$?

8. Find the vector product of $3\mathbf{i} - 2\mathbf{j}$ and $2\mathbf{i} + 3\mathbf{j}$.

*9. Show that if **a** and **b** have position vectors $a_1\mathbf{i} + a_2\mathbf{j} + a_3\mathbf{k}$ and $b_1\mathbf{i} + b_2\mathbf{j} + b_3\mathbf{k}$, respectively, then an equation of the plane of **a** and **b** is

$$(a_2b_3 - a_3b_2)x + (a_3b_1 - a_1b_3)y + (a_1b_2 - a_2b_1)z = 0.$$

Assume that vector multiplication is distributive.

10. Show that the plane of Problem 9 has a unit normal

$$\mathbf{u} = \frac{(a_2b_3 - a_3b_2)}{d}\mathbf{i} + \frac{(a_3b_1 - a_1b_3)}{d}\mathbf{j} + \frac{(a_1b_2 - a_2b_1)}{d}\mathbf{k}$$

where

$$d = \sqrt{(a_2b_3 - a_3b_2)^2 + (a_3b_1 - a_1b_3)^2 + (a_1b_2 - a_2b_1)^2}\,.$$

11-8. THE COMPUTATION OF VECTOR PRODUCTS

It is desirable to be able to compute the vector product of two vectors in terms of the components of the two vectors. The following theorem gives a formula for doing this.

THEOREM 11-11

If

$$\mathbf{a} = a_1\mathbf{i} + a_2\mathbf{j} + a_3\mathbf{k} \qquad and \qquad \mathbf{b} = b_1\mathbf{i} + b_2\mathbf{j} + b_3\mathbf{k},$$

then

$$\mathbf{a} \times \mathbf{b} = (a_2b_3 - a_3b_2)\mathbf{i} + (a_3b_1 - a_1b_3)\mathbf{j} + (a_1b_2 - a_2b_1)\mathbf{k}. \quad (1)$$

Proof. Although it is possible to derive formula (1) without knowing it in advance, it is much easier to simply *verify* that (1) is, indeed, correct. This is what we shall do.

If either $\mathbf{a} = \mathbf{0}$ or $\mathbf{b} = \mathbf{0}$, then $\mathbf{a} \times \mathbf{b} = \mathbf{0}$ and formula (1) also gives $\mathbf{0}$. Suppose now that neither $\mathbf{a}$ nor $\mathbf{b}$ is $\mathbf{0}$ but that $\mathbf{b}$ has the same direction as, or the opposite direction from, $\mathbf{a}$. Then $\mathbf{b} = \lambda\mathbf{a}$ for some real number λ, and $\mathbf{a} \times \mathbf{b} = \mathbf{0}$. But if $\mathbf{b} = \lambda\mathbf{a}$, then $b_1 = \lambda a_1$, $b_2 = \lambda a_2$, $b_3 = \lambda a_3$ and the right-hand member of (1) is also $\mathbf{0}$. Hence in this case also, $\mathbf{a} \times \mathbf{b}$ is given by formula (1).

Suppose now that neither $\mathbf{a}$ nor $\mathbf{b}$ is $\mathbf{0}$ and $\mathbf{b} \neq \lambda\mathbf{a}$ for any real number λ. Then not all of the numbers

$$a_2b_3 - a_3b_2, \qquad a_3b_1 - a_1b_3, \qquad a_1b_2 - a_2b_1 \qquad (2)$$

are zero.† Therefore the vector $\mathbf{v}$ defined by

$$\mathbf{v} = (a_2b_3 - a_3b_2)\mathbf{i} + (a_3b_1 - a_1b_3)\mathbf{j} + (a_1b_2 - a_2b_1)\mathbf{k} \qquad (3)$$

is not the zero vector.

---

† This may be seen as follows. Since $\mathbf{a} \neq \mathbf{0}$, at least one of its components is not 0. Suppose that $a_1 \neq 0$ and that all the numbers in (2) are zero. Then

$$b_2 = \frac{a_2b_1}{a_1}, \qquad b_3 = \frac{a_3b_1}{a_1},$$

and

$$\mathbf{b} = b_1\mathbf{i} + \frac{a_3b_1}{a_1}\mathbf{j} + \frac{a_3b_1}{a_1}\mathbf{k} = \frac{b_1}{a_1}(a_1\mathbf{i} + a_2\mathbf{j} + a_3\mathbf{k})$$

$$= \frac{b_1}{a_1}\mathbf{a}.$$

But this equation asserts that $\mathbf{b} = \lambda\mathbf{a}$, with $\lambda = b_1/a_1$, which is contrary to assumption. If $a_1 = 0$, then either a_2 or a_3 does not equal 0, and a similar argument leads to a contradiction. Therefore if $\mathbf{b} \neq \lambda\mathbf{a}$, not all of the numbers (2) are zero.

315

We shall now verify that $\mathbf{v}$ is perpendicular to both $\mathbf{a}$ and $\mathbf{b}$ (Fig. 11–30), and therefore to the plane of $\mathbf{a}$ and $\mathbf{b}$. This will show that $\mathbf{v}$ has either the correct direction or the opposite direction. We have

$$\begin{aligned} \mathbf{v}\cdot\mathbf{a} &= (a_2b_3 - a_3b_2)a_1 + (a_3b_1 - a_1b_3)a_2 + (a_1b_2 - a_2b_1)a_3 = 0, \\ \mathbf{v}\cdot\mathbf{b} &= (a_2b_3 - a_3b_2)b_1 + (a_3b_1 - a_1b_3)b_2 + (a_1b_2 - a_2b_1)b_3 = 0, \end{aligned} \tag{4}$$

where it is easily checked that the right-hand members of (4) are 0.

We now verify that $\mathbf{v}$ has the correct magnitude. We have

$$\begin{aligned} |\mathbf{v}|^2 &= (a_2b_3 - a_3b_2)^2 + (a_3b_1 - a_1b_3)^2 + (a_1b_2 - a_2b_1)^2 \\ &= a_2^2b_3^2 + a_3^2b_2^2 + a_3^2b_1^2 + a_1^2b_3^2 + a_1^2b_2^2 + a_2^2b_1^2 \\ &\qquad -2a_2a_3b_2b_3 - 2a_1a_3b_1b_3 - 2a_1a_2b_1b_2, \end{aligned} \tag{5}$$

and, if θ is the angle between $\mathbf{a}$ and $\mathbf{b}$,

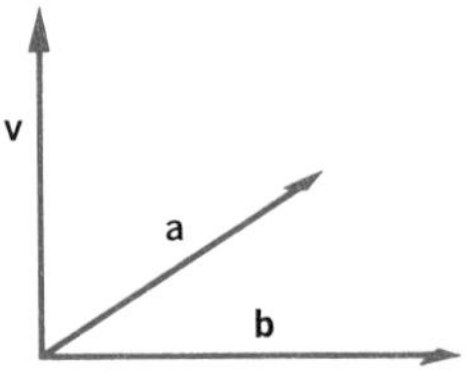

Fig. 11–30

$$\begin{aligned} |\mathbf{a}\times\mathbf{b}|^2 &= |\mathbf{a}|^2|\mathbf{b}|^2\sin^2\theta = |\mathbf{a}|^2|\mathbf{b}|^2(1 - \cos^2\theta) \\ &= |\mathbf{a}|^2|\mathbf{b}|^2\left(1 - \frac{(\mathbf{a}\cdot\mathbf{b})^2}{|\mathbf{a}|^2|\mathbf{b}|^2}\right) \\ &= |\mathbf{a}|^2|\mathbf{b}|^2 - (\mathbf{a}\cdot\mathbf{b})^2 \\ &= (a_1^2 + a_2^2 + a_3^2)(b_1^2 + b_2^2 + b_3^2) - (a_1b_1 + a_2b_2 + a_3b_3)^2 \\ &= a_2^2b_3^2 + a_3^2b_2^2 + a_3^2b_1^2 + a_1^2b_3^2 + a_1^2b_2^2 + a_2^2b_1^2 \\ &\qquad - 2a_2a_3b_2b_3 - 2a_1a_3b_1b_3 - 2a_1a_2b_1b_2. \end{aligned} \tag{6}$$

Comparison of (5) and (6) shows that $|\mathbf{v}|^2 = |\mathbf{a}\times\mathbf{b}|^2$.

We have now proved that $\mathbf{v}$ is the correct magnitude and a perpendicular to $\mathbf{a}$ and $\mathbf{b}$. It remains but to verify that $\mathbf{v}$ has the correct one of the two possible directions. For this purpose it suffices to observe that the formula for $\mathbf{v}$ gives $\mathbf{a}\times\mathbf{b}$ when $\mathbf{a}$ and $\mathbf{b}$ are pairs of the unit vectors $\mathbf{i}, \mathbf{j}, \mathbf{k}$. This last is left as an exercise for the student.

Remark

The components of $\mathbf{a}\times\mathbf{b}$ may seem difficult to remember, but if you have studied determinants (see Appendix A), it should be clear that $\mathbf{a}\times\mathbf{b}$ can be expressed as a third-order determinant, namely,

$$\mathbf{a}\times\mathbf{b} = \begin{vmatrix} \mathbf{i} & \mathbf{j} & \mathbf{k} \\ a_1 & a_2 & a_3 \\ b_1 & b_2 & b_3 \end{vmatrix}.$$

Furthermore, we may show that vector multiplication is distributive with respect to addition of vectors (see Problem 2 below), so that memorization of the components of $\mathbf{a}\times\mathbf{b}$ is not really necessary.

Problems

1. Use Theorem 11-11 to find the vector products below.

   (a) $(\mathbf{i} + \mathbf{j} - \mathbf{k}) \times (2\mathbf{i} - \mathbf{j} + \mathbf{k})$ (b) $(2\mathbf{i} + \mathbf{j}) \times (3\mathbf{j} + 2\mathbf{k})$

   (c) $(4\mathbf{i} - \mathbf{k}) \times (2\mathbf{i} - \mathbf{j})$ (d) $(2\mathbf{i} + 3\mathbf{j} + 4\mathbf{k}) \times (\mathbf{i} - 2\mathbf{j} + 2\mathbf{k})$

   (e) $(-\mathbf{i} + 5\mathbf{j} + 3\mathbf{k}) \times (3\mathbf{i} + \mathbf{j} - 4\mathbf{k})$

2. Show that vector multiplication is distributive with respect to addition, that is,

$$\mathbf{a} \times (\mathbf{b} + \mathbf{c}) = (\mathbf{a} \times \mathbf{b}) + (\mathbf{a} \times \mathbf{c}).$$

   [*Hint:* Let $\mathbf{a} = a_1\mathbf{i} + a_2\mathbf{j} + a_3\mathbf{k}$, $\mathbf{b} = b_1\mathbf{i} + b_2\mathbf{j} + b_3\mathbf{k}$, and $\mathbf{c} = c_1\mathbf{i} + c_2\mathbf{j} + c_3\mathbf{k}$.]

3. Is $\mathbf{a} \times (\mathbf{b} + \mathbf{c}) = (\mathbf{b} \times \mathbf{a}) + (\mathbf{c} \times \mathbf{a})$?

4. Use the distributive law for vector multiplication to compute the following cross products.

   (a) $2\mathbf{i} \times (\mathbf{j} + 3\mathbf{k})$ (b) $3\mathbf{i} \times (\mathbf{i} + \mathbf{j} + \mathbf{k})$

   (c) $(3\mathbf{i} + \mathbf{j}) \times (4\mathbf{j} + \mathbf{k})$ (d) $(\mathbf{i} + \mathbf{j} + \mathbf{k}) \times (3\mathbf{i})$

   (e) $(3\mathbf{i} - \mathbf{j} + \mathbf{k}) \times (\mathbf{i} + 2\mathbf{j} - 3\mathbf{k})$

11-9. APPLICATIONS OF VECTOR PRODUCTS

AREAS OF PARALLELOGRAMS AND TRIANGLES IN SPACE. Let us suppose that B, A, and C are successive vertices of a parallelogram, as in Fig. 11-31. Then by the definition of vector multiplication,

$$\text{area } \square BACD = |\overrightarrow{AB} \times \overrightarrow{AC}|$$

and

$$\text{area } \triangle BAC = \tfrac{1}{2}|\overrightarrow{AB} \times \overrightarrow{AC}|.$$

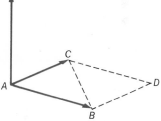

Fig. 11-31

EXAMPLE

Find the area of $\triangle ABC$, where $A = P(2, 1, 3)$, $B = P(-1, 0, 4)$ and $C = P(4, 2, 2)$.

We proceed as follows:

$$\overrightarrow{AB} = -3\mathbf{i} - \mathbf{j} + \mathbf{k}, \qquad \overrightarrow{AC} = 2\mathbf{i} + \mathbf{j} - \mathbf{k},$$

$$\overrightarrow{AB} \times \overrightarrow{AC} = [(-1)(-1) - 1 \cdot 1]\mathbf{i} + [1 \cdot 2 - (-3)(-1)]\mathbf{j}$$
$$+ [(-3)1 - (-1)2]\mathbf{k} = -\mathbf{j} - \mathbf{k};$$

$$\text{area } \triangle ABC = \tfrac{1}{2}|\overrightarrow{AB} \times \overrightarrow{AC}| = \tfrac{1}{2}\sqrt{(-1)^2 + (-1)^2} = \sqrt{2}/2.$$

317

PLANES PERPENDICULAR TO TWO INTERSECT-
ING PLANES. If a plane, π_3, is perpendicular to
each of two intersecting planes, π_1 and π_2, then
the normals of π_1 and π_2 must be perpendicular to
the normals of π_3. (See Fig. 11-32.) Therefore the
cross product of vectors normal to the intersecting
planes π_1 and π_2 will produce a vector which will
be normal to the set of planes perpendicular to π_1
and π_2.

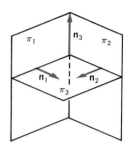

Fig. 11-32

EXAMPLE

Find an equation of the plane π which contains the point $P_1 = P(3, 2, 4)$
and is perpendicular to each of the intersecting planes

$$\pi_1: x + y - z - 4 = 0 \quad \text{and} \quad \pi_2: x - 2y + 3z - 6 = 0.$$

The given planes have normals

$$\mathbf{n}_1 = \mathbf{i} + \mathbf{j} - \mathbf{k} \quad \text{and} \quad \mathbf{n}_2 = \mathbf{i} - 2\mathbf{j} + 3\mathbf{k},$$

respectively. The required plane will have a normal $\mathbf{n}$ given by

$$\mathbf{n} = \mathbf{n}_1 \times \mathbf{n}_2 = \mathbf{i} - 4\mathbf{j} - 3\mathbf{k}.$$

The plane π must contain $P_1 = P(3, 2, 4)$; so if $P = P(x, y, z)$ is any point
in π, then $\mathbf{n} \cdot \overrightarrow{P_1 P} = 0$. Hence

$$(x - 3) \cdot 1 + (y - 2)(-4) + (z - 4)(-3) = 0,$$

so $x - 4y - 3z + 17 = 0$ is an equation of the plane π.

MOMENT OF FORCE. A force F acting on
a lever of length d from a fixed point O tends
to rotate the lever about O. (See Fig. 11-33.)
The vector product, $\mathbf{d} \times \mathbf{F}$, is called the
moment of force about O. Numerous appli-
cations of moments of force occur in physics.

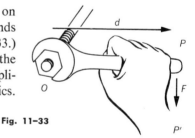

Fig. 11-33

EXAMPLE

The vector $\overrightarrow{PP'}$ acts on $\overrightarrow{OP}$ to produce a moment of force about O. What
is this moment if $P = P(2, 3, 1)$ and $P' = (-2, 6, 4)$?

$$\overrightarrow{OP} = 2\mathbf{i} + 3\mathbf{j} + \mathbf{k}. \quad \overrightarrow{PP'} = -4\mathbf{i} + 3\mathbf{j} + 3\mathbf{k}.$$

$$\text{Moment of force about } O = \overrightarrow{OP} \times \overrightarrow{PP'} = 6\mathbf{i} - 10\mathbf{j} + 18\mathbf{k}.$$

318

Problems

1. Using cross products, find the area of each triangle whose vertices have the following coordinates.

   (a) $(0, 0, 0)$, $(1, 1, 1)$, $(0, 0, 3)$ (b) $(2, 0, 0)$, $(0, 2, 0)$, $(0, 0, 2)$

   (c) $(2, 0, 0)$, $(0, 3, 0)$, $(0, 0, 4)$ (d) $(1, -1, 1)$, $(2, 2, 2)$, $(4, -2, 1)$

   *(e) (x_1, y_1, z_1), (x_2, y_2, z_2), (x_3, y_3, z_3)

2. Check Problem 1(b) by using the formula for the area of an equilateral triangle $(A = s^2\sqrt{3}/4)$.

3. The volume of a tetrahedron is given by the formula $V = \frac{1}{3}Bh$, where B is the area of a base and h is the length of the altitude to this base. (See figure.) Find the volume of a tetrahedron whose base has vertices at $(3, 1, 0)$, $(1, 4, 0)$, and $(5, 5, 0)$. The fourth vertex is at $(3, 1, 6)$.

4. Find an equation of a plane through $(0, 2, 0)$ which will be perpendicular to the pair of intersecting planes $x + 2z = 6$ and $x + y = 6$. Sketch a picture of all three planes.

5. Find an equation of a plane that contains the origin and is perpendicular to each of the planes $x + y + z = 4$ and $x - y + z = 4$. Sketch a picture.

6. Find the point of intersection of the three planes of Problem 5.

7. In each part, find an equation of the plane through the given noncollinear points.

   (a) $(1, 2, 2)$, $(3, 3, -1)$, $(-1, 5, 1)$ (b) $(0, -1, 0)$, $(2, 1, -2)$, $(1, 0, 1)$

   (c) $(1, 1, 0)$, $(3, 0, 1)$, $(-1, 2, 1)$ (d) $(1, 1, 1)$, $(2, 4, -2)$, $(5, 1, 0)$

   (e) $(2, 0, 0)$, $(0, 3, 0)$, $(0, 0, 4)$ (f) $(2, 2, 1)$, $(4, 2, -1)$, $(6, -3, 2)$

   [*Hint:* In part (a), for example, the arrows $((1, 2, 2), (3, 3, -1))$ and $((1, 2, 2), (-1, 5, 1))$ lie in the plane. Therefore, the vector product of the vectors represented by these arrows, $(2i + j - 3k) \times (-2i + 3j - k)$, will be a normal to the plane.]

8. A force $\mathbf{F} = 2i - 4j + k$ acts at P, where $\overrightarrow{OP} = 5i + 2j + 4k$. What is the moment of force about the point O? What is the magnitude of the moment of force?

9. In mechanics, a useful theorem due to Varignon states that the sum of the moments of force about a point O is equal to the moment of the sum of the forces about O. Use the diagram at the right to verify that the sum of the moments of $\mathbf{F}_1$ and $\mathbf{F}_2$ about O is the same as the moment of force of $\mathbf{F}_1 + \mathbf{F}_2$ about O. What property of vectors does this illustrate?

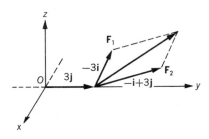

319

SUMMARY

Some of the more important concepts and formulas developed in this chapter are listed below. You should make certain that you understand the concepts and can apply the formulas.

1. The angle between two vectors or two rays.

2. Direction angles of a vector.

3. The cosine of the angle between the vectors $\mathbf{a} = a_1\mathbf{i} + a_2\mathbf{j} + a_3\mathbf{k}$ and $\mathbf{b} = b_1\mathbf{i} + b_2\mathbf{j} + b_3\mathbf{k}$:

$$\cos\theta = \frac{a_1b_1 + a_2b_2 + a_3b_3}{|\mathbf{a}|\,|\mathbf{b}|}.$$

4. The scalar product of $\mathbf{a}$ and $\mathbf{b}$:

$$\mathbf{a}\cdot\mathbf{b} = |\mathbf{a}|\cdot|\mathbf{b}|\cos\theta,$$

where θ is the measure of the angle between $\mathbf{a}$ and $\mathbf{b}$.

5. If the components of $\mathbf{a}$ and $\mathbf{b}$ are (a_1, a_2, a_3) and (b_1, b_2, b_3), respectively, then

$$\mathbf{a}\cdot\mathbf{b} = a_1b_1 + a_2b_2 + a_3b_3.$$

6. Two vectors $\mathbf{a}$ and $\mathbf{b}$ are perpendicular if and only if

$$\mathbf{a}\cdot\mathbf{b} = 0.$$

7. The line $ax + by + c = 0$ has a positive unit normal

$$\mathbf{n} = \frac{a}{\pm\sqrt{a^2 + b^2}}\mathbf{i} + \frac{b}{\pm\sqrt{a^2 + b^2}}\mathbf{j},$$

where the sign of the radical is chosen opposite to that of c. The distance p from the origin to the line is

$$p = \frac{|c|}{\sqrt{a^2 + b^2}}.$$

The distance d of the point $P_1 = P(x_1, y_1)$ from the line is

$$d = \frac{|ax_1 + by_1 + c|}{\sqrt{a^2 + b^2}}.$$

8. The plane $Ax + By + Cz + D = 0$ has positive unit normal

$$\mathbf{n} = \frac{A\mathbf{i}}{\pm\sigma} + \frac{B\mathbf{j}}{\pm\sigma} + \frac{C\mathbf{k}}{\pm\sigma},$$

where $\sigma = \sqrt{A^2 + B^2 + C^2}$, and the sign of the radical is chosen opposite to that of D.

320

The distance p from the origin to the plane is

$$p = \frac{|D|}{\sqrt{A^2 + B^2 + C^2}}.$$

The distance d from a point $P_1 = P(x_1, y_1, z_1)$ to the plane is

$$d = \frac{|Ax_1 + By_1 + Cz_1 + D|}{\sqrt{A^2 + B^2 + C^2}}.$$

9. The cross product of vectors: If

$$\mathbf{a} = a_1\mathbf{i} + a_2\mathbf{j} + a_3\mathbf{k} \qquad \text{and} \qquad \mathbf{b} = b_1\mathbf{i} + b_2\mathbf{j} + b_3\mathbf{k},$$

then

$$\mathbf{a} \times \mathbf{b} = (a_2b_3 - a_3b_2)\mathbf{i} + (a_3b_1 - a_1b_3)\mathbf{j} + (a_1b_2 - a_2b_1)\mathbf{k}.$$

Review Problems

1. Find the direction cosines and the measures of the direction angles of

$$\overrightarrow{OP} = 3\mathbf{i} - 6\mathbf{j} + 6\mathbf{k}.$$

2. The measures of the x- and y-direction angles of a vector are $\pi/3$ and $3\pi/4$, respectively. Find the measure of the z-direction angle. Draw a picture.

3. What is the cosine of the angle between $\overrightarrow{P_1P_2}$ and $\overrightarrow{P_3P_4}$ if $P_1 = P(2, 1, 3)$, $P_2 = P(-4, 4, 5)$, $P_3 = P(0, 7, 0)$, and $P_4 = P(-3, 4, -2)$?

4. What are the components of a unit vector that has the same direction as $\mathbf{v} = 2\mathbf{i} - \mathbf{j} + \mathbf{k}$?

5. Find $(\mathbf{a} + \mathbf{b}) \cdot (\mathbf{a} - \mathbf{b})$ if $\mathbf{a} = \mathbf{i} + 2\mathbf{j} + 3\mathbf{k}$ and $\mathbf{b} = 2\mathbf{i} - \mathbf{j} + \mathbf{k}$.

6. Prove that for every pair of vectors $\mathbf{a}$ and $\mathbf{b}$,

$$(\mathbf{a} + \mathbf{b}) \cdot (\mathbf{a} - \mathbf{b}) = |\mathbf{a}|^2 - |\mathbf{b}|^2.$$

7. Find the length of the projection of $\mathbf{v} = \mathbf{i} + 3\mathbf{j} - 4\mathbf{k}$ on each of the unit vectors below.

(a) $\mathbf{i}$ (b) $\mathbf{j}$ (c) $\mathbf{k}$

(d) $\dfrac{1}{\sqrt{26}}\mathbf{i} + \dfrac{3}{\sqrt{26}}\mathbf{j} - \dfrac{4}{\sqrt{26}}\mathbf{k}$ (e) $\dfrac{3}{5}\mathbf{i} - \dfrac{4}{5}\mathbf{k}$

(f) $\dfrac{2}{3}\mathbf{i} + \dfrac{2}{3}\mathbf{j} - \dfrac{1}{3}\mathbf{k}$ (g) $\dfrac{-1}{\sqrt{26}}\mathbf{i} + \dfrac{-3}{\sqrt{26}}\mathbf{j} + \dfrac{4}{\sqrt{26}}\mathbf{k}$

8. A boy pushes against a brick wall with a force of 100 lb until he is tired. How much work has he done?

9. A child lifts a toy weighing 2 lb from a floor to a table 3 ft above the floor. How much work is done? If the toy is pulled 3 ft along the floor, is the same amount of work done?

10. If a force $\mathbf{F} = 12\mathbf{i} - 4\mathbf{j} + 6\mathbf{k}$ acts through a distance $\mathbf{d} = 2\mathbf{i} + 3\mathbf{j} + 4\mathbf{k}$, what is the work done?

11. Parametric equations of a line in the xy-plane are

$$\begin{cases} x = 4 + \dfrac{1}{\sqrt{5}} d, \\[2mm] y = 2 + \dfrac{2}{\sqrt{5}} d. \end{cases}$$

What are the direction cosines of the positive unit normal to the line?

12. Find the distance from each point below to the line $3x - 4y + 7 = 0$.
   (a) (6, 2)   (b) (−2, −3)   (c) (−4, 0)
   (d) (0, 0)   (e) (11, 10)

13. Which of the following points are on the same side of the line $x - 6y + 8 = 0$ as the origin?
   (a) (2, 3)   (b) (−2, 3)   (c) (3, −2)
   (d) (−2, −3)   (e) (−3, 2)   (f) (−3, −2)

14. Find the cosines of the angles between the lines $x + 2y - 4 = 0$ and $x - y + 3 = 0$.

15. Write an equation of the plane whose positive unit normal has direction cosines $1/\sqrt{11}$, $-3/\sqrt{11}$, and $1/\sqrt{11}$, and whose distance from the origin is $2\sqrt{11}$.

16. Find the distance from each of the following points to the plane $6x - y - 2\sqrt{3}\, z - 4 = 0$.
   (a) (0, 0, 0)   (b) $(\sqrt{3}, 4\sqrt{3}, 0)$ (c) (1, 2, 0)   (d) (1, 2, 2)

17. Find the area of a triangle whose vertices have coordinates (2, 2, 0), (0, 4, 3), and (4, 0, 4).

18. What is the positive unit normal to the plane of the triangle of Problem 17?

19. Compute $\mathbf{a} \times \mathbf{b}$, given that $\mathbf{a} = 2\mathbf{i} + \mathbf{j} + 3\mathbf{k}$ and $\mathbf{b} = \mathbf{i} - 4\mathbf{j} - 2\mathbf{k}$.

20. Find an equation of the plane which contains the point $P = P(1, 1, 1)$ and is perpendicular to each of the planes

$$2x - y + 4z - 3 = 0 \quad \text{and} \quad x + 5y - 2z + 10 = 0.$$

HISTORICAL NOTE

Josiah Willard Gibbs (1839–1903)
(Courtesy The Bettman Archive)

During the nineteenth century, physicists were looking for a convenient notation and algebra for vectors. They were not groping in the dark, however; they knew what they wanted because they knew what arose naturally in the problems of mechanics.

The scalar product, for example, occurs as *work:* If a constant force **F** acts through a displacement **d**, then the work done is **F · d**. The vector product, on the other hand, occurs as a *torque*, or *moment:* If a force **F** acts at a point P with position vector $\overrightarrow{OP} = $ **v**, then the *moment* of the force is the vector **v** × **F**.

Physicists were accustomed to computing these scalars and vectors directly in terms of the rectangular components of the vectors. This direct approach of writing everything out in terms of components was referred to as "Cartesian

323

methods." What was needed was a formalism to expedite thought—an ability to think of vectors as separate entities, not as triples of numbers. When the physicist today *thinks* of the work done by the force as $\mathbf{F} \cdot \mathbf{d}$ (or the moment as $\mathbf{v} \times \mathbf{F}$), he knows that if he wishes, he can compute either product from the components. However, vector algebra carries him along without effort, enabling him to pay attention to the physical concepts without having to spend a lot of effort on computation.

Sir William Rowan Hamilton discovered quaternions in 1843. (See the Historical Note of Chapter 4.) In quaternions one can find both scalar and vector products. To understand how this is so, let

$$\mathbf{v} = ai + bj + ck \qquad \text{and} \qquad \mathbf{F} = xi + yj + zk,$$

where i, j, k are the quaternion units. Then the quaternion product of $\mathbf{F}$ and $\mathbf{v}$ is

$$\mathbf{vF} = (ai + bj + ck)(xi + yj + zk)$$
$$= -(ax + by + cz) + [(bz - cy)i + (cx - az)j + (ay - bx)k].$$

The real part of this quaternion is $-(ax + by + cz)$ and is simply the *negative* of the *scalar product* $(\mathbf{v} \cdot \mathbf{F})$ of the vectors $\mathbf{F}$ and $\mathbf{v}$. The vector part of this quaternion is $(bz - cy)i + (cx - az)j + (ay - bx)k$, and this is simply the *vector product* $(\mathbf{v} \times \mathbf{F})$ of the vectors $\mathbf{F}$ and $\mathbf{v}$. Thus we see that in quaternions we have an algebra which does what might be desired by the physicists. Hamilton and the British physicist, P. G. Tait (1831–1901), tried to popularize the use of quaternions but with little success. It is not quite clear why quaternions were never widely used, but perhaps it was the strangeness of the *extra* component, r, of the quaternion $r + xi + yj + zk$ which put off the physicists, who were after all mainly interested in the vector part, $xi + yj + zk$. It is interesting to note that James Clark Maxwell (1831–1879) in his path-breaking work *Electricity and Magnetism* (1873) used Cartesian methods in dealing with vectors.

In 1844, Hermann Grassmann, (1809–1877), published *Die Lineale Aus-dehnungslehre* (*The Theory of Linear Extension*). This outstanding work could have been the answer to the physicists' needs, but his expository style and notation proved to be a formidable barrier. Only in recent years, with better notation, has the importance of Grassmann's work been fully recognized.

One's immediate reaction to the lack of acceptance of Hamilton's quaternions is that of regret. It at first seems unreasonable that Hamilton's elegant solution was essentially discarded. But, strangely enough, the pure vector approach when generalized as anticipated by Grassmann has proved to be the more fruitful one. From vectors, one goes on to mathematical objects called *tensors*, and these are the tools of relativity theory.

324

Throughout the latter half of the nineteenth century certain notations in vector algebra came into fairly common use. In 1881, Josiah Willard Gibbs (1839–1903), professor of mathematical physics at Yale, published for his students a small pamphlet called *The Elements of Vector Analysis*. The Gibbs approach (which is what we have followed in this book) became well known and widely used. In the quaternions-versus-vectors controversy, the English physicist, Oliver Heaviside (1850–1925), should be mentioned as a leader in the vector approach. Eventually, the vector approach became *the* accepted one (with minor variations in notation), and is found in all modern texts on vector analysis.

12

CONICS

12–1. INTRODUCTION

We have seen that a first-degree (linear) equation in x and y has a graph which is a straight line; and conversely that every straight line in the plane has such an equation. It is reasonable, therefore, to ask, "What kind of graphs do second-degree equations have?" We shall see, in this chapter, that graphs of second-degree equations are the curves called *conic sections*.

These curves, the conic sections, were extensively studied by the ancient Greeks, and especially by Apollonius (third century B.C.). The Greeks considered the conics to be the curves of intersection of a plane and a right circular cone (see Fig. 12–1), and studied them in a purely geometric way. However, in this chapter, we shall study them by means of their equations. We shall give different definitions of these curves. From our definitions, it would be possible to show that these curves are actually sections of a cone, but we shall not do so.

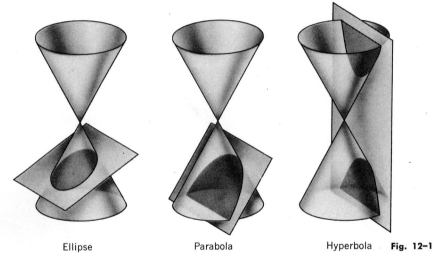

Ellipse   Parabola   Hyperbola   **Fig. 12–1**

We shall see that all these conic sections have equations that are of the second degree in the rectangular coordinates x and y. And we shall see how to recognize the curve quickly from its equation. Finally, we shall see that every second-degree equation which has a graph consisting of more than one point, and which does not *factor* (give two straight lines), must be an equation of one of the conic sections.

12–2. THE CONIC SECTIONS

There are two common definitions of these curves. We shall choose the one which clearly includes all three types (ellipse, parabola, hyperbola) in a single family of curves.

328

DEFINITION 12-1

Let l be a given line, called the *directrix*, and F be a given point, not on l, called the *focus*. Let e be a given positive number, called the *eccentricity*. Let $\mathfrak{C}$ be the set of all points P such that the ratio of the distance $|PF|$ from P to the focus F to the distance $|PM|$ from P to the directrix l is e. The point set $\mathfrak{C}$ is called a *conic*.

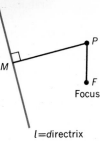

$$\text{The conic } \mathfrak{C} \text{ is } \begin{cases} \text{an } \textit{ellipse} \text{ if } e < 1, \\ \text{a } \textit{parabola} \text{ if } e = 1, \\ \text{a } \textit{hyperbola} \text{ if } e > 1. \end{cases}$$

Thus P is on the conic (see Fig. 12–2) if and only if

$$\frac{|PF|}{|PM|} = e. \qquad (1)$$

l=directrix

Fig. 12-2

EXAMPLE

Let us suppose that F and l are as shown in Fig. 12–3 and that $e = \frac{1}{2}$.

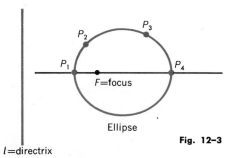

Fig. 12-3

By trial, one can approximately locate points P_1, P_2, P_3, and P_4 on the conic. The conic is an ellipse. It appears that the ellipse has the same shape at both ends. We shall see later that this is so.

Problems

1. Draw a directrix l and choose a point F as a focus. Plot many points on the ellipse with eccentricity $\frac{1}{2}$. Then draw circles C_r of different radii r with center F. For each radius r draw a line l_r parallel to l and at a distance $2r$ from l. Points where the circle C_r meets l_r will be on the ellipse. Why? How large must r be for this construction to yield points of the conic? Can r be too large?

2. Draw a directrix and choose a point as a focus. Draw several points on the parabola with eccentricity 1 and your focus and directrix. Draw circles C_r with radius r and center at the focus. Draw lines l_r parallel to the directrix and at a distance r from it. What are points of intersection of C_r and l_r? How large must r be for C_r and l_r to intersect? Can r be too large?

329

3. Draw a directrix and choose a point as a focus. Draw several points on the hyperbola with eccentricity $\frac{3}{2}$ and your focus and directrix. Draw circles C_r with radius r and center at the focus. Draw lines l_r parallel to the directrix and at distance $\frac{2}{3}r$ from it. What are points of intersection of C_r and l_r? How large must r be for C_r and l_r to intersect? Can r be too large? Can lines l_r that are on the side of the directrix opposite to the focus meet C_r?

4. A parabola has focus at $(1, 0)$ and as directrix the line with the equation $x = -1$. Find an equation satisfied by the coordinates of all points (x, y) on the parabola.

*5. Show that any conic has an equation of the second degree in x and y. [Hint: Suppose that the directrix is the line

$$ax + by + c = 0$$

and that the focus is at (h, k). Then use equation (1) of Definition 12–1.]

12-3. THE PARABOLA

If the focus and directrix of a parabola are placed conveniently with respect to the coordinate axes, then the equation of the parabola will be especially simple.

Let us suppose that the focus is at $(c, 0)$, and that the directrix has an equation $x = -c$, as in Fig. 12–4.

Then the point $P(x, y)$ is on the parabola if and only if

$$|PF| = |PM|e, \quad \text{but} \quad e = 1,$$

or

$$\sqrt{(x - c)^2 + y^2} = |x + c|. \quad (1)$$

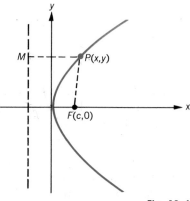

Fig. 12–4

Equation (1) is equivalent to the following equations:

$$(x - c)^2 + y^2 = (x + c)^2,$$
$$y^2 = 4cx. \quad (2)$$

Equation (2) is an equation to remember. It is the *standard form* for a parabola with its vertex at the origin and its axis along the *x*-axis. (The *axis* of a parabola is the line through the focus perpendicular to the directrix. The *vertex* is the point midway between the focus and directrix.) *It is to be emphasized that all points (x, y) on the parabola satisfy* (2), *and conversely if x and y satisfy* (2), *then the point (x, y) is on the parabola.*

330

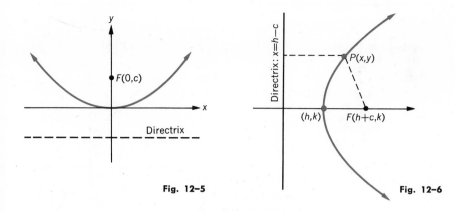

Fig. 12-5   Fig. 12-6

Several observations can be made from equation (2).

(a) The parabola is *symmetric* with respect to its axis. If (x, y) is on the parabola, so is $(x, -y)$, because then

$$y^2 = (-y)^2 = 4cx.$$

(b) The derivation of equation (2) is valid when c is either positive or negative. Figure 12–4 shows the parabola for $c > 0$. For $c < 0$, the focus would be to the left of the origin and the parabola would "open" to the left.

(c) If the parabola has its focus on the y-axis and its directrix parallel to the x-axis, then it appears as shown in Fig. 12–5 and has the standard equation

$$x^2 = 4cy.$$

(d) If the vertex is at a point (h, k) other than the origin and the directrix is parallel to the y-axis, then the focus is at $(h + c, k)$ and the directrix is $x = h - c$. (See Fig. 12–6.)

Just as before, an equation of the parabola is

$$\sqrt{(x - h - c)^2 + (y - k)^2} = |x - h + c|,$$

which is easily seen to be equivalent to

$$(y - k)^2 = 4c(x - h). \tag{3}$$

Equation (3) is the standard form for a parabola with vertex at (h, k) and axis parallel to the x-axis. If the axis were parallel to the y-axis, the standard form would be

$$(x - h)^2 = 4c(y - k). \tag{4}$$

331

EXAMPLES

1. Sketch the parabola whose equation is $y^2 = -6x$. Find its focus and directrix.

Comparing $y^2 = -6x$ with the standard form $y^2 = 4cx$, we see that

$$4c = -6$$

and

$$c = -\tfrac{3}{2}.$$

The focus is at $(-\tfrac{3}{2}, 0)$ and the directrix is the line $x = \tfrac{3}{2}$. The parabola is sketched in Fig. 12-7. Observe that the segment $\overline{AB}$ through the focus has a length $|AB| = 6 = |4c|$. Note that the segment corresponding to $\overline{AB}$ in a parabola always has a length of $4|c|$.

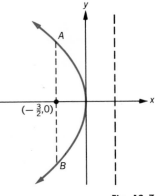

Fig. 12-7

2. Find the standard form for the parabola with the equation $x^2 + 2x + 6y - 11 = 0$. Find its vertex, focus, and equation of directrix, and sketch the figure.

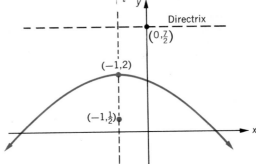

Fig. 12-8

The equation is equivalent to

$$x^2 + 2x = -6y + 11, \qquad (x+1)^2 = -6(y-2).$$

This last is in the standard form (4). Therefore the vertex is at $(-1, 2)$, with the parabola opening down. We have $4c = -6$, where $c = -\tfrac{3}{2}$. The focus is at $(-1, \tfrac{1}{2})$, and an equation of the directrix is $y = \tfrac{7}{2}$. (See Fig. 12-8.)

Problems

1. Find the focus and equation of the directrix, and sketch each of the following parabolas:

   (a) $y^2 = 6x$ (b) $y^2 = -6x$ (c) $x^2 = \tfrac{1}{2}y$ (d) $x^2 = -2y$

2. A parabola has its vertex at the origin, its axis parallel to the y-axis, and passes through $(-1, 3)$. Find its equation and sketch the parabola.

3. Sketch, on the same coordinate system, the parabolas $x^2 = 4cy$ for $c = \frac{1}{4}$, $\frac{1}{2}$, 1, 2, and 4.

4. Find vertex, focus, and equation of directrix, and sketch each of the following parabolas:

(a) $3x^2 = 8y - 16$ (b) $y^2 - 4y - 2x - 8 = 0$

(c) $y^2 + 4y = 4x$ (d) $3x^2 + 4y = 12$

5. Use the definition of a parabola to find equations of the following parabolas.

(a) Focus at $(4, 3)$, directrix $x + 2 = 0$

(b) Focus at $(-1, 1)$, directrix $2y = 5$

6. Find the points of intersection of each of the following pairs of curves and sketch the curves.

(a) $x = 3y - y^2$
$x - 2y + 2 = 0$

(b) $x^2 - y - 2 = 0$
$y - x = 0$

(c) $y^2 - 2y + 3x = 3$
$y^2 = 3x + 1$

(d) $y^2 - 4y - 6x + 24 = 0$
$x^2 - 4x - 2y = 0$

*7. A parabola has a focusing property that has many practical applications. Imagine light rays parallel to the axis of a parabolic surface, say a parabolic mirror (see figure). All these rays are reflected from the parabola toward the focus. Show that this is the case by proceeding as follows. (a) First show that the line $yy_0 = 2cx + 2cx_0$ is tangent to the parabola at a point (x_0, y_0) on it. This may be proved by showing that the line and the parabola intersect at one point only, namely (x_0, y_0). (b) Then prove that $\angle AP_0N \cong \angle NP_0F$. [*Hint:* Show that the angles have the same cosines.]

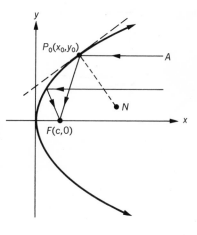

12-4. THE ELLIPSE

Like the parabola, the ellipse also has a very simple equation if the focus and directrix are suitably placed with respect to the axes. However, for the ellipse, this "conveniently chosen" coordinate system is much less obvious. Let us anticipate how things will work out in order to justify our choice of the coordinate system. From the example of Section 12-2 and Fig. 12-3 we may

333

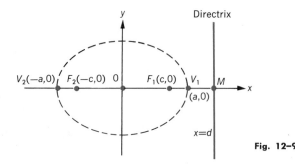

Fig. 12-9

expect the ellipse to have "the same shape at both ends." So there should be two foci F_1 and F_2, and two points V_1 and V_2 on the ellipse and on the line through the foci. Let us choose the origin midway between the foci, and the line through the foci as the x-axis. Then we may give coordinates to F_1, F_2, V_1, and V_2, as shown in Fig. 12-9. If the directrix is at a distance d from the origin, then it has an equation $x = d$. Consider the relation of V_1 and V_2 of the ellipse, to F and the directrix; by Definition 12-1 we have

$$\frac{|V_1 F_1|}{|V_1 M|} = e = \frac{|V_2 F_1|}{|V_2 M|},$$

$$\frac{|c - a|}{|d - a|} = e = \frac{|c - (-a)|}{|d - (-a)|}.$$

Since $-a < -c < 0 < c < a < d$, it follows that

$$\frac{a - c}{d - a} = e = \frac{a + c}{d + a},$$

and hence

$$a - c = de - ae,$$

$$a + c = de + ae.$$

Solving these simultaneous equations, we obtain

$$c = ae \quad \text{and} \quad a = de \quad \text{or} \quad d = \frac{c}{e^2}.$$

These last equations show where we should locate the focus and directrix in order to get a simple equation for the ellipse.

We have now arrived at a choice for the location of the ellipse with respect to the axes. Let us now see how this works out. Accordingly, suppose that the focus is at $(c, 0)$, $c > 0$, and that the directrix has the equation (see Fig. 12-10)

$$x = \frac{c}{e^2},$$

334

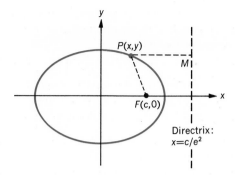

Directrix:
x=c/e²

Fig. 12–10

where e is the eccentricity and, of course, $e < 1$. Then $P(x, y)$ is on the ellipse if and only if $|PF| = |PM|e$:

$$\sqrt{(x - c)^2 + y^2} = \left|\frac{c}{e^2} - x\right| e. \tag{1}$$

This equation is equivalent to the following equations:

$$(x - c)^2 + y^2 = \left(\frac{c}{e^2} - x\right)^2 e^2,$$

$$x^2 - 2cx + c^2 + y^2 = \frac{c^2}{e^2} - 2cx + e^2 x^2,$$

$$x^2(1 - e^2) + y^2 = \frac{c^2(1 - e^2)}{e^2},$$

$$\frac{x^2}{\frac{c^2}{e^2}} + \frac{y^2}{\frac{c^2(1 - e^2)}{e^2}} = 1.$$

Let us now introduce new positive constants a and b such that

$$a^2 = \frac{c^2}{e^2}, \qquad b^2 = \frac{c^2(1 - e^2)}{e^2}. \tag{2}$$

Then the equation of the ellipse assumes the *standard form*,

$$\frac{x^2}{a^2} + \frac{y^2}{b^2} = 1. \tag{3}$$

Solving the first equation of (2) for c^2 and substituting in the second, we get $b^2 = a^2 - a^2 e^2$. From a second substitution in the last equation, we find that $a^2 = b^2 + c^2$.

If a point (x, y) is on the ellipse, then x and y satisfy equation (3), and conversely, if x and y satisfy (3), then the point (x, y) is on the ellipse.

The points $(-a, 0)$ and $(a, 0)$ are *vertices* of the ellipse and the ends of the *major axis*, so that a is the length of the semimajor axis. Likewise, the

335

points $(0, b)$ and $(0, -b)$ are *vertices* and the ends of the *minor axis* of the ellipse, so that b is the length of the semiminor axis. We observe that $b < a$. The origin is the *center* of the ellipse.

A number of observations can be made from equation (3).

(a) As we surmised earlier, the ellipse is *symmetric* with respect to both coordinate axes. If (x, y) is on the ellipse, so are $(x, -y)$, $(-x, y)$, and $(-x, -y)$. The two "ends" of the ellipse look alike.

(b) As a consequence of this symmetry, there must be another directrix at the other end of the ellipse. The equation of this second directrix would be $x = d' = -c/e^2$. Equation (3) could also be derived by choosing F_2 (or $c < 0$) and the directrix at $-c/e^2$. The ellipse with its two foci and directrices is shown in Fig. 12–11.

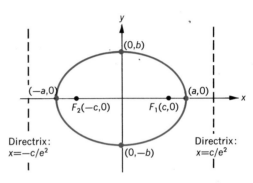

Fig. 12–11

(c) If the ellipse has its foci on the y-axis, the standard equation of the ellipse is

$$\frac{x^2}{b^2} + \frac{y^2}{a^2} = 1,$$

where a and b are the semiaxes.

(d) If the center of the ellipse is at the point (h, k) and the two foci are at $(h + c, k)$ and $(h - c, k)$, then an equation of the ellipse is

$$\sqrt{(x - h - c)^2 + (y - k)^2} = \left| h + \frac{c}{e^2} - x \right| e,$$

which can be shown to be equivalent to

$$\frac{(x - h)^2}{a^2} + \frac{(y - k)^2}{b^2} = 1. \tag{4}$$

Equation (4) is the standard form for an ellipse with center at (h, k) and major axis parallel to the x-axis. If the major axis were parallel to the y-axis, a and b would be interchanged in the equation.

EXAMPLES

1. We graph the ellipse having an equation $4x^2 + 3y^2 = 48$, and find its foci, eccentricity, and equations of directrices.

Dividing both sides of the equation by 48, we get the standard form

$$\frac{x^2}{12} + \frac{y^2}{16} = 1.$$

Then $a = 4$, $b = \sqrt{12} = 2\sqrt{3}$, and the major axis is along the y-axis. (See Fig. 12–12.)

From equations (2), $a^2 = b^2 + c^2$, or $16 = 12 + c^2$, and $c = 2$. Therefore the foci are at $(0, \pm 2)$. The eccentricity is obtained from equations (2):

$$e = \frac{c}{a} = \frac{2}{4} = \frac{1}{2}.$$

Therefore,

$$\frac{c}{e^2} = \frac{2}{(1/2)^2} = 8$$

and the directrices have equations $y = \pm 8$.

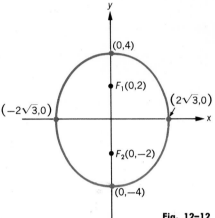

Fig. 12–12

2. An ellipse has its center at $(-2, 3)$ and semiaxes of lengths 2 and 1, with the major axis parallel to the x-axis. We wish to find the standard form of the equation of the ellipse, its foci, and directrices, and sketch the curve.

In this case, $a = 2$ and $b = 1$; therefore, the standard form is

$$\frac{(x + 2)^2}{4} + \frac{(y - 3)^2}{1} = 1. \tag{5}$$

From $a^2 = b^2 + c^2$ we obtain $4 = 1 + c^2$ and $c = \sqrt{3}$. The foci are $(-2 \pm \sqrt{3}, 3)$. (See Fig. 12–13.)

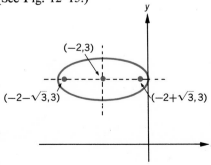

Fig. 12–13

337

Remark

Another form of an equation of the ellipse is obtained if we expand $(x + 2)^2$ and $(y - 3)^2$ in (5) and clear of fractions. We then have

$$x^2 + 4y^2 + 4x - 24y + 32 = 0, \tag{6}$$

which is also an equation of the ellipse. Had we been given (6) we would complete the squares on the x- and y-terms to obtain the standard form (5). See the next example.

EXAMPLE **3**

Let us show that the graph of $3x^2 + y^2 - 12x + 2y + 4 = 0$ is an ellipse. We will find its center, foci, eccentricity, and directrices, and sketch the ellipse.

We rewrite the equation as

$$3(x^2 - 4x \quad) + (y^2 + 2y \quad) = -4,$$

and complete the squares of the terms in parentheses to obtain

$$3(x - 2)^2 + (y + 1)^2 = 9,$$

which is equivalent to

$$\frac{(x - 2)^2}{3} + \frac{(y + 1)^2}{9} = 1.$$

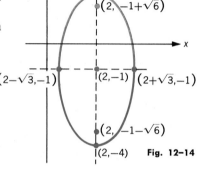

Fig. 12–14

This last is the standard form for the ellipse with semiaxes $a = 3$, $b = \sqrt{3}$ and center at $(2, -1)$. (See Fig. 12–14.) Then $c^2 = 9 - 3$ and $c = \sqrt{6}$. The eccentricity is $e = c/a = \sqrt{6}/3$.

Remark on ellipses and circles

An ellipse, as we have defined it, is never a circle. Yet it is clear that when b is close to a, the ellipse is very nearly a circle. If b is close to a, then $c = \sqrt{a^2 - b^2}$ is very nearly zero, and the eccentricity $e = c/a$ is also nearly zero. The directrices $x = \pm c/e^2 = \pm a^2/c$ recede farther and farther from the center as b approaches a. (See Fig. 12–15.)

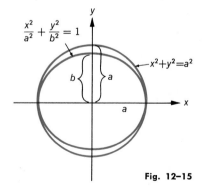

Fig. 12–15

338

By agreement we shall say that a circle is a special ellipse with *eccentricity zero*, even though the circle does not satisfy the definition of an ellipse. The two foci then coincide with the center of the circle and there are no directrices.

Problems

1. Sketch the following ellipses. Find the eccentricity, foci, and equations of directrices of each.

   (a) $x^2 + 4y^2 = 25$ \qquad\qquad (b) $5x^2 + y^2 = 80$

   (c) $4x^2 + 4y^2 = 25$ \qquad\qquad (d) $2x^2 + y^2 = 16$

2. Write the equations of each of the following ellipses and sketch the curves.

   (a) Foci at $(\pm\sqrt{3}, 0)$ and semimajor axis $\sqrt{6}$

   (b) Vertices at $(\pm 3, 0)$ and $(0, \pm 2)$

   (c) Center at $(0, 0)$, eccentricity $1/\sqrt{2}$, and semiminor axis along the x-axis and 2 units long

   (d) Foci at $(0, \pm 5)$ and eccentricity $\sqrt{5}/4$.

3. Find the points of intersection of the following pairs of curves and sketch each pair of curves.

   (a) $x^2 + 3y^2 = 52$ \qquad\qquad (b) $3x^2 + y^2 = 16$
   $\quad\ x^2 = 3y + 16$ \qquad\qquad\quad $3x + y = 1$

   (c) $2x^2 + y^2 = 18$ \qquad\qquad (d) $x^2 + 2y^2 = 9$
   $\quad\ x^2 + 5y^2 = 45$ \qquad\qquad\quad $x^2 + y^2 - 4x = 1$

4. Find an equation of the ellipse which has foci at $(\pm 2\sqrt{5}, 0)$ and passes through $(-3\sqrt{2}, 2\sqrt{2})$.

5. A rod 6 units long moves so that its ends are on two perpendicular lines. (See figure.) Show that a point two units from one end describes an ellipse.

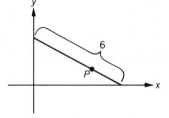

6. Find an equation of a parabola with vertex at the origin and focus at a focus of the ellipse $x^2 + 5y^2 = 10$.

7. Sketch the following ellipses. Find center and foci of each.

   (a) $9x^2 + 16y^2 - 18x - 64y = 71$

   (b) $9x^2 + 5y^2 + 36x - 30y + 36 = 0$

   (c) $25x^2 + 9y^2 + 150x + 18y + 9 = 0$

   (d) $9x^2 + y^2 - 8y + 7 = 0$

   (e) $2x^2 + y^2 + 12x + 4y = 0$

339

8. Show that the graphs of the following equations either consist of one point or are the empty set.

(a) $3x^2 + y^2 = 0$

(b) $4x^2 + y^2 - 16x - 2y + 17 = 0$

(c) $4x^2 + y^2 - 16x - 2y + 18 = 0$

9. Write equations of the following ellipses and sketch the curves.

(a) Major axis 8 units long and foci at $(0, 2)$ and $(6, 2)$

(b) Eccentricity $1/\sqrt{2}$ and foci at $(-1, -2 \pm 2\sqrt{2})$

(c) Minor axis 10 units long and parallel to the y-axis, with eccentricity $2/3$ and center $(1, 1)$

10. Find the points of intersection of the graphs of the following pairs of equations and sketch the graphs.

(a) $9x^2 + y^2 - 18x - 4y - 72 = 0$ (b) $x^2 + 2y^2 = 4$
     $y - 3x = 6$ $x^2 + 3y^2 - 2x = 0$

(c) $25x^2 + 12y^2 + 50x - 48y = 27$ (d) $x^2 + y^2 + 6x + 4y = 0$
     $4y^2 - 4y = 5x + 3$ $2y^2 + 8y - 9x = 19$

*11. The ellipse has several properties which serve to characterize it. One of these is the following, which is sometimes used as the definition. If P is on an ellipse with foci F_1 and F_2, then

$$|PF_1| + |PF_2| \text{ is a constant, and conversely.}$$

Prove that if $P = (x, y)$ is on the ellipse $b^2x^2 + a^2y^2 = a^2b^2$ with foci $F_1 = (c, 0)$ and $F_2 = (-c, 0)$, then $|PF_1| + |PF_2| = 2a$.

12-5. THE HYPERBOLA

We choose the focus and directrix such that they are conveniently located with respect to the axes. Our choice of location is formally identical with the one we made for the ellipse.

Accordingly, let us suppose that the focus is at $(c, 0)$, where $c \neq 0$ ($c > 0$ in Fig. 12–16). Let us further suppose that the directrix is

$$x = \frac{c}{e^2},$$

where e is the eccentricity and, of course, $e > 1$.

Then $P(x, y)$ is on the hyperbola if and only if $|PF| = |PM|e$, or

$$\sqrt{(x - c)^2 + y^2} = \left| \frac{c}{e^2} - x \right| e. \quad (1)$$

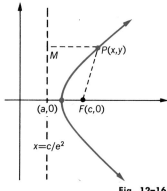

Fig. 12–16

This equation is formally the same as equation (1) of Section 12–4 and so by the same algebraic steps is equivalent to

$$\frac{x^2}{\dfrac{c^2}{e^2}} - \frac{y^2}{\dfrac{c^2(e^2-1)}{e^2}} = 1.$$

Note that the sign of the second fraction is negative because in the denominator we have $(e^2 - 1)$, which is greater than zero.

As for the ellipse, we introduce new positive constants a and b according to

$$a^2 = \frac{c^2}{e^2}, \quad b^2 = \frac{c^2(e^2-1)}{e^2} = c^2 - a^2, \quad \text{so that} \quad c^2 = a^2 + b^2. \qquad (2)$$

Unlike the ellipse, the hyperbola may have $a > b$ or $b > a$, or even $a = b$, since $c^2 = a^2 + b^2$. The equation of the hyperbola then assumes the *standard form*

$$\frac{x^2}{a^2} - \frac{y^2}{b^2} = 1. \qquad (3)$$

If a point (x, y) is on the hyperbola, then x and y satisfy (3), and conversely, if x and y satisfy (2), then the point (x, y) is on the hyperbola. The points $(a, 0)$ and $(-a, 0)$ are the *vertices* of the hyperbola. The number a is the length of the *semitransverse axis*. The number b is the length of the *semiconjugate axis*. (Geometric interpretations for a and b are given below.) The *center* of the hyperbola is at $(0, 0)$.

A number of observations can be made from equation (3).

(a) The hyperbola is *symmetric* with respect to the coordinate axes, which are called the *axes* of the hyperbola, and has its center at $(0, 0)$.

(b) From observation (a) we see that there must be a second focus and directrix. This fact may also be seen by observing that equations (1), (2), and (3) are not dependent on the sign of c. Figure 12–16 shows the focus and directrix when $c > 0$.

(c) If the hyperbola has its foci on the y-axis, the standard form of the equation is

$$\frac{y^2}{a^2} - \frac{x^2}{b^2} = 1.$$

(d) If we solve (3) for y, we obtain

$$y = \pm \frac{b}{a}\sqrt{x^2 - a^2}, \qquad (4)$$

from which we see that x^2 must be greater than or equal to a^2, and that the hyperbola does not meet the y-axis.

From equation (4) we can also see that there are two straight lines, called *asymptotes*, that are intimately related to the hyperbola. From (4) we have

$$y = \pm \frac{b|x|}{a} \sqrt{1 - \frac{a^2}{x^2}} \qquad \text{if} \qquad |x| > a.$$

This last equation suggests that for large $|x|$, and therefore small a^2/x^2, the hyperbola should be very near the straight lines

$$y = \pm \frac{bx}{a}.$$

That this is indeed the case can be shown as follows (where, because of symmetry, we may restrict ourselves to the first quadrant):

$$\begin{aligned}
y_{\text{line}} - y_{\text{hyperbola}} &= \frac{b}{a}x - \frac{b}{a}\sqrt{x^2 - a^2} \\
&= \frac{b}{a}(x - \sqrt{x^2 - a^2}) \\
&= \frac{b}{a}\frac{(x - \sqrt{x^2 - a^2})(x + \sqrt{x^2 - a^2})}{x + \sqrt{x^2 - a^2}} \\
&= \frac{ab}{x + \sqrt{x^2 - a^2}}.
\end{aligned}$$

When x is very large, this last fraction represents a small number. Therefore the ordinate on the line is very near the corresponding ordinate on the hyperbola if x is very large.

Such a line is called an *asymptote*. That is, *an asymptote is a line which a curve approaches as a point on the curve "recedes to infinity."* An asymptote is *not* a part of the hyperbola.

A hyperbola with both foci, both directrices, and asymptotes is shown in Fig. 12–17.

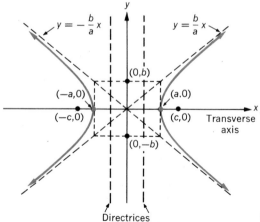

Fig. 12–17

We note that the asymptotes are very helpful in drawing the hyperbola. The asymptotes are easy to draw if one constructs the dotted rectangle of dimensions $2a$ and $2b$ shown in Fig. 12–17. We see that geometrically, a and b are equal to half the respective measures of this rectangle. The axis of the hyperbola containing the two foci is called the *transverse* axis.

(e) If the center of the hyperbola is at (h, k) and the two foci are at $(h \pm c, k)$, then an equation of the hyperbola is

$$\sqrt{(x - h - c)^2 + (y - k)^2} = \left| h + \frac{c}{e^2} - x \right| e,$$

which is equivalent to

$$\frac{(x - h)^2}{a^2} - \frac{(y - k)^2}{b^2} = 1. \qquad (5)$$

Equation (5) is the standard form for a hyperbola with center (h, k) and transverse axis parallel to the x-axis. If the transverse axis were parallel to the y-axis, the equation would be

$$\frac{(y - k)^2}{a^2} - \frac{(x - h)^2}{b^2} = 1.$$

EXAMPLES

1. We wish to graph the hyperbola having an equation $8x^2 - 3y^2 = 48$, and find its foci, equations of directrices and asymptotes, and eccentricity.

Dividing both sides of the equation by 48, we get the standard form

$$\frac{x^2}{6} - \frac{y^2}{16} = 1.$$

Therefore (see Fig. 12–18),

$$a = \sqrt{6}, \qquad b = 4,$$
$$c = \sqrt{6 + 16} = \sqrt{22}.$$

The foci are $(\pm\sqrt{22}, 0)$. The eccentricity is

$$e = \sqrt{\frac{22}{6}} = \sqrt{\frac{11}{3}}.$$

The directrices are

$$x = \pm \frac{c}{e^2} = \pm \frac{3\sqrt{22}}{11}.$$

The asymptotes are

$$y = \pm \frac{4}{\sqrt{6}} x.$$

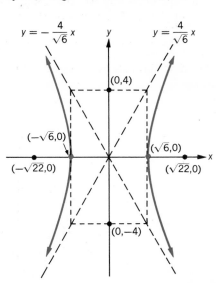

Fig. 12–18

2. We wish to find the standard form for the equation of the hyperbola with center at $(-2, 3)$, transverse axis parallel to the y-axis, and semiaxes of lengths a and b equal to 4 and 2, respectively. What are the equations of the asymptotes? We shall sketch the hyperbola and its asymptotes.

Since $c^2 = a^2 + b^2$, we have $c = \sqrt{20} = 2\sqrt{5}$. The foci are at $(-2, 3 \pm 2\sqrt{5})$. (See Fig. 12–19.) The vertices are at $(-2, 7)$ and $(-2, -1)$. The asymptotes have slopes ± 2 and pass through the center. Their equations are

$$y - 3 = \pm 2(x + 2).$$

The equation of the hyperbola is

$$\frac{(y-3)^2}{16} - \frac{(x+2)^2}{4} = 1,$$

which is equivalent to

$$y^2 - 4x^2 - 16x - 6y = 23.$$

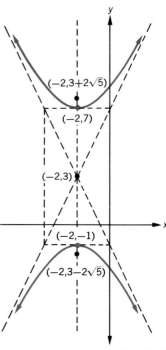

Fig. 12–19

3. We wish to show that the graph of $-4x^2 + 9y^2 + 36y + 8x + 68 = 0$ is a hyperbola, find its center, equations of asymptotes, and make a sketch.

Completing the squares on the x- and y-terms, we have

$$-4(x^2 - 2x + 1) + 9(y^2 + 4y + 4) = -68 - 4 + 36 = -36.$$

Dividing through by -36, we obtain the equivalent equation and standard form

$$\frac{(x-1)^2}{9} - \frac{(y+2)^2}{4} = 1,$$

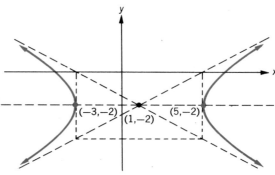

Fig. 12–20

344

which is recognized as the equation of a hyperbola with center at $(1, -2)$ and axis parallel to the x-axis. We have $a = 3$, $b = 2$, and asymptotes with equations $y + 2 = \pm\frac{2}{3}(x - 1)$. (See Fig. 12–20.)

Problems

1. Sketch the following hyperbolas. Find eccentricity, foci, and equations of asymptotes of each.

   (a) $16x^2 - 9y^2 = 144$ (b) $4x^2 - 5y^2 + 20 = 0$

   (c) $2x^2 - y^2 = 8$ (d) $10x^2 - 16y^2 + 25 = 0$

2. Write equations of each of the following hyperbolas, and sketch them.

   (a) Foci at $(\pm\sqrt{3}, 0)$ and semitransverse axis $\sqrt{2}$

   (b) Center at $(0, 0)$, eccentricity $\sqrt{2}$, and semiconjugate axis is 2 units long along the x-axis.

   (c) Vertices at $(\pm 3, 0)$ and asymptotes with slopes $\pm 1/3$

   (d) Foci at $(0, \pm 5)$ and eccentricity $\frac{5}{4}$

3. Find the points of intersection of the following pairs of curves and sketch each pair.

   (a) $3x^2 + 2y^2 = 8$ (b) $x^2 - y^2 = 1$
       $x^2 - y^2 = 1$ $y = 2x + 1$

   (c) $x^2 - 2y^2 = 2$ (d) $3y^2 - 4x^2 = 12$
       $y^2 = x$ $2x = (2\sqrt{6} + 3)y - 8\sqrt{6} - 18$

4. Find an equation of the hyperbola which has foci at $(0, \pm 2\sqrt{5})$ and passes through $(-2\sqrt{6}, 4\sqrt{3})$.

5. Sketch the following hyperbolas. Find center, foci, eccentricity, and equations of asymptotes.

   (a) $9x^2 - 16y^2 - 18x - 64y = 19$

   (b) $9x^2 - 5y^2 + 36x + 30y + 36 = 0$

   (c) $25x^2 - 9y^2 + 150x + 18y = 9$

   (d) $9x^2 - y^2 + 8y = 7$ (e) $y^2 - 2x^2 + 12x + 4y = -4$

6. Write equations of the following hyperbolas and sketch them.

   (a) Transverse axis 8 units long and foci at $(-2, 2)$ and $(8, 2)$

   (b) Eccentricity $\sqrt{2}$ and foci at $(-1, -2 \pm 2\sqrt{2})$

   (c) Semiconjugate axis 5, with eccentricity $3/2$, center at $(1, 1)$, and transverse axis parallel to the x-axis.

7. The hyperbola has several properties which serve to characterize it. One of these is sometimes used as the definition, namely: If P is on a hyperbola with foci F_1 and F_2, then $|PF_2| - |PF_1| = \pm 2a$ (depending on which branch P lies), and conversely.

   Show that if $P(x, y)$ is on the right-hand branch of the hyperbola of Figure 12–17, then $|PF_2| - |PF_1| = 2a$ if $F_1 = (c, 0)$ and $F_2 = (-c, 0)$.

345

12-6. DEGENERATE CONICS

In the preceding sections we have seen that the conics, ellipses, parabolas, and hyperbolas (with axes parallel to the coordinate axes), have equations which are of the second degree in x and y. In this and the following section we shall complete our study of what the graphs of second-degree equations in x and y can be. We shall see that except for *degenerate cases*, these graphs are always conics. In this section we investigate these degenerate cases by a study of examples.

From Fig. 12–1 we see that there are intersections of a plane with a cone that are not ellipses, parabolas, or hyperbolas. If the plane passes through the vertex of the cone, it can intersect the cone in two intersecting straight lines. The plane can also intersect the cone in a single point, the vertex. Thus there are other sections of a cone than the ones we have studied so far.

If a plane intersects a cone at a point or in two intersecting straight lines, or if the plane does not intersect the cone, then we usually call these cases *degenerate conics*.

EXAMPLES

1. The equation $x^2 + 2y^2 = 0$ has a graph consisting of only one point.

2. The equation $x^2 + 2y^2 + 1 = 0$ has an empty graph.

3. Sometimes it is not easy to recognize the types shown in Examples 1 and 2; they may be disguised as shown here. The equation

$$x^2 + 2y^2 - 4x + 8y + 13 = 0$$

becomes, on completion of the squares on x and y,

$$(x - 2)^2 + 2(y + 2)^2 + 1 = 0.$$

The graph of this equation is empty. Sometimes the graph is described as being *imaginary*. This means that the only numbers x and y which satisfy the equation are complex numbers with at least one of them having a nonzero imaginary part.

These examples illustrate one type of degeneracy of second-degree equations. The examples below illustrate the other type of degeneracy.

4. We wish to sketch the graph of $x^2 - xy - 2y^2 - x + 11y - 12 = 0$.
The polynomial happens to factor, so the equation is

$$x^2 - xy - 2y^2 - x + 11y - 12 = (x - 2y + 3)(x + y - 4) = 0.$$

Therefore its graph is the union of the graphs of $x - 2y + 3 = 0$ and $x + y - 4 = 0$. It is shown in Fig. 12–21.

346

The student may very well wonder how one is to determine whether or not a given equation factors. Inspection of the quadratic terms will usually show how to proceed. Thus in the above example, the quadratic terms alone factor: $x^2 - xy - 2y^2 = (x - 2y)(x + y)$. It remains then to see if there are suitable choices of a and b for which we can have

$$x^2 - xy - 2y^2 - x + 11y - 12 = (x - 2y + a)(x + y + b).$$

A few trials will usually decide the issue.

However, if there is *no xy-term* in the equation, then simple completion of the squares on x and y will show whether or not the equation factors. The next example illustrates this case.

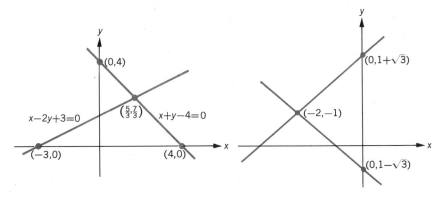

Fig. 12-21   Fig. 12-22

5. The equation $3x^2 - 4y^2 + 12x + 8y + 8 = 0$ becomes, after completion of the squares,

$$3(x + 2)^2 - 4(y - 1)^2 = 0.$$

The left-hand member of this last equation is the difference of two squares and it factors as the product of a sum and a difference:

$$[\sqrt{3}(x + 2) + 2(y - 1)][\sqrt{3}(x + 2) - 2(y - 1)] = 0.$$

The graph of the equation is the union of the graphs of

$$\sqrt{3}(x + 2) + 2(y - 1) = 0,$$
$$\sqrt{3}(x + 2) - 2(y - 1) = 0,$$

and is shown in Fig. 12-22.

347

Problems

1. Identify and sketch the following degenerate conics.

   (a) $3x^2 + 4y^2 = 0$ (b) $3x^2 + 4y^2 + 6x + 4y + 5 = 0$

   (c) $x^2 - 4y^2 = 0$ (d) $x^2 - 4y^2 + 2x + 4y = 0$

   (e) $2x^2 - 3y^2 + 3y - \frac{3}{4} = 0$ (f) $xy = 0$

   (g) $y^2 = 2xy$

   (h) $x^2 + 2xy + y^2 - 2x - 2y + 1 = 0$

   (i) $x^2 + 2xy + y^2 + x + y = 0$

2. Show that the graph of $Ax^2 + By^2 + Cx + Dy + E = 0$ consists of two intersecting straight lines if

$$AB < 0 \quad \text{and} \quad E = \frac{C^2}{4A} + \frac{D^2}{4B}.$$

   (Without loss of generality you may assume that $A > 0$ and $B < 0$. Why?)

12–7. THE GENERAL SECOND-DEGREE EQUATION

From the last section we see that if there is no xy-term, then by completing the square it is easy to determine whether or not the conic is degenerate. If the conic, given by

$$Ax^2 + Cy^2 + Dx + Ey + F = 0 \quad (A^2 + C^2 \neq 0)$$

is not degenerate, then from the preceding sections it follows that after completing the squares, we obtain the equation of an ellipse, parabola, or hyperbola in standard form—and the type of graph obtained depends only on the signs of A and C. (Remember that we call a circle a special ellipse.) Our present state of knowledge is summarized in the following theorem.

THEOREM 12–1

If the graph of

$$Ax^2 + Cy^2 + Dx + Ey + F = 0$$

is not degenerate, and not both A and C are zero, then the graph is

       (a) an ellipse   if $AC > 0$,

       (b) a parabola   if $AC = 0$,

       (c) a hyperbola   if $AC < 0$.

348

EXAMPLE 1

Let us consider the equation $2x^2 - 9y^2 + 4x + 18y + 1 = 0$. Assuming that its graph is not degenerate, we see that Theorem 12–1(c) applies, $AC = -18 < 0$, and we must have a hyperbola. It is easy to verify that this is indeed the case. We obtain

$$2(x + 1)^2 - 9(y - 1)^2 = 1 + 2 - 9 = -8,$$

and a standard form for a hyperbola,

$$\frac{(y - 1)^2}{\frac{8}{9}} - \frac{(x + 1)^2}{4} = 1.$$

We turn now to the general quadratic equation in x and y:

$$Ax^2 + Bxy + Cy^2 + Dx + Ey + F = 0, \tag{1}$$

where not all of A, B, and C are zero. In Chapter 13 we shall see that the xy-term in (1) can be eliminated by rotation of the axes through a suitably selected angle θ. (See Fig. 12–23.) In other words, if a second coordinate system were chosen, with axes x', y' as indicated in Fig. 12–23, then in terms of the new coordinates equation (1) would become the equivalent equation

$$A'x'^2 + C'y'^2 + D'x' + E'y' + F' = 0, \tag{2}$$

(note that $B' = 0$ for the special value of θ), where the coefficients $A', \ldots, F'$ can be found in terms of $A, \ldots, F$, and θ. We see therefore that equation (1) must represent a conic, degenerate or not.

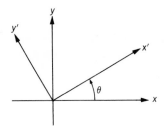

Fig. 12–23

When this transformation to the $x'y'$-coordinate system is carried out (and we shall do this in Chapter 13) it is an easy calculation to show that

$$B^2 - 4AC = B'^2 - 4A'C',$$

no matter through what angle θ the axes may be rotated. In other words, $B^2 - 4AC$ remains *invariant* under rotation of coordinate axes. Because the graph of equation (2) is readily identified by application of Theorem 12–1, we are able to distinguish the graph of (1) with little effort.

349

We state our conclusions as follows:

THEOREM 12-2

If not all of A, B, and C are zero, and if the graph of

$$Ax^2 + Bxy + Cy^2 + Dx + Ey + F = 0,$$

is not degenerate, then the graph is

(a) an ellipse   if $B^2 - 4AC < 0,$

(b) a parabola   if $B^2 - 4AC = 0,$

(c) a hyperbola   if $B^2 - 4AC > 0.$

Armed with knowledge of this theorem, one can make a rather good sketch of the graph of a second-degree equation without bothering to remove the xy-term. The following example may serve to illustrate the method.

EXAMPLE 2

Let us consider the equation

$$4x^2 + 3xy + y^2 - 12 = 0.$$

Here $A = 4$, $B = 3$, $C = 1$, and $B^2 - 4AC = 9 - 16 = -7 < 0.$ Therefore the graph, if not degenerate, is an ellipse.

Let us try to sketch the graph directly. First we observe that the given equation is quadratic in y and hence can easily be solved for y by the quadratic formula

$$y^2 + 3xy + (4x^2 - 12) = 0,$$

$$y = \frac{-3x + \sqrt{9x^2 - 4(4x^2 - 12)}}{2}$$

$$= -\frac{3x}{2} \pm \frac{\sqrt{48 - 7x^2}}{2}.$$

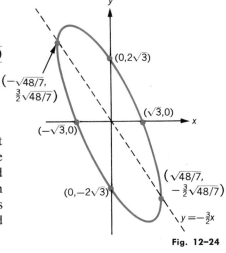

From this last equation we see that $|x|$ cannot exceed $\sqrt{\frac{48}{7}}$. Therefore the graph is confined to a bounded portion of the plane and must be an ellipse. (See Fig. 12–24.) The points of the ellipse must lie above and below the line $y = -3x/2$.

Fig. 12-24

Problems

1. Assume that the graphs of the following conics are not degenerate. In each case use Theorem 12–2 to predict the type of conic.

   (a) $x^2 - xy + y^2 + x + y = 0$ (b) $x^2 - xy - y^2 + x + y = 0$

   (c) $x^2 + 2xy + y^2 + x - y = 0$

   (d) $17x^2 + 12xy + 8y^2 - 60x + 24y - 12 = 0$

   (e) $xy - 7 = 0$ (f) $xy - x - 1 = 0$

2. Using Theorem 12–2, determine the kinds of graphs described by the following equations. Then sketch the graph of each by solving for y and plotting a few points.

   (a) $5x^2 - 4xy + 4y^2 = 12$ (b) $3x^2 + 4xy - 4y^2 - 12 = 0$

   (c) $x^2 - 4xy + 4y^2 - 4x + 8 = 0$ (d) $xy + y + x = 0$.

3. A conic has focus $(1, 1)$, directrix $x + y + 1 = 0$, and eccentricity $\sqrt{2}$. Use the definition to find a second-degree equation of the conic. Verify that Theorem 12–2 predicts the correct type of conic.

12–8. HIGHER-DEGREE CURVES

At this point our position is such that we can predict the kinds of graphs of the following equations:

$$Ax + By + C = 0,$$
$$Ax^2 + Bxy + Cy^2 + Dx + Ey + F = 0.$$

We can also sketch the graphs of such equations fairly quickly. It therefore is natural to wonder about the graphs of equations obtained from polynomials of degree three or more in x and y, for example *cubic* curves which have an equation of the form

$$Ax^3 + Bx^2y + Cxy^2 + Dy^3 + Ex^2 + Fxy + Gy^2 + Hx + Iy + J = 0.$$

Such curves are called *algebraic curves*, and the classification of the kinds one can obtain is part of *algebraic geometry*. We cannot go into these questions here, partly for lack of space, but also because more advanced methods are needed for such a study. Nevertheless, a few of these curves are quite easy to graph by the methods we have at our disposal. If the algebraic equation is either linear or quadratic in y, then it is easy to solve for y, and the graph can usually be sketched after a few points have been plotted. Consider the following examples.

EXAMPLES

1. Sketch the graph of $y^2 = x(x - 1)^2$.

We observe that the graph is symmetric with respect to the x-axis because if x and y satisfy the equation, so do x and $-y$. We also observe that we must have $x \geq 0$, for otherwise y could not be a real number. The graph is as shown in Fig. 12–25.

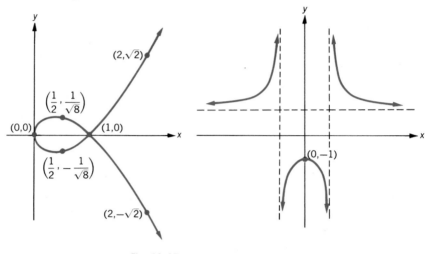

Fig. 12–25   Fig. 12–26

2. Let us sketch the graph of $x^2y - x^2 - y = 0$.

This equation is also a cubic (of degree three) because of the x^2y-term. It is of the first degree in y, and

$$y = \frac{x^2}{x^2 - 1}.$$

The graph is symmetric with respect to the y-axis. This curve has asymptotes just as a hyperbola does. We observe that as $|x| \to 1$, $y \to \pm\infty$, depending on whether $|x| > 1$ or $|x| < 1$. Furthermore, as $|x|$ becomes infinite, y approaches 1. The graph is shown in Fig. 12–26.

Problems

Sketch the graphs of the following equations.

1. $x^2y = 4a^2(2a - y)$, $a > 0$ (the witch of Agnesi)

2. $y^2 = ax^3$, $a > 0$ (a semicubical parabola)

3. $y^2 = x^2(x - 1)$ (curve with an isolated point)

4. $y^2 = x(x - 1)(x - 2)$ 5. $y = (x - 1)(x - 2)(x - 3)$

352

6. $y = \dfrac{(x - 1)(x - 3)}{x - 2}$

7. $y = \dfrac{x - 1}{(x - 2)(x - 3)}$

*8. $(x^2 + y^2)^2 = a^2(x^2 - y^2)$ (Lemniscate).

*9. $x^3 + y^3 - 3axy, a > 0$ (the folium of Descartes)

12–9. QUADRIC SURFACES

Thus far we have considered curves in the *plane*, and mainly curves represented by second-degree equations in x and y. One generalization was suggested in Section 12–8, where we briefly mentioned curves represented by algebraic equations of higher degree.

A different generalization is to consider the graphs of second-degree equations in *three* variables:

$$Ax^2 + By^2 + Cz^2 + Dxy + Eyz + Fzx + Gx + Hy + Iz + J = 0. \quad (1)$$

The graphs of such equations are called *quadric surfaces*. A complete description of these surfaces would take us too far afield, so we shall content ourselves with sketching a few examples. In Fig. 12–27 the nondegenerate quadric surfaces are shown along with the equations they have when the axes are conveniently chosen.

Actually, the ideas of this section were anticipated in Chapter 5, where cylinders and spheres were discussed. The method we follow is that of examining the intersections of these surfaces with planes parallel to the coordinate planes. These sections will be conics and therefore easy for us to sketch. When a few of these sections have been drawn, the appearance of the surface will usually be clear.

EXAMPLES

1. Sketch the quadric surface whose equation is

$$2x^2 + y^2 = z.$$

First we examine the *traces* of this surface in the coordinate planes. They are

xy-trace: $2x^2 + y^2 = 0$, $z = 0$ (the trace is a point),
yz-trace: $y^2 = z$, $x = 0$ (the trace is a parabola),
zx-trace: $2x^2 = z$, $y = 0$ (the trace is a parabola).

The parabolic traces (half of each) are drawn as red lines in Fig. 12–28.

353

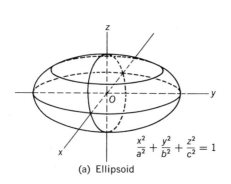

$$\frac{x^2}{a^2} + \frac{y^2}{b^2} + \frac{z^2}{c^2} = 1$$

(a) Ellipsoid

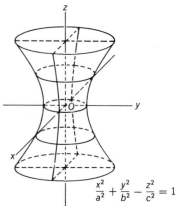

$$\frac{x^2}{a^2} + \frac{y^2}{b^2} - \frac{z^2}{c^2} = 1$$

(b) Hyperboloid of one sheet

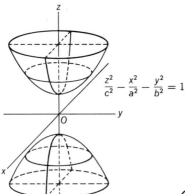

$$\frac{z^2}{c^2} - \frac{x^2}{a^2} - \frac{y^2}{b^2} = 1$$

(c) Hyperboloid of two sheets

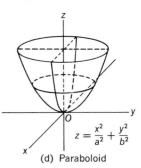

$$z = \frac{x^2}{a^2} + \frac{y^2}{b^2}$$

(d) Paraboloid

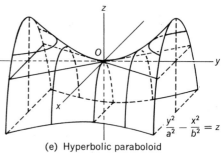

$$\frac{y^2}{a^2} - \frac{x^2}{b^2} = z$$

(e) Hyperbolic paraboloid

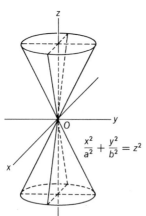

$$\frac{x^2}{a^2} + \frac{y^2}{b^2} = z^2$$

(f) Quadric cone (elliptic sections)

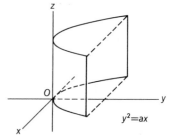

$$y^2 = ax$$

(g) Parabolic cylinder   **Fig. 12-27**

354

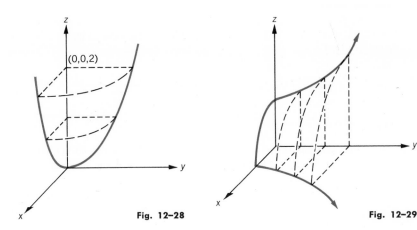

Fig. 12-28   Fig. 12-29

Let us consider the intersections of the surface with planes $z = c =$ constant. These curves are ellipses for all positive c. Two are shown in Fig. 12–28. Actually only one-fourth of the quadric is shown in Fig. 12–28. The full surface is shown in Fig. 12–27(d).

2. Sketch the graph of

$$2x^2 - y^2 + z^2 = 4.$$

The traces in the coordinate planes are:

$$xy\text{-trace:} \quad 2x^2 - y^2 = 4, \quad z = 0 \quad \text{(a hyperbola)},$$
$$yz\text{-trace:} \quad -y^2 + z^2 = 4, \quad x = 0 \quad \text{(a hyperbola)},$$
$$zx\text{-trace:} \quad 2x^2 + z^2 = 4, \quad y = 0 \quad \text{(an ellipse)}.$$

Parts of these traces are drawn as solid lines in Fig. 12–29. To make the surface "stand out" we slice it by planes parallel to one of the coordinate planes. Which plane to use is dictated by ease in drawing the sections. Since all sections determined by the planes $y = c =$ constant are ellipses and therefore easy to draw, we shall use these planes. Parts of these ellipses are drawn as dashed lines for $c = 1, 2, 3$ in Fig. 12–29.

Problems

1. In each of the following quadrics, sketch the traces in the coordinate planes and sections produced by several planes parallel to the coordinate plane.
   (a) $x^2 + 2y^2 + 3z^2 = 6$ (b) $x^2 + 2y^2 - 3z^2 = 6$
   (c) $-x^2 + 2y^2 - 3z^2 = 6$ (d) $x^2 - y^2 + z^2 = 0$
   (e) $x^2 + z^2 - y = 0$ (f) $y^2 - x^2 = z$
   (g) $(x + z - 1)(x - y) = 0$ (h) $x^2 + 2y^2 = 6$
   (i) $y^2 = 4x$ *(j) $xz = y^2$

2. For the following quadrics, first complete the squares on the appropriate variables, and then sketch each surface. Identify the kind of quadric by reference to Fig. 12–27.

(a) $x^2 + y^2 + z^2 - 4z = 0$

(b) $x^2 + 2y^2 + 3z^2 - 2x - 8y + 3 = 0$

(c) $x^2 + y^2 - z^2 - 2x - 4y + 1 = 0$

(d) $y^2 + 4x - 4y + 8 = 0$

3. Show that sections of the general quadric surface of equation (1), page 353, made by planes parallel to the coordinate planes are conic sections.

SUMMARY

The emphasis of this chapter has been on the graphs of second-degree equations. These graphs are called *conic* sections.

The principal nondegenerate conic sections are the parabola, ellipse, and hyperbola. Definition 12–1, which defines the conic sections, is of primary importance. The eccentricity e of a conic tells us the kind of conic we are considering. Thus, if

(a) $e < 1$, the conic is an ellipse,

(b) $e = 1$, the conic is a parabola,

(c) $e > 1$, the conic is a hyperbola.

If the focus and directrix of one of the conic sections is suitably placed with respect to the coordinate axes, then an equation of the conic is quite simple.

1. $y^2 = 4cx$. Parabola with vertex at the origin and axis along the x-axis; c is the focus.

2. $\dfrac{x^2}{a^2} + \dfrac{y^2}{b^2} = 1$. Ellipse with *semimajor axis a* and *semiminor axis b*. $a^2 = b^2 + c^2$. The foci are at $(c, 0)$ and $(-c, 0)$. $e = (c/a) < 1$.

3. $\dfrac{x^2}{a^2} - \dfrac{y^2}{b^2} = 1$. Hyperbola with *semitransverse axis* of length a and *semiconjugate axis* of length b. The foci are at $(\pm c, 0)$, where $c^2 = a^2 + b^2$. Equations of the *asymptotes* are $y = \pm(b/a)x$.

4. The graph of the equation

$$Ax^2 + Cy^2 + Dx + Ey + F = 0,$$

if not degenerate, is

(a) an ellipse   if $AC > 0$;

(b) a parabola   if $AC = 0$;

(c) a hyperbola   if $AC < 0$.

5. The graph of the equation

$$Ax^2 + Bxy + Cy^2 + Dx + Ey + F = 0,$$

if not degenerate, is

(a) an ellipse   if $B^2 - 4AC < 0$;

(b) a parabola   if $B^2 - 4AC = 0$;

(c) a hyperbola if $B^2 - 4AC > 0$.

In addition to the conic sections we considered a few *algebraic curves* of a degree greater than two. Our method of graphing such higher-degree equations was that of plotting enough points to visualize the shape of the curve.

Finally, we extended the idea of conic sections to space by considering equations of the form

$$Ax^2 + By^2 + Cz^2 + Dxy + Eyz + Fzx + Gx + Hy + Iz + J = 0.$$

The method of plotting the *quadric surfaces* given by this equation was to examine the traces of the surface in planes parallel to the coordinate planes.

Review Problems

1. Find an equation of the parabola, and sketch it, given that:

   (a) the focus is $(1, -2)$ and the directrix is $y = 4$.

   (b) the vertex is $(2, 2)$ and the focus is $(4, 2)$.

2. Find the focus and an equation of the directrix of the parabola with the equation

   $$y^2 + 2y - 6x + 13 = 0.$$

   Sketch the parabola.

3. An ellipse with eccentricity e has center at the origin O, vertex $A = (a, 0)$, and focus $F = (c, 0)$. The directrix, $x = d$, cuts the x-axis at D. Express each of the following distances in terms of a or e.

   (a) $|OF|$ (b) $|OA|$ (c) $|OD|$

4. An ellipse has eccentricity $e = \sqrt{3}/2$ and foci $(\pm 2\sqrt{3}, 0)$. Write an equation of the ellipse.

5. Find the length of the semimajor axis and the eccentricity of the ellipse $x^2 + 9y^2 = 144$.

6. The coordinates of the endpoints of the major axis of an ellipse are $(4, 7)$ and $(4, -1)$. The coordinates of the endpoints of the minor axis are $(2, 3)$ and $(6, 3)$. What is an equation of the ellipse?

357

7. (a) Sketch the graphs of the pair of concentric circles

$$x^2 - 4x + y^2 - 2y + 1 = 0,$$
$$x^2 - 4x + y^2 - 2y - 4 = 0.$$

(b) Sketch an ellipse which has the same center as the circles; the major axis is parallel to the x-axis and its length is the same as a diameter of the larger circle; its minor axis has the same length as a diameter of the smaller circle.

(c) Write an equation of the ellipse of part (b).

8. The vertices of the major axis of an ellipse are $(\pm 3, 0)$, and the foci are $(\pm 2, 0)$. What is an equation of the ellipse?

9. (a) What is the area of a rectangle circumscribing an ellipse whose equation is

$$x^2/121 + y^2/49 = 1$$

if the sides of the rectangle are parallel to the axes of the ellipse?

(b) What is the area of the parallelogram inscribed in the ellipse of part (a) if the vertices of the parallelogram are the ends of the major and minor axes of the ellipse?

(c) Estimate the area of the ellipse.

10. The foci of a hyperbola are $(\pm 4, 0)$, and its eccentricity is $\sqrt{5}$. What is an equation of the hyperbola? Sketch the hyperbola. What are the equations of its asymptotes?

11. Express the eccentricity of a hyperbola $b^2 x^2 - a^2 y^2 = a^2 b^2$ in terms of a and b. Express the distance from center to directrix in terms of a and b.

12. Sketch the pair of hyperbolas given below on the same axis.

$$x^2/9 - y^2/4 = 1$$
and
$$y^2/4 - x^2/9 = 1$$

What are equations of the asymptotes of the hyperbolas? Two hyperbolas in which the transverse axis of either one is the conjugate axis of the other are called *conjugate hyperbolas*. Conjugate hyperbolas have the same asymptotes.

13. Determine the kind of conic given by the equations below and sketch the curve.

(a) $x^2 - 4y^2 + 6x + 32y - 59 = 0$

(b) $x^2 - 4x - 8y + 28 = 0$ (c) $2x^2 - 2x + 3y^2 - 2y = \frac{19}{6}$

(d) $4x^2 - 9y^2 = 0$ (e) $x^2 - 2x + y^2 + 6y + 10 = 0$

(f) $x^2 - 2xy + y^2 - 4 = 0$

14. Find the points of intersection of the graphs of the following pairs of equations. Check by sketching the graphs of the equations.

(a) $x^2/25 + y^2/9 = 1$
    $x^2/25 - y^2/9 = 1$

(b) $xy = 4$
    $x - y - 1 = 0$

(c) $x^2/12 + y^2/9 = 1$
    $x^2 = 12(y + 3)$

(d) $x^2/9 + y^2/4 = 1$
    $x^2/4 + y^2/9 = 1$

(e) $3x - y - 8 = 0$
    $9x^2 - y^2 - 18x - 4y - 72 = 0$

(f) $4x^2 + y^2 + 8x = 0$
    $4x^2 + 9y^2 - 8x = 32$

15. Sketch a portion of each of the following quadric surfaces by considering traces of the surface in planes parallel to the coordinate planes.

(a) $x^2/4 - y^2/9 + z^2 = 1$

(b) $y = x^2/9 + z^2/25$

(c) $y^2 - 6y - 4x + 17 = 0$

(d) $9x^2 + y^2 + 9z^2 = 9$

HISTORICAL NOTE

Why do we study the conics? There are several reasons. First, these curves are encountered with astonishing frequency in all sorts of real problems. For example, because of Newton's law of gravitation, the path of a planet around the sun is an ellipse, except for the slight disturbing effect of the other planets. Second, next to straight lines, the conics are the simplest curves in the plane; they have equations of the second degree in x and y. Third, the conics are interesting in themselves for the variety of surprising properties which they possess.

Apart from these mathematical reasons, there is also the influence of the past. The conics have attracted mathematicians for 2000 years. As in so many fields, we are indebted to the ancient Greeks, who, with a sure intuition as to what is elegant and important, developed an extensive theory of the conics. A great part of that theory is the work of one man, *Apollonius of Perga* (262?–200? B.C.), one of the three great geometers of the third century B.C., the other two being Euclid and Archimedes. In his remarkable book *Conic Sections*, Apollonius systematized and vastly extended the work of earlier writers. The 400 (approximately) propositions of the book include much more material than has been mentioned in this brief chapter.

Before Apollonius, the definitions of the conics were based on the requirement that the sectioning plane be perpendicular to a generator of the cone. Hence one obtained the three kinds of conics by making the vertex angle of the cone acute, right, or obtuse (see Fig. 12–30). Note that since this construction used only one nappe, or half of the complete cone, only half of the hyperbola was obtained. Apollonius obtained all the conics from a single, complete cone (using both nappes) by permitting the sectioning plane to cut a generator at any angle.

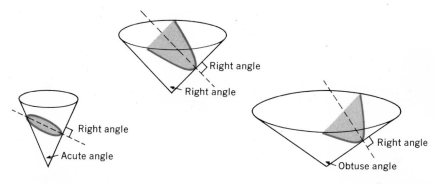

Fig. 12–30

Apollonius also gave us the names *ellipse, parabola,* and *hyperbola.* To catch the spirit of his writing we shall paraphrase his terminology with respect to the eccentricity. Thus he said that a conic suffers *ellipsis* if the eccentricity *falls short* of 1, *parabole* if the eccentricity is *precisely* 1, or *hyperbole* if the eccentricity *exceeds* 1.

Up to the time of Descartes, all treatises on the conics used the synthetic methods familiar to the student of plane geometry. With the advent of algebraic methods the view of geometry was vastly expanded, all functions were available for geometric exploitation, and synthetic methods fell into disfavor. This happened in spite of the significant developments in synthetic geometry due to the mark of Pascal, Desargues, and La Hire. One hundred years, and more, were to pass before the development of projective geometry brought about the revival of synthetic methods.

OTHER COORDINATE

13

YSTEMS

13-1. INTRODUCTION

What is a coordinate system in the plane? On reflection one sees that *a coordinate system is a mapping* that associates with each point P an ordered pair of numbers called the coordinates of P:

$P \rightarrow$ (first coordinate, second coordinate).

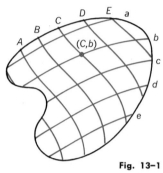

Fig. 13-1

Let us suppose that we have, in a region, two families of curves labeled A, B, C, ... and a, b, c, ..., as in Fig. 13-1. And let us further suppose that each point of the region is on exactly one curve of each family. Then the two families of curves give a coordinate system in the region. Each point of the region has associated with it a unique ordered pair of numbers, for example, (C, b).

In the preceding chapters we have concerned ourselves with rectangular coordinates, but clearly there are infinitely many kinds of coordinate systems because of the infinite variety of curve families we can choose. In this chapter we shall investigate some of the more important of these nonrectangular coordinate systems.

13-2. TRANSLATION OF AXES

We first study the relations between the different rectangular coordinate systems that can be chosen.

Let us suppose that we have two rectangular coordinate systems in the plane, with origins at O and O', and with the first and second coordinate axes parallel in the two systems, as in Fig. 13-2.

Then the point P in the plane has two sets of coordinates, x, y and x', y' with respect to the two sets of coordinate axes. We say that the origin of the xy-coordinate system has been *translated* to the point O'.

If the coordinates of O' are (h, k) with respect to the old axes, then how are the coordinates (x, y) and (x', y') related? An easy geometric argument will show that for all real numbers h and k,

$$x' = x - h,$$
$$y' = y - k. \tag{1}$$

Equations (1) are called the *translation equations*.

An equation in x and y may become considerably simpler if the origin O is translated to a properly selected point O'.

364

EXAMPLE

Find an equation of the conic

$$2x^2 + 3y^2 - 4x + 9y = \tfrac{13}{4},$$

after the origin has been translated to the point $(1, -\tfrac{3}{2})$. (See Fig. 13–3.)

Since $O' = (1, -\tfrac{3}{2})$, we have $h = 1$ and $k = -\tfrac{3}{2}$. The translation equations are

$$x' = x - 1,$$
$$y' = y + \tfrac{3}{2},$$

where $x = x' + 1$ and $y = y' - \tfrac{3}{2}$. Substitution of these for x and y in the given equation results in

$$2(x' + 1)^2 + 3(y' - \tfrac{3}{2})^2 - 4(x' + 1) + 9(y' - \tfrac{3}{2}) = \tfrac{13}{4}.$$

This equation reduces to

$$2x'^2 + 3y'^2 = 12, \tag{2}$$

which is an ellipse with center at O' and semiaxes $\sqrt{6}$ and 2.

When we complete the squares in the original equation, we are led automatically to the proper point O' to which we should translate the origin:

$$2(x^2 - 2x \quad) + 3(y^2 + 3y \quad) = \tfrac{13}{4},$$
$$2(x - 1)^2 + 3(y + \tfrac{3}{2})^2 = \tfrac{13}{4} + 2 + \tfrac{27}{4},$$

or

$$2(x - 1)^2 + 3(y + \tfrac{3}{2})^2 = 12.$$

This last equation is our previous equation (2) with $x' = x - 1$ and $y' = y + \tfrac{3}{2}$.

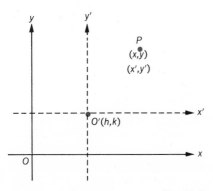

Fig. 13–2

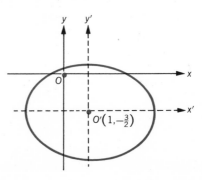

Fig. 13–3

Problems

1. If the origin is translated to the point $(-2, 3)$, what are the new coordinates of the point $(x, y) = (-1, -1)$? What are the new coordinates of the old origin?

2. Transform the equation $4x^2 - 9y^2 - 16x - 18y = 18$ by translating the origin to the point $(2, -1)$. Then sketch the graph.

3. Transform the equation $4x^2 + y^2 - 24x + 4y + 24 = 0$ by translating the origin to the point (h, k). Determine h and k so that the x'- and y'-terms are absent. Complete the squares in the original equation. How do you interpret your result?

4. Transform the equation $y^2 - 6y - 2x + 7 = 0$ by translating the origin to the point (h, k). Determine h and k so the y'- and the constant terms are absent.

5. Prove that the formula for the slope of the line through (x_1, y_1) and (x_2, y_2) remains valid after translation of axes. [*Hint:* Translate the origin to the point (h, k).]

13-3. ROTATION OF AXES

In addition to a translation of the origin, two rectangular coordinate systems can also be related by a *rotation of axes*, as indicated in Fig. 13-4. The positive x'-axis meets the unit circle in a point $\phi(\theta)$, where ϕ is the standard map introduced in Chapter 7. Then the positive y'-axis meets the unit circle in the point $\phi(\theta + \pi/2)$.

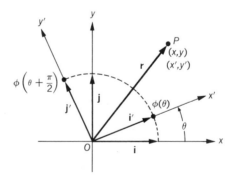

Fig. 13-4

A point P has two sets of coordinates (x, y) and (x', y'). The relation between these coordinates is easily obtained by examining the position vector $\overrightarrow{OP} = \mathbf{r}$ in the two coordinate systems. Let $\mathbf{i}, \mathbf{j}$ and $\mathbf{i}', \mathbf{j}'$ be the unit vectors along the axes in the two systems. Then

$$\mathbf{r} = x\mathbf{i} + y\mathbf{j} = x'\mathbf{i}' + y'\mathbf{j}'.$$

Because $\mathbf{r} \cdot \mathbf{i} = x$ and $\mathbf{r} \cdot \mathbf{j} = y$, we have

$$x = \mathbf{r} \cdot \mathbf{i} = (x'\mathbf{i}' + y'\mathbf{j}') \cdot \mathbf{i} \quad \text{and} \quad y = \mathbf{r} \cdot \mathbf{j} = (x'\mathbf{i}' + y'\mathbf{j}') \cdot \mathbf{j}.$$

Finally, we get

$$x = x'(\mathbf{i}' \cdot \mathbf{i}) + y'(\mathbf{j}' \cdot \mathbf{i}), \qquad y = x'(\mathbf{i}' \cdot \mathbf{j}) + y'(\mathbf{j}' \cdot \mathbf{j}), \tag{1}$$

and all that remains is to find the dot products in (1). Clearly,

$$\mathbf{i}' \cdot \mathbf{i} = \mathbf{j}' \cdot \mathbf{j} = \cos \theta,$$
$$\mathbf{i}' \cdot \mathbf{j} = \cos (\pi/2 - \theta) = \sin \theta,$$
$$\mathbf{j}' \cdot \mathbf{i} = \cos (\pi/2 + \theta) = -\sin \theta.$$

Therefore, *the equations for rotation of axes through an angle θ are*

$$x = x' \cos \theta - y' \sin \theta, \qquad y = x' \sin \theta + y' \cos \theta. \tag{2}$$

Formulas for x' and y' in terms of x and y can be found by solving the linear equations (2) for x' and y'. (See Problem 6 below.)

It may happen that after rotation of axes through a suitably chosen angle, the equation for a curve takes a simpler form. An important instance of this is given in the following theorem.

THEOREM 13-1

The general quadratic in x and y,

$$Ax^2 + Bxy + Cy^2 + Dx + Ey + F = 0, \tag{3}$$

can be transformed into

$$A'x'^2 + C'y'^2 + D'x' + E'y' + F' = 0 \tag{4}$$

by rotation of the axes through an angle θ such that

$$\tan 2\theta = \frac{B}{A - C} \quad \text{if} \quad A \neq C,$$

or by rotation through

$$\theta = \pi/4 \quad \text{if} \quad A = C.$$

Proof. We use the equations for rotation (2) and substitute these expressions for x and y in the general quadratic. We obtain

$$A(x' \cos \theta - y' \sin \theta)^2 + B(x' \cos \theta - y' \sin \theta)(x' \sin \theta + y' \cos \theta)$$
$$+ C(x' \sin \theta + y' \cos \theta)^2 + D(x' \cos \theta - y' \sin \theta)$$
$$+ E(x' \sin \theta + y' \cos \theta) + F = 0.$$

367

After carrying out the multiplications and collecting terms containing x'^2, $x'y'$, y'^2, x', and y', we obtain

$$(A \cos^2 \theta + B \sin \theta \cos \theta + C \sin^2 \theta)x'^2$$
$$+ [-2A \sin \theta \cos \theta + B(\cos^2 \theta - \sin^2 \theta) + 2C \sin \theta \cos \theta]x'y'$$
$$+ (A \sin^2 \theta - B \sin \theta \cos \theta + C \cos^2 \theta)y'^2$$
$$+ (D \cos \theta + E \sin \theta)x' + (E \cos \theta - D \sin \theta)y' + F = 0. \quad (5)$$

This last equation has the same graph in the plane as does the original equation. It has the form

$$A'x'^2 + B'x'y' + C'y'^2 + D'x' + E'y' + F = 0, \quad (6)$$

where A', B', C', D', and E' can be obtained from Equation (5) in terms of A, B, C, D, and E and functions of θ. The $x'y'$-term will be absent from (6) if

$$B' = -2A \sin \theta \cos \theta + B(\cos^2 \theta - \sin^2 \theta) + 2C \sin \theta \cos \theta = 0. \quad (7)$$

This is a trigonometric equation which is relatively easy to solve. Recall that $\sin 2\theta = 2 \sin \theta \cos \theta$ and $\cos 2\theta = \cos^2 \theta - \sin^2 \theta$. Then equation (7) becomes

$$B \cos 2\theta + (C - A) \sin 2\theta = 0,$$

so that

$$\tan 2\theta = \frac{B}{A - C} \quad \text{if} \quad A \neq C.$$

However, if $A = C$, then $\cos 2\theta = 0$, and $\theta = \pi/4$ will satisfy the equation. This completes the proof.

EXAMPLE

Rotate the axes to remove the xy-term from the equation $34x^2 - 24xy + 41y^2 = 200$, and sketch the graph.

If θ is the angle of Theorem 13–1, then

$$\tan 2\theta = \frac{-24}{34 - 41} = \frac{24}{7}.$$

We may therefore choose 2θ in the first quadrant, as has been done in Fig. 13–5. Then $\cos 2\theta = \frac{7}{25}$, and

$$\sin \theta = \sqrt{\frac{1 - \cos 2\theta}{2}} = \sqrt{\frac{1 - \frac{7}{25}}{2}} = \frac{3}{5},$$

$$\cos \theta = \sqrt{\frac{1 + \cos 2\theta}{2}} = \sqrt{\frac{1 + \frac{7}{25}}{2}} = \frac{4}{5}.$$

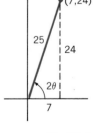

Fig. 13–5

368

The equations of the transformation are therefore

$$x = \frac{4}{5}x' - \frac{3}{5}y' = \frac{4x' - 3y'}{5},$$

$$y = \frac{3}{5}x' + \frac{4}{5}y' = \frac{3x' + 4y'}{5}.$$

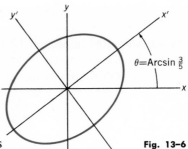

$\theta = \text{Arcsin } \frac{3}{5}$

Fig. 13–6

Substitution in the original equation yields

$$34(4x' - 3y')^2 - 24(4x' - 3y')(3x' + 4y') + 41(3x' + 4y')^2 = 200(25).$$

This equation simplifies to $x'^2 + 2y'^2 = 8$, and its graph is the ellipse of Fig. 13–6.

In Chapter 12 we used, without proof, the result of the following theorem, for which we can now give a straightforward, though long, proof by reference to equations (5) and (6).

THEOREM 13-2

For arbitrary rotations of the axes [and in the notation of Equations (5) and (6)],

$$B^2 - 4AC = B'^2 - 4A'C'.$$

Problems

1. Rotate the axes through a positive acute angle to remove the xy-term from each of the following equations. Sketch the graph showing both sets of axes.
   (a) $xy = 4$
   (b) $3x^2 - 4xy + 8x - 3y - 1 = 0$
   (c) $4x^2 - 24xy + 11y^2 = 0$
   (d) $x^2 - 2xy + y^2 + 2x + 4y - 4 = 0$
   (e) $21x^2 + 10\sqrt{3}\,xy + 31y^2 = 144$
   (f) $17x^2 + 12xy + 8y^2 = 20$

2. Using the notations in equations (5) and (6), solve for A', B', and C', and prove Theorem 13–2.

3. Show that in Theorem 13–1 we may always choose θ so that $0 < \theta < \pi/2$ if B is not already zero.

4. Show that the graph of $Ax^2 + Bxy + Cy^2 + F = 0$ is a hyperbola if $AC < 0$ and $F \neq 0$.

5. Given two points $P(x_1, y_1)$ and $P(x_2, y_2)$, prove that the distance $|P_1P_2|$ is invariant under rotation of axes by showing that the distance formula gives the same number in both coordinate systems.

6. Solve equations (2) for x', y' in terms of x and y. Show that the same result can be obtained as a rotation from x'-, y'-axes to x-, y-axes.

369

13-4. POLAR COORDINATES

As was suggested in Section 13–1, there are infinitely many coordinate systems. Among the nonrectangular ones the most important are the *polar coordinate systems* in a plane, which we now define.

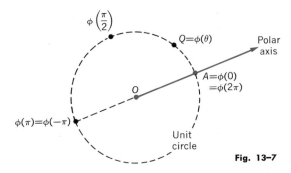

Fig. 13–7

We will *choose* a point O in the plane, which will be called the *pole*, and a ray emanating from O, called the *polar axis*. The unit circle with center at O meets the polar axis at a point A. (See Fig. 13–7.) Next *choose* a positive sense around the unit circle and map the real numbers on the circle by the standard map ϕ with $\phi(0) = A$. Each point Q on the unit circle then corresponds to infinitely many real numbers, $Q = \phi(\theta + 2k\pi)$, where $k = 0$, $\pm 1, \pm 2, \ldots$

Let us consider any point $P \neq O$ in the plane. The ray from O through P meets the unit circle in a point $Q = \phi(\theta)$, where θ is a real number. We suppose that P is at a distance r from the pole. Then the pair of numbers (r, θ) uniquely determine the point P in the plane. With this notation, we can give the definition of polar coordinates.

DEFINITION 13–1

> With the above notation (shown in Fig. 13–8), the ordered pairs of numbers $(r, \theta + 2k\pi)$, $k = 0$, $\pm 1, \ldots$, are polar coordinates of P. If $P = O$, then $r = 0$ and θ is arbitrary.

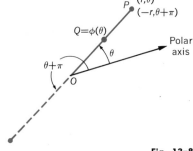

Fig. 13–8

We shall also permit negative values for r. If r is negative, we simply measure distance along the ray *oppositely* directed to the ray through O and $\phi(\theta)$. (See Fig. 13–8.)

370

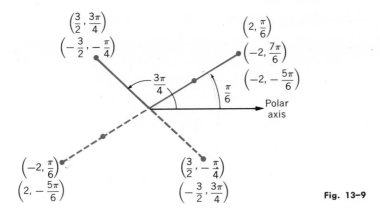

Fig. 13-9

Some points with some of their polar coordinates are shown in Fig. 13-9.

Remarks

1. Even when the pole and polar axis are fixed, *there are infinitely many polar coordinates for each point.* However, given an ordered pair (r, θ), of real numbers, there is a unique point that has these numbers as polar coordinates.

2. Consider the $r\theta$-plane, where r and θ are now rectangular coordinates. The shaded portion of Fig. 13–10(a) maps onto the whole plane with r and θ as polar coordinates, as indicated in Fig. 13–10(b).

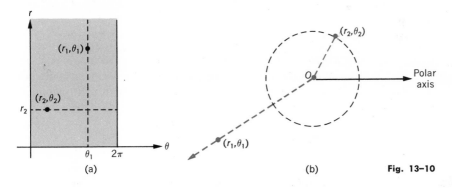

(a) (b) Fig. 13-10

The vertical ray of Fig. 13–10(a) maps onto the dashed ray from the pole in Fig. 13–10(b).

The horizontal segment in Fig. 13–10(a) maps onto the circle in Fig. 13–10(b).

3. We have already had some contact with polar coordinates in Chapter 9, where we made use of the polar form of a complex number.

371

Problems

1. Plot the points with the following polar coordinates.
   (a) $(4, \pi/3)$, $(-4, -2\pi/3)$, $(-4, 4\pi/3)$, $(-4, \pi/3)$, $(4, -2\pi/3)$
   (b) $(1/2, 5\pi/4)$, $(-1/2, -\pi/4)$, $(1/2, 13\pi/4)$, $(1/2, -\pi/4)$
   (c) $(2, 1)$, $(-2, \pi + 1)$, $(-2, 1)$, $(-2, -1)$, $(-2, 1 - \pi)$, $(2, 1 - \pi)$

2. Find three other pairs of polar coordinates for each of the points with the following polar coordinates.
   (a) $(3, \pi/3)$ (b) $(2, 1/2)$ (c) $(-1, -\pi/4)$ (d) (π, π) (e) $(-1, \pi/2)$

3. Sketch the graphs of the following polar equations. In other words, sketch the set of points $P(r, \theta)$ whose coordinates satisfy the equations below.
   (a) $r = 3$ (b) $r = -3$ (c) $\theta = 5\pi/6$
   (d) $\theta = 5\pi/6$ and $r > 0$ *(e) $\cos \theta = 1/r$

13–5. CURVES IN POLAR COORDINATES

Just as certain curves have simple equations in rectangular coordinates (for example, lines and conics), so in polar coordinates some curves will have simple equations. However, a new variety of curves comes to our attention, and equations with familiar graphs in rectangular coordinates will now have different graphs in polar coordinates. Since many of our examples involve the circular functions, it will be very helpful if the variations of the circular functions are kept in mind.

Remark

Observe that the graphs of the same equation, $r = f(\theta)$, are quite different, depending on whether r and θ are polar coordinates or rectangular coordinates. Whenever the graph of $r = f(\theta)$ is known for either rectangular or polar coordinates, it may be helpful to use it to help with the drawing of the other.

EXAMPLES

1. Sketch the graph of $r = a \cos \theta$.

We first observe that the cosine has period 2π, and hence we may restrict our attention to the interval $0 \le \theta \le 2\pi$. Moreover, the cosine is an even function, so the full graph can be inferred from the graph for $0 \le \theta \le \pi$. We make a small table of r versus θ.

θ	0	$\pi/4$	$\pi/2$	$3\pi/4$	π	$5\pi/4$	$3\pi/2$	$7\pi/4$	2π
r	a	$a\sqrt{2}/2$	0	$-a\sqrt{2}/2$	$-a$	$-a\sqrt{2}/2$	0	$a\sqrt{2}/2$	a

372

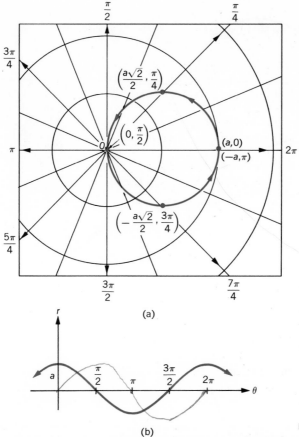

(a)

(b)

Fig. 13-11

Figure 13–11(a) shows the graph of $0 \le \theta \le \pi$ in polar coordinates. The arrowheads indicate how the point (r, θ) moves as θ increases from 0 to π. For $\pi \le \theta \le 2\pi$, the same points are obtained, although not the same coordinates. The graph appears to be a circle. We shall see in the next section that it actually is.

Note that the graph of $r = a \cos \theta$ in rectangular coordinates is the cosine wave of Fig. 13–11(b). From this graph the polar graph of the equation is quickly sketched.

2. Sketch the graph of $r = 1 + \cos \theta$.

In this example, we observe that $r \ge 0$ for all θ. As in Example 1, the periodicity of the cosine permits us to restrict θ to the interval $0 \le \theta \le 2\pi$. Because the cosine is even, the graph for $\pi \le \theta \le 2\pi$ can be inferred from the graph for $0 \le \theta \le \pi$. The graph, shown in Fig. 13–12(a), is called a *cardioid*. The solid curve is $0 \le \theta \le \pi$. The dashed curve is the graph of $\pi \le \theta \le 2\pi$.

373

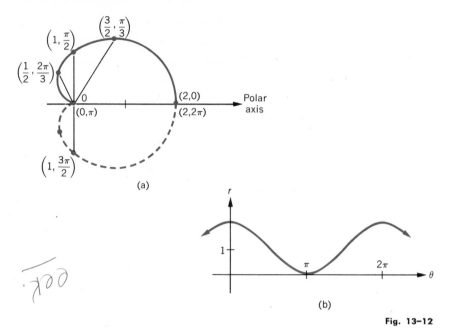

Fig. 13–12

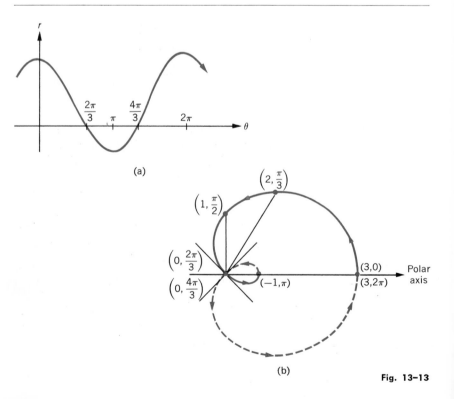

Fig. 13–13

Note that the graph of $r = 1 + \cos\theta$ in rectangular coordinates is the wave of Fig. 13–12(b). Obviously r is never negative.

3. Sketch the graph of $r = 1 + 2\cos\theta$.

The same remarks concerning periodicity and the interesting range on θ can be made as in Examples 1 and 2. The graph of $r = 1 + 2\cos\theta$ in rectangular coordinates appears in Fig. 13–13(a). Note the range on θ when r is negative.

The graph in polar coordinates for $0 \le \theta \le \pi$ is shown in Fig. 13–13(b) as a solid curve. The graph for $\pi \le \theta \le 2\pi$ is shown dashed. The arrows indicate how the curve is traversed as θ increases from 0 to 2π. We observe that for $0 \le \theta \le 2\pi/3$, r is nonnegative. But for $2\pi/3 < \theta \le \pi$, r is negative, and the lower part of the loop to the right of the pole is obtained. The curve is called a *limaçon*.

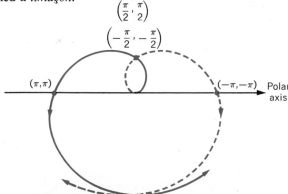

Fig. 13–14

4. Sketch the graph of $r = \theta$.

In this case, there is no periodicity, and r simply increases with θ. The graph for positive θ is shown as the solid curve in Fig. 13–14. The graph for negative θ is shown dashed. The curve is a *spiral of Archimedes*.

5. Sketch the graph of $r = a\cos 2\theta$, $a > 0$.

This interesting curve (a four-leaved rose) is shown in Fig. 13–15. The graph for $0 \le \theta \le \pi$ is shown as a solid curve. That for $\pi \le \theta \le 2\pi$ is shown dashed. For $\pi/4 < \theta < 3\pi/4$, r is negative, and we get the bottom petal on the rose.

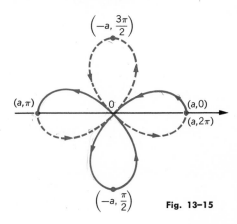

Fig. 13–15

375

A selection of other interesting polar curves is shown in Fig. 13–16.

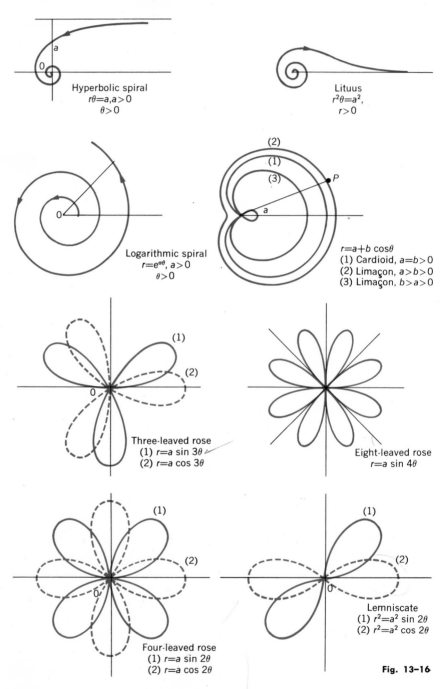

Hyperbolic spiral
$r\theta=a, a>0$
$\theta>0$

Lituus
$r^2\theta=a^2,$
$r>0$

Logarithmic spiral
$r=e^{a\theta}, a>0$
$\theta>0$

$r=a+b\ \cos\theta$
(1) Cardioid, $a=b>0$
(2) Limaçon, $a>b>0$
(3) Limaçon, $b>a>0$

Three-leaved rose
(1) $r=a\ \sin 3\theta$
(2) $r=a\ \cos 3\theta$

Eight-leaved rose
$r=a\ \sin 4\theta$

Four-leaved rose
(1) $r=a\ \sin 2\theta$
(2) $r=a\ \cos 2\theta$

Lemniscate
(1) $r^2=a^2\ \sin 2\theta$
(2) $r^2=a^2\ \cos 2\theta$

Fig. 13–16

Problems

1. Sketch the graphs of the following equations in polar coordinates.

(a) $r = 3 \sin \theta$ (b) $r = 2 \cos \theta$

(c) $r = 1 + \sin \theta$ (d) $r = 1 - \sin \theta$

(e) $r = 1 - \sqrt{2} \cos \theta$ (f) $r = 2 + \cos \theta$

(g) $r = 1/\sin \theta$ (h) $r = 1/\sin (\theta - \pi/3)$

(i) $r = a \sin 2\theta$ (j) $r = a \cos 3\theta$

(k) $r = a \cos 4\theta$ (l) $r = 1/\theta^2, \quad \theta > 0$

(m) $r^2 = a^2 \sin 2\theta$ (n) $r^2 = a^2 \sec 2\theta$

(o) $r^2 = a^2 \cos 3\theta$ (p) $r = a \cos^2 \theta, \quad a > 0$

*2. The limaçon of Example 3 can be used to trisect angles. Let A be a given acute angle of measure α placed with respect to the limaçon, $r = 1 + 2 \cos \theta$, as in the figure. The unit circle with center at A has a polar equation $r = 2 \cos \theta$. Referring to the figure, explain why the following statements are true.

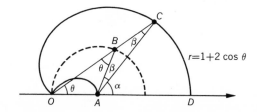

(a) $\angle AOB \cong \angle OBA$ (b) $\alpha + \beta = 2\theta$

(c) $|BC| = 1$ (d) $\angle BAC \cong \angle BCA$

(e) $\theta = 2\beta$

(f) Therefore $\alpha = 3\beta$, and $\angle BAC$ is the desired trisection of $\angle CAD$.

13-6. POLAR AND RECTANGULAR COORDINATES

There are infinitely many polar coordinate systems, differing by the choices made for pole and polar axis. Likewise, there are infinitely many rectangular coordinate systems with different origins and axes. Relations between arbitrary polar and rectangular coordinate systems could be quite complicated. However, if the pole and the origin coincide, if the positive x-axis is the polar axis, and if the unit circle with center O is oriented in the same way in both systems, then the two coordinate systems are simply related. (See Fig. 13–17.) In this section we shall assume that the two systems are so related.

It is clear from the figure that

$$x = r \cos \theta,$$
$$y = r \sin \theta. \tag{1}$$

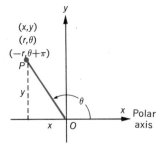

Fig. 13–17

Equations (1) are satisfied by the polar coordinates (r, θ), or by $(r, \theta + 2k\pi)$, or by $(-r, \theta + (2k + 1)\pi)$ where k is an integer. This is the case because

$$\cos (\theta + \pi) = -\cos \theta$$

and

$$\sin (\theta + \pi) = -\sin \theta.$$

Equations (1) permit us to find a polar equation of a curve from a rectangular equation.

EXAMPLES

1. Find a polar equation of the circle $x^2 + y^2 - ax = 0$.
From equations (1) we have

$$r^2 \cos^2 \theta + r^2 \sin^2 \theta - ar \cos \theta = 0$$

or

$$r^2 - ar \cos \theta = r(r - a \cos \theta) = 0.$$

The last equation is satisfied if either $r = 0$ (the pole) or $r - a \cos \theta = 0$. Because the graph of $r - a \cos \theta = 0$ contains the pole ($r = 0$ at $\theta = \pi/2$) (see Fig. 13–18), we *do not omit any point of the graph by neglecting the factor r*. Therefore, an equation of the circle in polar coordinates is

$$r = a \cos \theta.$$

Equations (1) can be solved for r and θ. We have

$$x^2 + y^2 = r^2 \cos^2 \theta + r^2 \sin^2 \theta = r^2,$$

$$\frac{y}{x} = \frac{\sin \theta}{\cos \theta} = \tan \theta,$$

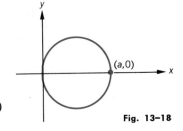

Fig. 13–18

and therefore

$$r = \pm\sqrt{x^2 + y^2},$$
$$\theta = \arctan \frac{y}{x}. \tag{2}$$

Note that we do not select the principal value of the inverse tangent. *Any* θ such that $\tan \theta = y/x$ will suffice *if* we select a suitable sign for r, so that (π, θ) is in the same quadrant as (x, y).

378

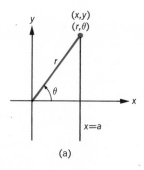

(a)

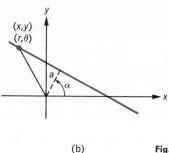

(b)

Fig. 13-19

2. Find a rectangular equation of the curve with the polar equation $r \cos \theta = a$.

Since $x = r \cos \theta$, the graph is the straight line with equation $x = a$ (Fig. 13–19a).

Similarly, the equation

$$r \cos (\theta - \alpha) = a$$

is equivalent to

$$r \cos \theta \cos \alpha + r \sin \theta \sin \alpha = a,$$

or the straight-line equation (Fig. 13–19b)

$$x \cos \alpha + y \sin \alpha = a.$$

We note that the dot product of $\mathbf{r}$ and the unit position vector $\cos \alpha \mathbf{i} + \sin \alpha \mathbf{j}$ is equal to a:

$$\mathbf{r} \cdot (\cos \alpha \, \mathbf{i} + \sin \alpha \, \mathbf{j}) = a.$$

Problems

1. Find the rectangular coordinates of the points with polar coordinates $(3, \pi/6)$, $(4, -5\pi/6)$, $(-4, -5\pi/4)$, $(2, 2)$.

2. Find polar coordinates of the points with rectangular coordinates $(2, -2\sqrt{3})$, $(-3, 4)$, $(-2, -2)$.

3. Find polar equations of the following curves and sketch them.
   (a) $x^2 + y^2 = a^2$ (b) $x + 5 = 0$
   (c) $x + y = 2$ (d) $x^2 + y^2 = 4y$
   (e) $(x^2 + y^2)^2 = a^2(x^2 - y^2)$ (f) $xy = 1$
   (g) $(x^2 + y^2)^3 = a^2(x^2 - y^2)^2$ (h) $y = b$
   (i) $x \cos \gamma + y \sin \gamma = p$ (j) $4x^2 + 3y^2 - 2y - 1 = 0$
   (k) $y^2 = x^3$

379

4. Find rectangular equations of the curves with the following polar equations and sketch them.

(a) $r = a \sin \theta$ (b) $r = 4$

(c) $r = 1/(1 - \cos \theta)$ (d) $r^2 = a^2 \sin 2\theta$

(e) $r = \tan \theta$ (f) $r^2 = \tan \theta \sec^2 \theta$

(g) $r = a \sin 2\theta$ (h) $r = \cos \theta - \sin \theta$

(i) $r = \theta$ *(j) $r = \tan \frac{1}{2}\theta$

5. Find a formula for the distance between the points (r_1, θ_1) and (r_2, θ_2).

6. Prove that a straight line not passing through the origin has an equation of the form $r(A \cos \theta + B \sin \theta) = 1$. If the line passes through the origin, what is the form of a polar equation for it?

13-7. INTERSECTIONS

To find the intersections of curves given in rectangular coordinates, one simply solves the two simultaneous equations, because we know that a point is on both curves if and only if its (unique) coordinates satisfy both equations.

To find the intersection of curves with polar equations, more care must be taken because a point has many sets of polar coordinates. Thus on one curve, the point may be given by one pair of coordinates while on the other curve, it is given by a different pair. Naturally, solution of the two simultaneous polar equations (if any solution exists) will yield points on both curves, but it may not give all of them. The procedure we shall follow is to (a) solve the two polar equations, and (b) graph the two equations to see whether all points of intersection have been obtained.

EXAMPLE

Find the points of intersection of the circle, $r = \sin \theta$, and the cardioid, $r = 1 - \sin \theta$.

Eliminating θ between the two equations gives $r = 1 - r$ and $r = \frac{1}{2}$, where $\sin \theta = \frac{1}{2}$ and $\theta = \pi/6$ or $5\pi/6$. The two points of intersection so obtained are shown in Fig. 13–20. Furthermore, we see from the figure that the curves also intersect at the pole. As a point of the circle, the pole has coordinates $(0, 0)$, $(0, \pi)$, $(0, 2\pi)$, and as a point of the cardioid, it has coordinates $(0, \pi/2)$. We may visualize this situation by thinking of two ships, both starting at P and sailing along the

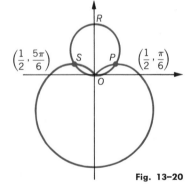

Fig. 13–20

two curves to O. They pass through O at different times because their paths from their starting point to O are different. One would go from P to O directly; the other would go from P to R to S and then to O.

Problem

1. Find the points of intersection of the pairs of curves with the following polar equations. Sketch each pair.

(a) $r = 3$, $r = 3 + 2 \cos \theta$ (b) $r = 2$, $r = 2 \sin 2\theta$

(c) $r = \sin \theta$, $r = \cos 2\theta$ (d) $r = \cos \theta$, $r = \sin 2\theta$

(e) $r = \sin 2\theta$, $r = \cos 2\theta$ (f) $r = 2$, $r^2 = 8 \cos 2\theta$

(g) $r = 2$, $r = \sec^2 \frac{1}{2}\theta$ (h) $r^2 = a^2 \cos 2\theta$, $r^2 = a^2 \sin 2\theta$

(i) $r^2 = \sin 2\theta$, $r = \sin \theta$

13–8. CONICS

Equations of conics in polar coordinates are quite simple if the focus is at the pole and the directrix is perpendicular to the polar axis. The polar form for an equation of a conic is often used in calculation of orbits of planets or satellites.

Let us suppose that the focus and direc-trix of a conic are as in Fig. 13–21. Then P is on the conic of eccentricity e if and only if $|PF| = |PM|e$. Since $|PM| = p + r \cos \theta$, we have $r = (p + r \cos \theta)e$ or

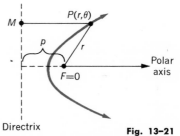

Fig. 13–21

$$r = \frac{pe}{1 - e \cos \theta}. \qquad (1)$$

Equation (1) can be used to quickly sketch the conic, as the following example shows.

EXAMPLE

Sketch the curve with the equation

$$r = \frac{4}{2 - \cos \theta}.$$

The equation, as it stands, is not in the standard form (1). Dividing numerator and denominator of the fraction by 2 gives

$$r = \frac{2}{1 - \frac{1}{2} \cos \theta},$$

381

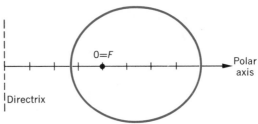

Fig. 13–22

which is the equation of an ellipse with eccentricity $\frac{1}{2}$. From (1) we see that the distance from focus to directrix is $p = 4$. The ellipse is shown in Fig. 13–22.

Problems

1. Sketch the following conics:

(a) $r = \dfrac{2}{3 - 2\cos\theta}$

(b) $r = \dfrac{1}{1 - \cos\theta}$

(c) $r = \dfrac{4}{1 - 2\cos\theta}$

(d) $r = \dfrac{9}{10 - 9\cos\theta}$

2. Find the equation of the conic if the directrix is perpendicular to the polar axis and a distance p to the right of the pole.

3. Find the equation of the conic if the directrix is parallel to the polar axis and a distance p above it.

4. Show that $r = 2p\sec^2\frac{1}{2}\theta$ represents a parabola.

5. Find the equation of the conic if the directrix is at a distance p from the pole and is inclined, as shown in the figure.

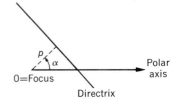

*6. A *reciprocal transformation* is defined as follows (see figure). The point P' is the transform of the point P if

$$|OP'| = 1/|OP|.$$

The reciprocal transformation maps, one-to-one, the exterior of the unit circle onto the interior (except for the center).

Show that a conic with focus at the pole is transformed into a limaçon or cardioid by a reciprocal transformation.

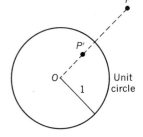

382

13-9. CYLINDRICAL COORDINATES

We turn now to nonrectangular coordinate systems in space. Two of these systems are of major importance, and we shall examine them briefly in this and the next section. As with rectangular and polar coordinates in a plane, there are infinitely many choices for the placement of these new systems. In these sections, we shall place them in the simple *standard* position with respect to a rectangular system. We are concerned primarily with two aspects: (1) the surfaces which are the graphs of very simple equations, and (2) the relations between the new coordinates and the rectangular coordinates for space.

The *cylindrical* and rectangular systems are shown in Fig. 13–23. We choose polar coordinates in the *xy*-plane (with the two systems related as in Section 13–6). The segment $\overline{PQ}$ is parallel to the *z*-axis. The third coordinate is the rectangular *z*-coordinate. *The cylindrical coordinates of P are (r, θ, z).*

The two coordinate systems are related by

$$
\begin{aligned}
x &= r \cos \theta, & r &= \pm\sqrt{x^2 + y^2}, \\
y &= r \sin \theta, \quad \text{or} \quad & \theta &= \arctan y/x, \\
z &= z; & z &= z.
\end{aligned}
\tag{1}
$$

As with polar coordinates, the choice of $\theta = \arctan (y/x)$ will dictate which sign to use for $r = \pm\sqrt{x^2 + y^2}$.

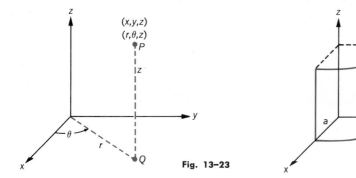

Fig. 13–23   Fig. 13–24

EXAMPLE

The graph of the equation $r = a$ is the right circular cylinder of radius a with its axis along the *z*-axis. A portion of the cylinder is sketched in Fig. 13–24.

It is rather clear that physical problems involving axial symmetry might be conveniently described in terms of cylindrical coordinates. Some examples are the flow of fluids in straight pipes, heat transfer in long tubes, and the magnetic fields surrounding long straight wires.

383

Problems

1. Sketch the surfaces having the following equations in cylindrical coordinates. Where convenient, change to rectangular coordinates.

   (a) $\theta = \pi/6$ (b) $r^2 + z^2 = 1$ (c) $r = z$

   (d) $r = 2a \sin \theta$ (e) $r = c \sec^2 \frac{1}{2}\theta$ (f) $r = 1 + \cos \theta$

2. Derive a formula in cylindrical coordinates for the distance between two points.

13-10. SPHERICAL COORDINATES

The *spherical* and rectangular coordinate systems are shown in Fig. 13-25. The point P is projected by a line parallel to the z-axis into a point R in the xy-plane. Suppose that r, θ are polar coordinates of R. If the position vector, $\overrightarrow{OP}$, makes an angle φ with the positive z-axis, and if $|\overrightarrow{OP}| = \rho$, then *the spherical coordinates of P are (ρ, θ, φ).*

From the definitions one has

$$0 \le \varphi \le \pi \qquad \text{and} \qquad \rho \ge 0,$$
$$r = \rho \sin \varphi \qquad \text{and} \qquad r^2 + z^2 = \rho^2.$$

Thus the two coordinate systems are related by

$$x = r \cos \theta = \rho \sin \varphi \cos \theta,$$
$$y = r \sin \theta = \rho \sin \varphi \sin \theta,$$
$$z = \rho \cos \varphi. \tag{1}$$

If these equations are solved for ρ, θ, φ, one obtains

$$\rho = \sqrt{x^2 + y^2 + z^2}, \qquad \theta = \arctan \frac{y}{x}, \qquad \varphi = \frac{\text{Arccos } z}{\sqrt{x^2 + y^2 + z^2}}. \tag{2}$$

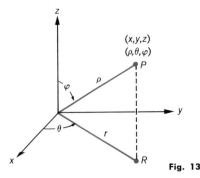

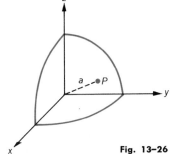

Fig. 13-25   Fig. 13-26

EXAMPLE

The graph of the equation $\rho = a$ is the sphere of radius a with center at the origin. One-eighth of the sphere is shown in Fig. 13–26.

Problems

1. Sketch the surfaces having the following equations in spherical coordinates.
   (a) $\rho = 4$ and $\varphi \geq \pi/2$ (b) $\varphi = \pi/6$
   (c) $\theta = \pi/4$ (d) $\rho \sin \varphi = a$

2. If the earth is a sphere and spherical coordinates are chosen with origin at the center, the z-axis toward the North Pole, and the plane $\theta = 0$ through Greenwich, England, what are the relations between θ and φ and longitude and latitude?

3. Derive a formula for the distance between two points in spherical coordinates.

*13–11. OTHER COORDINATES

As would be expected, we have come nowhere near exhausting the variety of possible coordinate systems for a plane or space. In this section we give an example and a problem that may suggest the possibilities.

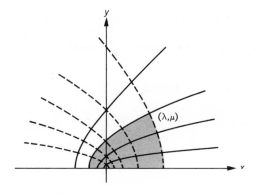

Fig. 13–27

EXAMPLE   *(Parabolic coordinates)*

Consider the two families of parabolas, where $\lambda > 0, \mu > 0$:

$$y^2 = 4\lambda(x + \lambda),$$
$$y^2 = -4\mu(x - \mu).$$

Through each point of the plane there is exactly one parabola of each family. The parabolas (the upper half) of the λ-family are drawn as solid lines in Fig. 13–27. Those of the μ-family are represented by the dashed lines.

385

Points symmetrically located with respect to the x-axis will lie on the same two parabolas. This is why we restrict our attention to the upper half-plane.

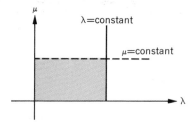

Fig. 13–28

The two numbers, λ and μ (*parabolic coordinates*), establish a coordinate system for the upper half-plane. The first quadrant of the $\lambda\mu$-plane is mapped one-to-one on the upper half of the xy-plane. The shaded region of Fig. 13–27 corresponds to the shaded region of Fig. 13–28.

Problems

1. Show that all parabolas of the example have focus at the origin. Hence we can say that we have families of *confocal* (having the same foci) *conics*.

2. What are the rectangular coordinates of the point with parabolic coordinates $(2, 3)$?

3. What are the parabolic coordinates of the point with rectangular coordinates $(1, 2\sqrt{2})$?

*4. Draw several members of each of the following families:

$$\frac{x^2}{\lambda - b^2} + \frac{y^2}{\lambda - a^2} = 1,$$

where

$$a^2 > b^2 \quad \text{and} \quad \lambda > a^2 \qquad \text{(ellipses)},$$

$$\frac{x^2}{\mu - b^2} - \frac{y^2}{a^2 - \mu} = 1,$$

where

$$b^2 < \mu < a^2 \qquad \text{(hyperbolas)}.$$

Show that:

(a) all ellipses and the hyperbolas have the same foci;

(b) the (elliptic) coordinates λ and μ establish a coordinate system for the first quadrant of the xy-plane.

SUMMARY

There are infinitely many ways of setting up a coordinate system for the plane, space, or portions of either. The most important ones are:

1. Different rectangular coordinates related by
   (a) Translation of axes:

$$x' = x - h,$$
$$y' = y - k.$$

If a second-degree equation does not contain an xy-term, we can find a convenient point to translate the origin by completing the squares.
   (b) Rotation of axes:

$$x' = x \cos \theta - y \sin \theta,$$
$$y' = x \sin \theta + y \cos \theta.$$

The xy-term can be removed from

$$Ax^2 + Bxy + Cy^2 + Dx + Ey + F = 0$$

by rotating axes through an angle θ given by

$$\tan 2\theta = B/(A - C).$$

2. A point in the plane has infinitely many polar coordinates. If rectangular axes are placed in the standard position with respect to the polar axis, the two coordinate systems are connected by

$$x = r \cos \theta, \quad \text{or} \quad r = \pm\sqrt{x^2 + y^2},$$
$$y = r \sin \theta, \qquad \theta = \arctan (y/x).$$

Simple polar equations give a variety of new curves.
When finding intersections of curves given by polar equations, we must be careful to get all points of intersection.

3. Cylindrical coordinates are simply related to rectangular coordinates if the two sets of axes are suitably placed.

$$x = r \cos \theta, \qquad r = \pm\sqrt{x^2 + y^2},$$
$$y = r \sin \theta, \qquad \theta = \arctan (y/x),$$
$$z = z, \qquad\qquad z = z.$$

4. Spherical coordinates are simply related to rectangular coordinates if the two sets of axes are suitably placed.

$$x = \rho \sin \varphi \cos \theta, \qquad \rho = \sqrt{x^2 + y^2 + z^2},$$
$$y = \rho \sin \varphi \sin \theta, \qquad \theta = \arctan (y/x),$$
$$z = \rho \cos \varphi, \qquad\qquad \varphi = \text{Arccos} (z/\sqrt{x^2 + y^2 + z^2}).$$

387

Review Problems

1. The origin is translated to the point $(-3, 3)$.

   (a) What are the new coordinates of the point $(-7, -5)$?

   (b) What were the original coordinates of the point whose new coordinates are $(1, 2)$?

2. Where should the origin be translated to simplify the following equations? Sketch each graph.

   (a) $4x^2 + 3y^2 + 16x - 6y + 12 = 0$

   (b) $2x^2 - y^2 + 12x - 8y + 5 = 0$

   (c) $x^2 + 8x + 3y + 13 = 0$

3. The axes are rotated through $\pi/6$. If the new coordinates of a point are $(\sqrt{3}, 2)$, what were the original coordinates?

4. Rotate the axes to remove the xy-term from each of the following equations, and sketch each curve.

   (a) $3x^2 + 12xy - 2y^2 + 84 = 0$

   (b) $3x^2 + 2\sqrt{3}\,xy + y^2 - 8x + 8\sqrt{3}\,y = 0$

   (c) $x^2 - xy + y^2 - 12x - 6y + 66 = 0$

5. Sketch the graphs of the following equations in polar coordinates.

   (a) $r = 5\cos 2\theta$ (b) $r = a\cos\theta,\quad a < 0$

   (c) $r^2 = 16\cos 2\theta$ (d) $r = 2^{-\theta},\quad \theta \ge 0$

   (e) $r = 2/(1 - \cos\theta)$ (f) $r = a\sin 3\theta,\quad a > 0$

6. Find the points of intersection of the following curves given by their polar equations. Sketch each graph.

   (a) $r = 2\sin\theta,\quad r = 2\cos 2\theta$ (b) $r = 1 + \cos\theta,\quad r = 3\cos\theta$

   (c) $r = 1,\quad r = \tan\theta$

7. Find rectangular equations of, and sketch, each of the curves whose equations in polar coordinates are

   (a) $r = a\cos\theta + a\sin\theta$

   (b) $r^2 = a^2\cos 2\theta$

   (c) $r = \tan\theta\sec\theta$

8. Find polar equations for, and sketch, the curves whose rectangular equations are:

   (a) $x^3 + xy^2 = y$ (b) $x^2 + y^2 + ax + by = 0$

   (c) $3x^2 - y^2 - 12x + 9 = 0$

388

9. Sketch the surfaces whose equations in cylindrical coordinates are

   (a) $r = 6 \cos \theta$ (b) $r = 2z$

   (c) $b^2 r^2 \cos^2 \theta + a^2 r^2 \sin^2 \theta = a^2 b^2$

   (d) $r^2 + 2z^2 = 4$ (e) $r^2 - 2z^2 = 4$

10. Sketch the surfaces whose equations in spherical coordinates are

   (a) $\rho = 2, \quad \pi/4 \le \theta \le \pi/2$ (b) $\rho \cos \varphi = 3$

   (c) $b^2 \rho^2 \sin^2 \varphi + a^2 \rho^2 \cos^2 \varphi = a^2 b^2$

HISTORICAL NOTE

Jakob Bernoulli (1654–1705)

In a sense, a variety of coordinate systems have been with us since ancient times. Latitude and longitude on the celestial sphere, as used by the ancient astronomers, have a close connection with spherical coordinates. However, with the exception of Descartes' invention (and he used only Cartesian coordinates), there are no great landmarks in the theory of coordinate systems until modern times. Gradually, new coordinate systems appeared in order to help solve special problems.

Polar coordinates were introduced by the Swiss Jakob Bernoulli (1654–1705) of the distinguished Bernoulli family of mathematicians. Initially, polar coordinates were applied chiefly to spirals, but Jakob Bernoulli also made use of them in other situations.

No new coordinate systems were conceived until the end of the eighteenth century, and it was only in the nineteenth century, after analysis and physics had become sufficiently sophisticated, that mathematicians developed a systematic notion of general coordinate systems. Highly instrumental and suggestive to the development of a general point of view was the work of Karl Friedrich Gauss (1777–1855) in 1827 on the curvature of surfaces. The Gaussian point of view was generalized (in 1861) by Georg Friedrich Bernhard Riemann (1826–1866), who founded n-dimensional differential geometry. In this discipline the properties of n-dimensional space are studied in terms of the n coordinates, $x_1 \ldots, x_n$, of a point. The fundamental work of Riemann was elaborated by a number of geometers and was later found to be the natural mathematical language needed for the theory of relativity.

A book by the engineer G. Lamé, published in 1859, contains material on curvilinear coordinates. In this book are found numerous applications to problems of physics. Today the theory of general coordinate systems is taught to most engineering students.

REPRESENTATION O

14

PARAMETRIC
CURVES AND SURFACES

14-1. INTRODUCTION

What is a curve? What is a surface? These are questions we propose to answer by giving natural, intuitively satisfying, *definitions*.

A definition of curve that might be given by "the man in the street" is as follows:

"A curve is a bent (and/or stretched or compressed) line." (See Fig. 14–1.)

In the same spirit a definition of a surface might be:

"A surface is a bent (and/or stretched or compressed) flat plate." (See Fig. 14–2.)

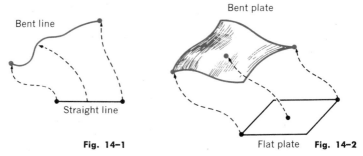

Fig. 14–1   Flat plate   **Fig. 14–2**

These tentative, and as yet vague, definitions will be made precise in the sections to follow.

It should be noted that a set of points which is a "bent and stretched line" could be obtained by bending and stretching many different lines. In other words, there is no one single way of bending and stretching a line to give a curve.

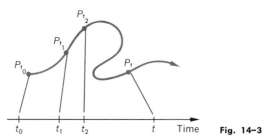

Fig. 14–3

When we "bend and stretch" a line to get a curve, we naturally do not permit the line to be broken and then bent or stretched in piecemeal fashion. This will be reflected later in our requirement that the functions which define a curve, or surface, be continuous.

394

A final geometric illustration of a curve (and a most important one in physics) is the following: Imagine a particle moving continuously in such a manner that at each instant of time t, after an initial time t_0, the particle is at the point P_t (see Fig. 14–3). The set of points occupied by the moving particle is a curve because it is simply the image in space of an interval of the time axis. Time has been "bent and stretched" into a curve in space.

14–2. PARAMETRIC CURVES

In accordance with the intuitive ideas of the preceding section, we shall make a precise definition of a parametrized curve.

DEFINITION 14–1

A *parametrized curve* is a *continuous function* from an interval of the real numbers into space (or into the plane if we are concerned with plane curves).

This implies that the three coordinates which fix a point in space are continuous functions on the given interval. A variable which represents a real number in the domain of a function is called a *parameter*.

A line can be parametrized, as in Fig. 14–3, by the coordinates on a line. That is, the coordinates t_0, t_1, t_2, etc., of the time line can be used to locate the position of a point $P(x, y, z)$ in space. Therefore, when we bend and stretch a line into space, we have a mapping of an interval of real numbers into space.

Thus, if rectangular coordinates are used to locate the point, and if the interval of the real line on which the mapping is defined is $a \leq t \leq b$, then a parametrized curve is given by the equations

$$\begin{cases} x = f(t), \\ y = g(t), \quad \text{for} \quad a \leq t \leq b, \\ z = h(t), \end{cases} \tag{1}$$

where the functions f, g, and h are *continuous*. The variable t is the *parameter*. Equations (1) are *parametric equations* of the parametrized curve.

Remarks

1. One need not be restricted to rectangular coordinates.

2. Most of our examples will be plane curves given by $x = f(t)$ and $y = g(t)$, where f and g are very simple functions.

3. The domain of the parameter may be the whole real line, in which case $-\infty < t < \infty$.

395

4. In this section our technique for drawing parametrized curves will be to make a table of values of the coordinates versus the parameter. After these points are plotted, it will then be clear how to draw the curve.

5. We have already met with parametrized curves in Chapters 1 and 3, where we discussed parametric equations of lines:

$$x = x_0 + c_1d, \qquad y = y_0 + c_2d, \qquad z = z_0 + c_3d$$

for $-\infty < d < \infty$.

EXAMPLES

1. Sketch the parametrized curve

$$\begin{cases} x = t, \\ y = t^2, \end{cases} \qquad -\infty < t < \infty.$$

t	0	± 1	± 2	$\pm\frac{1}{2}$	$\pm\frac{3}{2}$
x	0	± 1	± 2	$\pm\frac{1}{2}$	$\pm\frac{3}{2}$
y	0	1	4	$\frac{1}{4}$	$\frac{9}{4}$

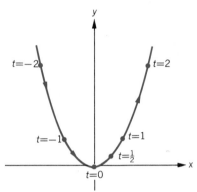

Fig. 14-4

The points on the curve corresponding to some of the values of t are shown in Fig. 14-4. The arrowheads on the curve indicate the direction of increasing t.

2. If ϕ is the standard map of the real numbers (Chapter 7) onto the unit circle, then ϕ makes the unit circle a parametrized curve. The parametric equations are

$$x = \cos\theta, \qquad y = \sin\theta, \qquad -\infty < \theta < \infty.$$

Observe that we also have the polar parametric representation of the unit circle:

$$r = 1, \qquad \theta = \theta, \qquad -\infty < \theta < \infty.$$

(See Fig. 14-5.)

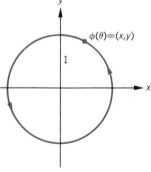

Fig. 14-5

3. Consider the parametrized curve

$$\begin{cases} x = 2^t, \\ y = 2^{-t}, \end{cases} \qquad -\infty < t < \infty.$$

The curve with some parameter values is shown in Fig. 14-6(a).

396

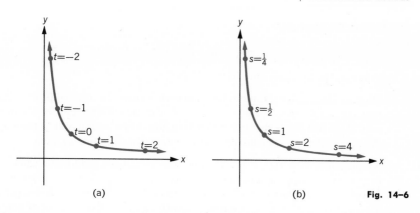

(a)　　　　　　　　　　　(b)　　　　Fig. 14-6

The same set of points can be parametrized in other ways. For example, the equations

$$\left.\begin{array}{l} x = s \\ y = \dfrac{1}{s} \end{array}\right\}, \qquad 0 < s < \infty,$$

also give the same set of points. Observe how the parameter values in this case are spread along the curve in Fig. 14-6(b).

Problems

1. Sketch the following parametrized curves by plotting enough points to see where the graphs go. Mark on each graph some points with their parameter values.

    (a) $x = s^2$, $y = s$, $\quad -\infty < s \le 0$
    (b) $x = 1/(t + 1)$, $y = t + 2$, $\quad 0 \le t < \infty$
    (c) $x = \sin t$, $y = \tan t$, $\quad 0 \le t < \pi/2$
    (d) $x = 1/(t^2 + 1)$, $y = t$, $\quad -\infty < t < \infty$
    (e) $x = 2 \sin t$, $y = 3 \cos t$, $\quad -\infty < t < \infty$
    (f) $x = 2 + 3 \cos t$, $y = 4 + 3 \sin t$, $\quad -\infty < t < \infty$
    (g) $x = \sin t$, $y = \cos 2t$, $\quad -\infty < t < \infty$
    (h) $x = \sin t$, $y = 2 \sin t$, $\quad -\infty < t < \infty$

2. Sketch the graph of

    (a) $x = \cos t$, $y = \sin t$, $z = 1$, $\quad 0 \le t \le 2\pi$.
    (b) $x = \cos t$, $y = \sin t$, $z = \frac{1}{3}t$, $\quad 0 \le t \le 2\pi$.

3. Sketch the graph of

    (a) $x = 1 - t$, $y = t$, $z = 1$, $\quad 0 \le t \le 1$.
    (b) $x = 1 - t$, $y = t$, $z = t^2$, $\quad 0 \le t \le 1$.

4. Sketch the graph of

$$x = 2 + t, \quad y = -2 - 2t, \quad z = -t, \quad -\infty < t < \infty.$$

What geometric significance does t have?

5. Suppose that f is a continuous function with domain the interval $[a, b]$. Show that the graph of $y = f(x)$, $a \le x \le b$, can be parametrized in a natural way. This will prove that our earlier language, when we referred to the graph of f as a curve, is now consistent with our present definition of a curve.

*6. Suppose that $x = f(t)$, $y = g(t)$, and $a \le t \le b$, are parametric equations of a curve. Suppose also that $t = \varphi(s)$, for $c \le s \le d$, is a continuous mapping of the interval $[c, d]$ onto the interval $[a, b]$. Show that $x = f(\varphi(s))$, $y = g(\varphi(s))$, $c \le s \le d$, is a new parametrization of the same set of points. Hence you may conclude that there are infinitely many parametrizations of a given parametrized set of points.

14-3. ELIMINATION OF THE PARAMETER

Parametric equations for a plane curve may not have a form that permits one to recognize the curve at a glance. In previous chapters we have regarded curves as graphs of equations in rectangular (or polar) coordinates, and we have developed some skill in recognizing at once some of these curves from their equations. Therefore, in drawing parametrized curves it will frequently help to *eliminate the parameter*. This will result in a rectangular (or polar) equation which we can perhaps recognize. But *one must be careful because the parametrized curve may not be all of the graph of the rectangular* (or polar) *equation*. Examples will illustrate this idea.

EXAMPLES

1. Graph the parametrized curve

$$x = \cos^2 t, \qquad y = \sin^2 t, \qquad -\infty < t < \infty.$$

If the point (x, y) is on the parametrized curve, then

$$x + y = \cos^2 t + \sin^2 t = 1.$$

Therefore the point (x, y) is on the straight line

$$x + y = 1.$$

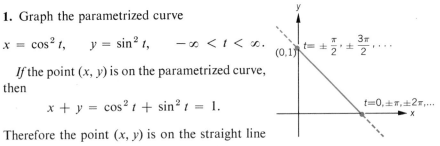

Fig. 14-7

(See Fig. 14-7.) But the parametrized curve cannot be all of this line because x and y on the parametrized curve must be between 0 and 1. Clearly the point (x, y) on the parametrized curve moves back and forth on the line between $(1, 0)$ and $(0, 1)$ as t increases.

398

2. Let us assume that the earth is flat, that there is no air resistance, and that the only force acting on a projectile is the force of gravity. It is shown in physics that a projectile fired at an angle of elevation α with the horizontal will trace a path given by the parametric equations

$$\begin{cases} x = v_0 t \cos \alpha, \\ y = v_0 t \sin \alpha - \frac{1}{2}gt^2. \end{cases}$$

These equations are based on the assumptions that the axes are chosen as in Fig. 14–8, that t is the time in seconds from the instant of firing, g is the acceleration of gravity (say, in feet per second per second), and v_0 is the initial velocity (in feet per second).

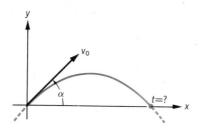

Fig. 14-8

If we eliminate t by solving for t in terms of x and substitute in the equation for y, we obtain

$$y = x \tan \alpha - \frac{g}{2v_0^2 \cos^2 \alpha} x^2,$$

which is recognized as the equation of a parabola. Clearly, not all of the parabola is the path, or trajectory, of the projectile. The projectile begins its motion at $t = 0$. It is also clear that when the projectile strikes the earth, there is an end to the parabolic path.

Problems

1. Eliminate the parameter, identify the curve if possible, and sketch it. Show how a point on the parametrized curve moves as the parameter increases.

   (a) $x = 2 + \sin \theta, \quad y = \cos \theta, \qquad -\infty < \theta < \infty$

   (b) $x = 2 + t, \quad y = 1 - t, \qquad 0 \le t < \infty$

   (c) $x = 1 - t^2, \quad y = 1 + t^2, \qquad -\infty < t < \infty$

   (d) $x = 4 \cos s, \quad y = 3 \sin s, \qquad -\infty < s < \infty$

   (e) $x = 3 \sin \theta - 1, \quad y = 2 \cos \theta + 1, \qquad -\infty < \theta < \infty$

   (f) $r = 1 + 2 \cos t^2, \quad \theta = t^2, \qquad -\infty < t < \infty \quad$ (polar coordinates)

   (g) $x = \tan \theta, \quad y = \sec^2 \theta, \qquad -\pi/2 < \theta < \pi/2$

   (h) $x = u + 1/u, \quad y = u - 1/u, \qquad 0 < u < \infty$

   (i) $x = \cos^2 \theta - 1, \quad y = \cos \theta - 1, \qquad -\infty < \theta < \infty$

   (j) $r = 2\sqrt{\cos t}, \quad \theta = \frac{1}{2}t, \qquad -\pi/2 \le t \le \pi/2 \quad$ (polar coordinates)

399

2. Show that $x = A \cos t + B \sin t$, and $y = A \sin t - B \cos t$ are parametric equations of a circle. Find its center and radius and show how a point moves on the circle as t increases from 0 to ∞.

3. At what instant and where does the projectile of Example 2 above reach the earth? What is the maximum height of the projectile?

4. Show that the parametric equations $x = h + a \cos \theta$ and $y = k + b \sin \theta$, $-\infty < \theta < \infty$, represent an ellipse.

5. Show that the parametric equations

$$x = at/(1 + t^2), \quad y = a/(1 + t^2), \qquad -\infty < t < \infty, \qquad \text{and} \qquad a > 0,$$

represent almost a full circle.

*6. The *folium of Descartes* is given by the parametric equations

$$x = 3t^2/(1 + t^3), \qquad y = 3t/(1 + t^3), \qquad t \neq -1.$$

(a) Sketch the curve.

(b) Show that its rectangular equation is $x^3 + y^3 - 3xy = 0$.

(c) Show that $x + y + 1 = 0$ is an asymptote.
[*Hint:* Show that when t is near -1, then $x + y + 1$ is near zero.]

14-4. ON THE PARAMETRIZATION OF CURVES

We have defined *parametrized* curves, and we have seen that they can be parametrized in different ways. We have not yet defined what we mean by *curve*, without any qualifying adjective. We now fill this gap in our set of mathematical concepts.

DEFINITION 14-2

A set C of points in space is a *curve* if this set can be parametrized.

In other words, C is a curve if there are continuous functions f, g, and h such that the points (x, y, z) of C are given by

$$x = f(t), \qquad y = g(t), \qquad z = h(t),$$

for numbers t in an interval $a \leq t \leq b$.

Remarks

1. We have seen many examples of sets that can be parametrized. In this section we shall see other examples in which the parameter can be chosen in a quite natural way.

400

2. Curves according to Definitions 14–1 and 14–2 can be exceedingly complicated. The single requirement of continuity of the functions f, g, and h is
not enough to prevent rather strange sets from being curves. (See Historical
Note at the end of Chapter 14.) However, *if f, g, and h are elementary functions*, then we always get sets of points which it seems natural to call curves.
The surprising cases do not occur.

3. The union of two curves (see Fig. 14–9),
with nonempty intersection, is also a curve.
In other words, the combined set can be
parametrized. The next example suggests
why this is the case.

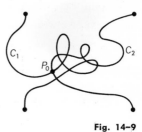

Fig. 14-9

EXAMPLES

1. Let C be the union of two segments, one on each of the x- and y-axes,
as shown in Fig. 14–10(a). We shall parametrize C so that it is the continuous
image of the interval $0 \leq t \leq 1$.

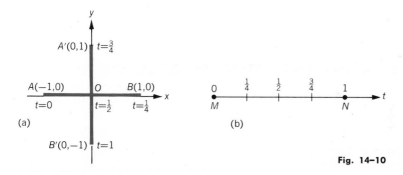

Fig. 14-10

Divide the unit interval $\overline{MN}$ of the t-axis into fourths. (See Fig. 14–10b.)
We shall map successive fourths of $\overline{MN}$ into $\overline{AB}$, $\overline{BO}$, $\overline{OA'}$, and $\overline{A'B'}$ in that
order. Let

$$x = -1 + 8t, \quad y = 0 \qquad \text{if} \qquad 0 \leq t \leq \tfrac{1}{4},$$
$$x = 2 - 4t, \quad y = 0 \qquad \text{if} \qquad \tfrac{1}{4} \leq t \leq \tfrac{1}{2},$$
$$x = 0, \quad y = -2 + 4t \qquad \text{if} \qquad \tfrac{1}{2} \leq t \leq \tfrac{3}{4},$$
$$x = 0, \quad y = 7 - 8t \qquad \text{if} \qquad \tfrac{3}{4} \leq t \leq 1.$$

These equations give a parametrization of C because x and y are continuous
functions of t. In each of the subintervals, the continuity is clear because the
functions are linear functions of t. At the ends of the intervals, that is, at
$t = \tfrac{1}{4}, \tfrac{1}{2}$, and $\tfrac{3}{4}$, the values of x and y given by the two formulas agree.

401

2. Consider two circles of radii a and $b < a$ with center at the origin (see Fig. 14–11). Let A and B be the points at which a ray from O meets these circles. Let P be the intersection of the vertical and horizontal lines through A and B, respectively.

Let C be the set of all such points P. Each point of C is on a unique ray from the origin. Therefore, if we parametrize these rays, we will obtain a parametrization of C.

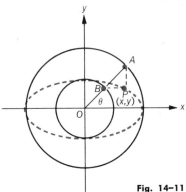

Fig. 14-11

Let (a, θ) be polar coordinates of A. Then to each real number θ there is a unique ray from O. If the rectangular coordinates of P are x and y, then

$$\begin{cases} x = a \cos \theta, \\ y = b \sin \theta, \end{cases} \qquad -\infty < \theta < \infty. \quad (1)$$

Equations (1) parametrize C because $a \cos \theta$ and $b \sin \theta$ are continuous functions of θ. They are seen to be parametric equations of an ellipse because

$$\frac{x^2}{a^2} + \frac{y^2}{b^2} = \cos^2 \theta + \sin^2 \theta = 1.$$

3. Imagine a circle of radius a rolling on a horizontal line with one point P marked on the circle. The set of points described by the moving point P is called a *cycloid*.

We shall parametrize the cycloid. We first choose axes so that the circle rolls along the x-axis and one point of contact of P with the x-axis is at the origin. (See Fig. 14–12.) We select as our parameter the angle θ through which the circle has rotated since P coincided with O. It is convenient to use vectors. We have

$$\overrightarrow{OP} = \overrightarrow{OA} + \overrightarrow{AC} + \overrightarrow{CP},$$

where

$$\overrightarrow{OP} = x\mathbf{i} + y\mathbf{j},$$
$$\overrightarrow{OA} = a\theta\mathbf{i},$$
$$\overrightarrow{AC} = a\mathbf{j},$$
$$\overrightarrow{CP} = -a \sin \theta\mathbf{i} - a \cos \theta\mathbf{j}.$$

Then

$$x\mathbf{i} + y\mathbf{j} = (a\theta - a \sin \theta)\mathbf{i} + (a - a \cos \theta)\mathbf{j},$$

and, equating components, we have

$$x = a\theta - a \sin \theta,$$
$$y = a - a \cos \theta.$$

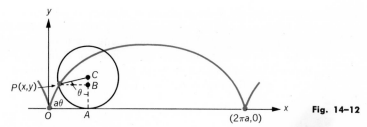

Fig. 14-12

These equations are valid for all θ, and give x and y as continuous functions of θ. Thus the cycloid is parametrized by

$$x = a(\theta - \sin \theta),$$
$$y = a(1 - \cos \theta).$$

Problems

1. Given the following rectangular equations, make the suggested substitution (t is the parameter) and so parametrize the graph of each equation.
   (a) $9x^2 + y^2 = 1$. Let $y = \sin t$.
   (b) $x^2 y + xy + 1 = 0$. Let $x = t$.
   (c) $y = f(x)$. Let $x = t$.
   (d) $x^{2/3} + y^{2/3} = a^{2/3}$. Let $y = a \sin^3 t, a > 0$.
   (e) $(x + 2)^2 + 4(y - 3)^2 = 16$. Let $y = 3 + 2 \cos t$.
   (f) $x^2 - y^2 = a^2$. Let $x = a \sec t$.

2. Parametrize, in some way, the graphs of the following equations.
   (a) $(x - 1)^2 + 2(y + 2)^2 = 4$ (b) $xy^2 = x + y$
   (c) $y(a^2 + x^2) = 2ax$ (d) $x^3 + y^3 = a^3$

3. Consider the family of lines $y = mx + b$, where m is the parameter and b is fixed and not zero. Each of these lines meets (if $m \neq 0$) the x-axis at a point A. If $B = (0, b)$, parametrize in terms of m the set of midpoints of the segments $\overline{AB}$.

4. Parametrize the unit circle in terms of the slope m of a line through $(-1, 0)$. (See figure.)

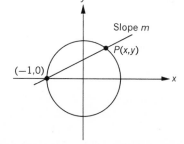

5. Use the result of Problem 4 to generate Pythagorean triples, that is, *whole* numbers r, s, t such that $r^2 + s^2 = t^2$. [*Hint:* Let $m = p/q$, where $p < q$ and p and q are relatively prime integers.]

403

6. The curve called the *Witch of Agnesi* is obtained as suggested in the figure on the left below. A ray from O in the upper half-plane meets the circle $r = a \sin \theta$ (polar coordinates) in a point A, and the line $y = a$ in a point B. The point P on the Witch has the x-coordinate of B and the y-coordinate of A. Parametrize the Witch with θ, the polar angle, as parameter. Sketch the curve and find a rectangular equation for it.

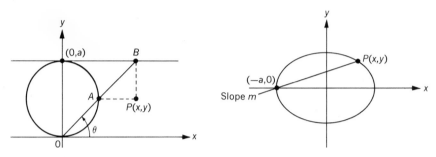

7. Parametrize the ellipse $x^2/a^2 + y^2/b^2 = 1$ in terms of the parameter m which is equal to the slope of the line through $(-a, 0)$ (see the figure on the right above). Do you get all of the ellipse?

8. Find a rectangular equation for the cycloid.

9. If a cycloid is generated by a rolling circle with its center below the x-axis, what are parametric equations for it?

10. The *prolate cycloid* is generated by a point P fixed with respect to a circle rolling on a line, where the distance P from the center of the circle, b, is greater than the radius, a, of the circle. Choose axes and parameter as in Example 3, p. 402. Show that parametric equations of the prolate cycloid are $x = a\theta - b \sin \theta$ and $y = a - b \cos \theta$. Sketch the curve. [*Hint:* Use vectors. Note that $\overrightarrow{CP} = -b \sin \theta \mathbf{i} - b \cos \theta \mathbf{j}$.]

11. The *curtate* cycloid is generated similarly to the prolate cycloid in Problem 10 but with $b < a$. Find parametric equations for the curtate cycloid and sketch.

12. The *hypocycloids* are generated by a small circle rolling inside a larger circle. They are curves generated by a point P fixed on the small circle. Use the notation and axes of the figure to parametrize the *hypocycloid of four cusps* which is obtained when $4b = a$, and $P = (a, 0)$ when $\theta = 0$. Using vectors, show that $x = a \cos^3 \varphi$ and $y = a \sin^3 \varphi$. Note that $\overrightarrow{OP} = \overrightarrow{OC} + \overrightarrow{CP}$ and $\varphi = \frac{1}{4}\theta$.

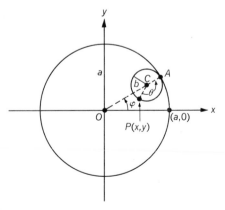

13. Show that if for a hypocycloid (see Problem 12) the ratio of the radii, a/b, is an irrational number, then the curve never "closes up," or repeats itself.

14. The *epicycloids* are generated by a point P on a small circle which rolls on the outside of a larger circle. If the radii are a and $b < a$, and if P is at $(a, 0)$ when $\theta = 0$ (see the figure on the left below), show that the parametric equations of the epicycloid are

$$\begin{cases} x = (a + b) \cos \varphi - b \cos \dfrac{a + b}{b} \varphi, \\[2mm] y = (a + b) \sin \varphi - b \sin \dfrac{a + b}{b} \varphi. \end{cases}$$

[*Hint:* $\overrightarrow{OP} = \overrightarrow{OC} + \overrightarrow{CP}$ and $b\theta = a\varphi$.]

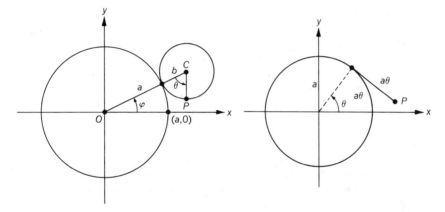

15. A string (zero thickness) is wrapped round a circle and then unwrapped keeping the string taut. (See the figure on the right above for notation and choice of axes.) The set of points occupied by the end of the string is called an *involute* of the circle. Show that parametric equations of the involute are

$$x = a(\cos \theta + \theta \sin \theta), \qquad y = a(\sin \theta - \theta \cos \theta).$$

16. Show that the three sets of parametric equations

$$\begin{aligned} x &= \cos^4 t, & y &= \sin^4 t, \\ x &= \sec^4 t, & y &= \tan^4 t, \\ x &= \tan^4 t, & y &= \sec^4 t \end{aligned}$$

represent different arcs of the same parabola. [*Hint:* Show that in the three cases $x^{1/2} + y^{1/2} = 1$, $x^{1/2} - y^{1/2} = 1$, and $-x^{1/2} + y^{1/2} = 1$, respectively. Then show that each is a part of the parabola

$$x^2 - 2xy + y^2 - 2x - 2y + 1 = 0.$$

405

14–5. SURFACES

We now give definitions for surfaces and parametric surfaces which are similar to those definitions we gave for curves. Our development of these ideas will be quite brief.

First we must decide what set, in parameter space, is to replace the parameter interval that we used for curves. In Section 14–1 we regarded a surface as a "bent plate." We must now decide what "plates" to use.

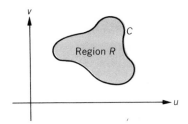

Fig. 14–13

As shown in Fig. 14–13, we let C be a simple closed curve (a bent circle) in the uv-plane (the plane of the parameters). We will call R the interior of C. (We shall also allow R to be the whole plane.) Such regions, with or without their boundaries, will be our "plates."

DEFINITION 14–3

A *parametrized surface* is *the image of a continuous function* from a region R in a uv-plane into space. The variables u and v are *parameters*.

Thus, if rectangular coordinates are used to locate points, the parametrized surface is given by†

$$\begin{aligned} x &= f(u, v), \\ y &= g(u, v), \qquad \text{for } (u, v) \text{ in } R, \\ z &= h(u, v), \end{aligned} \qquad (1)$$

where f, g, h are continuous real-valued functions.

DEFINITION 14–4

A set S of points in space is a *surface* if this set can be parametrized.

In other words, S is a surface if a region R and continuous real functions f, g, and h, with domain R can be found, such that S is the graph of Equations (1).

---

† The symbol "$f(u, v)$" is standard functional notation for the value of the function f (of two variables) corresponding to the values u and v.

406

We shall be interested in only the simplest examples.

EXAMPLES

1. The plane $z = 2 - 2x - y$ (see Fig. 14–14) can be parametrized by

$$x = u, \qquad y = v, \qquad z = 2 - 2u - v,$$

where u and v are arbitrary real numbers. The region R of parameter space is the whole uv-plane.

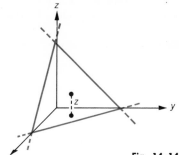

Fig. 14–14

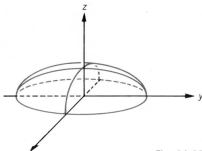

Fig. 14–15

2. Consider the upper half of the ellipsoid $2x^2 + y^2 + 4z^2 = 8$. (See Fig. 14–15.)

This set of points is parametrized by

$$x = u, \qquad y = v, \qquad z = \tfrac{1}{2}\sqrt{8 - 2u^2 - v^2}$$

The region R of the parameters is the ellipse $2u^2 + v^2 = 8$ plus its interior.

3. The sphere with center at the origin and radius a (Fig. 14–16a) is parametrized by spherical coordinates:

$$x = a \sin \varphi \cos \theta, \qquad y = a \sin \varphi \sin \theta, \qquad z = a \cos \varphi.$$

The region R of parameter space is the rectangle (Fig. 14–16b) $0 \le \theta \le 2\pi$, $0 \le \varphi \le \pi$.

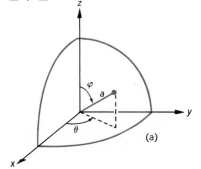

(a)

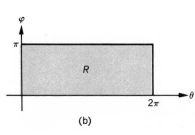

(b)

Fig. 14–16

407

Problems

1. Parametrize the hemisphere $x^2 + y^2 + z^2 = a^2$, $y \geq 0$, by solving for y. What is the region R of parameter space?

2. Parametrize the cylinder $x^2 + y^2 = a^2$ by using cylindrical coordinates. What is the region R?

3. Parametrize the paraboloid $z = x^2 + y^2$. What is R?

4. Suppose in Definition 14–3 that the three functions f, g, and h are constant functions. We say that the surface is degenerate. What surface is it? Suppose that only two of the three functions f, g, and h are constant. In what way is the surface "degenerate"? Suppose that only one of the three functions f, g, and h is a constant. Must the surface be degenerate in some way?

SUMMARY

In this chapter we have finally defined precisely the meaning of *curve* and *surface*. The sequence of ideas is as follows:

1. A *parametrized curve* is a continuous mapping (a continuous function) from an interval of real numbers into space.

2. A *curve* is a set of points that can be parametrized. There are infinitely many ways to parametrize a curve.

3. A rectangular equation of a parametrized plane curve is obtained by eliminating the parameter between the two parametric equations.

4. A *parametrized surface* is a continuous mapping from a plane region into space. Coordinates in the plane region are parameters.

5. A *surface* is a set of points that can be parametrized to give a parametrized surface.

Review Problems

1. Sketch the plane curves given by the following parametric equations. Where it is possible to do so, identify the curve by finding a rectangular equation for the curve.

   (a) $x = 1 - \cos t$, $y = 2 - 2 \sin t$, $-\pi/2 \leq t \leq \pi/2$

   (b) $x = at/(1 + t^2)$, $y = a/(1 + t^2)$, $-\infty < t < \infty$

   (c) $x = t^2 - t$, $y = t^2 + t$, $-1 \leq t \leq 1$

   (d) $x = 2 \sin^2 t$, $y = 3 \cos^2 t$, $-\infty < t < \infty$

(e) $x = 1/(1 + \lambda^2)$, $y = \lambda$, $\quad 0 \leq \lambda < \infty$

(f) $x = a \sec \theta$, $y = b \tan \theta$, $\quad -\pi/2 < \theta < \pi/2$

(g) $x = \tan \theta$, $y = \cot \theta$, $\quad \pi/2 < 0 < \pi$

(h) $x = 1 + 2\sqrt{\mu}$, $y = \mu$, $\quad 0 \leq \mu < \infty$

(i) $x = \sin^2 t - 2$, $y = \sin t + 1$, $\quad -\infty < t < \infty$

(j) $x = 50t$, $y = 50t - 16t^2$, $\quad$ with t restricted so that $x \geq 0$ and $y \geq 0$

(k) $x = 5(\theta - \sin \theta)$, $y = 5(1 - \cos \theta)$, $\quad 0 \leq \theta \leq 2\pi$

(l) $x = 4\theta - 2 \sin \theta$, $y = 4 - 2 \cos \theta$, $\quad -\infty < \theta < \infty$

(m) $x = 2 \cos \theta + \cos 2\theta$, $y = 2 \sin \theta - \sin 2\theta$, $\quad 0 \leq \theta \leq 2\pi$

(n) $x = \dfrac{a(1 - t^2)}{1 + t^2}$, $y = \dfrac{bt}{1 + t^2}$, $\quad a, b > 0$, $\quad -\infty < t < \infty$

(o) $r = t$, $\theta = a^2/t^2$, $\quad 0 < t < \infty$, polar coordinates

*(p) $x = \sin t$, $y = 2^t$, $\quad -\infty < t < \infty$

2. Find parametrizations of the graphs of the following equations.

(a) $x^2 - y^2 = 1$ $\qquad\qquad$ (b) $xy^2 = 4$

(c) $xy^2 + x + y = 1$

(d) $y = F(x)$, where F is continuous with domain $[a, b]$.

3. Show how to parametrize the following curves C with the parameter t in the interval $[0, 1]$. (There are many answers.)

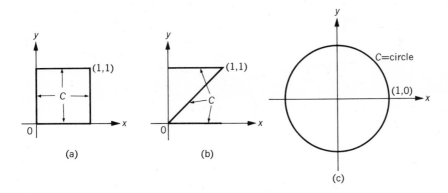

(a) $\qquad\qquad\qquad$ (b) $\qquad\qquad\qquad$ (c)

4. Sketch the following parametrized space curves.

(a) $x = a \cos t$, $y = a \sin t$, $z = t$

(b) $x = a \cos t$, $y = a \sin t$, $z = a \sin t$

*(c) $x = 2^{-t/\pi} \cos t$, $y = 2^{-t/\pi} \sin t$, $z = 2^{-t/\pi}$

*(d) $x = \dfrac{a \cos t}{1 + t^2}$, $y = \dfrac{a \sin t}{1 + t^2}$, $z = t$, $\quad 0 \leq t < \infty$

409

5. Sketch the following parametrized surfaces:

   (a) $x = a \sin u, \quad y = v, \quad z = a \cos u, \qquad 0 \le u \le \pi/2, \; 0 \le v \le 2$

   (b) $x = \cos u, \quad y = \cos v, \quad z = \cos^2 u + \cos^2 v, \qquad 0 \le u, \; v \le \pi/2$

   (c) $x = u/\sqrt{2}, \quad y = v/\sqrt{2}, \quad z = 1 - (u + v)/\sqrt{2}$, where $0 \le u, \; 0 \le v$, and $u + v \le \sqrt{2}$

*6. The *Folium of Descartes* has the rectangular equation $x^3 + y^3 - 3axy = 0$, $a > 0$. Find parametric equations for the curve by letting $y = mx$ and solving for x and y in terms of the parameter m. Sketch the curve. Show that the line $x + y + a = 0$ is an asymptote by showing that as m approaches -1, both x and y become infinite while $x + y + a$ is a very small number.

*7. The *Conchoid of Nicomedes†* is generated as suggested by the accompanying figure. The point $B = (0, -b)$ and $a > b > 0$. A directed line through B makes an angle θ (measured positively clockwise) with the y-axis, and meets the axis in a point C. Along the directed line choose the point P at a distance a from C. The set of all such points P (except for θ, an odd multiple of $\pi/2$) is the Conchoid. Obtain parametric equations for the Conchoid in terms of the parameter θ. Find a rectangular equation for it. [*Hint:* Note the position vector $\overrightarrow{OP} = \overrightarrow{OC} + \overrightarrow{CP}$.]

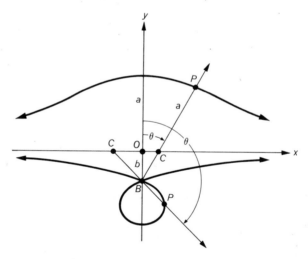

† See Thomas L. Heath, *Euclid's Elements*, p. 160.

HISTORICAL NOTE

Georg Cantor (1845–1918)

The notion of a parametrized curve is as old as the idea of curve itself. From the beginning, geometers have imagined the path of a moving point—a natural parametrization with time as the parameter. Newton, in the seventeenth century, imagined a point moving in the plane and tracing out the graph of a function.

A vast literature exists about curves of special kinds: cubic curves, quartic curves, algebraic curves, polar curves, etc. Most of the earlier writers took it for granted that the reader knew what a curve was, and then went on to discuss those special curves which were of interest to them. There was no attempt, on the part of these writers, to look for "the most general curve." They were not concerned with "pathological cases." For them, curves were the "nice curves" which they dealt with in the special cases they had in mind.

However, during the years 1874–1895, Georg Cantor (1845–1918) published a series of papers on the general *theory of sets*. These revolutionary papers gave rise to a totally new view of mathematics as a whole, a view whose repercussions persist to the present day. One effect of Cantor's work was that mathematicians began to look for *very general*, yet quite precise, formulations of mathematical concepts, and thus the notion of curve came under close scrutiny. Camille Jordan (1838–1922) in his lectures at the Ecole Polytechnique suggested that a curve was a "continuous line"—which is essentially the definition of parametrized curve given in this book. At this period, toward the end of the nineteenth century, it was not known how peculiar, or "pathological," a continuous line might be. Jordan himself raised the question as to whether a continuous line might possibly fill up an area. This question, which at first hearing sounds absurd, was answered in 1890 in the affirmative by Giuseppi Peano (1858–1922). He gave an example of a continuous line (parametrized curve) that *fills up a square*!

Specifically, Peano showed that there are continuous real functions, *f* and *g*, such that the curve defined by

$$x = f(t), \quad 0 \le t \le 1, \qquad (1)$$
$$y = g(t),$$

maps the unit interval [0, 1] on the *whole* unit square, as indicated in Fig. 14–17. *Every* point of the square, as well as every point in the interior of the square, is the image of at least one point, *t*, in the interval [0, 1].

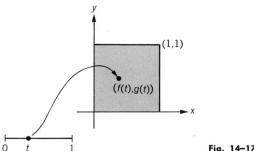

Fig. 14–17

This astonishing discovery by Peano made it clear that if the concept "curve" were not to include such astonishing examples, then, in addition to continuity, other restrictions would have to be imposed on the functions *f* and *g* of Eq. (1). (Note that the functions *f* and *g* of the Peano example must be very "wiggly" in order for the points (*f(t)*, *g(t)*) to fill out the square.

412

Many modifications in the continuous line definition of curve have been suggested. Each of these modifications of the definition of curve excludes the pathological behavior of the Peano example. Today a mathematician uses whichever modification seems appropriate for his purposes. The important thing to know for the problems of this book is that if the functions f and g of (1) are elementary functions, or if they are composed of finitely many elementary functions, then examples of "diseased behavior," as in the Peano example, do not occur.

OF TANGENTS AN

15

THE PROBLEM

HE PROBLEM OF AREAS

15-1. INTRODUCTION

In this final chapter we shall be concerned with two problems which had occupied mathematicians from ancient times (notably the Greek mathematician Archimedes), and which were the focus of attention for several of the great mathematicians of the middle seventeenth century. The problems are concerned with *tangents* to curves and *areas* under curves.

The names of some of the mathematicians who worked on these problems are Pierre de Fermat (1601–1665); Isaac Newton (1642–1727); Isaac Barrow (1630–1677), the teacher of Newton; and Gottfried Leibniz (1646–1716), who, independently of Newton, also discovered the calculus. For an excellent account of these men and their accomplishments, the student is urged to read *Men of Mathematics* by E. T. Bell.

The history of the two problems mentioned is long and interesting but we cannot pursue it here. After you have studied the calculus, you will find the history of the problems both entertaining and beneficial.

Although we shall be dealing with problems of the seventeenth century we will be able to attack them with modern concepts and modern notation. Examples will be used to illustrate the problems. We have on purpose chosen simple functions so that the algebra will not obscure the ideas. We shall try to bring to your attention the need for simple rules of calculation. (Find the meaning of the word *calculus* in a dictionary.) We shall do a fair amount of arithmetical computation and we shall make a few definitions. For the most part, however, the formulation of the basic concepts will be left to you. If all goes well, you will be able to discover the solutions to the basic problems yourself.

In Part I of this chapter we shall consider the problem of tangents and in Part II we shall treat, in an introductory manner, the problem of areas. In Part III we shall examine briefly the relation between these two problems.

PART I | THE PROBLEM OF TANGENTS

15-2. THE PROBLEM

We will consider the graph of a function f which is continuous on its domain $[a, b]$, as in Fig. 15–1. The problem is to discover a device, rule, or algorithm which will enable one to easily compute the slope of the tangent line at an arbitrary point $(x_0, f(x_0))$ of the graph of f.

416

The utility of such a rule is easy to see. For example, it seems reasonable that if the slope of the tangent line were positive for every point on the graph of f, then the function would be an increasing function. Another application might be the determination of "maximum points" or "minimum points" such as the points A and B in Fig. 15–1. At such points the slope of the tangent should be zero.

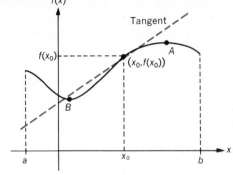

Fig. 15–1

The first question which arises is: "What is a good definition of the tangent line?" Let us defer answering this question for the time being and instead consider a definition of *secant lines*.

DEFINITION 15–1

A *secant line* of a continuous function f is a line joining points $(a, f(a))$ and $(b, f(b))$, $b \neq a$. (See Fig. 15–2.)

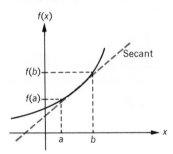

Fig. 15–2   Fig. 15–3

EXAMPLES

1. Suppose that f is a linear function. Then every secant line of f coincides with the graph of f. (See Fig. 15–3.) The slope of the secant is constant, for if f is given by

$$f(x) = Ax + B,$$

then

$$f(a) = Aa + B \quad \text{and} \quad f(b) = Ab + B.$$

417

Then, slope of secant $= \dfrac{f(b) - f(a)}{b - a} = \dfrac{(Ab + B) - (Aa + B)}{b - a}$

$$= \dfrac{A(b - a)}{b - a} = A.$$

We have shown in this example that the slope of the secant line to $f(x) = Ax + B$ is simply what we have always called the slope of the line given by $f(x) = Ax + B$.

2. Let f be the function given by

$$f(x) = x^2 \qquad \text{for all} \quad x$$

and consider the various secants which pass through $(\frac{3}{2}, \frac{9}{4})$ on the graph of f. (See Fig. 15-4.) We can select any real number $h \neq 0$ and consider the slopes of the secant lines through the points

$(\frac{3}{2}, \frac{9}{4})$ and $((\frac{3}{2} + h), (\frac{3}{2} + h)^2)$

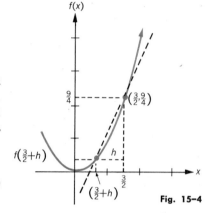

Fig. 15-4

for different values of h. Computation yields the values listed in Table 15-1. From the table it appears that when h is small, the slope m of the secant line through $(\frac{3}{2}, \frac{9}{4})$ is near 3.

TABLE 15-1

h	$f(\frac{3}{2} + h)$	$m = \dfrac{f(\frac{3}{2} + h) - f(\frac{3}{2})}{h}$
-1	$\frac{1}{4}$	$2 = 3 - 1$
1	$\frac{25}{4}$	$4 = 3 + 1$
$-\frac{1}{2}$	1	$\frac{5}{2} = 3 - \frac{1}{2}$
$\frac{1}{2}$	4	$\frac{7}{2} = 3 + \frac{1}{2}$
$-\frac{1}{4}$	$\frac{25}{16}$	$\frac{11}{4} = 3 - \frac{1}{4}$
$\frac{1}{4}$	$\frac{49}{16}$	$\frac{13}{4} = 3 + \frac{1}{4}$
-0.1	1.96	$2.9 = 3 - 0.1$
0.1	2.56	$3.1 = 3 + 0.1$
h	$\frac{9}{4} + 3h + h^2$	$3 + h$

418

Particularly important is the last line of the table, which presents us with a formula for the slope of the secant for any choice of h. From this formula it is easy to see what happens to the slope m as h approaches zero.

Let us now develop a formula for the slope of the secants through *any* point (x_0, x_0^2) of the graph of f and for *any* choice of $h \neq 0$.

We have

$$f(x_0 + h) = x_0^2 + 2x_0 h + h^2,$$

whence the slope of the secant

$$m = \frac{f(x_0 + h) - f(x_0)}{(x_0 + h) - x_0} = \frac{x_0^2 + 2x_0 h + h^2 - x_0^2}{h} = 2x_0 + h. \qquad (1)$$

From (1) we see that when h is small, the slope of the secant through (x_0, x_0^2) is near $2x_0$.

What do you think is meant by "the slope of the tangent line" at x_0? Can you now think of a good *definition* of the tangent line at x_0?

Let us agree on the following rough definition of the tangent line at x_0.

DEFINITION 15-2

The tangent line to the graph of a function f at x_0 is the line through $(x_0, f(x_0))$ which is the *limiting position*† of the secant line through $(x_0, f(x))$ and $(x_0 + h, f(x + h))$.

Problems

1. As in Example 1 above, show that for the linear function f, where $f(x) = 3x + 4$, the slopes of the secants through any two points, $(x_1, f(x_1))$ and $(x_2, f(x_2))$, are the same constant 3.

2. What are the slopes of the secants through any two points of
   (a) $f(x) = -\frac{1}{2}x - 7$ (b) $g(x) = x + 1$ (c) $h(x) = \frac{3}{4}x + \pi$

3. Compute the slopes of the secants through $(\frac{3}{2}, \frac{9}{4})$ of $f(x) = x^2$ for the following values of h.
   (a) 0.01 (b) 0.001 (c) -0.01 (d) -0.001

4. (a) Consider the set of numbers one gets for the slopes of the secants through $(\frac{3}{2}, \frac{9}{4})$ of $f(x) = x^2$ for $h > 0$. Is this set of numbers bounded below? What is the greatest lower bound of this set of numbers?

---

† This is not a precise definition because we have not been precise about what we mean by "the limiting position." What is meant is that the slope of the line through $(x_0, f(x_0))$ is equal to the *limit* of the slope of the secant line through $(x_0, f(x_0))$ and $(x_0 + h, f(x_0 + h))$. See Appendix C for an introduction to limits. Observe that the concept of tangent line *requires* the use of limits.

(b) Consider the set of numbers which are slopes of the secants through $(\frac{3}{2}, \frac{9}{4})$ of the same function but for $h < 0$. Is this set bounded above? What is the least upper bound?

(c) What do you think the slope of the tangent line is through $(\frac{3}{2}, \frac{9}{4})$?

5. Using a large scale, draw as accurately as possible the graph of $f(x) = x^2$ for $0 \le x \le 1.5$. Draw the secant lines through $(1, 1)$ for the values of h in the table below and complete the table.

h	1	-1	$\frac{1}{2}$	$-\frac{1}{2}$	$\frac{1}{4}$	$-\frac{1}{4}$	0.1	-0.1
$f(1 + h)$								
$m = \dfrac{f(1 + h) - f(1)}{h}$								

6. What is a formula for the slope of the tangent of $f(x) = x^2$ at the point where $x = x_0$? Use this formula to find the slope of the tangents and draw the tangent lines to the graph of f at the points where $x = -2, -1, -\frac{1}{2}, 0, \frac{1}{2}$, 1, and 2.

7. Sketch the graph of $f(x) = \frac{1}{2}x^2 + 4$ and the secant lines which pass through $(2, 6)$ for the choices of h in the table below. Complete the table.

h	1	-1	$\frac{1}{2}$	$-\frac{1}{2}$	$\frac{1}{4}$	$-\frac{1}{4}$	0.1	-0.1	0.0001
$f(2 + h)$									
$m = \dfrac{f(2 + h) - f(2)}{h}$									

8. Compute the slope of the secant through the points $(x_0, f(x_0))$ and $(x_0 + h, f(x_0 + h))$ on the graph of $f(x) = \frac{1}{2}x^2 + 4$. What is the slope of the tangent line at $(x_0, f(x_0))$?

9. (a) Sketch the graph of $y = f(x) = x - x^2$.
   (b) Draw several secant lines through $(\frac{1}{2}, \frac{1}{4})$, some for $h > 0$ and some for $h < 0$.
   (c) What is the slope of the tangent line through $(\frac{1}{2}, \frac{1}{4})$?
   (d) What is the slope of a secant line through $(x_0, f(x_0))$?
   (e) What is the slope of the tangent line through $(x_0, f(x_0))$?

10. (a) Sketch the graph of $y = f(x) = x^3 - x$.
    (b) Draw several secant lines through $(\frac{1}{2}, -\frac{3}{8})$.
    (c) What is the slope of the tangent line through $(\frac{1}{2}, -\frac{3}{8})$?
    (d) What is the slope of a secant line through $(x_0, f(x_0))$?
    (e) What is the slope of the tangent line at $(x_0, f(x_0))$?

HISTORICAL NOTE

Sir Isaac Newton (1642–1727)

Sir Isaac Newton (1642–1727) was one of the great minds of all time. He is acclaimed by physicists for his mechanics, his theory of gravitation, and his optics. He is acclaimed by mathematicians for his discovery of the calculus. However, these great achievements are only part of the contributions he made to science.

Newton was the son of a small farmer in Lincolnshire, England, and unlike many men of genius, did not give early promise of his greatness. He entered Trinity College, Cambridge, in June of 1661 and soon became absorbed in mathematics and physics under his brilliant teacher, Isaac Barrow. He took his undergraduate degree in January 1664. The following year there was a recurrence of the bubonic plague, and the university was closed for about two years. These two years, which he spent at home in Woolthorpe, were the most productive of his life. In this time he invented the calculus (which he called the *method of fluxions*), discovered universal gravitation, and showed that white light is a blend of all colors. In these years he laid the basis for most of his later work in science.

Newton was reluctant to have his work appear in print. He was content to communicate his discoveries to friends in letters. Finally, at the continued and urgent insistence of his friends, he published his great masterpiece, *Philosophiae Naturalis Principia Mathematica* (*Mathematical Principles of Natural Philosophy*), in 1687, almost twenty years after his discovery of much of it. This tardiness of publication contributed greatly to the unfortunate, and bitter, controversy with Leibniz over priority in the invention of the calculus.

421

15-3. SOME NOTATION

If $m(x)$ is the slope of the tangent line to the graph of f at the point $(x, f(x))$, then one has a new function m, the slope function. (See Fig. 15–5.) There are many notations used for this function. We shall content ourselves with the one given in the following definition.

DEFINITION 15-3

The slope function for the graph of f is called the *derived function* (or *derivative*) of f. It is denoted by f'. From f one gets another function $f': f \rightarrow f'$.

If the graph of f has been drawn, then the graph of the derived function, or derivative, can be roughly sketched as follows. We draw (approximately) several tangent lines and estimate their slopes, either "by eye" or by counting squares on the graph. These rough data will give several points on the graph of f'. With these points, it is usually not difficult to sketch the general shape of the graph of f'.

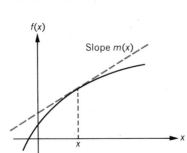

Fig. 15-5

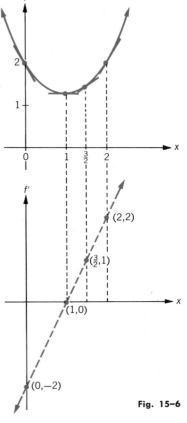

EXAMPLES

1. The graph of $y = f(x) = 1 + (x - 1)^2$ is shown in Fig. 15–6 with the tangent lines sketched at $x = 0, 1, \frac{3}{2},$ and 2. Estimating slopes by eye, one has approximately

$$f'(0) = -2, \qquad f'(1) = 0,$$
$$f'(\tfrac{3}{2}) = 1, \qquad f'(2) = 2.$$

These points are plotted in the graph directly below that of f. The points apparently lie on a straight line, the graph of f', shown dashed in the figure.

Fig. 15-6

422

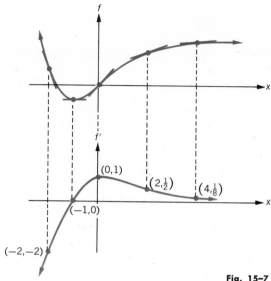

Fig. 15-7

2. Consider the function f whose graph is drawn in Fig. 15-7. The tangent lines are sketched at $x = -2, -1, 0, 2$, and 4, where the slopes appear to be $-2, 0, 1, \frac{1}{2}$, and $\frac{1}{8}$, respectively. The graph of f' must look something like that shown in the figure.

Even though a function is continuous, the graph need not have a tangent line at all points. There may be "corners" as in the next example.

3. The graph of $f(x) = |x|$ is shown in Fig. 15-8. At $x = 0$ there is no tangent line. At other values of $x, f'(x)$ is either $+1$ or -1. $f'(0)$ *does not exist;* it is *not defined.*

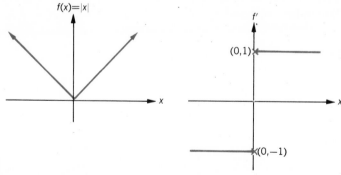

Fig. 15-8

It can be shown that there are continuous functions f for which $f'(x)$ does not exist for any x in the domain of f—but they are exceedingly complicated. *For the elementary functions the derived function always exists, except perhaps at a finite set of points.*

423

Much of the calculus notation in use today was invented by Leibniz in the seventeenth century. Among the notations which he introduced is the "Δ-notation" for increments. This notation is described in the next definition.

DEFINITION 15-4

Suppose the real variable x changes from x_1 to x_2. Then the change in x is called the *increment* of x and is denoted by Δx (where the Greek letter Δ reminds us that it is a *difference*):

$$\Delta x = x_2 - x_1.$$

Thus, the increment of x as x changes from

$$
\begin{aligned}
2 \text{ to } 4 \quad &\text{is} \quad \Delta x = 4 - 2 = 2, \\
1 \text{ to } 1.3 \quad &\text{is} \quad \Delta x = 1.3 - 1 = 0.3, \\
x \text{ to } x + h \quad &\text{is} \quad \Delta x = (x + h) - x = h.
\end{aligned}
$$

If $y = f(x)$, then the change in y as x changes from x to $x + h$ (or $x + \Delta x$) is

$$\Delta y = f(x + h) - f(x) = f(x + \Delta x) - f(x).$$

Sometimes this increment is denoted by Δf. Then the slope of the secant line between $(x, f(x))$ and $(x + \Delta x, f(x + \Delta x))$ is

$$\frac{\Delta y}{\Delta x} = \frac{f(x + \Delta x) - f(x)}{\Delta x}. \tag{1}$$

To find the derived function, f' for a function f, one must examine (1) to see what happens to $\Delta y / \Delta x$ as Δx approaches zero. In other words, what is $\Delta y / \Delta x$ close to for small Δx?

Problems

1. Sketch the following graphs of functions on coordinate paper. Then sketch, as in Examples 1 and 2, the graphs of the derived functions *without doing* any computations.

(a)

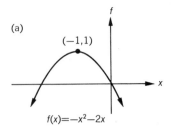

$f(x) = -x^2 - 2x$

(b)

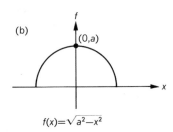

$f(x) = \sqrt{a^2 - x^2}$

424

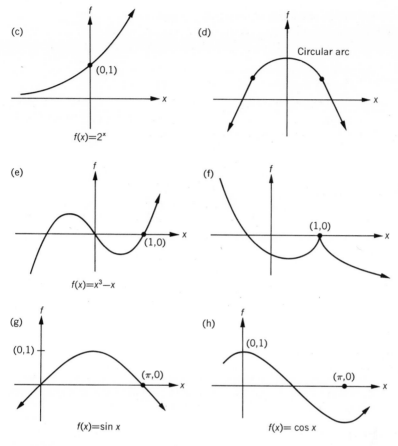

(c) $f(x)=2^x$

(d) Circular arc

(e) $f(x)=x^3-x$

(f) (1,0)

(g) $f(x)=\sin x$

(h) $f(x)=\cos x$

2. In Problem 1, by inspection of the graph of f, state where the derivative, f', is positive, and where it is negative.

3. Show that $f(x) = x^2$ is increasing for $x \geq 0$, and decreasing for $x \leq 0$. Graph f and f', using the results of Example 2, Section 15–2. Observe that where $f'(x) > 0$, $f(x)$ is increasing.

4. (a) Sketch the graph of the polynomial function g, where

$$g(x) = \tfrac{1}{4}x^2 + x \qquad \text{for all } x.$$

(b) Sketch the graph of g' *without making any computations.*

(c) Develop a formula for the slope of the secants of g through the points $(x_0, g(x_0))$ and $(x_0 + h, g(x_0 + h))$.

(d) What is a formula for g'? Compare the graph of g' with your previous guess.

(e) Show that if $x > -2$, then g is increasing. How does this check with your graph of g? with the graph of g'?

425

5. (a) Sketch the graph of the function f given by

$$f(x) = x^3 \quad \text{for all } x.$$

(b) Sketch the secants through $(1, 1)$ on the graph of f for the values of h given in the table below. Complete the table.

(c)

h	1	-1	$\frac{1}{2}$	$-\frac{1}{2}$	$\frac{1}{4}$	$-\frac{1}{4}$	0.1	-0.1
$f(1 + h)$								
m								

(d) Find a formula for the slope of the secants through (x_0, x_0^3) and $(x_0 + h, (x_0 + h)^3)$.

(e) What is the formula for the slope of the tangent of f at x_0? What is the slope of the tangent at $x = 1$? at $x = \frac{1}{2}$? at $x = 0$?

(f) Sketch the graph of f'. Is $f'(x)$ always positive?

6. What is the slope of the graph of a function h where $h(x) = f(x) + g(x)$ in terms of the slopes to the graphs of f and g?

7. Sketch the graph of

$$f(x) = x^3 + x^2 - 2x.$$

Make a guess as to the shape of the graph of f' by inspecting the graph of f. Compute $f'(x)$ and draw the graph of f'. Compare the graph of f' with your previous guess. Sketch several tangent lines to f.

8. Using a short cut, if you can, compute the slope of the tangent to the graph of

$$f(x) = x^4 - 2x^3 + 6x^2 - x - 2$$

at the point where $x = 1$; at the point where $x = 0.1$.

*9. Show that the parabola defined by $y = x^2$ has the optical property that any ray of light parallel to the y-axis is reflected so as to pass through the focus $(0, \frac{1}{4})$ of the parabola. [*Hint:* The ray of incidence and the ray of reflection form congruent angles with the normal to the tangent of the parabola, as shown in the accompanying figure.]

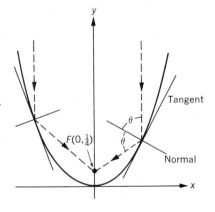

426

*10. The upper half of a circle with center at $(0, 0)$ is given by

$$f(x) = \sqrt{a^2 - x^2}.$$

Compute the slope of the tangent to f at $(x, f(x))$. (See figure.) [*Hint:* After $[f(x + h) - f(x)]/h$ has been found, rationalize the *numerator*.] Verify your answer from elementary geometry.

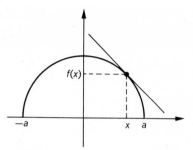

*11. Suppose f has domain $[0, 1]$, $f(0) = 1$, and also that $0 < f'(x) < 1$ for x in $[0, 1]$. How large do you think $f(1)$ can be? Why?

15–4. RATES

In the last section we derived for certain functions f another function f', whose value at x was the slope of the tangent line at $(x, f(x))$. In this section we shall interpret this derived function f' in another way.

EXAMPLES

1. Suppose that a tank is being emptied (see Fig. 15–9), and the volume V of liquid in the tank, measured in gallons, at any time t in minutes, is given by

$$V = f(t) = 4(t - 10)^2, \qquad 0 \le t \le 10.$$

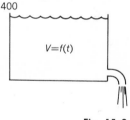

At $t = 0$ there are 400 gallons in the tank, while at the end of 10 minutes the tank is empty. Therefore, the *average rate of flow* is

$$\frac{\text{volume of liquid emptied}}{\text{elapsed time}} = \frac{400}{10} = 40 \,\frac{\text{gal}}{\text{min}}.$$

Fig. 15–9

At the end of 5 minutes there are 100 gallons left in the tank, therefore during the first 5 minutes the average rate of flow was

$$\frac{400 - 100}{5} = 60 \,\frac{\text{gal}}{\text{min}}.$$

During the first minute the average rate was

$$\frac{400 - 324}{1} = 76 \,\frac{\text{gal}}{\text{min}}.$$

427

These different rates are given by

$$\frac{f(0) - f(10)}{10}, \qquad \frac{f(0) - f(5)}{5},$$

and

$$\frac{f(0) - f(1)}{1}.$$

The rates computed above are, *except for sign*, equal to the slopes of the secant lines through the points $(0, 400)$ and $(t, f(t))$ of the graph of $V = f(t)$ shown in Fig. 15–10. Our signs are reversed because we have computed the rate of *decrease* of V.

Let us compute the rate at which V changes over a time interval from t_0 to $t_0 + \Delta t$, where $t_0 + \Delta t \leq 10$. The change in V is

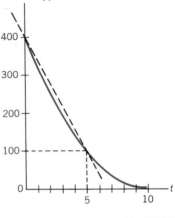

$$V = f(t_0 + \Delta t) - f(t_0).$$

The average rate of change of V is

$$V = \frac{f(t_0 + \Delta t) - f(t_0)}{\Delta t}.$$

Therefore, the average rate of change of V is

$$V = \frac{4[(t_0 + \Delta t) - 10]^2 - 4(t_0 - 10)^2}{\Delta t}$$

$$= \frac{8 \Delta t(t_0 - 10) + 4 \Delta t^2}{\Delta t}$$

$$= 8(t_0 - 10) + 4 \Delta t.$$

Fig. 15–10

By examining our final result, what do you think is meant by the *instantaneous rate of change of V*?

What is this instantaneous rate at $t = 0$? at $t = 5$? at $t = 10$?

2. A body falls from rest in a vacuum and after t seconds has fallen a distance S, in feet, given by (Fig. 15–11)†

$$S = 16t^2.$$

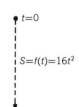

Fig. 15–11

---

† In this formula we have approximated the acceleration due to gravity by using $g = 32$, rather than $g = 32.2$.

TABLE 15–2

t	0	0.1	0.5	1	2	2.1	2.5	3	4
S	0	0.16	4	16	64	70.56	100	144	256

Let us compute the distance S at various times in order to obtain the average rates (velocities) in several time intervals. The values obtained are listed in Table 15–2. Since the average velocity v is given by

$$\frac{\text{distance}}{\text{elapsed time}},$$

then the average velocities for several time intervals starting at $t = 0$ are as listed in Table 15–3.

TABLE 15–3

Time interval	Average velocity, v ft/sec
$t = 0$ to $t = 2$	$64/2 = 32$
$t = 0$ to $t = 1$	$16/1 = 16$
$t = 0$ to $t = \frac{1}{2}$	$4/\frac{1}{2} = 8$
$t = 0$ to $t = 0.1$	$0.16/0.1 = 1.6$

From the table, it appears that as $t \to 0$, then $v \to 0$. Does this conform to the physical situation?

The average velocities starting at $t = 2$ over several time intervals are given in Table 15–4.

TABLE 15–4

Time interval	Average velocity, v ft/sec
$t = 2$ to $t = 3$	$(144 - 64)/1 = 80$
$t = 2$ to $t = 2.5$	$(100 - 64)/0.5 = 72$
$t = 2$ to $t = 2.1$	$(70.56 - 64)/0.1 = 65.44$

What do you think is meant by *instantaneous velocity*? What is the instantaneous velocity at the time $t = 0$? at $t = 2$? at $t = t_0$?

In these two examples we have seen that the number obtained for the slope of a secant line could also be interpreted as a rate of change of the function in the case where the independent variable is *time*. But this physical (time) restriction is extraneous to the mathematics of the situation. Hence we make the following definition.

429

DEFINITION 15–5

The *average rate of change of a function f over the interval* x_0 to $x_0 + \Delta x$ is the number

$$\frac{f(x_0 + \Delta x) - f(x_0)}{\Delta x}.$$

EXAMPLE 3

The average rate of change of the function f given by

$$f(x) = 3x^2 - 2x + 1$$

in the interval from $x = 1$ to $x = 3$ is

$$\frac{f(3) - f(1)}{2} = \frac{22 - 2}{2} = 10.$$

The average rate of change of f in the interval from $x = 1$ to $x = 2$ is

$$\frac{f(2) - f(1)}{1} = \frac{9 - 2}{1} = 7.$$

What do you think is the instantaneous rate of change of f at $x = 1$?

Problems

1. Use the function

$$V = f(t) = 4(t - 10)^2$$

of Example 1 and compute the average rate of flow (rate of change of volume) in the time intervals from $t = 4$ to

(a) $t = 5$ (b) $t = 4\frac{1}{2}$ (c) $t = 4\frac{1}{4}$ (d) $t = 4.1$

What is the instantaneous rate of flow at $t = 4$?

2. A body falls from rest according to the formula

$$S = 16t^2,$$

where S is in feet at t in seconds. Compute the average velocity of the object, neglecting air resistance, in the following time intervals.

(a) $t = 0$ to $t = 4$ (b) $t = 2$ to $t = 4$

(c) $t = 3$ to $t = 4$ (d) $t = 3.9$ to $t = 4$.

What is the instantaneous velocity at $t = 4$?

430

3. A point "moves" on a coordinatized line so that its coordinate d at any time t is

$$d = f(t) = 3t^2 - 2t + 1.$$

(a) Sketch the graph of f for $t \geq 0$.

(b) Compute the average velocity of the point between the times:

(i) $t = 0$ and $t = 1$ (ii) $t = 0$ and $t = \frac{1}{2}$

(iii) $t = 0$ and $t = 0.1$ (iv) $t = 0$ and $t = h$

(c) What is the instantaneous velocity at $t = 0$?

(d) What is the average velocity in the interval from t_0 to $t_0 + h$?

(e) What is the velocity at t_0?

(f) Sketch a graph of the velocity function f'.

(g) What is the velocity at $t = 2$? at $t = \frac{1}{2}$?

(h) When is the point at rest? That is, at what time t is the velocity zero?

*(i) *Acceleration* is defined as the rate of change of velocity. What is the acceleration of the point? [*Hint:* Look at the graph of f'.]

4. A point "moves" along a line so that its distance from the origin is given by

$$d = f(t) = t^3 - t.$$

(a) Find the average velocities between $t = -1$ and the following:

(i) 1   (ii) 0.5   (iii) 0   (iv) -0.5

(v) -0.8 (vi) -0.9 (vii) -0.99

(b) What is the velocity at any time t?

(c) When is the velocity zero?

5. A point moves along the x-axis and is at the following positions at various times t, in seconds.

x	5	17	21	17	5	-15	-43	-79
t	0	0.5	1.0	1.5	2.0	2.5	3.0	3.5

(a) Plot these values of x versus the time and connect by a smooth curve.

(b) Estimate the instantaneous velocity at $t = 1$ and at $t = 2$.

(c) Sketch the graph of the velocity. Is the acceleration of the point positive or negative?

6. If

$$f(x) = x^3 - x^2 + x - 1,$$

what is the average rate of change of f between x and $x + \Delta x$? What is the "instantaneous" rate of change of f with respect to x?

7. What is the average rate of change of the area of a circle between radii of r and $r + \Delta r$? What is the instantaneous rate of change of the area with respect to the radius?

HISTORICAL NOTE

**Gottfried Wilhelm Leibniz
(1646–1716)**

Gottfried Wilhelm Leibniz (1646–1716) made notable contributions to law, diplomacy, history, logic, mathematics, and philosophy.

He was largely self-taught when he began the study of law, obtaining a doctor's degree at the age of 20 in 1666. He then began a roving career as lawyer and diplomat.

In 1672 Leibniz persuaded the physicist Christian Huygens to tutor him in mathematics. It was at once clear that Leibniz was a natural mathematician, for he was soon making his own discoveries. He even invented a calculating machine.

By 1676 he had worked out the essential features of the calculus, both differential and integral, which he published in 1677. This was eleven years after Newton's discovery and ten years before Newton's *Principia*. Leibniz had developed a particularly happy notation (a notation we use today). Hence his ideas were seized upon by the mathematicians of the continent, who during the ensuing twenty years developed them into a powerful tool. In England, owing to Newton's reluctance to publish, and perhaps also to his less accessible notation, the calculus remained a curiosity.

Thus came about the bitter controversy between English and continental mathematicians over priority in the discovery of the calculus. The consensus of modern scholarship is that the two men made their discoveries independently of each other. And so we have another noteworthy example of the fact that new ideas can occur simultaneously to two men who have little or no connection with each other.

PART II | THE PROBLEM OF AREA

15-5. WHAT IS AREA?

In elementary geometry you found areas only of figures bounded by straight lines and areas of circles or portions of circles. As soon as we consider other plane figures it becomes necessary to decide what it is we are trying to find. In other words, we need a precise definition of the thing to be calculated.

Of course, everyone has strong intuitive feelings about the meaning of area and, given an irregular shape drawn on coordinate paper, as in Fig. 15-12, could estimate the area by counting squares.

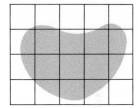

Fig. 15-12

There are two distinct problems associated with the notion of area. One is a suitable definition for the *area of any set*. We shall not try to formulate such a definition in this section, for even after such a formulation has been made it would be necessary to *prove* that area, so defined, has the properties that we might like it to have. Instead we shall *postulate* that there is an *area function* with a few very natural properties.

The second problem, after area has been defined and certain elementary properties established, is that of *calculation of areas*. It is this problem to which we shall devote most of our attention.

POSTULATES FOR AREA

There is an *area function* A mapping bounded subsets S of the plane into real numbers $A(S)$ with the following properties:

P1. $A(S) \geq 0$, for every set S.

P2. Congruent sets have the same area.

P3. If S_1 is a subset of S_2, then $A(S_1) \leq A(S_2)$.

P4. If a set S is separated by a straight line into two sets (see Fig. 15-13), S_1 and S_2, then
$$A(S) = A(S_1) + A(S_2).$$

P5. If S is a rectangle plus its interior and S has dimensions l and w, then $A(S) = l \cdot w$.

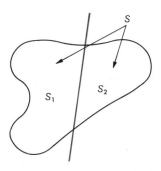

Fig. 15-13

433

Some applications of the postulates to familiar polygons are given in the examples that follow.

EXAMPLES

1. By continued use of P4, the area of the rectangle of Fig. 15–14 is seen to be 40 times the area of a square whose side is 1 unit in length. We also get the same result by direct use of P5.

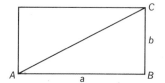

Fig. 15–14

2. Using P2 and P4, we see that the area of the right triangle ABC of Fig. 15–15 is one-half the area of the rectangle. Therefore by P5, $A(\triangle ABC) = \frac{1}{2}ab$.

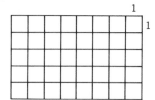

Fig. 15–15

3. Figure 15–16 illustrates P3 and P4.

> **P3:** $A(S_1) \leq A(S_1 \cup S_2)$.
> **P4:** $A(S_1 \cup S_2) = A(S_1) + A(S_2)$.

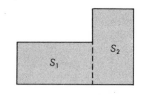

Fig. 15–16

4. Let S_2 be a rectangle plus its interior and let S_1 be the same rectangle plus its interior except that one edge is missing. Then $S_1 \subset S_2$, so by P3, $A(S_1) \leq A(S_2)$. That S_1 and S_2 actually have the same area may be seen as follows. Let us consider a somewhat smaller rectangle S_0 inside S_1 as in Fig. 15–17. Then, using P3 and P5,

$$w(l - \epsilon) = A(S_0) \leq A(S_1) \leq A(S_2) = wl. \quad (1)$$

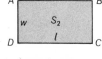

The left-hand side of (1) is $wl - w\epsilon$. Now, $w\epsilon$ can be made arbitrarily small if ϵ is made small enough. Therefore

$$A(S_1) \geq wl - \text{an arbitrarily small number,}$$

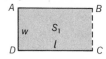

and so

$$A(S_1) \geq wl.$$

Consequently, from (1), we have

$$wl \leq A(S_1) \leq A(S_2) = wl.$$

Therefore $A(S_1) = wl = A(S_2)$.

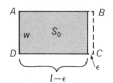

Fig. 15–17

434

5. In Fig. 15–18 two congruent, but differently oriented, triangles are drawn on coordinate paper. Let us consider the problem of estimating the area of the triangles by counting squares. If we use a finer mesh of squares, what happens? Can you use P3 or P4?

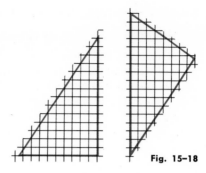

Fig. 15–18

Problems

1. S_1 and S_2 are subsets of the plane and S_1 is congruent to S_2. What can you conclude?

2. If $A(S_1) = A(S_2)$, is S_1 necessarily congruent to S_2?

3. Circles C_1 and C_2 are concentric circles such that the points of C_1 are in the interior of C_2. Compare $A(C_1)$ to $A(C_2)$. Which postulate have you used?

4. Prove that if $A(S_1) \neq A(S_2)$, then S_1 is not congruent to S_2.

5. In the accompanying figure a 3-4-5 right triangle is drawn on coordinate paper with the sides not parallel to the paper rulings. Estimate the area of the triangle by counting squares. Find the area by applying Postulates P3, P4, and P5. Explain how these postulates are used.

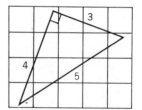

6. Find an upper bound for the area of the shaded region in the figure. Find a lower bound for the area of the region. Estimate the area of the region. Which area postulates have been used?

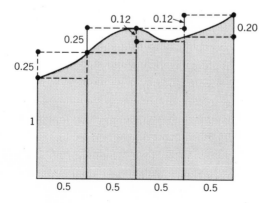

435

7. Give an example of a nonempty subset S of the plane such that $A(S) = 0$.

8. Is there a subset K of the plane such that $A(K) < 0$?

9. Find upper and lower bounds for the area of a quadrant of a unit circle. (See the figure on the left below.) From the areas computed, estimate the area of the quadrant. Check your result by using the formula for the area of a circle. Would your estimate be better if we chose smaller divisions of the x-axis?

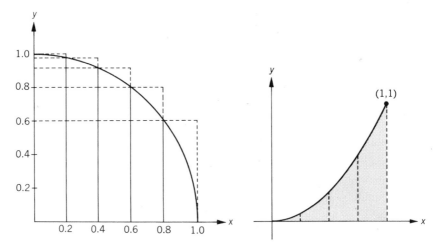

10. The shaded area in the figure on the right above is the area under the graph of $y = x^2$, and above the x-axis between $x = 0$ and $x = 1$. Divide the interval $0 \le x \le 1$ into four congruent subintervals and find upper and lower bounds for the area.

15–6. AREA UNDER GRAPHS OF FUNCTIONS

Let us consider a function which is continuous and which has always positive values on $[a, b]$, as in Fig. 15–19. We shall investigate the area of the set S of all points $P(x, y)$ such that

$$a \le x \le b$$

and

$$0 \le y \le f(x).$$

Our approach will be to examine some cases for simple functions.

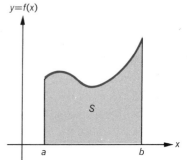

Fig. 15–19

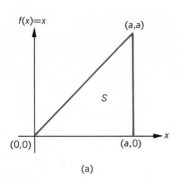

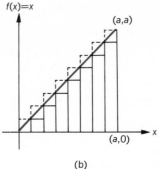

(a)

(b)

Fig. 15-20

EXAMPLES

1. Suppose f is the identity function,

$$f(x) = x \qquad \text{for all } x,$$

and we wish to find the area under the graph of f between $x = 0$ and $x = a$ (Fig. 15-20a). Of course, from elementary geometry,

$$A(S) = \tfrac{1}{2}a^2,$$

but suppose we try to obtain this result in another way.

Let us partition the interval $[0, a]$ into n congruent subintervals of equal length, a/n. Then we obtain rectangular strips, as in Fig. 15-20(b), and we can calculate the sum of the areas of these strips.

Let $\underline{S}_n$ denote the union of the shorter rectangles plus their interiors. Then

$$A(\underline{S}_n) = \frac{a}{n} \cdot \frac{a}{n} + \frac{a}{n} \cdot \frac{2a}{n} + \frac{a}{n} \cdot \frac{3a}{n} + \cdots + \frac{a(n-1)}{n} \cdot \frac{a}{n}$$

$$= \frac{a^2}{n^2} (1 + 2 + 3 + \cdots + (n-1)).$$

Now it happens (fortunately) that the sum of the first $n - 1$ natural numbers (the sum in parentheses) is (see Appendix B–2)

$$1 + 2 + 3 + \cdots + (n-1) = \frac{n(n-1)}{2}.$$

Therefore

$$A(\underline{S}_n) = \frac{a^2}{n^2} \cdot \frac{n(n-1)}{2} = \frac{a^2}{2} \left(1 - \frac{1}{n} \right). \tag{1}$$

Evidently the number $A(\underline{S}_n)$ is a lower bound of the area of the set S.

In the same manner, if we denote the larger rectangles [those with the dotted tops in Fig. 15–20(b)] plus their interiors by $\bar{S}_n$, then

$$A(\bar{S}_n) = \frac{a}{n} \cdot \frac{a}{n} + \frac{a}{n} \cdot \frac{2a}{n} + \frac{a}{n} \cdot \frac{3a}{n} + \cdots + \frac{a}{n} \cdot \frac{na}{n}$$

$$= \frac{a^2}{n^2}(1 + 2 + 3 + \cdots + n)$$

$$= \frac{a^2}{n^2} \cdot \frac{n(n+1)}{2} = \frac{a^2}{2}\left(1 + \frac{1}{n}\right). \tag{2}$$

We see that the number $A(\bar{S}_n)$ given in (2) is an upper bound of the area of the set S. Therefore, by P3, if S is the set of points of the triangle plus its interior, then

$$\frac{a^2}{2}\left(1 - \frac{1}{n}\right) \le A(S) \le \frac{a^2}{2}\left(1 + \frac{1}{n}\right). \tag{3}$$

What happens to (3) when the number n gets large? What can you conclude?

2. We now consider the area of the set of points under the graph of $f(x) = x^2$ and between $x = 0$ and $x = a$.

Elementary geometry does not supply an immediate answer in this case. We must try some scheme, and the one which was successful in the previous example suggests itself.

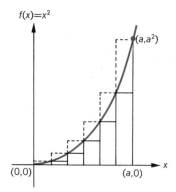

Fig. 15–21

We partition the interval $[0, a]$ into n congruent subintervals of length a/n and construct the upper and lower rectangles as shown in Fig. 15–21. Let $\underline{S}_n$ be the set of points of the lower rectangles plus their interiors. Then

$$A(\underline{S}_n) = \frac{a}{n} \cdot \left(\frac{a}{n}\right)^2 + \frac{a}{n} \cdot \left(\frac{2a}{n}\right)^2 + \frac{a}{n} \cdot \left(\frac{3a}{n}\right)^2 + \cdots + \frac{a}{n}\left[\frac{(n-1)a}{n}\right]^2$$

$$= \frac{a^3}{n^3}(1 + 4 + 9 + \cdots + (n-1)^2).$$

As in the previous example there is a fine formula (see Appendix B–2) for the sum of the squares of the first k integers:

$$1^2 + 2^2 + 3^2 + \cdots + k^2 = \frac{k(k+1)(2k+1)}{6}.$$

438

Therefore

$$A(\underline{S}_n) = \frac{a^3}{n^3} \cdot \frac{(n-1)(n)(2n-1)}{6} = \frac{a^3}{3} \left(1 - \frac{3}{2n} + \frac{1}{2n^2} \right). \qquad (4)$$

Similarly, we let $\overline{S}_n$ be the set of points in and on the upper rectangles. Then

$$A(\overline{S}_n) = \frac{a}{n} \cdot \left(\frac{a}{n}\right)^2 + \frac{a}{n} \cdot \left(\frac{2a}{n}\right)^2 + \cdots + \frac{a}{n} \cdot \left(\frac{na}{n}\right)^2$$

$$= \frac{a^3}{n^3} (1 + 2^2 + \cdots + n^2) = \frac{a^3}{n^3} \cdot \frac{n(n+1)(2n+1)}{6}$$

$$= \frac{a^3}{3} \left(1 + \frac{3}{2n} + \frac{1}{2n^2} \right). \qquad (5)$$

Therefore, by P3, if S is the set of points under the graph of $f(x) = x^2$ between $x = 0$ and $x = a$, then equations (4), (5), and P3 imply that

$$\frac{a^3}{3} \left(1 - \frac{3}{2n} + \frac{1}{2n^2} \right) \le A(S) \le \frac{a^3}{3} \left(1 + \frac{3}{2n} + \frac{1}{2n^2} \right).$$

Now, as before, we ask what happens as n becomes large? Is it clear to you why this scheme is sometimes referred to as "the mathematical vise"?

Problems

1. If f is a constant function, $f(x) = c$ for all x, $c > 0$, show that the area under the graph of f for $0 \le x \le a$ is $a \cdot c$, using the technique of Examples 1 and 2 of this section.

2. What is the area under the graph of f where $f(x) = x + 2$, $0 \le x \le a$?

3. Compute, approximately, the area under the graph of $y = x^2$ between 0 and 1 by counting squares. Draw the curve on graph paper with each small square 0.1 unit on a side. Check by using the formula of Example 2.

4. What is the area under the graph of $f(x) = x^2$ between $x = 1$ and $x = 2$?

5. What is the area under the graph of $f(x) = 2x^2$ between $x = 0$ and $x = a$? Justify your answer.

6. How do the areas under the graphs of $y = Ax$ and $y = Bx$ between $x = 0$ and $x = a$ compare, if $A > B > 0$? (See the accompanying figure.)

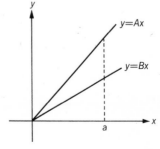

439

7. What is the area under the graph of $f(x) = x^2 + 1$ between $x = 0$ and $x = a$? Can you think of different ways of finding the area?

8. Obtain a formula for the area under $f(x) = x^2$ between $x = a$ and $x = b$, where $b > a$. Using P1 through P5, why do you think your result is exact?

9. The figure on the left below is a graph of a continuous, positive function f defined for $x > 0$. Draw an approximate graph of the area function, A, where $A(x)$ is the area under the graph of f between $x = 0$ and x.

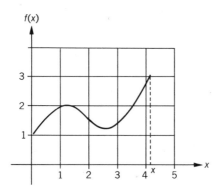

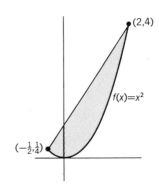

*10. What is the area of the shaded region shown in the figure on the right above? Can you be sure of your answer from P1 through P5 and the examples?

*11. What is the area under

$$F(x) = \sqrt{x}$$

between $x = 0$ and $x = a$?

*12. Find the area under $f(x) = x^3$ between $x = 0$ and $x = a$. *Hint:* Use the fact that

$$1^3 + 2^3 + 3^3 + \cdots + n^3 = \frac{n^2(n + 1)^2}{4}.$$

*13. Use your answer to Problem 12 to compute the area under $y = \sqrt[3]{x}$ between $x = 0$ and $x = a$.

*14. Suppose that f is a function which is not always positive. What do you think is meant by the "area under the graph of f"? [*Hint:* We should, perhaps, like the process of the illustrative examples to be the same in all cases.]

*15. In physics when a constant force F acts in a straight line through a distance d, the work done is $F \cdot d$. Suppose that the force is not constant. How does one then compute the work? Suppose that the force is proportional to the distance x (as is the case of a spring stretched an amount x). What is the work in this case?

440

PART III | THE PROBLEMS ARE RELATED

15-7. LIMITS

In Parts I and II of this chapter the basic problems of tangents and areas were attacked directly for some special functions. By the middle of the seventeenth century, mathematicians were familiar with all the results we have obtained to date in this chapter and many more. They could compute tangents to graphs of a considerable variety of functions. Furthermore, they could compute areas under a variety of curves—using the same painful methods that we have used. But there was no real system to all this work. Problems which today can be handled with dispatch often called for exceedingly clever algebraic manipulation. What was needed was a set of calculation rules, easy to apply, which would work on "most" of the functions and which would solve each kind of problem. On reading the history of those times, the beginning student will probably wonder why the light did not dawn sooner.

One of the troubles was that each object to be calculated, namely slope of the tangent and area under the curve, was a *limit*.

For slope, the desired number is

$$m = \operatorname*{limit}_{\Delta x \to 0} \frac{f(x_0 + \Delta x) - f(x_0)}{\Delta x} \tag{1}$$
$$= f'(x_0).$$

For area, one has areas of smaller and larger sets $\underline{S}_n$ and $\overline{S}_n$, and the true area $A(S)$ is

$$A(S) = \operatorname*{limit}_{n \to \infty} A(\underline{S}_n) \tag{2}$$
$$= \operatorname*{limit}_{n \to \infty} A(\overline{S}_n).$$

This common limit is called the *integral* of the function f over the given interval.

In those days a precise definition of limit had not been given, with the result that each worker was guided solely by his intuition of what was proper. Furthermore, notation was not so well developed as it is today, and the discovery of the desired algorithms was not at all easy.

The *differential calculus* consists of a set of *rules* which enable one to compute the limit in (1) for a large class of functions, *without doing* all the tedious details.

441

The *integral calculus* consists of a set of *rules* which enable one to compute the limit in (2) for a large class of functions, *without doing* all the tedious details.

From our examples in Part I of this chapter we know that

$$\text{if} \quad f(x) = x, \qquad \text{then} \quad m = f'(x_0) = 1;$$
$$\text{if} \quad f(x) = x^2, \qquad \text{then} \quad m = f'(x_0) = 2x_0;$$
$$\text{if} \quad f(x) = x^3, \qquad \text{then} \quad m = f'(x_0) = 3x_0^2.$$

You may have found other rules for other functions and, if so, you have begun to tackle the problem of differential calculus.

From the examples of Part II of this chapter we know that the area $A(x)$ under the graph of f and over the interval from 0 to x_0 is

$$A(x_0) = x_0 \qquad \text{if} \quad f(x) = 1;$$

$$A(x_0) = \frac{x_0^2}{2} \qquad \text{if} \quad f(x) = x;$$

$$A(x_0) = \frac{x_0^3}{3} \qquad \text{if} \quad f(x) = x^2.$$

Hence, for these simple functions, both problems of differential and integral calculus are solved. For these functions we can calculate quite complicated limits by the simple rules given above.

15-8. THE RELATION BETWEEN THE PROBLEMS

It so happens that the problem of the differential calculus, namely, the discovery of algorithms for computing slopes of tangent lines, can be solved completely *for the elementary functions*. In other words, rules can be given such that for each elementary function f, the slope function f' can be written quite easily. To go into additional detail would be to write half of a calculus book. Let it suffice to say that there are no inherent difficulties here as soon as the notion of limit is made precise.

With regard to area, the problem is more complicated, and it apparently took the insight of men of genius (Newton and Leibniz) to see the "trick" involved. The trick, if we may call it that, lies in the observation that the two problems are related. The exercises below are chosen to suggest to you this relation. Once the relation between the problems is understood, the solution to the problem of the differential calculus furnishes a solution to the problem of the integral calculus.

442

Problems

1. What is the area $A(x_0)$, under the graph of f if $f(x) = 1$ for all x, between 0 and x_0? Graph the area function A. Compute the slope of the tangent at x on the graph of A.

2. What is the area $A(x_0)$ between 0 and x_0 under the graph of f if $f(x) = x$ for all x? Graph the area function A. Compute the slope of the tangent at x on the graph of A.

3. What is the area $A(x_0)$ between 0 and x_0 under the graph of $f(x) = x^2$, for all x? Graph the area function A. Compute the slope of the tangent at x on the graph of A.

4. Suppose that f is an increasing function and is continuous. (The requirement that f be increasing is not necessary, but is convenient here for clarity.) Let $A(x)$ be the area under the graph of f between 0 and x. Obtain upper and lower bounds for

$$A(x + h) - A(x), \qquad h > 0.$$

Show that the slope of $A(x)$ at x is between $f(x)$ and $f(x + h)$. From this result decide what $A'(x)$ is equal to.

SUMMARY

The basic problem in differential calculus and the basic problem of integral calculus have been examined in a very cursory way in this chapter. In this brief examination of the problems we have not gone into detail nor have we attempted to pursue the innumerable applications of the calculus. All that we have done is present the two fundamental concepts, each of which is a *limit*. The two concepts are *derivative* and *integral;* the derivative we interpreted as a slope and a rate of change; the integral we interpreted as an area.

1. The derivative f' of a function f has, at a point x, the value

$$f'(x) = \lim_{\Delta x \to 0} \frac{f(x + \Delta x) - f(x)}{\Delta x}.$$

There are short-cut rules for calculating f' for the elementary functions. These rules comprise a part of the *differential calculus*. We have found a few of these rules.

2. The area under the graph of f over a given interval is also a limit, called the *integral* of f over the interval:

$$A(S) = \lim_{n \to \infty} A(\underline{S}_n) = \lim_{n \to \infty} A(\overline{S}_n).$$

There also exist short-cut rules for finding this limit. These short cuts exist because the problem of area is related to the problem of tangents (see Problem 4 of Section 15–6).

443

Review Problems

1. What is the slope of the tangent at any point of a constant function, $f(x) = c$ for all x?

2. At what point is the slope of the tangent to the graph of $f(x) = x^2$ equal to zero?

3. Draw the graph of the function f given by

$$f(x) = x^2 - 6x + 4 \qquad \text{for all } x.$$

   Estimate from the graph of f a "minimum point" of f. Using the formulas developed in this chapter, compute the slope of the tangent at this point.

4. Find a "maximum point" of the function g given by

$$g(x) = -2x^2 + 6x - 1$$

5. Show that the slope of the secant of the function f, given by

$$f(x) = 1/x, \qquad x > 0,$$

   through the points $(a, f(a))$ and $(b, f(b))$, $0 < a < b$, is $-1/ab$. What is $f'(a)$?

6. Find a formula for the slope of the secants through $(x_0, f(x_0))$ and $((x_0 + h), f(x_0 + h))$ of the function f of Problem 5. What is the slope of the tangent of f at x_0?

7. A certain continuous function f defined on $[0, \pi]$ is such that the slopes of the tangents to f at various points are as given in the table below.

x	0	$\pi/6$	$\pi/4$	$\pi/3$	$\pi/2$	$2\pi/3$	$3\pi/4$	$5\pi/6$	π
$f'(x) = m$	1	$\sqrt{3}/2$	$\sqrt{2}/2$	$1/2$	0	$-1/2$	$-\sqrt{2}/2$	$-\sqrt{3}/2$	-1

   Sketch the graph of the derived function f'. Are such functions f and f' familiar to you?

8. A car is moving according to the formula $d = 48t - 3t^2$, where d is distance in feet and t is time in seconds.

   (a) What is the average velocity in the interval from $t = 0$ to $t = 1$?

   (b) What is the average velocity in the interval from $t = 0$ to $t = 2$? Is the car accelerating or slowing down?

   (c) What is the velocity at any time t_0?

   (d) At what time will the car be motionless?

9. Compare the areas under the graph of $f(x) = x$ between $x = 0$ and $x = 1$ and between $x = 0$ and $x = 2$.

10. The area under the graph of a function f from $x = 0$ to x is given by $A(x) = 2x^2$. What is a formula for $f(x)$?

11. Find the area of the region under the graph of the function f between $x = 2$ and $x = 5$ if $f(x) = x^2$. What constant function will have the same area under its graph in the same interval?

12. Prove that

$$1 + 2 + 3 + \cdots + n = \frac{n(n + 1)}{2}.$$

13. If $f(x) = 3x^2$ and $A(x)$ is the area under the graph of f between 0 and x, what is the rate of change of A at x?

445

APPENDIX A | Systems of Linear Equations and Determinants

A-1. OUTLINE

In this appendix we treat second- and third-order determinants rather fully with their relations to systems of linear equations in two and three variables. Properties of determinants of order four, and higher, will only be suggested by analogy with the properties of determinants of orders two and three.

A-2. GEOMETRIC ASPECTS

Systems of linear equations can be interpreted geometrically if the number of variables is two or three. For linear equations in more variables, the same geometric language (borrowed from the plane and from space) is used but without the physical interpretation. One has to *invent higher-dimensional spaces* in which to carry out the discussion.

Consider two linear equations in x and y:

$$a_1x + b_1y = c_1,$$
$$a_2x + b_2y = c_2, \tag{1}$$

where a_1, b_1, c_1, a_2, b_2, and c_2 are real numbers and not both a_1 and b_1 nor a_2 and b_2 are zero, $(a_1^2 + b_1^2 \neq 0$ and $a_2^2 + b_2^2 \neq 0)$. These equations have graphs which are lines l_1 and l_2. Exactly one of the following three possibilities is true (see Fig. A–1):

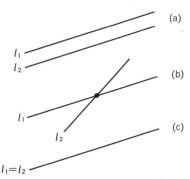

Fig. A–1

(a) l_1 is parallel to l_2. There is no solution of the system (1).

(b) l_1 intersects l_2 in a unique point. There is exactly one solution of the system (1).

(c) $l_1 = l_2$. There are infinitely many solutions of the system (1).

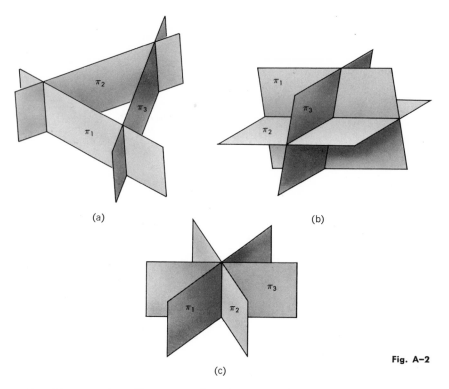

(a)

(b)

(c)

Fig. A–2

Consider now three linear equations in x, y, and z:

$$a_1x + b_1y + c_1z = d_1,$$
$$a_2x + b_2y + c_2z = d_2, \tag{2}$$
$$a_3x + b_3y + c_3z = d_3,$$

where the coefficients $a_1, \ldots, d_3$ are real numbers and in any one equation not all a_i, b_i, and c_i are zero, $i = 1, 2, 3$ ($a_i^2 + b_i^2 + c_i^2 \neq 0$). These equations have graphs which are planes π_1, π_2, and π_3. Exactly one of the following three possibilities is true.

(a) There is no solution of system (2). Either all three planes are parallel or the line of intersection of two of them is parallel to the third plane (Fig. A–2a).

(b) There is exactly one solution of system (2). Two of the planes meet in a line which pierces the third plane (Fig. A–2b).

(c) There are infinitely many solutions. There is at least one line on all three planes, for if two distinct points were on all planes, the line containing these points would be on all planes (Fig. A–2c).

448

To summarize: For either two lines in the plane, or three planes in space, exactly one of the three possibilities (a), (b), or (c) is true.

We shall be concerned with algebraic criteria which will distinguish these cases.

A-3. TWO LINEAR EQUATIONS IN TWO VARIABLES

Let us consider the system of two linear equations

$$a_1x + b_1y = c_1,$$
$$a_2x + b_2y = c_2. \tag{1}$$

The following theorem gives a complete description of the possible solutions of this system.

THEOREM A-1

System (1) has exactly one solution if and only if $a_1b_2 - a_2b_1 \neq 0$. In this case the solution is

$$x = \frac{c_1b_2 - c_2b_1}{a_1b_2 - a_2b_1}, \qquad y = \frac{a_1c_2 - a_2c_1}{a_1b_2 - a_2b_1}. \tag{2}$$

If $a_1b_2 - a_2b_1 = 0$, then there is a unique real number $k \neq 0$ such that $a_2 = ka_1$ and $b_2 = kb_1$. There is no solution if $c_2 \neq kc_1$. There are infinitely many solutions if $c_2 = kc_1$.

Proof. We multiply the members of the first equation of (1) by b_2, and the members of the second equation by b_1 and subtract. We obtain

$$(a_1b_2 - a_2b_1)x = c_1b_2 - c_2b_1. \tag{3}$$

In a similar manner, we get

$$(a_1b_2 - a_2b_1)y = a_1c_2 - a_2c_1. \tag{4}$$

Then, if $a_1b_2 - a_2b_1 \neq 0$, equations (2) are obtained from equations (3) and (4). Therefore (2) must be the solution, if there is one. It is easy to check that (2) is a solution. This proves the first half of the theorem.

Suppose now that $a_1b_2 - a_2b_1 = 0$. Then there is a unique real number k such that $a_2 = ka_1$ and $b_2 = kb_1$. (The reader should establish this fact.) From equations (3) and (4) we see that the system is *inconsistent* (no solution) if either $c_1b_2 - c_2b_1 \neq 0$ or $a_1c_2 - a_2c_1 \neq 0$. If both $c_1b_2 - c_2b_1 = 0$ and $a_1c_2 - a_2c_1 = 0$, then one also has $c_2 = kc_1$. In this case the lines are identical, and there are infinitely many solutions.

449

Corollary

If $a_1b_2 - a_2b_1 \neq 0$, the only solution of the homogeneous† system

$$a_1x + b_1y = 0,$$
$$a_2x + b_2y = 0$$

is the trivial solution $x = y = 0$.

One could, of course, memorize equations (2) and use those equations as a formula to solve system (1). It will turn out that with determinants, one learns without effort formulas (2), along with their generalization to n equations in n variables.

A-4. MATRICES AND DETERMINANTS

The concept of determinant is based on that of matrix. Hence we shall first define a matrix.

DEFINITION A-1

An $m \times n$ *matrix* is a *rectangular array* of m rows and n columns of numbers:

$$\begin{pmatrix} a_{11} & a_{12} & \cdots & a_{1n} \\ a_{21} & a_{22} & \cdots & a_{2n} \\ \vdots & & & \vdots \\ a_{m1} & a_{m2} & \cdots & a_{mn} \end{pmatrix}. \tag{1}$$

The *elements* of the matrix are the numbers a_{ij}. A *square matrix* has the same number of rows as columns: $m = n$.

For example, the following are matrices:

$$\begin{pmatrix} a & b \\ c & d \end{pmatrix}, \quad \begin{pmatrix} a & b & c \\ d & e & f \\ g & h & i \end{pmatrix}, \quad \begin{pmatrix} a & b \\ c & d \\ e & f \end{pmatrix}, \quad \begin{pmatrix} a & b & c \\ d & e & f \end{pmatrix}.$$

$$2 \times 2 \qquad 3 \times 3 \qquad 3 \times 2 \qquad 2 \times 3$$

There is an algebra of matrices, which we cannot pursue here, that is an important part of what is called *linear algebra*. For our purposes, however, all that we need is the concept of a rectangular array. Two matrices are *equal* if and only if they have the same number of rows and the same number of columns, and the numbers appearing in the same row and column of the two matrices are equal.

---

† A linear equation is *homogeneous* if the constant term is zero. Then every term is of the first degree in the variables. Every homogeneous equation has the *trivial* solution $x = y = 0$.

450

PRELIMINARY TO A DEFINITION. It is possible to define certain useful functions, called determinant functions, which map $n \times n$ square matrices into the real numbers. The natural number n is called the order of the determinant function. To evaluate a determinant function at a given square matrix is to find the real number associated with the matrix.

We do not use the usual functional notation for determinant functions. We replace the rounded parentheses enclosing the array of the matrix by vertical lines. Then, if D is the determinant function, say of order three, we have

$$D \begin{pmatrix} a & b & c \\ d & e & f \\ g & h & i \end{pmatrix} = \begin{vmatrix} a & b & c \\ d & e & f \\ g & h & i \end{vmatrix}.$$

A-5. SECOND-ORDER DETERMINANTS

We need the following definition.

DEFINITION A-2

If D is the determinant function of order 2, then

$$D \begin{pmatrix} a_1 & b_1 \\ a_2 & b_2 \end{pmatrix} = \begin{vmatrix} a_1 & b_1 \\ a_2 & b_2 \end{vmatrix} = a_1 b_2 - a_2 b_1.$$

Remarks

1. The real number $(a_1 b_2 - a_2 b_1)$ is the value of the determinant function D at the matrix

$$\begin{pmatrix} a_1 & b_1 \\ a_2 & b_2 \end{pmatrix}.$$

It is convenient to refer to $(a_1 b_2 - a_2 b_1)$ as the value of the determinant, and we shall even say that $(a_1 b_2 - a_2 b_1)$ *is* the determinant although you should realize that we are abusing the language when we do this.

2. The number $a_1 b_2 - a_2 b_1$ is the sum of two terms $a_1 b_2$ and $-a_2 b_1$. Observe that each term is plus or minus a product of a number from one row and column and a number from a different row and column. We shall see later that this carries over to determinants of arbitrary order.

3. There is a mnemonic device for Definition A-2. One forms the products, with the proper signs, according to the arrows of Fig. A-3 and takes their sum.

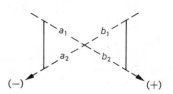

Fig. A-3 $(-)$ $(+)$

Now let us examine Theorem A–1. Definition A–2 permits us to restate part of the theorem as follows.

THEOREM A–2

The system
$$a_1x + b_1y = c_1, \tag{1}$$
$$a_2x + b_2y = c_2$$

has the unique solution

$$x = \frac{\begin{vmatrix} c_1 & b_1 \\ c_2 & b_2 \end{vmatrix}}{\begin{vmatrix} a_1 & b_1 \\ a_2 & b_2 \end{vmatrix}}, \qquad y = \frac{\begin{vmatrix} a_1 & c_1 \\ a_2 & c_2 \end{vmatrix}}{\begin{vmatrix} a_1 & b_1 \\ a_2 & b_2 \end{vmatrix}} \tag{2}$$

if Δ, the denominator determinant, in (2) is not zero. If $\Delta = 0$, then either there is no solution or there are infinitely many solutions.

We note that when the two equations are in the standard form (1), the rows of the determinant Δ are the same as the coefficients of x and y. The numerator determinants are obtained by replacing the coefficients in Δ of the variable sought by the constant terms. Equations (2) are known as *Cramer's Rule*, so called after the Swiss mathematician, Gabriel Cramer (1701–1752).

Problems

1. Evaluate:

(a) $\begin{vmatrix} 1 & 2 \\ -1 & -1 \end{vmatrix}$ 　　(b) $\begin{vmatrix} a & b \\ ka & kb \end{vmatrix}$ 　　(c) $\begin{vmatrix} \cos\theta & -\sin\theta \\ \sin\theta & \cos\theta \end{vmatrix}$

(d) $\begin{vmatrix} a & b \\ c & d \end{vmatrix}$ and $\begin{vmatrix} a + kc & b + kd \\ c & d \end{vmatrix}$ 　　(e) $\begin{vmatrix} x & 1 \\ 2 & x-1 \end{vmatrix}$

2. Solve the following equations.

(a) $\begin{vmatrix} 3 & 1 \\ x & 2 \end{vmatrix} = 0$ 　　(b) $\begin{vmatrix} x-1 & 1 \\ -1 & x-2 \end{vmatrix} = 0$

3. Solve the inequality below.

$$\begin{vmatrix} x & x-2 \\ 5 & 10 \end{vmatrix} < 0$$

4. Show that:

(a) $\begin{vmatrix} a & b \\ c & d \end{vmatrix} = -\begin{vmatrix} c & d \\ a & b \end{vmatrix} = \begin{vmatrix} a & c \\ b & d \end{vmatrix} = -\begin{vmatrix} c & a \\ d & b \end{vmatrix}$

(b) $\begin{vmatrix} a & b \\ kc & kd \end{vmatrix} = k\begin{vmatrix} a & b \\ c & d \end{vmatrix} = \begin{vmatrix} ka & b \\ kc & d \end{vmatrix}$

5. State the results of Problem 4 in words. Properties concerning rows and columns analogous to these are valid for determinants of any order.

6. Solve the following systems by determinants (Theorem A–2) if there is a unique solution. If there is no unique solution, decide whether there is any solution.

(a) $\begin{cases} 2x + y = 5 \\ x + 3y = 5 \end{cases}$ (b) $\begin{cases} 3x + 2y = -11 \\ 2x - 3y = 10 \end{cases}$ (c) $\begin{cases} 6x - 9y = 11 \\ 2x - 3y = 7 \end{cases}$

(d) $\begin{cases} 4x + 12y = 20 \\ 2x + 6y = 10 \end{cases}$ (e) $\begin{cases} 2x + 5 = 3y \\ 1 + y = -2x \end{cases}$ (f) $\begin{cases} 3/x - 2/y = 2 \\ 9/x + 4/y = 1 \end{cases}$

A–6. THIRD-ORDER DETERMINANTS

We first present the definition.

DEFINITION A–3

$$\begin{vmatrix} a_1 & b_1 & c_1 \\ a_2 & b_2 & c_2 \\ a_3 & b_3 & c_3 \end{vmatrix} = \begin{array}{l} a_1 b_2 c_3 + a_2 b_3 c_1 + a_3 b_1 c_2 \\ - a_3 b_2 c_1 - a_1 b_3 c_2 - a_2 b_1 c_3. \end{array}$$

Remarks

1. The determinant is the sum of products each of which has a plus or minus sign. Each product contains a factor from each row and each column. The sign is plus or minus depending on whether or not the number of *inversions on the subscripts is even or odd,* when the product has its factors in the order "*abc*" of the columns.

The number of *inversions* is the number of times a larger number precedes a smaller number in a sequence of numbers. Thus in "43125" there are five inversions. ("4" precedes "3," "1," and "2," and "3" precedes "1" and "2.") Then, for example, the term $a_3 b_2 c_1$ in the expansion of the determinant must have a minus sign because in "321" there are three inversions.

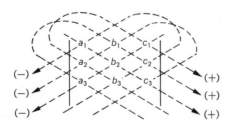

Fig. A–4

2. There is a mnemonic device for Definition A–3. One forms the products, with the proper signs, according to the arrows of Fig. A–4 and takes their sum.

453

Problems

1. Evaluate:

(a) $\begin{vmatrix} 1 & -1 & 1 \\ 2 & 1 & -1 \\ 1 & 2 & 3 \end{vmatrix}$ (b) $\begin{vmatrix} 2 & 1 & 3 \\ 1 & 1 & 6 \\ 1 & 2 & 13 \end{vmatrix}$ (c) $\begin{vmatrix} -2 & 3 & 7 \\ 4 & -2 & 6 \\ -1 & 3 & 5 \end{vmatrix}$

2. Prove that

$$\begin{vmatrix} a & b & c \\ a & b & c \\ d & e & f \end{vmatrix} = 0.$$

A–7. THIRD-ORDER DETERMINANTS (Cont.)

Before showing how determinants apply to linear systems in three variables we establish some important theorems that are valid for determinants of any order. Most of the proofs will be left to the reader.

DEFINITION A-4

The *minor* of an element of a determinant is the determinant of one lower order† that is obtained by deleting the row and column containing that element.

For example, the minor of b_3 in

$$\begin{vmatrix} a_1 & b_1 & c_1 \\ a_2 & b_2 & c_2 \\ a_3 & b_3 & c_3 \end{vmatrix} \quad \text{is} \quad \begin{vmatrix} a_1 & c_1 \\ a_2 & c_2 \end{vmatrix}.$$

The *cofactor* of an element of a determinant is the minor of that element multiplied by 1 or -1, according to whether the sum of the row number and the column number for that element is even or odd.

For example, in the above determinant the element b_3 is in the third row and second column. Since $3 + 2 = 5$ and this sum is odd, the cofactor of b_3 is

$$-\begin{vmatrix} a_1 & c_1 \\ a_2 & c_2 \end{vmatrix}.$$

THEOREM A-3

A determinant is the sum of the elements of any row (or column) multiplied by their corresponding cofactors.

---

† The order of a determinant is the number of rows or columns it contains. Hence a determinant of lower order would be one containing fewer rows and columns.

EXAMPLE

Using the elements of the second row, we have

$$\begin{vmatrix} a_1 & b_1 & c_1 \\ a_2 & b_2 & c_2 \\ a_3 & b_3 & c_3 \end{vmatrix} = -a_2 \begin{vmatrix} b_1 & c_1 \\ b_3 & c_3 \end{vmatrix} + b_2 \begin{vmatrix} a_1 & c_1 \\ a_3 & c_3 \end{vmatrix} - c_2 \begin{vmatrix} a_1 & b_1 \\ a_3 & b_3 \end{vmatrix} . \quad (1)$$

Proof of the example. We compute the right-hand side of (1):

$$-a_2 \begin{vmatrix} b_1 & c_1 \\ b_3 & c_3 \end{vmatrix} + b_2 \begin{vmatrix} a_1 & c_1 \\ a_3 & c_3 \end{vmatrix} - c_2 \begin{vmatrix} a_1 & b_1 \\ a_3 & c_3 \end{vmatrix}$$

$$= -a_2 b_1 c_3 + a_2 b_3 c_1 + a_1 b_2 c_3 - a_3 b_2 c_1 - a_1 b_3 c_2 + a_3 b_1 c_2.$$

This last expression is the value of the determinant according to Definition A–3.

We note that the sum in (1) when multiplied out is a sum of products of elements from each row and column. Thus to prove this theorem for determinants of higher orders it is necessary only to see that each product has the correct sign. The proof, however, is not trivial. (See Section A–8.)

Corollaries

1. If a row (or column) of a determinant is multiplied by k, then the determinant is multiplied by k.

2. If two adjacent rows (or columns) are interchanged, the determinant is changed in sign.

Proof. The minors of one row are the same as the minors of the other row in the changed determinant. All the cofactors have been changed in sign.

3. If any two rows (or columns) are interchanged, the determinant is changed in sign.

Proof. To interchange any two rows requires an odd number of interchanges of adjacent rows. Apply Corollary 2.

4. If two rows (or columns) of a determinant are the same, the determinant is zero.

THEOREM A–4

If the elements of any row (or column) are multiplied by the cofactors of any other row (column) and summed, the result is zero.

455

For example, referring to the determinants of (1) and using the second row and the cofactors of the first row, we have

$$-a_2 \begin{vmatrix} b_2 & c_2 \\ b_3 & c_3 \end{vmatrix} + b_2 \begin{vmatrix} a_2 & c_2 \\ a_3 & c_3 \end{vmatrix} - c_2 \begin{vmatrix} a_2 & b_2 \\ a_3 & b_3 \end{vmatrix} = 0.$$

[*Proof hint.* Apply Corollary 4 to a determinant which contains two identical rows.]

We are now ready to state, and prove, Cramer's Rule for a third-order system.

THEOREM A–5

The system

$$\begin{aligned} a_1x + b_1y + c_1z &= d_1, \\ a_2x + b_2y + c_2z &= d_2, \\ a_3x + b_3y + c_3z &= d_3 \end{aligned} \tag{2}$$

has the unique solution

$$x = \dfrac{\begin{vmatrix} d_1 & b_1 & c_1 \\ d_2 & b_2 & c_2 \\ d_3 & b_3 & c_3 \end{vmatrix}}{\begin{vmatrix} a_1 & b_1 & c_1 \\ a_2 & b_2 & c_2 \\ a_3 & b_3 & c_3 \end{vmatrix}}, \quad y = \dfrac{\begin{vmatrix} a_1 & d_1 & c_1 \\ a_2 & d_2 & c_2 \\ a_3 & d_3 & c_3 \end{vmatrix}}{\begin{vmatrix} a_1 & b_1 & c_1 \\ a_2 & b_2 & c_2 \\ a_3 & b_3 & c_3 \end{vmatrix}}, \quad z = \dfrac{\begin{vmatrix} a_1 & b_1 & d_1 \\ a_2 & b_2 & d_2 \\ a_3 & b_3 & d_3 \end{vmatrix}}{\begin{vmatrix} a_1 & b_1 & c_1 \\ a_2 & b_2 & c_2 \\ a_3 & b_3 & c_3 \end{vmatrix}}, \tag{3}$$

if the denominator determinant Δ in (3) is not zero. If $\Delta = 0$, then either there is no solution or there are infinitely many solutions.

Proof. Let us denote the cofactors of the elements a_i, b_i, c_i by A_i, B_i, C_i, respectively; $i = 1, 2, 3$. We eliminate y and z by multiplying the three equations of (2) by A_1, A_2, and A_3, respectively and adding. We obtain

$$(a_1A_1 + a_2A_2 + a_3A_3)x + (b_1A_1 + b_2A_2 + b_3A_3)y$$
$$+ (c_1A_1 + c_2A_2 + c_3A_3)z = d_1A_1 + d_2A_2 + d_3A_3.$$

By Theorem A–4 the coefficients of y and z are zero. The coefficient of x is Δ; so hence

$$\Delta x = d_1A_1 + d_2A_2 + d_3A_3. \tag{4}$$

Similarly, we obtain

$$\begin{aligned} \Delta y &= d_1B_1 + d_2B_2 + d_3B_3, \\ \Delta z &= d_1C_1 + d_2C_2 + d_3C_3. \end{aligned} \tag{5}$$

The right-hand members of equations (4) and (5) are recognized as the numerator determinants in (3). Therefore, if $\Delta \neq 0$, the solution to equations (2) must be given by (3). That (3) is actually a solution can be shown by obtaining equations (2) from equations (4) and (5). This is most easily done as follows. To get the first of equations (2) use (4) and (5) to compute $a_1 \Delta x + b_1 \Delta y + c_1 \Delta z$; then (after some rearrangement) Theorems 3 and 4 will reduce the equality to

$$\Delta(a_1 x + b_1 y + c_1 z) = \Delta d_1.$$

Since $\Delta \neq 0$, we get the first equation. The other equations of (2) are similarly obtained.

If $\Delta = 0$ and not all the right-hand members of (4) and (5) are zero, then there is no solution. If $\Delta = 0$ and all the right-hand members of (4) and (5) are zero, then it can be shown that there are infinitely many solutions, but we omit the proof.

Corollary

If the homogeneous equations

$$a_1 x + b_1 y + c_1 z = 0,$$
$$a_2 x + b_2 y + c_2 z = 0,$$
$$a_3 x + b_3 y + c_3 z = 0$$

have a solution different from $x = y = z = 0$, then $\Delta = 0$, and they have infinitely many solutions.

Problems

1. Solve the following systems, using Cramer's Rule.

(a) $x + y + z = 1$
$3x + 3y - 3z = 2$
$x - y - z = 0$

(b) $x - y + 1 = 0$
$y - z + 2 = 0$
$x + z + 3 = 0$

*(c) $x - y + 1 = 0$
$x + z - 6 = 0$
$y + z - 7 = 0$

2. Evaluate the determinant

$$\begin{vmatrix} -1 & 2 & -3 \\ 2 & 1 & -1 \\ 1 & -1 & 2 \end{vmatrix}$$

by cofactors of (a) the elements of the second row and (b) the elements of the third column.

3. Verify Theorem A–4 for the determinant of Problem 2, using the elements of the third row and the cofactors of the first row.

457

*4. Show in two ways that the equation

$$\begin{vmatrix} x & y & 1 \\ x_1 & y_1 & 1 \\ x_2 & y_2 & 1 \end{vmatrix} = 0$$

is an equation of the line through the distinct points (x_1, y_1) and (x_2, y_2).

[*Hint* 1. There is such a line: $Ax + By + C = 0$. Therefore $Ax_1 + By_1 + C = 0$ and $Ax_2 + By_2 + C = 0$. These three homogeneous equations have a nontrivial solution. Apply the Corollary to Theorem A–5.]

[*Hint* 2. The determinant equation is a linear equation in x and y and therefore represents a line. Show that (x_1, y_1) and (x_2, y_2) are on it.]

*5. Use the procedure of Problem 4 to find the line through $(1, -2)$ and $(-2, -4)$.

*6. Prove that if k times one row (or column) is added to another row (or column), then the determinant is unchanged.

*7. The theorem of Problem 6 can be used to get zeros in a determinant array. Thus the determinant   can be changed into

$$\begin{vmatrix} 1 & 2 & 3 \\ 3 & 4 & 6 \\ 3 & 2 & 1 \end{vmatrix} \qquad \begin{vmatrix} 1 & 2 & 3 \\ 1 & 0 & 0 \\ 3 & 2 & 1 \end{vmatrix}$$

by adding (-2) times the first row to the second row. The second determinant is easy to expand by cofactors of the second row.

Apply this method to get some zero elements into the following determinants. Then evaluate the determinants.

(a) $\begin{vmatrix} 1 & 2 & 3 \\ 4 & 5 & 6 \\ 7 & 8 & 9 \end{vmatrix}$ (b) $\begin{vmatrix} 1 & -1 & 1 \\ -2 & 3 & 2 \\ 1 & 2 & 3 \end{vmatrix}$ (c) $\begin{vmatrix} 1 & 1 & -2 \\ 2 & -1 & 1 \\ 4 & 1 & -2 \end{vmatrix}$.

*8. The use of the theorem of Problem 6 to get zeros in the determinant array corresponds to what one does in solving a linear system by successively eliminating the unknowns. To illustrate we shall solve a third-order system, but the same method applies to any system. Consider the system

(a) $a_1 x + b_1 y + c_1 z = d_1,$

(b) $a_2 x + b_2 y + c_2 z = d_2,$ (6)

(c) $a_3 x + b_3 y + c_3 x = d_3,$

and suppose that† $a_1 \neq 0$. We eliminate x from equations (6b) and (6c) by

---

† If not all of the a_i are zero, we can remember the equations so that $a_1 \neq 0$. If all of the a_i are zero, then either the equations are inconsistent or one of them is a linear combination of the other two. In the latter case we are really dealing with a lower-order system.

458

subtracting multiples of the first equation from these two equations, and so obtain

(a) $a_1x + b_1y + c_1z = d_1,$

(b) $\left(b_2 - \dfrac{a_2b_1}{a_1}\right)y + \left(c_2 - \dfrac{a_2c_1}{a_1}\right)z = d_2 - \dfrac{a_2d_1}{a_1},$ $\qquad$ (7)

(c) $\left(b_3 - \dfrac{a_3b_1}{a_1}\right)y + \left(c_3 - \dfrac{a_3c_1}{a_1}\right)z = d_3 - \dfrac{a_3d_1}{a_1}.$

System (7) is equivalent to system (6) because one can obtain (6) by adding multiples of (7a) to each of (7b) and (7c).

The last pair of equations in (7) constitute a lower-order system, and the same technique can be applied to this lower-order system. If we eliminate y between equations (7b) and (7c), we obtain a system in the form

$$a_1x + b_1y + c_1z = d_1,$$
$$B_2y + C_2z = D_2,$$
$$C_3z = D_3.$$

Such a system is said to be in *triangular form*. A system in this form is easily solved by inspection.

Solve the system
$$x - y - z = 5,$$
$$3x + 6y - 7z = 5, \qquad (8)$$
$$2x - y = 4,$$

by reducing it to triangular form.
We first get

$$x - y - z = 5, \qquad 9y - 4z = -10, \qquad y + 2z = -6.$$

Then, applying the same technique to the last two equations, we get

$$x - y - z = 5, \qquad 9y - 4z = -10, \qquad \tfrac{22}{9}z = -\tfrac{44}{9}.$$

The solution is evidently $z = -2, y = -2, x = 1$.

Show how each step in your reduction to triangular form corresponds to obtaining a zero in the determinant array of system (8).

*9. Solve the following equations by reducing each to triangular form.

(a) $\begin{cases} x + y + z = 1 \\ 3x + 3y - 3z = 2 \\ x - y - z = 0 \end{cases}$
$\qquad$
(b) $\begin{cases} x - y + 1 = 0 \\ x + z - 6 = 0 \\ y + z - 6 = 0 \end{cases}$

(c) $\begin{cases} 2x - 5y - 7z = 18 \\ x + y + 8z = -35 \\ 4x + 6y + z = 13 \end{cases}$
$\qquad$
(d) $\begin{cases} x + 2y - z = 8 \\ -w + y + 3z = 3 \\ 4w - x + z = -20 \\ w + 5x - y = 9 \end{cases}$

(e) $\begin{cases} x + 2y - z = 3 \\ 3x + y - 2z = 4 \end{cases}$

A–8. HIGHER-ORDER DETERMINANTS

To simplify the notation, we formulate the definition of higher-order determinants in terms of fourth-order ones. The extension to orders greater than four will be clear.

DEFINITION A–5

The *fourth-order determinant* $\begin{vmatrix} a_1 & b_1 & c_1 & d_1 \\ a_2 & b_2 & c_2 & d_2 \\ a_3 & b_3 & c_3 & d_3 \\ a_4 & b_4 & c_4 & d_4 \end{vmatrix}$

is the sum of all products $\pm a_i b_j c_k d_l$ with $i, j, k,$ and l all different. The positive sign is used if the symbol "$ijkl$" has an even number of inversions. The negative sign is used when the number of inversions is odd.

On the basis of this definition it is possible (but not trivial) to prove all of the theorems of Section A–6. Basic to the development of properties of higher-order determinants are Theorems A–3 and A–4. Theorem A–3 is illustrated by the following example, where we have expanded by cofactors of the second row.

EXAMPLE

$$\begin{vmatrix} 1 & 2 & 0 & -1 \\ 2 & -1 & 1 & 2 \\ -2 & -3 & -4 & 1 \\ 1 & -1 & 1 & 2 \end{vmatrix} = -2\begin{vmatrix} 2 & 0 & 1 \\ -3 & -4 & 1 \\ -1 & 1 & 2 \end{vmatrix} + (-1)\begin{vmatrix} 1 & 0 & -1 \\ -2 & -4 & 1 \\ 1 & 1 & 2 \end{vmatrix}$$

$$-(1)\begin{vmatrix} 1 & 2 & -1 \\ -2 & -3 & 1 \\ 1 & -1 & 2 \end{vmatrix} + 2\begin{vmatrix} 1 & 2 & 0 \\ -2 & -3 & -4 \\ 1 & -1 & 1 \end{vmatrix}$$

$$= -2(-17) + (-1)(-7) + (0) + 2(-11) = 9.$$

Problems

1. Evaluate:

(a) $\begin{vmatrix} 1 & 2 & 3 & 4 \\ 1 & 4 & 10 & 20 \\ 1 & 3 & 6 & 10 \\ 1 & 1 & 1 & 1 \end{vmatrix}$
   (b) $\begin{vmatrix} 1 & -1 & -1 & -1 \\ -1 & -1 & 1 & -1 \\ -1 & -1 & -1 & 1 \\ -1 & 1 & -1 & 1 \end{vmatrix}$

2. Apply the theorem of Problem 6, Section A–7 to get zeros as elements of determinants which are equal to those of Problem 1. Then evaluate the determinants.

3. Use Theorem A–5 to prove that if the equations

$$a_1x + b_1y + c_1z - d_1 = 0,$$
$$a_2x + b_2y + c_2z - d_2 = 0,$$
$$a_3x + b_3y + c_3z - d_3 = 0,$$
$$a_4x + b_4y + c_4z - d_4 = 0$$

are consistent (that is, have a solution), then

$$\begin{vmatrix} a_1 & b_1 & c_1 & d_1 \\ a_2 & b_2 & c_2 & d_2 \\ a_3 & b_3 & c_3 & d_3 \\ a_4 & b_4 & c_4 & d_4 \end{vmatrix} = 0.$$

4. Show that an equation of the plane through the three noncollinear points

$$(x_1, y_1, z_1), \quad (x_2, y_2, z_2), \quad (x_3, y_3, z_3)$$

is the determinant equation

$$\begin{vmatrix} x & y & z & 1 \\ x_1 & y_1 & z_1 & 1 \\ x_2 & y_2 & z_2 & 1 \\ x_3 & y_3 & z_3 & 1 \end{vmatrix} = 0.$$

5. Show that an equation of the circle through the three noncollinear points,

$$(x_1, y_1), \quad (x_2, y_2), \quad (x_3, y_3),$$

in the xy-plane is the determinant equation.

$$\begin{vmatrix} x^2 + y^2 & x & y & 1 \\ x_1^2 + y_1^2 & x_1 & y_1 & 1 \\ x_2^2 + y_2^2 & x_2 & y_2 & 1 \\ x_3^2 + y_3^2 & x_3 & y_3 & 1 \end{vmatrix} = 0.$$

6. Solve the following system by use of Cramer's Rule:

$$x + y + z + w = -1,$$
$$2x - y + z - 2w = 11,$$
$$x - y + 2z - w = 9,$$
$$3x + y - z + w = -3.$$

APPENDIX B | Mathematical Induction—Combinatorial Problems

B–1. INTRODUCTION

In this appendix we discuss certain problems relating to the natural numbers. There is a common thread running through the various topics, namely that statements, or formulas, are proved for *every* natural number n. Most of these statements can be proved by the technique called *mathematical induction*, an important method of proof which is encountered in all sorts of contexts.

Moreover, each topic in this appendix has independent importance. Some familiarity with this material is a necessity for further study in mathematics. The reader is urged to rely as little as possible on his memory (apart from the definitions) and to think the problems through on his own.

B–2. MATHEMATICAL INDUCTION

The natural numbers,

$$N = \{1, 2, 3, \ldots, n, \ldots\},$$

have an important property called the *Induction Principle*, which is the basis for many otherwise inaccessible proofs.

THE INDUCTION PRINCIPLE

If S is a set of natural numbers with the following two properties:

(a) 1 is in S,

(b) For any k, if k is in S, then $k + 1$ is in S,
   then S is the set of all natural numbers: $S = N$.

This principle simply describes the set which we *define* as the natural numbers. It states carefully what each of us learned as a child. "The whole numbers are those you get by counting from 1—that is, starting with 1 and adding 1 again and again."

One amusing way of looking at the principle is to regard it as the "domino effect." Imagine an infinite set of dominoes (one for each natural number)

462

lined up not too far apart (Fig. B–1). Then, if the first one is toppled over, eventually each one must fall. But

Fig. B–1

(a) one must be sure to topple the first domino;

(b) one must be sure that the kth domino topples the $(k + 1)$th domino.

Part (a) of the induction principle is called the *anchor*. If part (a) is true, the induction is *anchored*. Part (b) begins "If k is in S . . ." The assumption "k is in S" is called the *inductive hypothesis*. Let us see how the induction principle can supply proofs.

EXAMPLE 1

Prove that the sum of the first n natural numbers is $n(n + 1)/2$, that is

$$P_n: \quad 1 + 2 + 3 + \cdots + n = \frac{n(n + 1)}{2},$$

for all natural numbers n.

We wish to prove that P_n is true for all n. Let S be the set of all natural numbers n for which P_n is true. To prove that P_n is true for all n we must show that $S = N$. We do this as follows:

(a) 1 is in S because P_1 asserts that

$$1 = \frac{1(1 + 1)}{2} = 1,$$

which is true. The induction is *anchored*.

(b) Suppose k is in S. Then P_k is true, that is,

$$1 + 2 + 3 + \cdots + k = \frac{k(k + 1)}{2}.$$

This is the *inductive hypothesis* and therefore is *assumed* to be true.

We wish to prove that P_{k+1} is true. We have, by the inductive hypothesis,

$$1 + 2 + \cdots + k = \frac{k(k + 1)}{2}.$$

Adding $(k + 1)$ to both sides of the equation we get

$$1 + 2 + \cdots + k + (k + 1) = (1 + 2 + \cdots + k) + (k + 1)$$
$$= \frac{k(k + 1)}{2} + (k + 1)$$
$$= \frac{(k + 1)(k + 2)}{2}.$$

463

But this is precisely P_{k+1}. Therefore, P_{k+1} is true if P_k is true. This proves part (b) and completes the induction; $S = N$ and P_n is true for all n.

Remark

The simple theorem of the example above can be established in ways other than by induction. For example, if

$$S_n = 1 + 2 + \cdots + n \qquad \text{(there are } n \text{ summands)}, \tag{1}$$

then, reversing the order of the summands, we have

$$S_n = n + (n - 1) + \cdots + 1. \tag{2}$$

Adding S_n given by (1) and (2), we obtain

$$2S_n = (n + 1) + (n + 1) + \cdots + (n + 1)$$
$$= n(n + 1) \qquad \text{(there are } n \text{ summands)}.$$

Therefore

$$S_n = \frac{n(n + 1)}{2},$$

which was to be proved.

The importance of the induction principle lies in its use in proofs where no such simple trick works.

EXAMPLE 2

Find the sum of the first n odd numbers.

With no clues as to how to proceed we do some computing:

$1 = 1^2$,   the first odd number;

$1 + 3 = 4 = 2^2$,   the sum of the first two odd numbers;

$1 + 3 + 5 = 9 = 3^2$,   the sum of the first three odd numbers.

Because the nth odd number is $2n - 1$, we conjecture that

$$P_n: \quad 1 + 3 + \cdots (2n - 1) = n^2,$$

for all natural numbers n.

We prove our conjecture by induction.

(a) The induction is anchored by the computation that led to the conjecture, that is, $1 = 1^2$.

(b) Assume that P_k is true. Then $1 + 3 + 5 + \cdots + (2k - 1) = k^2$.

The $(k + 1)$th odd number is $2k + 1$; hence by the inductive hypothesis,

464

and by adding $2k + 1$ to both sides of the equation, we have

$$1 + 3 + \cdots + (2k - 1) + (2k + 1) = k^2 + (2k + 1),$$
$$1 + 3 + \cdots + (2k - 1) + (2k + 1) = (k + 1)^2.$$

But this is precisely the statement of P_{k+1}. This completes the induction. P_n is true for all natural numbers n.

Problems

1. Prove by induction that the following statements are true for all natural numbers n.

(a) $2 + 4 + \cdots + 2n = n(n + 1)$

(b) $1^2 + 2^2 + \cdots + n^2 = \frac{1}{6}n(n + 1)(2n + 1)$

(c) $1^2 + 3^2 + \cdots + (2n - 1)^2 = \frac{1}{3}n(2n - 1)(2n + 1)$

(d) $1^3 + 2^3 + \cdots + n^3 = \frac{1}{4}n^2(n + 1)^2$

(e) $\dfrac{1}{1 \cdot 2} + \dfrac{1}{2 \cdot 3} + \cdots + \dfrac{1}{n(n + 1)} = \dfrac{n}{n + 1}$

[*Hint:* There is a neat short proof if one observes that

$$\frac{1}{k(k + 1)} = \frac{1}{k} - \frac{1}{k + 1}.$$

Then most of the terms cancel to give the desired result.]

(f) $2^n > n$

(g) $n^3 + 2n$ is divisible by 3

(h) $x^n - y^n$ is divisible by $x - y$

(i) $x^{2n+1} + y^{2n+1}$ is divisible by $x + y$

(j) $1 \cdot 2 + 2 \cdot 3 + \cdots + n(n + 1) = \frac{1}{3}n(n + 1)(n + 2)$

(k) $\frac{1}{2} + \frac{1}{3} + \frac{1}{4} + \frac{1}{5} + \cdots + 1/2^n < n$

(l) If $t \geq 0$, then $(1 + t)^n \geq 1 + nt$

*(m) $\cos x + \cos 3x + \cdots \cos (2n - 1)x = \dfrac{\sin 2nx}{2 \sin x}$

2. The laws of exponents for positive-integer exponents can be established by induction. Recall that

$$a^{n+1} = a \cdot a^n \qquad \textit{by definition.}$$

To prove that

$$a^n \cdot a^m = a^{n+m}$$

for all positive integers n and m (natural numbers), we proceed as follows.

Let S be the set of all positive integers n such that $a^n \cdot a^m = a^{n+m}$ is true for *all positive integers m*. Explain why each of the following is true.

(a) 1 is in S because $a^1 \cdot a^m = a^{m+1}$.   (Why?)

(b) If k is in S, then $a^k \cdot a^m = a^{k+m}$.   (Why?)

Then

$$
\begin{aligned}
a^{k+1} \cdot a^m &= (a \cdot a^k) \cdot a^m & &\text{(Why?)}\\
&= a \cdot (a^k \cdot a^m) & &\text{(Why?)}\\
&= a \cdot a^{k+m} & &\text{(Why?)}\\
&= a^{k+m+1} & &\text{(Why?)}\\
&= a^{(k+1)+m}. & &\text{(Why?)}
\end{aligned}
$$

This completes the induction.   (Why?)

3. What is wrong with the "proof" of the following "theorem"?

   In any group of people, all members are of the same sex.

   The proof is by induction on the number in a group.

   (a) If there is only one person in the group, the theorem is obvious. This anchors the induction.

   (b) Suppose that the theorem is true for groups of k persons and consider a group of $k + 1$ members. Take one person aside. This will leave k persons, and all of these necessarily are of the same sex. Now return the person you took aside to the group and remove another. Again the remaining group is all of one sex. Therefore the person first taken aside has the same sex as the others.

4. Prove that

$$
a + (a + d) + \cdots + (a + (n - 1)d) = \tfrac{1}{2}n(2a + (n - 1)d).
$$

5. Prove that

$$
a + ar + \cdots + ar^{n-1} = \frac{a - ar^n}{1 - r}.
$$

B-3. SEQUENCES

We define some special functions called *sequences*.

DEFINITION B-1

A *sequence* of real numbers is a real-valued function whose domain is the set of natural numbers.

Thus, a sequence f is known when its nth term $f(n)$ is known. Instead of representing sequences by the usual functional symbols f, g, a, etc., and their values at n by $f(n)$, $g(n)$, $a(n)$, etc., it is customary to use a subscript notation. The values of the sequences at the natural number n are denoted by $f_n, g_n, a_n, \ldots$ The sequences as a whole are denoted by $\{f_n\}, \{g_n\}, \{a_n\}, \ldots$

466

A sequence is said to be *finite* if all the terms are zero for n sufficiently large.

There is a bewildering variety of sequences, some of which are quite bizarre. The two important types we mainly wish to consider are:

(1) Arithmetic sequences (progressions†),

$$a, a + d, a + 2d, \ldots, a + (n - 1)d, \ldots,$$

where a and d are given numbers (the *first term* and the *common difference*) and n is a natural number. The nth term of the sequence is $a + (n - 1)d$.

(2) Geometric sequences (progressions†),

$$a, ar, ar^2, \ldots, ar^{n-1}, \ldots,$$

where a and r are given numbers (the *first term* and the *common ratio*) and n is a natural number. The nth term of the sequence is ar^{n-1}.

Other examples of sequences are given below.

(3) *Harmonic sequences* are sequences whose terms are reciprocals of the terms of arithmetic sequences. When we speak of *the* harmonic sequence we mean the sequence

$$1, \frac{1}{2}, \frac{1}{3}, \ldots, \frac{1}{n}, \ldots$$

(4) Let p_n be the perimeter of a regular polygon of n sides inscribed in a circle of radius a. (Necessarily now $n \geq 3$.) We have the sequence

$$3\sqrt{3}\, a, 4\sqrt{2}\, a, \ldots, p_n, \ldots$$

When n is large, what does p_n approach?

(5) Consider the decimal expansion of π,

$$\pi = 3.141592653589 \ldots$$

Let a_n be 0 if the digit in the nth decimal place is even. Let a_n be 1 if the nth digit is odd. We get the sequence

$$1, 0, 1, 1, 1, 0, 0, 1, 1, 1, 0, 1, \ldots, a_n, \ldots$$

---

† The term "progression" is sometimes used for sequence, especially in older books, and with reference to arithmetic or geometric sequences.

Our main purpose is to find the sums of the first n terms of arithmetic and geometric sequences:

$$A_n = a + (a + d) + \cdots + (a + (n - 1)d),$$
$$G_n = a + ar + \cdots + ar^{n-1}.$$

Formulas for both these sums can be found by a little manipulation. (See Example 1, Section B–2, and the Problem Section below.) However, in conformity to the theme of this appendix we proceed by induction.

The formulas we obtain are

$$A_n = \tfrac{1}{2}n(2a + (n - 1)d),$$
$$G_n = \frac{a - ar^n}{1 - r}, \qquad r \neq 1.$$

You will be asked to prove the formula for A_n in Problem 7 of the next set of problems.

Proof of the formula for G_n

(a) G_1 is true because

$$a = \frac{a - ar}{1 - r}.$$

(b) Suppose that G_k is true. Then

$$G_{k+1} = a + ar + \cdots + ar^{k-1} + ar^k = \frac{a - ar^k}{1 - r} + ar^k \qquad \text{(Why?)}$$

$$= \frac{a - ar^{k+1}}{1 - r},$$

which is precisely the formula for G_{k+1}. Therefore G_{k+1} is true if G_k is true. The induction is complete.

For geometric sequences we can also sum the terms of the entire infinite sequence if the absolute value of the common ratio is less than one. In order to "sum" infinitely many terms, we must *define* what we mean by an infinite geometric series.

An *infinite geometric series* is an expression

$$G = a + ar + ar^2 + \cdots + ar^{n-1} + \cdots$$

The sum, G, of the series is *defined* to be

$$G = \lim_{n \to \infty} G_n \qquad \text{if } |r| < 1.$$

Here, again, the object of study is *defined* to be a limit. Just as in geometry, where the circumference of a circle is defined to be the limit of the perimeters of inscribed polygons, so the object of our study is a limit of a sequence of finite approximations. See Appendix C for a more detailed discussion of limits. In this situation we have the limit of the infinite sequence

$$G_1, G_2, \ldots, G_n, \ldots$$

The limit is a number G (if such a number exists) such that $|G - G_n|$ is arbitrarily small if n is sufficiently large. The limit G *does exist* because

$$G_n = \frac{a - ar^n}{1 - r} = \frac{a}{1 - r} - \frac{ar^n}{1 - r}.$$

The second term,

$$\frac{-ar^n}{1 - r},$$

is a very small number provided $|r| < 1$. Then

$$G = \lim_{n \to \infty} G_n = \frac{a}{1 - r}.$$

EXAMPLES

1. The geometric series

$$\tfrac{1}{2} + \tfrac{1}{4} + \tfrac{1}{8} + \cdots + 1/2^n + \cdots$$

has as its first term $a = \tfrac{1}{2}$ and as its ratio $r = \tfrac{1}{2} < 1$. Its sum, by the formula above, is

$$\frac{\tfrac{1}{2}}{1 - \tfrac{1}{2}} = 1.$$

The geometric significance of this series on the real line is shown in Fig. B–2.

Fig. B–2

2. Repeating decimals are infinite geometric series. For example,

$$0.78181\overline{81} = 0.7 + 0.081 + 0.00081 + \cdots$$

The terms following the first form a geometric series with ratio $r = 0.01$. Therefore

$$0.78181\overline{81} = 0.7 + \frac{0.081}{1 - 0.01} = \frac{7}{10} + \frac{81}{990}$$

$$= \frac{7}{10} + \frac{9}{110} = \frac{86}{110} = \frac{43}{55}.$$

We can check this by dividing 43 by 55 to obtain the original decimal.

469

Problems

1. What are the first five terms of the arithmetic sequence with $a = 5$ and $d = -\frac{2}{3}$? Find the sum of 32 terms.

2. Find the sum of 10 terms of the geometric sequence with $a = 1$ and $r = 2$. About how many digits is the sum of 50 terms?

3. Suppose that $d > 0$ in an arithmetic sequence. Show that the sum, A_n, of the first n terms becomes arbitrarily large as n becomes infinite.

4. A ball rolls down an inclined plane, traveling 3.43 feet during the first second. In each succeeding second it travels 6.86 feet more than in the preceding one. How far does it roll in 8 seconds?

5. A ball is dropped from a height h and bounces to 0.9 its previous height after each bounce. What is the total distance traveled?

6. The fifth term of an arithmetic sequence is 3; the fifteenth term is 8. What is the sequence?

7. Prove the formula for A_n by induction.

8. Derive the formula for A_n by reversing the order of the summands.

9. Derive the formula for G_n by showing that

$$G_{n+1} = G_n + ar^n = a + rG_n.$$

10. Using geometric series, express as quotients of integers the rational numbers given by the following repeating decimals.

    (a) $0.444\ldots$ (b) $0.\overline{27}$ (c) $31.\overline{09}$

11. A person contributes 1 cent to the Red Cross and writes letters to two friends requesting each to contribute 1 cent and write similar letters to two friends. Let us assume that all comply. How many dollars would the Red Cross receive after 100 sets of letters were written?

12. Show that the sum of the infinite geometric series

$$1 + x + x^2 + x^3 + \cdots + x^n + \cdots,$$

with $|x| < 1$, is $1/(1 - x)$. Use long division on this result to recover the original series.

B-4. PERMUTATIONS

In this section and the next, we are concerned with certain combinatorial problems—*counting* problems in which we count the ways in which finite sets of objects can be arranged or selected. The formulas which we derive have important applications to probability and statistics but we pursue them here for their own interest.

Basic to problems of counting is the following principle:

PRINCIPLE

If an event can occur in m ways, and if a second independent event can occur in n ways, then the two events can occur in mn ways.

Let us suppose that we have a set of n distinct objects and we select r ($\leq n$) of them. We shall derive a formula for the number of ways in which r objects of the set of n objects can be arranged on a line.

EXAMPLE 1

We have three objects a, b, and c. Using two of the three objects, let us enumerate all the arrangements (permutations) that can be made. They are

$$ab, ac, ba, bc, ca, cb.$$

If we enumerate all the arrangements obtained by using all three objects, we have

$$abc, acb, bac, bca, cab, cba.$$

In each case there are 6 possible arrangements.

How many arrangements can one make of four objects, using all of the objects each time? List all possibilities. There are 24 arrangements.

DEFINITION B–2

A *permutation* of a set of n different objects is an arrangement of the n objects in order, so that there is a first, a second, a third, . . . , an nth object.

Every permutation of a set of r objects taken from a set of n different objects is called a *permutation of n objects taken r at a time*.

The number of different permutations of n objects taken r at a time is denoted† by $P(n, r)$.

From Example 1 we observe that $P(3, 2) = 6$ and $P(3, 3) = 6$. It was noted above that $P(4, 4) = 24$. It is an easy conjecture that

$$P(n, n) = n(n - 1)(n - 2) \cdots (1). \tag{1}$$

The right-hand member of equation (1) occurs with great frequency in all parts of mathematics and hence is denoted by the special symbol "$n!$":

$$n! = n(n - 1)(n - 2) \cdots (1),$$

---

† The notation $_nP_r$ is also used.

where, of course, n must be a natural number. The number $n!$ is called "n-factorial." Then $1! = 1$, $2! = 2$, $3! = 6$, $4! = 24$, etc.

Let us verify the conjecture mentioned above:

$$P(n, n) = n!$$

The result is really quite obvious because of the Principle: The first object can be selected in n ways. This leaves $n - 1$ objects from which to choose a second object. Therefore the first two objects can be selected in $n(n - 1)$ ways. The next object can be selected in $n - 2$ ways, *and so on*. Continuing in this manner, we obtain the desired result.

We can also give an inductive proof that avoids the phrase "and so on."

(a) If $n = 1$, there is only one arrangement and $1 = 1!$. This anchors the induction.

(b) If $P(k, k) = k!$, then a permutation of $k + 1$ objects is made by first selecting one object ($k + 1$ possible ways to select the first in order). When this has been done, there remain k objects, and furthermore it is a different set of k objects for each choice of the first object. For each of the $k + 1$ sets of k objects there are, by the inductive hypothesis, $k!$ ways of arranging them. Therefore, by the Principle,

$$P(k + 1, k + 1) = (k + 1)P(k, k) = (k + 1)k!$$
$$= (k + 1)!.$$

This completes the induction and the proof.

We now wish to find a formula for $P(n, r)$. We first prove that

$$P(n, r) = P(n, r - 1)(n - r + 1).$$

Proof. We can select a permutation of $r - 1$ objects in $P(n, r - 1)$ ways. Then the next object can be selected in $n - r + 1$ ways. Every permutation r of the objects is obtained in this manner. Therefore, by the Principle,

$$P(n, r) = P(n, r - 1)(n - r + 1).$$

THEOREM B-1†

$$P(n, r) = n(n - 1) \cdots (n - r + 1)$$
$$= \frac{n!}{(n - r)!}.$$

Proof by induction

(a) $P(n, 1) = n = \dfrac{n!}{(n - 1)!}$

---

† If $r = n$, then the denominator $(n - r)! = 0!$. To make this formula valid in this case, we *define* $0! = 1$.

The induction is anchored.

(b) If $P(n, k) = \dfrac{n!}{(n - k)!}$ and $k < n$, then

$$P(n, k + 1) = P(n, k)(n - k)$$
$$= \frac{n!}{(n - k)!}(n - k)$$
$$= \frac{n!}{(n - k - 1)!},$$

which is the correct formula for $P(n, k + 1)$. The induction is complete.

The formula for $P(n, r)$ is almost obvious. The first of the r objects can be chosen in n ways, the second in $n - 1$ ways, *and so on*, until one reaches the rth object, which can be chosen in $n - r + 1$ ways. The *Principle* then gives $P(n, r) = n(n - 1) \cdots (n - r + 1)$.

EXAMPLE 2

A president, vice-president, and secretary are to be selected from a group of 15 people. How many different slates of candidates are possible?

A direct solution based on the *Principle* is possible. The president can be one of 15, the vice-president one of 14, and the secretary one of 13. There are therefore $15 \cdot 14 \cdot 13 = 2730$ different slates.

Theorem B–1 also provides a solution. There will be $P(15, 3)$ slates: $P(15, 3) = 15 \cdot 14 \cdot 13 = 2730$.

B–5. COMBINATIONS

We have been counting the number of permutations, or arrangements, of r objects from a set of n. We now turn to the number of such sets of r objects *without regard to order*.

DEFINITION B–3

A *subset* of r objects from a set of n objects is called a *combination of n objects taken r at a time*. The number of combinations of n objects taken r at a time is denoted† by $C(n, r)$.

THEOREM B–2

$$P(n, r) = r! \, C(n, r),$$

$$C(n, r) = \frac{n!}{r!(n - r)!}.$$

---

† There are several other notations for $C(n, r)$, the most common being $_nC_r$ and $\dbinom{n}{r}$.

Note that when we apply this formula for $C(n, r)$ to the case of $r = n$, we obtain

$$C(n, n) = \frac{n!}{n!0!}.$$

We must use the convention of the footnote on page 472, that $0! = 1$. Then the number of combinations of n things taken n at a time comes out to be 1.

Proof. One gets all permutations by choosing a combination of r objects [this may be done in $C(n, r)$ ways] and then arranging these r objects in all ways (there are $r!$ ways). Therefore, by the Principle,

$$P(n, r) = C(n, r)r!.$$

The formula for $C(n, r)$ follows from the one for $P(n, r)$.

EXAMPLES

1. Three representatives (of equal rank) are to be selected from a group of 15 persons. How many different sets of representatives are possible?

Since there is no concern with order, there are $C(15, 3)$ sets:

$$C(15, 3) = \frac{15!}{(3!)(12!)} = \frac{15 \cdot 14 \cdot 13}{3 \cdot 2 \cdot 1} = 455.$$

2. How many different 5-digit numbers can be formed with the digits 3, 4, 6, 6, 6?

Had the digits been all different the answer would be $P(5, 5) = 5! = 120$. However, there are three "6's" which in any five-digit number could be permuted among themselves without affecting the number. Since there are $3!$ such permutations of the "6's," the number of different numbers is $5!/3! = 20$.

Problems

1. How many different batting orders for a baseball team are possible?

2. How many three-letter "words" can be made from the alphabet if no letter is to be used more than once?

3. How many different basketball teams (without regard to position) can be selected from 12 players?

4. An examination has 10 questions from which the student is to select six to work on. How many different selections can be made?

5. An automobile manufacturer makes three differently named cars, with five body types and three types of engines available for each. How many different kinds of autos does he make?

474

6. Show that
$$\frac{(n + 1)!}{(n - 1)!} = n^2 + n.$$

7. Show that $n[n! + (n - 1)!] = (n + 1)!$.

8. If $C(n, 3) = 20$, what is n?

9. A coin is tossed eight times in succession. How many different outcomes are there for the eight tosses?

10. In how many different ways is it possible to arrange the letters in the word "cool"?

11. Prove that the number of different permutations of n objects of which p are the same and q are the same (but different from the p objects) is $n!/p!q!$.

12. How many different six-digit numbers can be formed from the digits 3, 3, 4, 4, 5, 6?

13. How many different arrangements are there of the letters of the words (a) pester? (b) Mississippi?

14. Prove that $C(n, r) = C(n - 1, r - 1) + C(n - 1, r)$, where $1 < r < n$.

15. How many selections of a five-man team can be made from 12 men if (a) one particular man must always be included? (b) one particular man must always be excluded?

16. Prove that $C(n, r) = C(n, n - r)$.

17. Thirteen cards are dealt from a pack of 52. How many different hands are possible? Leave your answer as a product, but estimate its magnitude.

18. Four people are seated at a round table. How many seating arrangements are there? ("Rotations" of an arrangement do not change the arrangement.) Suppose 5 people are at the table. How many seating plans are possible? Generalize your result.

19. Prove that if p is a prime, then $(p - 1)(p - 2) \cdots (p - r + 1)$ is divisible by $r!$, where $0 < r < p$.

20. In how many ways can 10 persons be split into two groups of 4 and 6 persons?

21. Prove that $n!/k!(n - k)!$ is always an integer, where $0 \leq k \leq n$.

22. In a 10-team league, how many league games are there if each team plays all other teams twice? Why is this number $P(10, 2)$?

*23. In how many ways can 10 people be lined up so that two forming a certain pair are (a) always next to each other? [*Hint:* (a) Arrange the other eight first.] (b) never next to each other? [*Hint:* (b) This part follows from part (a).]

*24. Six boys and six girls are to be lined up in such a way that boys and girls alternate. In how many different ways can this be done if (a) a certain boy and a certain girl must be together? (b) must never be together?

475

B-6. THE BINOMIAL THEOREM

The polynomial $a + x$ is called a *binomial*. Our purpose in this section is to obtain a formula (the binomial theorem) for $(a + x)^n$, where n is a natural number. First we make a few computations to see what develops.

$$(a + x)^0 = 1$$
$$(a + x)^1 = a + x$$
$$(a + x)^2 = a^2 + 2ax + x^2$$
$$(a + x)^3 = a^3 + 3a^2x + 3ax^2 + x^3$$
$$(a + x)^4 = a^4 + 4a^3x + 6a^2x^2 + 4ax^3 + x^4$$
$$(a + x)^5 = a^5 + 5a^4x + 10a^3x^2 + 10a^2x^3 + 5ax^4 + x^5$$

A pattern is beginning to emerge. Before reading on, you may wish to guess what the coefficients are in the next row.

To get $(a + x)^6$ we multiply $(a + x)^5$ by $a + x$. Let us suppose that we wish to find the coefficient of a^4x^2 in $(a + x)^6$:

$$a^5 + 5a^4x + 10a^3x^2 + 10a^2x^3 + 5ax^4 + x^5$$

$$a + x$$

$$\cdots + 10a^4x^2 + 5a^4x^2 + \cdots$$

The dashed lines indicate the products that give "a^4x^2-terms," namely $10a^4x^2 + 5a^4x^2 = 15a^4x^2$. What will be the "$a^5x$-term"?

Examination of the products in (1) and the coefficients in the expansion of $(a + x)^6$ makes the following conjecture reasonable:

Having computed $(a + x)^n$, we find that:
  (i) the expansion of $(a + x)^{n+1}$ begins with a^{n+1} and ends with x^{n+1};
  (ii) the coefficients are the same, in reverse order, at the end as they are at the beginning; and
  (iii) we can obtain the coefficient of $a^k x^{n-k+1}$ in $(a + x)^{n+1}$ from the coefficients of $a^{k-1}x^{n-k+1}$, and of $a^k x^{n-k}$ in the expansion of $(a + x)^n$. The desired coefficient is the sum of the coefficients of these two terms.

The pattern of coefficients described by (i), (ii), and (iii) is called Pascal's triangle (Blaise Pascal 1623–1662) and is shown in Fig. B–3. We therefore have an algorithm for computing any power of $(a + x)$.

```
                    1
                  1   1
                1   2   1
              1   3   3   1
            1   4   6   4   1
          1   5  10  10   5   1
        1   6  15  20  15   6   1
```

Fig. B–3

Yet what we have is not all we might desire, for we do not have a formula for, say, the coefficient of $a^{12}x^{13}$ in $(a + x)^{25}$ without doing a great deal of extraneous computation. Nevertheless, the insight we get from Pascal's triangle can lead us quickly to the binomial theorem.

Let us consider, for example,

$$(a + x)^6 = (a + x)(a + x)(a + x)(a + x)(a + x)(a + x).$$

The separate terms in the expanded form are obtained by taking one factor (an a or an x) from each of the parentheses. If we always take the factor a, then we get the term a^6; there is only one way of doing this. To obtain terms a^5x we must choose the factor a five times and the factor x once. However, a factor a can be chosen from the six parenthesis in $C(6, 5)$ ways. The coefficient of a^5x is therefore $C(6, 5)$. For the full expansion we would have

$$\begin{aligned}(a + x)^6 = \ & C(6, 6)a^6 + C(6, 5)a^5x + C(6, 4)a^4x^2 \\ & + C(6, 3)a^3x^3 + C(6, 2)a^2x^4 + C(6, 1)ax^5 \\ & + C(6, 0)x^6.\end{aligned}$$

The same type of argument must be valid for any exponent. It is therefore inescapable that we must have

THE BINOMIAL THEOREM

$$\begin{aligned}(a + x)^n = \ & C(n, n)a^n + C(n, n - 1)a^{n-1}x + \cdots \\ & + C(n, r)a^rx^{n-r} + \cdots + C(n, 0)x^n.\end{aligned}$$

Although the preceding argument should have convinced us of the truth of the binomial theorem—has it *proved* its validity? Rereading the preceding argument will show that what we have done is to show what the binomial theorem *ought* to be. A proof can now be made by induction.

(a) $(a + x)^1 = C(1, 1)a + C(1, 0)x = a + x$. The induction is anchored.

(b) Suppose that the theorem is true for $n = k$. Then

$$(a + x)^k = a^k + \cdots + C(k, r)a^rx^{k-r} + \cdots + x^r,$$

and

$$\begin{aligned}(a + x)^{k+1} = \ & (a + x)(a + x)^k \\ = \ & (a + x)(a^k + \cdots + C(k, r - 1)a^{r-1}x^{k-(r-1)} \\ & + C(k, r)a^rx^{k-r} + \cdots + x^k).\end{aligned}$$

It suffices to examine the coefficient of a^rx^{k+1-r}. This coefficient is

$$C(k, r - 1) + C(k, r). \tag{1}$$

477

It would appear that we have failed because we did not get $C(k + 1, r)$. However, it is easy to show that (1) is actually $C(k + 1, r)$:

$$
\begin{aligned}
C(k, r - 1) + C(k, r) &= \frac{k!}{(r - 1)!(k - (r - 1))!} + \frac{k!}{r!(k - r)!} \\
&= \frac{k!}{(r - 1)!(k - r)!} \left(\frac{1}{k + 1 - r} + \frac{1}{r} \right) \\
&= \frac{(k + 1)!}{r!(k + 1 - r)!} \\
&= C(k + 1, r).
\end{aligned}
$$

Therefore the coefficient of $a^r x^{k+1-r}$ is $C(k + 1, r)$. This completes the induction and the proof.

Remarks

1. The numbers $C(n, r)$ of combinations of n things r at a time are also called *binomial coefficients*.

2. If one needs a particular term in the expansion of $(a + x)^n$, he can quickly obtain it from the Binomial Theorem. But is the theorem the quickest way of writing the entire expansion of a power of $(a + x)$? Say $(a + x)^8$? The answer to this is "no." There is an algorithm one uses which is based on the following lemma.

LEMMA
$$ C(n, r - 1) = \frac{C(n, r)r}{n - r + 1} . $$

Proof

$$
\begin{aligned}
C(n, r - 1) &= \frac{n!}{(r - 1)!(n - (r - 1))!} \\
&= \frac{n!}{r!(n - r)!} \cdot \frac{r}{(n - r + 1)} \\
&= \frac{C(n, r)r}{(n - r + 1)} .
\end{aligned}
$$

We can now compute the binomial coefficients one after the other.

EXAMPLES

1. $(a + x)^7 = 1 \cdot a^7 + \dfrac{1 \cdot 7}{1} a^6 x^1 + \dfrac{7 \cdot 6}{2} a^5 x^2 + \dfrac{21 \cdot 5}{3} a^4 x^3$

$\qquad + \dfrac{35 \cdot 4}{4} a^3 x^4 + \dfrac{35 \cdot 3}{5} a^2 x^5 + \dfrac{21 \cdot 2}{6} ax^6 + \dfrac{7 \cdot 1}{7} x^7$

$\qquad = a^7 + 7a^6 x + 21a^5 x^2 + 35a^4 x^3 + 35a^3 x^4 + 21a^2 x^5$

$\qquad\quad + 7ax^6 + x^7.$

2. Find $(1 - 2\sqrt{2})^5 = (1 + (-2\sqrt{2}))^5$.
Here $a = 1$ and $x = -2\sqrt{2}$. Then

$$(1 + (-2\sqrt{2}))^5 = 1^5 + 5 \cdot 1^4 \cdot (-2\sqrt{2})^1 + 10 \cdot 1^3 \cdot (-2\sqrt{2})^2$$
$$+ 10 \cdot 1^2 \cdot (-2\sqrt{2})^3$$
$$+ 5 \cdot 1^1 \cdot (-2\sqrt{2})^4 + (-2\sqrt{2})^5$$
$$= 1 - 10\sqrt{2} + 10(8) - 10(16\sqrt{2})$$
$$+ 5(64) - 128\sqrt{2}$$
$$= 401 - 298\sqrt{2}.$$

Problems

1. Expand the following binomial powers and simplify where natural to do so.
   (a) $(a - b)^5$ (b) $(x - 1/x)^7$
   (c) $(a^{-1} + a^{-2})^3$ (d) $(\sqrt{a/b} + \sqrt{b/a})^6$
   (e) $(2 + \sqrt{3})^7 + (2 - \sqrt{3})^7$ (f) $(\frac{1}{2} + x)^8$
   (g) $(1 - ab)^7$ (h) $(x - 2y)^9$
   (i) $(x^{1/3} - y^{1/3})^6$ (j) $(a/2 - 2/a)^5$

2. Find the term indicated for the following binomial expansions.
   (a) $(a + b)^{11}$, the fifth term
   (b) $(\frac{1}{2} + \frac{1}{2})^{10}$, the fourth term
   (c) $(4x/5 - 5/2x)^{10}$, the eighth term
   (d) $(x^2 - y^2)^{10}$, the sixth term
   (e) $(1 - x^{1/3})^7$, the fourth term

3. Compute to three decimal places $(1 + 1/n)^n$ for $n = 4, 5, 10$. The limit

$$\lim_{n \to \infty} (1 + 1/n)^n = e = 2.718 \ldots$$

   is the base of the natural logarithms.

4. Compute $(0.99)^6$ to six decimal places.

5. Find $(i^2 = -1)$:
   (a) $(1 + i)^4 + (1 - i)^4$ (b) $(\sqrt{3} - i)^6$

6. The fourth term of a binomial expansion is

$$\frac{9!(x/2)^6 y^3}{6!3!}.$$

   What is the fifth term?

7. If $C(n, 5) = 21$, what is n?

8. Find the coefficient of x^{19} in $(2x^3 - 3x)^9$.

9. If a^k occurs in $(a + 1/a)^n$, what is the coefficient?

479

10. Show that

$$C(n, n) + C(n, n - 1) + \cdots + C(n, 0) = 2^n.$$

[*Hint:* Expand $(1 + 1)^n$.]

11. Show that the sum of the $C(n, r)$ for r even is equal to the sum of the $C(n, r)$ for r odd. [*Hint:* Expand $(1 - 1)^n$.]

12. Find the middle term in the expansion of $(1 + x)^{2n}$.

13. Use the binomial theorem to expand

$$(x^2 - 3x + 1)^3 = (x^2 + (1 - 3x))^3.$$

14. Expand $(1 + x)^{-1}$ by the binomial theorem. Then obtain the same series by long division.

*15. Show that

$$C(n, 1) + 2C(n, 2) + 3C(n, 3) + \cdots + nC(n, n) = n2^{n-1}.$$

*16. Show that

$$C(n, 0) + \frac{C(n, 1)}{2} + \frac{C(n, 2)}{3} + \cdots + \frac{C(n, n)}{n + 1} = \frac{2^{n+1} - 1}{n + 1}.$$

*17. Show that

$$\frac{C(n, 1)}{C(n, 0)} + \frac{2C(n, 2)}{C(n, 1)} + \frac{3C(n, 3)}{C(n, 2)} + \cdots + \frac{nC(n, n)}{C(n, n - 1)} = \frac{n(n + 1)}{2}.$$

*18. In the calculus it is shown that the Binomial Theorem can be formulated for exponents that are not positive integers. The coefficients are computed by the algorithm which follows the Lemma.

$$(1 + x)^n = 1 + nx + \frac{n(n - 1)}{2} x^2 + \frac{n(n - 1)(n - 2)}{3!} x^3 + \cdots \quad (2)$$

If n is not a positive integer, the expansion (2) does not terminate. Nevertheless, a finite number of terms of (2) approximates $(1 + x)^n$ for any x such that $|x| < 1$.

Use this fact to compute the following to three decimal places by means of the binomial theorem.

(a) $\sqrt{1.02} = (1 + 0.02)^{1/2}$ (b) $\sqrt[3]{1.06}$

(c) $(1.2)^{-1}$ (d) $(\frac{5}{4})^{1/2}$

(e) $\sqrt{48} = \sqrt{49 - 1} = 7\sqrt{1 - 1/49}$

*19. Assume that x is small enough that (for our purposes) one can neglect x^2, x^3, and higher powers in the binomial expansions. Find and simplify

$$\frac{(1 + x/2)^{-4} + 2(1 + x)^{1/2}}{8(1 + x/4)^{3/2}}.$$

APPENDIX C | Limits and Continuity

C–1. INTRODUCTION

Much of elementary mathematics is finite in nature. We are concerned with combinations of, or relations among, finitely many objects. This aspect includes most of geometry too. However, there are certain mathematical concepts which, by their very definition, require the consideration of infinite sets. In many of these cases, the concept of "infinite" is essential because the notion of *limit* is involved.

We have already encountered examples of the need for limits. Thus the circumference C of a circle is *defined* to be the limit of lengths p_n of inscribed polygons:

$$C = \lim_{n \to \infty} p_n.$$

Another example is furnished by the *definition* of the exponential function a^x for *irrational* exponents x:

$$a^x = \lim_{r \to x} a^r,$$

where r is a *rational* number. In Chapter 15 the derivative is *defined* as a limit:

$$f'(x) = \lim_{\Delta x \to 0} \frac{f(x + \Delta x) - f(x)}{\Delta x}.$$

In Appendix B the sum of the terms of an infinite geometric sequence is *defined* to be the limit of the sums G_n of the first n terms:

$$G = \lim_{n \to \infty} G_n.$$

In this appendix we formalize our earlier intuitive treatment of limits. It will be seen that the existence of limits is intimately associated with fundamental properties of the real number system. Hence a brief review of the real numbers is included here. Finally, we shall discuss how the concept of continuity is related to limits.

We wish to emphasize that in this appendix we are primarily concerned with *definitions*. The few problems and theorems are included solely to illuminate the concepts. Real facility in the use of limits will be attained in more advanced courses.

C-2. THE REAL FIELD

We are interested in real-valued functions. Therefore the validity of what we do must depend directly on properties of the field of real numbers. In other words, the concepts must admit of formulation *in purely arithmetical terms.*

Recall that in a field one can add, subtract, multiply, and divide (except by zero), and that the commutative, associative, and distributive properties are valid. There are many different fields but only *one* real field. What characterizes the real field R among other fields are the following two properties.

(1) R is an *ordered* field. This means that there is a relation, "$<$," between pairs of real numbers such that

(a) For any two real numbers x and y exactly one of the following relations is true:

$$x < y, \qquad x = y, \qquad x > y.$$

(b) If $x < y$ and $y < z$, then $x < z$.

(c) If $x < y$, then $x + z < y + z$ for all z.

(d) If $x < y$ and $z > 0$, then $xz < yz$.

(2) The ordered field R is *complete.* This means that if S is a (nonempty) set of real numbers that is bounded above, then S has a *least upper bound* (or *supremum*).

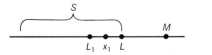

Fig. C-1

Let us suppose that S is a nonempty set of real numbers and that M is a real number such that $x \leq M$ for all numbers x in S. Then there is a least real number L such that $x \leq L$ for all x in S. Hence, if $L_1 < L$, then there is an x_1 in S such that $L_1 < x_1 \leq L$. (See Fig. C-1.) We write

$$L = \text{lub } S \qquad \text{or} \qquad \text{sup } S.$$

Remarks

1. For sets bounded below one has lower bounds and a *greatest lower bound* (or *infimum*), abbreviated "glb" (or "inf").

2. Properties 1 and 2, which are expressed in a purely algebraic, or arithmetic, manner permit one to assign coordinates to lines, where the order relation is a purely geometric concept. The completeness property (2) ensures that there are no "gaps" in the real numbers; or, speaking geometrically, that there are no "holes" in the line.

It is the completeness property which supplies a basis for proving that certain real numbers exist. For illustration, consider the following example.

EXAMPLE

Let S be the set of all real numbers x such that $x^3 < 2$. Then S is bounded above, for certainly 2 itself is an upper bound for S. (There are other upper bounds, for example, 5, 10,000, 1.5, etc.) From the completeness property, there is a *least* real number L such that if x is in S, then $x \leq L$. Furthermore, there are numbers in S arbitrarily close to L but less than L.

It should be clear that $L^3 = 2$, although a proof is not so easy as might be expected. In other words $L = \sqrt[3]{2}$.

Problems

1. Suppose $S = \langle 0, 1 \rangle$. Give several upper bounds for S. What is lub S? Does S have a greatest lower bound?

2. Let S be the set of numbers

$$S = \left\{ 1 - \frac{1}{1}, 1 - \frac{1}{2}, \ldots, 1 - \frac{1}{n}, \ldots \right\}, \qquad n = 1, 2, \ldots$$

What is lub S?

3. Show that if S is bounded above, and if S' is the set of all numbers $-x$ for x in S, then S' is bounded below. What is glb S'?

4. Suppose that S consists of a set of numbers x_n for $n = 1, 2, \ldots$, such that

    (a) $x_{n+1} > x_n$ for all n,   and   (b) $x_n < 3$ for all n.

Can lub $S = 3$? Can lub $S < 3$?

C–3. LIMITS OF SEQUENCES

In this and the next section we shall be concerned with limits of functions. There are two, rather different, kinds of functions which we shall consider. They are distinguished by the fact that they have different kinds of *domains*. The first kind, called sequences, have as their domain the set of natural numbers. The second kind have as their domain an interval. In this section we consider only sequences.

Recall (see Appendix B, p. 466) that a *sequence* of real numbers is a function, f, from the natural numbers to the real numbers. As is customary we exhibit the values of the function

$$f(1), f(2), \ldots, f(n), \ldots, \qquad n = 1, 2, \ldots,$$

by the subscript notation, $f_1, f_2, \ldots, f_n, \ldots$ We then speak of the sequence $\{f_n\}$ instead of the function f.

483

EXAMPLES

1. If
$$a_n = \frac{n+1}{3n}, \qquad n = 1, 2, \ldots,$$
then

$$a_1 = \tfrac{2}{3}, \quad a_2 = \tfrac{1}{2}, \quad a_3 = \tfrac{4}{9}, \quad \ldots, \quad a_n = \frac{1}{3} + \frac{1}{3n}, \quad \ldots$$

Clearly, when n is *large*, a_n is *close to* $\tfrac{1}{3}$. We then write (see Definition C–1 below)

$$A = \lim_{n \to \infty} a_n = \tfrac{1}{3}.$$

2. Let
$$S_n = \frac{1 - r^n}{1 - r},$$

which is the sum of the first n terms of the geometric sequence (see Appendix B, p. 467):
$$1, r, r^2, r^3, \ldots, r^n, \ldots$$
Then

$$S_n = \frac{1}{1 - r} - \frac{r^n}{1 - r}.$$

Now, if $|r| < 1$, then r^n is a very small number when n is a large number. Therefore, when n is *large*, S_n is *close to* $1/(1 - r)$,

$$S = \lim_{n \to \infty} S_n = \frac{1}{1 - r}.$$

These examples illustrate the general situation. The statement

$$\lim_{n \to \infty} f_n = L$$

means that "when n is *large*, then f_n is *close to L*." To make the idea precise and put in a form that can be used in proofs, it is necessary to clarify what "close to" means and how large "large" is. We need a definition.

DEFINITION C–1

Suppose that $\{a_n\}$ is a sequence of real numbers. Then $\{a_n\}$ has limit L as $n \to \infty$ if, given any *positive* number ϵ, there is a positive number N (which depends on ϵ) such that

$$|a_n - L| < \epsilon \qquad \text{when} \quad n \geq N.$$

Remarks

1. The *given* positive number ϵ specifies the closeness to L that one wishes to get. The number N (which, in general, must get larger as ϵ gets smaller) specifies how large n should be for the specified degree of closeness, ϵ.

484

2. The definition does not predict or supply a way of computing L. What the definition does is supply a criterion with which one can *test a number L* to see whether it is actually the limit of the sequence $\{a_n\}$.

EXAMPLES

3. Consider again the sequence of Example 1:

$$a_n = \frac{n+1}{3n} = \frac{1}{3} + \frac{1}{3n}.$$

We saw by inspection that the limit of the sequence is $\frac{1}{3}$. We must now verify this result by using Definition C–1. We have

$$|a_n - L| = \left| a_n - \frac{1}{3} \right| = \frac{1}{3n}.$$

According to the definition, we must find, for any $\epsilon > 0$, a number N such that

$$\frac{1}{3n} < \epsilon \qquad \text{if} \quad n \geq N.$$

Fortunately, this is easy; we simply choose $N > 1/3\epsilon$. Then if $n \geq N$, then

$$n > \frac{1}{3\epsilon} \qquad \text{and} \qquad \epsilon > \frac{1}{3n}.$$

4. This example is more difficult. Suppose that $S_n = \sqrt[n]{n} = n^{1/n}$. It is not clear what the limit of S_n might be. Some calculation gives the following data:

$$S_1 = 1, \quad S_2 = \sqrt{2} = 1.41..., \quad S_3 = 1.442..., \quad S_4 = 1.41...,$$
$$S_8 = 1.3..., \quad S_{16} = 1.2..., \quad S_{32} = 1.11..., \quad ...$$

It appears that S_n is approaching 1. Let us try $L = 1$ in the definition of limit. Set

$$S_n = 1 + \delta_n = \sqrt[n]{n}, \qquad \text{where} \qquad \delta_n > 0.$$

The problem is to estimate the size of δ_n. We have

$$n = (1 + \delta_n)^n = 1 + n\delta_n + \frac{n(n-1)}{2}\delta_n^2 + \cdots + \delta_n^n.$$

Then

$$n > \frac{n(n-1)}{2}\delta_n^2,$$

and

$$\delta_n < \sqrt{\frac{2n}{n(n-1)}} = \sqrt{\frac{2}{n-1}}, \qquad \text{if} \quad n \geq 2.$$

Therefore

$$1 < S_n < 1 + \sqrt{\frac{2}{n-1}}, \quad \text{or} \quad |S_n - 1| < \sqrt{\frac{2}{n-1}}.$$

In order to have $\sqrt{2/(n-1)} < \epsilon$, or $2/(n-1) < \epsilon^2$, we only need to have $n > 1 + 2/\epsilon^2$. Therefore, if $N > 1 + 2/\epsilon^2$, then $|S_n - 1| < \epsilon$ when $n \geq N$.

Problems

For each sequence, guess its limit L. Then show that given $\epsilon > 0$, there is a number N such that $|S_n - L| < \epsilon$ if $n \geq N$.

1. $S_n = 3 + 2/n$ 2. $S_n = (2n - 1)/n$

3. $S_n = a + (\sin n)/n$ 4. $S_n = r^n, \quad |r| < 1$

5. $S_n = \dfrac{1}{1 \cdot 2} + \dfrac{1}{2 \cdot 3} + \dfrac{1}{3 \cdot 4} + \cdots + \dfrac{1}{n(n+1)}.$

$$\left[Hint: \frac{1}{k(k+1)} = \frac{1}{k} - \frac{1}{k+1}. \right]$$

C–4. FUNCTIONS DEFINED ON INTERVALS

We now turn to functions that are defined near a point c of the real line. For sequences we saw that the limit L is the number which S_n approaches when n is very large. The same intuitive idea prevails for functions defined on an interval.

EXAMPLE 1

If $f(x) = 3 + (x - 2)$ for all real numbers x, then

$$\lim_{x \to 2} f(x) = \lim_{x \to 2} [3 + (x - 2)] = 3.$$

This is the case because when "x is near 2," then "$x - 2$ is near 0," and "$3 + (x - 2)$ is near 3."
    A definition will make these ideas of nearness precise.

DEFINITION C–2

Suppose that c is a real number and f is a function whose domain contains an open interval with c as an endpoint. Then the "limit of $f(x)$ as x approaches c" is L,

$$\lim_{x \to c} f(x) = L,$$

if to each positive number ϵ, there is a *positive* number δ such that

$$|f(x) - L| < \epsilon$$

if

$$0 < |x - c| < \delta.$$

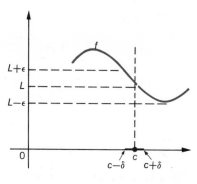

We see from Fig. C-2 that if x is different from c and is located between $c - \delta$ and $c + \delta$, then $f(x)$ is between $L - \epsilon$ and $L + \epsilon$.

Fig. C-2

Remarks

1. The number ϵ specifies the closeness to L which one wants to achieve. The number δ specifies a closeness to c which will ensure that $f(x)$ is within a distance ϵ from L.

2. The definition does not provide a technique for calculating L. What the definition does is supply a criterion which one uses to *test* a number L to see whether it is actually the limit of $f(x)$ as x approaches c.

3. The value of f at c does not matter so far as the limit is concerned. Indeed, f need not even be defined at c. (Just as with sequences, S_n is not defined at ∞.)

EXAMPLES

2. To determine $\lim_{x \to 2} (3x - 7)$ we first guess that the limit is $L = -1$. Hence we must show that

$$|f(x) - L| = |3x - 7 - (-1)| = |3x - 6|$$

is small when x is near 2. Let us suppose $\epsilon > 0$ is given; then

$$|f(x) - L| = |3x - 6| = 3|x - 2| < \epsilon$$

if

$$|x - 2| < \epsilon/3.$$

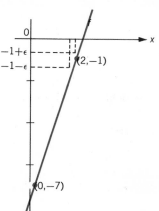

Therefore, if we choose $\delta = \epsilon/3$, we will have fulfilled the conditions of the definition. One can see from the graph in Fig. C-3 that $\delta = \epsilon/3$ will work.

Fig. C-3

487

3. To prove that $\lim_{x \to 1} x^2 = 1$, we must show that $|x^2 - 1|$ is small if $|x - 1|$ is small enough. Hence, let us suppose that $\epsilon > 0$ is given and let us consider

$$|x^2 - 1| = |x - 1| \cdot |x + 1|.$$

If x is near 1, then $|x + 1|$ is not too large. If we restrict x to the interval $0 \leq x \leq 2$, then $|x + 1| \leq 3$ and so

$$|x^2 - 1| \leq 3|x - 1| \quad \text{if} \quad 0 \leq x \leq 2 \quad \text{or} \quad |x - 1| \leq 1.$$

We are now in a satisfactory position to choose δ. Let us choose $\delta > 0$ such that $\delta \leq 1$ and

$$3|x - 1| < \epsilon \quad \text{if} \quad |x - 1| < \delta.$$

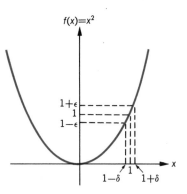

f(x)=x²

Remember that we should have $\delta \leq 1$ in order that $|x + 1| \leq 3$. Therefore, if we choose

$$\delta = \text{minimum of } \frac{\epsilon}{3} \text{ and } 1,$$

then

$$|x^2 - 1| = |x - 1| \cdot |x + 1| < \frac{\epsilon}{3} \cdot 3 = \epsilon$$

if $|x - 1| < \delta$. The conditions of the definition are satisfied (Fig. C–4).

Fig. C–4

Problems

1. Guess what the following limits are. Then apply Definition C–2 to prove that your guess is correct.

(a) $\lim_{x \to 6} (\frac{1}{3}x + 1)$

(b) $\lim_{x \to -1} (2x + 5)$

(c) $\lim_{x \to 2} x^2$

*(d) $\lim_{x \to -1} (x^2 + 3x)$

*(e) $\lim_{x \to 1} \frac{x + 1}{x + 2}$

*(f) $\lim_{x \to 1/2} \frac{1}{x}$

C–5. CONTINUITY

In this section we clarify the intuitive ideas about continuity presented in Chapter 6. First we give some examples of discontinuous functions to aid the intuition. Figure C–5 represents three graphs of functions, f, g, and h, defined on a closed interval (shown as a heavy line) containing the point c.

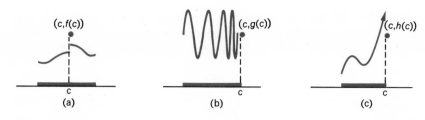

(a) $(c,f(c))$ (b) $(c,g(c))$ (c) $(c,h(c))$

Fig. C–5

Each is discontinuous at c. In (a) the limits of $f(x)$, from either side of c, appear to exist but do not equal the value of f at c. In (b) $\lim_{x \to c} g(x)$ does not exist. The graph oscillates near c. In part (c) the function becomes infinite near c, but at c it is finite.

DEFINITION C–3

If f is defined on an interval containing c, then f is *continuous at c* if

$$\lim_{x \to c} f(x) = f(c).$$

In other words, when x is close to c, then $f(x)$ is close to $f(c)$. In terms of "epsilons and deltas" this means that given $\epsilon > 0$, there is a $\delta > 0$ such that

$$|f(x) - f(c)| < \epsilon \quad \text{if} \quad |x - c| < \delta.$$

Definition C–3 defines continuity at a point. The functions in which one is usually interested are continuous at all points (where they are defined).

DEFINITION C–4

A function defined on an interval, open or closed, is *continuous on that interval* if it is continuous at each point of the interval.

In Chapter 6 the intermediate-value theorem was discussed and used. We restate this theorem here and give a proof. Observe that in the proof we have occasion to use the completeness property (2) of the real number system.

THEOREM C–1

Suppose that f is a real-valued function which is continuous on the interval $[a, b]$, and that $f(a) < f(b)$. Suppose now that d is a number between $f(a)$ and $f(b)$, so that $f(a) < d < f(b)$. Then there is at least one number c between a and b such that

$$d = f(c).$$

489

Proof. Let A be the subset of $[a, b]$ consisting of numbers x such that $f(x) < d$. (See Fig. C–6.) Then A is not empty because a is in A. Furthermore, since every member of A is less than b, the set A is bounded above. Let

$$c = \text{lub } A.$$

We shall prove that $f(c) = d$ by proving that $f(c) < d$ and $f(c) > d$ are impossible. Let us suppose that $f(c) < d$. (See Fig. C–7.) We will apply the definition of continuity at c to obtain a contradiction. We denote by ϵ the difference $\epsilon = d - f(c)$, which is positive. There is a positive number δ such that

$$|f(x) - f(c)| < \epsilon$$

if $|x - c| < \delta$. So we have

$$f(c) - \epsilon < f(x) < f(c) + \epsilon \quad \text{if} \quad -\delta < x - c < \delta.$$

In particular, we have

$$f(x) < d \quad \text{if} \quad c < x < c + \delta.$$

But this last inequality implies that $f(x) < d$ for numbers x larger than c. This contradicts the choice of c as an upper bound of A. Therefore $f(c)$ cannot be less than d, so $f(c) \geq d$. A similar argument can be made to show that $f(c)$ cannot be greater than d. Hence $f(c) = d$, and the proof is complete.

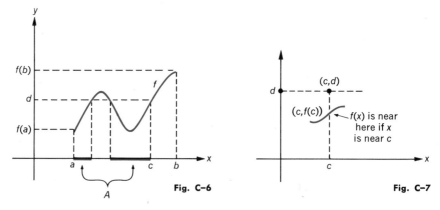

Fig. C–6

Fig. C–7

There are many theorems concerning continuous functions. One studies these theorems in analysis. They are beyond the scope of this book. Two of these numerous theorems are stated without proof below.

THEOREM C-2

If f is continuous on the closed interval $[a, b]$, then f is bounded on that interval. Furthermore, if M is the least upper bound of f on the interval, then there is a point c of the interval such that $f(c) = M$.

THEOREM C-3

If both f and g are continuous functions on an interval, then $f + g$, $f - g$, $f \cdot g$, and f/g (except where g is zero) are continuous functions on that interval.

Remarks

It is this last theorem which allows us to conclude rather easily that large classes of functions are continuous. Thus it is easy to see that constant functions are continuous. Likewise, it is easy to prove that the identity function, $f(x) = x$, also is continuous. Now we can utilize Theorem C–3 to conclude that the functions given by the following formulas are continuous:

$$5x, \quad x^2 = x \cdot x, \quad 2x^2 - 3x + 7,$$
$$x^3 = x^2 \cdot x, \quad 7x^3 - 34x, \quad \text{etc.}$$

Continuing in this way, one sees that all polynomials are continuous functions. Moreover, again from Theorem C–3, we can conclude that all rational functions are continuous at points where the function in the denominator does not vanish.

TABLE I

Four-Place Logarithms of Numbers

N	0	1	2	3	4	5	6	7	8	9
10	0000	0043	0086	0128	0170	0212	0253	0294	0334	0374
11	0414	0453	0492	0531	0569	0607	0645	0682	0719	0755
12	0792	0828	0864	0899	0934	0969	1004	1038	1072	1106
13	1139	1173	1206	1239	1271	1303	1335	1367	1399	1430
14	1461	1492	1523	1553	1584	1614	1644	1673	1703	1732
15	1761	1790	1818	1847	1875	1903	1931	1959	1987	2014
16	2041	2068	2095	2122	2148	2175	2201	2227	2253	2279
17	2304	2330	2355	2380	2405	2430	2455	2480	2504	2529
18	2553	2577	2601	2625	2648	2672	2695	2718	2742	2765
19	2788	2810	2833	2856	2878	2900	2923	2945	2967	2989
20	3010	3032	3054	3075	3096	3118	3139	3160	3181	3201
21	3222	3243	3263	3284	3304	3324	3345	3365	3385	3404
22	3424	3444	3464	3483	3502	3522	3541	3560	3579	3598
23	3617	3636	3655	3674	3692	3711	3729	3747	3766	3784
24	3802	3820	3838	3856	3874	3892	3909	3927	3945	3962
25	3979	3997	4014	4031	4048	4065	4082	4099	4116	4133
26	4150	4166	4183	4200	4216	4232	4249	4265	4281	4298
27	4314	4330	4346	4362	4378	4393	4409	4425	4440	4456
28	4472	4487	4502	4518	4533	4548	4564	4579	4594	4609
29	4624	4639	4654	4669	4683	4698	4713	4728	4742	4757
30	4771	4786	4800	4814	4829	4843	4857	4871	4886	4900
31	4914	4928	4942	4955	4969	4983	4997	5011	5024	5038
32	5051	5065	5079	5092	5105	5119	5132	5145	5159	5172
33	5185	5198	5211	5224	5237	5250	5263	5276	5289	5302
34	5315	5328	5340	5353	5366	5378	5391	5403	5416	5428
35	5441	5453	5465	5478	5490	5502	5514	5527	5539	5551
36	5563	5575	5587	5599	5611	5623	5635	5647	5658	5670
37	5682	5694	5705	5717	5729	5740	5752	5763	5775	5786
38	5798	5809	5821	5832	5843	5855	5866	5877	5888	5899
39	5911	5922	5933	5944	5955	5966	5977	5988	5999	6010
40	6021	6031	6042	6053	6064	6075	6085	6096	6107	6117
41	6128	6138	6149	6160	6170	6180	6191	6201	6212	6222
42	6232	6243	6253	6263	6274	6284	6294	6304	6314	6325
43	6335	6345	6355	6365	6375	6385	6395	6405	6415	6425
44	6435	6444	6454	6464	6474	6484	6493	6503	6513	6522
45	6532	6542	6551	6561	6571	6580	6590	6599	6609	6618
46	6628	6637	6646	6656	6665	6675	6684	6693	6702	6712
47	6721	6730	6739	6749	6758	6767	6776	6785	6794	6803
48	6812	6821	6830	6839	6848	6857	6866	6875	6884	6893
49	6902	6911	6920	6928	6937	6946	6955	6964	6972	6981
50	6990	6998	7007	7016	7024	7033	7042	7050	7059	7067
51	7076	7084	7093	7101	7110	7118	7126	7135	7143	7152
52	7160	7168	7177	7185	7193	7202	7210	7218	7226	7235
53	7243	7251	7259	7267	7275	7284	7292	7300	7308	7316
54	7324	7332	7340	7348	7356	7364	7372	7380	7388	7396

(Continued)

TABLE I

Four-Place Logarithms of Numbers

N	0	1	2	3	4	5	6	7	8	9
55	7404	7412	7419	7427	7435	7443	7451	7459	7466	7474
56	7482	7490	7497	7505	7513	7520	7528	7536	7543	7551
57	7559	7566	7574	7582	7589	7597	7604	7612	7619	7627
58	7634	7642	7649	7657	7664	7672	7679	7686	7694	7701
59	7709	7716	7723	7731	7738	7745	7752	7760	7767	7774
60	7782	7789	7796	7803	7810	7818	7825	7832	7839	7846
61	7853	7860	7868	7875	7882	7889	7896	7903	7910	7917
62	7924	7931	7938	7945	7952	7959	7966	7973	7980	7987
63	7993	8000	8007	8014	8021	8028	8035	8041	8048	8055
64	8062	8069	8075	8082	8089	8096	8102	8109	8116	8122
65	8129	8136	8142	8149	8156	8162	8169	8176	8182	8189
66	8195	8202	8209	8215	8222	8228	8235	8241	8248	8254
67	8261	8267	8274	8280	8287	8293	8299	8306	8312	8319
68	8325	8331	8338	8344	8351	8357	8363	8370	8376	8382
69	8388	8395	8401	8407	8414	8420	8426	8432	8439	8445
70	8451	8457	8463	8470	8476	8482	8488	8494	8500	8506
71	8513	8519	8525	8531	8537	8543	8549	8555	8561	8567
72	8573	8579	8585	8591	8597	8603	8609	8615	8621	8627
73	8633	8639	8645	8651	8657	8663	8669	8675	8681	8686
74	8692	8698	8704	8710	8716	8722	8727	8733	8739	8745
75	8751	8756	8762	8768	8774	8779	8785	8791	8797	8802
76	8808	8814	8820	8825	8831	8837	8842	8848	8854	8859
77	8865	8871	8876	8882	8887	8893	8899	8904	8910	8915
78	8921	8927	8932	8938	8943	8949	8954	8960	8965	8971
79	8976	8982	8987	8993	8998	9004	9009	9015	9020	9025
80	9031	9036	9042	9047	9053	9058	9063	9069	9074	9079
81	9085	9090	9096	9101	9106	9112	9117	9122	9128	9133
82	9138	9143	9149	9154	9159	9165	9170	9175	9180	9186
83	9191	9196	9201	9206	9212	9217	9222	9227	9232	9238
84	9243	9248	9253	9258	9263	9269	9274	9279	9284	9289
85	9294	9299	9304	9309	9315	9320	9325	9330	9335	9340
86	9345	9350	9355	9360	9365	9370	9375	9380	9385	9390
87	9395	9400	9405	9410	9415	9420	9425	9430	9435	9440
88	9445	9450	9455	9460	9465	9469	9474	9479	9484	9489
89	9494	9499	9504	9509	9513	9518	9523	9528	9533	9538
90	9542	9547	9552	9557	9652	9566	9571	9576	9581	9586
91	9590	9595	9600	9605	9609	9614	9619	9624	9628	9633
92	9638	9643	9647	9652	9657	9661	9666	9671	9675	9680
93	9685	9689	9694	9699	9703	9708	9713	9717	9722	9727
94	9731	9736	9741	9745	9750	9754	9759	9763	9768	9773
95	9777	9782	9786	9791	9795	9800	9805	9809	9814	9818
96	9823	9827	9832	9836	9841	9845	9850	9854	9859	9863
97	9868	9872	9877	9881	9886	9890	9894	9899	9903	9908
98	9912	9917	9921	9926	9930	9934	9939	9943	9948	9952
99	9956	9961	9965	9969	9974	9978	9983	9987	9991	9996

TABLE II

Four-Place Values of Trigonometric Ratios and Radians

Degrees	Radians	Sin	Cos	Tan	Cot	Sec	Csc		
0° 00′	.0000	.0000	1.0000	.0000	——	1.000	——	1.5708	90° 00′
10	029	029	000	029	343.8	000	343.8	679	50
20	058	058	000	058	171.9	000	171.9	650	40
30	.0087	.0087	1.0000	.0087	114.6	1.000	114.6	1.5621	30
40	116	116	.9999	116	85.94	000	85.95	592	20
50	145	145	999	145	68.75	000	68.76	563	10
1° 00′	.0175	.0175	.9998	.0175	57.29	1.000	57.30	1.5533	89° 00′
10	204	204	998	204	49.10	000	49.11	504	50
20	233	233	997	233	42.96	000	42.98	475	40
30	.0262	.0262	.9997	.0262	38.19	1.000	38.20	1.5446	30
40	291	291	996	291	34.37	000	34.38	417	20
50	320	320	995	320	31.24	001	31.26	388	10
2° 00′	.0349	.0349	.9994	.0349	28.64	1.001	28.65	1.5359	88° 00′
10	378	378	993	378	26.43	001	26.45	330	50
20	407	407	992	407	24.54	001	24.56	301	40
30	.0436	.0436	.9990	.0437	22.90	1.001	22.93	1.5272	30
40	465	465	989	466	21.47	001	21.49	243	20
50	495	494	988	495	20.21	001	20.23	213	10
3° 00′	.0524	.0523	.9986	.0524	19.08	1.001	19.11	1.5184	87° 00′
10	553	552	985	553	18.07	002	18.10	155	50
20	582	581	983	582	17.17	002	17.20	126	40
30	.0611	.0610	.9981	.0612	16.35	1.002	16.38	1.5097	30
40	640	640	980	641	15.60	002	15.64	068	20
50	669	669	978	670	14.92	002	14.96	039	10
4° 00′	.0698	.0698	.9976	.0699	14.30	1.002	14.34	1.5010	86° 00′
10	727	727	974	729	13.73	003	13.76	981	50
20	756	756	971	758	13.20	003	13.23	952	40
30	.0785	.0785	.9969	.0787	12.71	1.003	12.75	1.4923	30
40	814	814	967	816	12.25	003	12.29	893	20
50	844	843	964	846	11.83	004	11.87	864	10
5° 00′	.0873	.0872	.9962	.0875	11.43	1.004	11.47	1.4835	85° 00′
10	902	901	959	904	11.06	004	11.10	806	50
20	931	929	957	934	10.71	004	10.76	777	40
30	.0960	.0958	.9954	.0963	10.39	1.005	10.43	1.4748	30
40	989	987	951	992	10.08	005	10.13	719	20
50	.1018	.1016	948	.1022	9.788	005	9.839	690	10
6° 00′	.1047	.1045	.9945	.1051	9.514	1.006	9.567	1.4661	84° 00′
10	076	074	942	080	9.255	006	9.309	632	50
20	105	103	939	110	9.010	006	9.065	603	40
30	.1134	.1132	.9936	.1139	8.777	1.006	8.834	1.4573	30
40	164	161	932	169	8.556	007	8.614	544	20
50	193	190	929	198	8.345	007	8.405	515	10
7° 00′	.1222	.1219	.9925	.1228	8.144	1.008	8.206	1.4486	83° 00′
10	251	248	922	257	7.953	008	8.016	457	50
20	280	276	918	287	7.770	008	7.834	428	40
30	.1309	.1305	.9914	.1317	7.596	1.009	7.661	1.4399	30
40	338	334	911	346	7.429	009	7.496	370	20
50	367	363	907	376	7.269	009	7.337	341	10
8° 00′	.1396	.1392	.9903	.1405	7.115	1.010	7.185	1.4312	82° 00′
10	425	421	899	435	6.968	010	7.040	283	50
20	454	449	894	465	6.827	011	6.900	254	40
30	.1484	.1478	.9890	.1495	6.691	1.011	6.765	1.4224	30
40	513	507	886	524	6.561	012	6.636	195	20
50	542	536	881	554	6.435	012	6.512	166	10
9° 00′	.1571	.1564	.9877	.1584	6.314	1.012	6.392	1.4137	81° 00′
		Cos	Sin	Cot	Tan	Csc	Sec	Radians	Degrees

(Continued)

TABLE II

Four-Place Values of Trigonometric Ratios and Radians

Degrees	Radians	Sin	Cos	Tan	Cot	Sec	Csc		
9° 00′	.1571	.1564	.9877	.1584	6.314	1.012	6.392	1.4137	81° 00′
10	600	593	872	614	197	013	277	108	50
20	629	622	868	644	084	013	166	079	40
30	.1658	.1650	.9863	.1673	5.976	1.014	6.059	1.4050	30
40	687	679	858	703	871	014	5.955	1.4021	20
50	716	708	853	733	769	015	855	992	10
10° 00′	.1745	.1736	.9848	.1763	5.671	1.015	5.759	1.3963	80° 00′
10	774	765	843	793	576	016	665	934	50
20	804	794	838	823	485	016	575	904	40
30	.1833	.1822	.9833	.1853	5.396	1.017	5.487	1.3875	30
40	862	851	827	883	309	018	403	846	20
50	891	880	822	914	226	018	320	817	10
11° 00′	.1920	.1908	.9816	.1944	5.145	1.019	5.241	1.3788	79° 00′
10	949	937	811	974	066	019	164	759	50
20	978	965	805	.2004	4.989	020	089	730	40
30	.2007	.1994	.9799	.2035	4.915	1.020	5.016	1.3701	30
40	036	.2022	793	065	843	021	4.945	672	20
50	065	051	787	095	773	022	876	643	10
12° 00′	.2094	.2079	.9781	.2126	4.705	1.022	4.810	1.3614	78° 00′
10	123	108	775	156	638	023	745	584	50
20	153	136	769	186	574	024	682	555	40
30	.2182	.2164	.9763	.2217	4.511	1.024	4.620	1.3526	30
40	211	193	757	247	449	025	560	497	20
50	240	221	750	278	390	026	502	468	10
13° 00′	.2269	.2250	.9744	.2309	4.331	1.026	4.445	1.3439	77° 00′
10	298	278	737	339	275	027	390	410	50
20	327	306	730	370	219	028	336	381	40
30	.2356	.2334	.9724	.2401	4.165	1.028	4.284	1.3352	30
40	385	363	717	432	113	029	232	323	20
50	414	391	710	462	061	030	182	294	10
14° 00′	.2443	.2419	.9703	.2493	4.011	1.031	4.134	1.3265	76° 00′
10	473	447	696	524	3.962	031	086	235	50
20	502	476	689	555	914	032	039	206	40
30	.2531	.2504	.9681	.2586	3.867	1.033	3.994	1.3177	30
40	560	532	674	617	821	034	950	148	20
50	589	560	667	648	776	034	906	119	10
15° 00′	.2618	.2588	.9659	.2679	3.732	1.035	3.864	1.3090	75° 00′
10	647	616	652	711	689	036	822	061	50
20	676	644	644	742	647	037	782	032	40
30	.2705	.2672	.9636	.2773	3.606	1.038	3.742	1.3003	30
40	734	700	628	805	566	039	703	974	20
50	763	728	621	836	526	039	665	945	10
16° 00′	.2793	.2756	.9613	.2867	3.487	1.040	3.628	1.2915	74° 00′
10	822	784	605	899	450	041	592	886	50
20	851	812	596	931	412	042	556	857	40
30	.2880	.2840	.9588	.2962	3.376	1.043	3.521	1.2828	30
40	909	868	580	994	340	044	487	799	20
50	938	896	572	.3026	305	045	453	770	10
17° 00′	.2967	.2924	.9563	.3057	3.271	1.046	3.420	1.2741	73° 00′
10	996	952	555	089	237	047	388	712	50
20	.3025	979	546	121	204	048	356	683	40
30	.3054	.3007	.9537	.3153	3.172	1.049	3.326	1.2654	30
40	083	035	528	185	140	049	295	625	20
50	113	062	520	217	108	050	265	595	10
18° 00′	.3142	.3090	.9511	.3249	3.078	1.051	3.236	1.2566	72° 00′
		Cos	Sin	Cot	Tan	Csc	Sec	Radians	Degrees

(Continued)

TABLE II

Four-Place Values of Trigonometric Ratios and Radians

Degrees	Radians	Sin	Cos	Tan	Cot	Sec	Csc		
18° 00′	.3142	.3090	.9511	.3249	3.078	1.051	3.236	1.2566	72° 00′
10	171	118	502	281	047	052	207	537	50
20	200	145	492	314	018	053	179	508	40
30	.3229	.3173	.9483	.3346	2.989	1.054	3.152	1.2479	30
40	258	201	474	378	960	056	124	450	20
50	287	228	465	411	932	057	098	421	10
19° 00′	.3316	.3256	.9455	.3443	2.904	1.058	3.072	1.2392	71° 00′
10	345	283	446	476	877	059	046	363	50
20	374	311	436	508	850	060	021	334	40
30	.3403	.3338	.9426	.3541	2.824	1.061	2.996	1.2305	30
40	432	365	417	574	798	062	971	275	20
50	462	393	407	607	773	063	947	246	10
20° 00′	.3491	.3420	.9397	.3640	2.747	1.064	2.924	1.2217	70° 00′
10	520	448	387	673	723	065	901	188	50
20	549	475	377	706	699	066	878	159	40
30	.3578	.3502	.9367	.3739	2.675	1.068	2.855	1.2130	30
40	607	529	356	772	651	069	833	101	20
50	636	557	346	805	628	070	812	072	10
21° 00′	.3665	.3584	.9336	.3839	2.605	1.071	2.790	1.2043	69° 00′
10	694	611	325	872	583	072	769	1.2014	50
20	723	638	315	906	560	074	749	985	40
30	.3752	.3665	.9304	.3939	2.539	1.075	2.729	1.1956	30
40	782	692	293	973	517	076	709	926	20
50	811	719	283	.4006	496	077	689	897	10
22° 00′	.3840	.3746	.9272	.4040	2.475	1.079	2.669	1.1868	68° 00′
10	869	773	261	074	455	080	650	839	50
20	898	800	250	108	434	081	632	810	40
30	.3927	.3827	.9239	.4142	2.414	1.082	2.613	1.1781	30
40	956	854	228	176	394	084	595	752	20
50	985	881	216	210	375	085	577	723	10
23° 00′	.4014	.3907	.9205	.4245	2.356	1.086	2.559	1.1694	67° 00′
10	043	934	194	279	337	088	542	665	50
20	072	961	182	314	318	089	525	636	40
30	.4102	.3987	.9171	.4348	2.300	1.090	2.508	1.1606	30
40	131	.4014	159	383	282	092	491	577	20
50	160	041	147	417	264	093	475	548	10
24° 00′	.4189	.4067	.9135	.4452	2.246	1.095	2.459	1.1519	66° 00′
10	218	094	124	487	229	096	443	490	50
20	247	120	112	522	211	097	427	461	40
30	.4276	.4147	.9100	.4557	2.194	1.099	2.411	1.1432	30
40	305	173	088	592	177	100	396	403	20
50	334	200	075	628	161	102	381	374	10
25° 00′	.4363	.4226	.9063	.4663	2.145	1.103	2.366	1.1345	65° 00′
10	392	253	051	699	128	105	352	316	50
20	422	279	038	734	112	106	337	286	40
30	.4451	.4305	.9026	.4770	2.097	1.108	2.323	1.1257	30
40	480	331	013	806	081	109	309	228	20
50	509	358	001	841	066	111	295	199	10
26° 00′	.4538	.4384	.8988	.4877	2.050	1.113	2.281	1.1170	64° 00′
10	567	410	975	913	035	114	268	141	50
20	596	436	962	950	020	116	254	112	40
30	.4625	.4462	.8949	.4986	2.006	1.117	2.241	1.1083	30
40	654	488	936	.5022	1.991	119	228	054	20
50	683	514	923	059	977	121	215	1.1025	10
27° 00′	.4712	.4540	.8910	.5095	1.963	1.122	2.203	1.0996	63° 00′
		Cos	Sin	Cot	Tan	Csc	Sec	Radians	Degrees

(Continued)

TABLE II

Four-Place Values of Trigonometric Ratios and Radians

Degrees	Radians	Sin	Cos	Tan	Cot	Sec	Csc		
27° 00′	.4712	.4540	.8910	.5095	1.963	1.122	2.203	1.0996	63° 00′
10	741	566	897	132	949	124	190	966	50
20	771	592	884	169	935	126	178	937	40
30	.4800	.4617	.8870	.5206	1.921	1.127	2.166	1.0908	30
40	829	643	857	243	907	129	154	879	20
50	858	669	843	280	894	131	142	850	10
28° 00′	.4887	.4695	.8829	.5317	1.881	1.133	2.130	1.0821	62° 00′
10	916	720	816	354	868	134	118	792	50
20	945	746	802	392	855	136	107	763	40
30	.4974	.4772	.8788	.5430	1.842	1.138	2.096	1.0734	30
40	.5003	797	774	467	829	140	085	705	20
50	032	823	760	505	816	142	074	676	10
29° 00′	.5061	.4848	.8746	.5543	1.804	1.143	2.063	1.0647	61° 00′
10	091	874	732	581	792	145	052	617	50
20	120	899	718	619	780	147	041	588	40
30	.5149	.4924	.8704	.5658	1.767	1.149	2.031	1.0559	30
40	178	950	689	696	756	151	020	530	20
50	207	975	675	735	744	153	010	501	10
30° 00′	.5236	.5000	.8660	.5774	1.732	1.155	2.000	1.0472	60° 00′
10	265	025	646	812	720	157	1.990	443	50
20	294	050	631	851	709	159	980	414	40
30	.5323	.5075	.8616	.5890	1.698	1.161	1.970	1.0385	30
40	352	100	601	930	686	163	961	356	20
50	381	125	587	969	675	165	951	327	10
31° 00′	.5411	.5150	.8572	.6009	1.664	1.167	1.942	1.0297	59° 00′
10	440	175	557	048	653	169	932	268	50
20	469	200	542	088	643	171	923	239	40
30	.5498	.5225	.8526	.6128	1.632	1.173	1.914	1.0210	30
40	527	250	511	168	621	175	905	181	20
50	556	275	496	208	611	177	896	152	10
32° 00′	.5585	.5299	.8480	.6249	1.600	1.179	1.887	1.0123	58° 00′
10	614	324	465	289	590	181	878	094	50
20	643	348	450	330	580	184	870	065	40
30	.5672	.5373	.8434	.6371	1.570	1.186	1.861	1.0036	30
40	701	398	418	412	560	188	853	1.0007	20
50	730	422	403	453	550	190	844	977	10
33° 00′	.5760	.5446	.8387	.6494	1.540	1.192	1.836	.9948	57° 00′
10	789	471	371	536	530	195	828	919	50
20	818	495	355	577	520	197	820	890	40
30	.5847	.5519	.8339	.6619	1.511	1.199	1.812	.9861	30
40	876	544	323	661	501	202	804	832	20
50	905	568	307	703	1.492	204	796	803	10
34° 00′	.5934	.5592	.8290	.6745	1.483	1.206	1.788	.9774	56° 00′
10	963	616	274	787	473	209	781	745	50
20	992	640	258	830	464	211	773	716	40
30	.6021	.5664	.8241	.6873	1.455	1.213	1.766	.9687	30
40	050	688	225	916	446	216	758	657	20
50	080	712	208	959	437	218	751	628	10
35° 00′	.6109	.5736	.8192	.7002	1.428	1.221	1.743	.9599	55° 00′
10	138	760	175	046	419	223	736	570	50
20	167	783	158	089	411	226	729	541	40
30	.6196	.5807	.8141	.7133	1.402	1.228	1.722	.9512	30
40	225	831	124	177	393	231	715	483	20
50	254	854	107	221	385	233	708	454	10
36° 00′	.6283	.5878	.8090	.7265	1.376	1.236	1.701	.9425	54° 00′
		Cos	Sin	Cot	Tan	Csc	Sec	Radians	Degrees

(Continued)

TABLE II

Four-Place Values of Trigonometric Ratios and Radians

Degrees	Radians	Sin	Cos	Tan	Cot	Sec	Csc		
36° 00′	.6283	.5878	.8090	.7265	1.376	1.236	1.701	.9425	54° 00′
10	312	901	073	310	368	239	695	396	50
20	341	925	056	355	360	241	688	367	40
30	.6370	.5948	.8039	.7400	1.351	1.244	1.681	.9338	30
40	400	972	021	445	343	247	675	308	20
50	429	995	004	490	335	249	668	279	10
37° 00′	.6458	.6018	.7986	.7536	1.327	1.252	1.662	.9250	53° 00′
10	487	041	969	581	319	255	655	221	50
20	516	065	951	627	311	258	649	192	40
30	.6545	.6088	.7934	.7673	1.303	1.260	1.643	.9163	30
40	574	111	916	720	295	263	636	134	20
50	603	134	898	766	288	266	630	105	10
38° 00′	.6632	.6157	.7880	.7813	1.280	1.269	1.624	.9076	52° 00′
10	661	180	862	860	272	272	618	047	50
20	690	202	844	907	265	275	612	.9018	40
30	.6720	.6225	.7826	.7954	1.257	1.278	1.606	.8988	30
40	749	248	808	.8002	250	281	601	959	20
50	778	271	790	050	242	284	595	930	10
39° 00′	.6807	.6293	.7771	.8098	1.235	1.287	1.589	.8901	51° 00′
10	836	316	753	146	228	290	583	872	50
20	865	338	735	195	220	293	578	843	40
30	.6894	.6361	.7716	.8243	1.213	1.296	1.572	.8814	30
40	923	383	698	292	206	299	567	785	20
50	952	406	679	342	199	302	561	756	10
40° 00′	.6981	.6428	.7660	.8391	1.192	1.305	1.556	.8727	50° 00′
10	.7010	450	642	441	185	309	550	698	50
20	039	472	623	491	178	312	545	668	40
30	.7069	.6494	.7604	.8541	1.171	1.315	1.540	.8639	30
40	098	517	585	591	164	318	535	610	20
50	127	539	566	642	157	322	529	581	10
41° 00′	.7156	.6561	.7547	.8693	1.150	1.325	1.524	.8552	49° 00′
10	185	583	528	744	144	328	519	523	50
20	214	604	509	796	137	332	514	494	40
30	.7243	.6626	.7490	.8847	1.130	1.335	1.509	.8465	30
40	272	648	470	899	124	339	504	436	20
50	301	670	451	952	117	342	499	407	10
42° 00′	.7330	.6691	.7431	.9004	1.111	1.346	1.494	.8378	48° 00′
10	359	713	412	057	104	349	490	348	50
20	389	734	392	110	098	353	485	319	40
30	.7418	.6756	.7373	.9163	1.091	1.356	1.480	.8290	30
40	447	777	353	217	085	360	476	261	20
50	476	799	333	271	079	364	471	232	10
43° 00′	.7505	.6820	.7314	.9325	1.072	1.367	1.466	.8203	47° 00′
10	534	841	294	380	066	371	462	174	50
20	563	862	274	435	060	375	457	145	40
30	.7592	.6884	.7254	.9490	1.054	1.379	1.453	.8116	30
40	621	905	234	545	048	382	448	087	20
50	650	926	214	601	042	386	444	058	10
44° 00′	.7679	.6947	.7193	.9657	1.036	1.390	1.440	.8029	46° 00′
10	709	967	173	713	030	394	435	999	50
20	738	988	153	770	024	398	431	970	40
30	.7767	.7009	.7133	.9827	1.018	1.402	1.427	.7941	30
40	796	030	112	884	012	406	423	912	20
50	825	050	092	942	006	410	418	883	10
45° 00′	.7854	.7071	.7071	1.000	1.000	1.414	1.414	.7854	45° 00′
		Cos	Sin	Cot	Tan	Csc	Sec	Radians	Degrees

TABLE III

Four-Place Logarithms of Trigonometric Functions
Angle θ in Degrees

Attach -10 to logarithms obtained from this table

Angle θ	log sin θ	log csc θ	log tan θ	log cot θ	log sec θ	log cos θ	
0° 00′	No value	No value	No value	No value	10.0000	10.0000	90° 00′
10′	7.4637	12.5363	7.4637	12.5363	.0000	.0000	50′
20′	.7648	.2352	.7648	.2352	.0000	.0000	40′
30′	7.9408	12.0592	7.9409	12.0591	.0000	.0000	30′
40′	8.0658	11.9342	8.0658	11.9342	.0000	.0000	20′
50′	.1627	.8373	.1627	.8373	.0000	10.0000	10′
1° 00′	8.2419	11.7581	8.2419	11.7581	10.0001	9.9999	89° 00′
10′	.3088	.6912	.3089	.6911	.0001	.9999	50′
20′	.3668	.6332	.3669	.6331	.0001	.9999	40′
30′	.4179	.5821	.4181	.5819	.0001	.9999	30′
40′	.4637	.5363	.4638	.5362	.0002	.9998	20′
50′	.5050	.4950	.5053	.4947	.0002	.9998	10′
2° 00′	8.5428	11.4572	8.5431	11.4569	10.0003	9.9997	88° 00′
10′	.5776	.4224	.5779	.4221	.0003	.9997	50′
20′	.6097	.3903	.6101	.3899	.0004	.9996	40′
30′	.6397	.3603	.6401	.3599	.0004	.9996	30′
40′	.6677	.3323	.6682	.3318	.0005	.9995	20′
50′	.6940	.3060	.6945	.3055	.0005	.9995	10′
3° 00′	8.7188	11.2812	8.7194	11.2806	10.0006	9.9994	87° 00′
10′	.7423	.2577	.7429	.2571	.0007	.9993	50′
20′	.7645	.2355	.7652	.2348	.0007	.9993	40′
30′	.7857	.2143	.7865	.2135	.0008	.9992	30′
40′	.8059	.1941	.8067	.1933	.0009	.9991	20′
50′	.8251	.1749	.8261	.1739	.0010	.9990	10′
4° 00′	8.8436	11.1564	8.8446	11.1554	10.0011	9.9989	86° 00′
10′	.8613	.1387	.8624	.1376	.0011	.9989	50′
20′	.8783	.1217	.8795	.1205	.0012	.9988	40′
30′	.8946	.1054	.8960	.1040	.0013	.9987	30′
40′	.9104	.0896	.9118	.0882	.0014	.9986	20′
50′	.9256	.0744	.9272	.0728	.0015	.9985	10′
5° 00′	8.9403	11.0597	8.9420	11.0580	10.0017	9.9983	85° 00′
10′	.9545	.0455	.9563	.0437	.0018	.9982	50′
20′	.9682	.0318	.9701	.0299	.0019	.9981	40′
30′	.9816	.0184	.9836	.0164	.0020	.9980	30′
40′	8.9945	11.0055	8.9966	11.0034	.0021	.9979	20′
50′	9.0070	10.9930	9.0093	10.9907	.0023	.9977	10′
6° 00′	9.0192	10.9808	9.0216	10.9784	10.0024	9.9976	84° 00′
	log cos θ	log sec θ	log cot θ	log tan θ	log csc θ	log sin θ	Angle θ

(Continued)

Attach -10 to logarithms obtained from this table

Angle θ	log sin θ	log csc θ	log tan θ	log cot θ	log sec θ	log cos θ	
6° 00′	9.0192	10.9808	9.0216	10.9784	10.0024	9.9976	84° 00′
10′	.0311	.9689	.0336	.9664	.0025	.9975	50′
20′	.0426	.9574	.0453	.9547	.0027	.9973	40′
30′	.0539	.9461	.0567	.9433	.0028	.9972	30′
40′	.0648	.9352	.0678	.9322	.0029	.9971	20′
50′	.0755	.9245	.0786	.9214	.0031	.9969	10′
7° 00′	9.0859	10.9141	9.0891	10.9109	10.0032	9.9968	83° 00′
10′	.0961	.9039	.0995	.9005	.0034	.9966	50′
20′	.1060	.8940	.1096	.8904	.0036	.9964	40′
30′	.1157	.8843	.1194	.8806	.0037	.9963	30′
40′	.1252	.8748	.1291	.8709	.0039	.9961	20′
50′	.1345	.8655	.1385	.8615	.0041	.9959	10′
8° 00′	9.1436	10.8564	9.1478	10.8522	10.0042	9.9958	82° 00′
10′	.1525	.8475	.1569	.8431	.0044	.9956	50′
20′	.1612	.8388	.1658	.8342	.0046	.9954	40′
30′	.1697	.8303	.1745	.8255	.0048	.9952	30′
40′	.1781	.8219	.1831	.8169	.0050	.9950	20′
50′	.1863	.8137	.1915	.8085	.0052	.9948	10′
9° 00′	9.1943	10.8057	9.1997	10.8003	10.0054	9.9946	81° 00′
10′	.2022	.7978	.2078	.7922	.0056	.9944	50′
20′	.2100	.7900	.2158	.7842	.0058	.9942	40′
30′	.2176	.7824	.2236	.7764	.0060	.9940	30′
40′	.2251	.7749	.2313	.7687	.0062	.9938	20′
50′	.2324	.7676	.2389	.7611	.0064	.9936	10′
10° 00′	9.2397	10.7603	9.2463	10.7537	10.0066	9.9934	80° 00′
10′	.2468	.7532	.2536	.7464	.0069	.9931	50′
20′	.2538	.7462	.2609	.7391	.0071	.9929	40′
30′	.2606	.7394	.2680	.7320	.0073	.9927	30′
40′	.2674	.7326	.2750	.7250	.0076	.9924	20′
50′	.2740	.7260	.2819	.7181	.0078	.9922	10′
11° 00′	9.2806	10.7194	9.2887	10.7113	10.0081	9.9919	79° 00′
10′	.2870	.7130	.2953	.7047	.0083	.9917	50′
20′	.2934	.7066	.3020	.6980	.0086	.9914	40′
30′	.2997	.7003	.3085	.6915	.0088	.9912	30′
40′	.3058	.6942	.3149	.6851	.0091	.9909	20′
50′	.3119	.6881	.3212	.6788	.0093	.9907	10′
12° 00′	9.3179	10.6821	9.3275	10.6725	10.0096	9.9904	78° 00′
10′	.3238	.6762	.3336	.6664	.0099	.9901	50′
20′	.3296	.6704	.3397	.6603	.0101	.9899	40′
30′	.3353	.6647	.3458	.6542	.0104	.9896	30′
40′	.3410	.6590	.3517	.6483	.0107	.9893	20′
50′	.3466	.6534	.3576	.6424	.0110	.9890	10′
13° 00′	9.3521	10.6479	9.3634	10.6366	10.0113	9.9887	77° 00′
	log cos θ	log sec θ	log cot θ	log tan θ	log csc θ	log sin θ	Angle θ

(Continued)

Attach -10 to logarithms obtained from this table

Angle θ	log sin θ	log csc θ	log tan θ	log cot θ	log sec θ	log cos θ	
13° 00′	9.3521	10.6479	9.3634	10.6366	10.0113	9.9887	77° 00′
10′	.3575	.6425	.3691	.6309	.0116	.9884	50′
20′	.3629	.6371	.3748	.6252	.0119	.9881	40′
30′	.3682	.6318	.3804	.6196	.0122	.9878	30′
40′	.3734	.6266	.3859	.6141	.0125	.9875	20′
50′	.3786	.6214	.3914	.6086	.0128	.9872	10′
14° 00′	9.3837	10.6163	9.3968	10.6032	10.0131	9.9869	76° 00′
10′	.3887	.6113	.4021	.5979	.0134	.9866	50′
20′	.3937	.6063	.4074	.5926	.0137	.9863	40′
30′	.3986	.6014	.4127	.5873	.0141	.9859	30′
40′	.4035	.5965	.4178	.5822	.0144	.9856	20′
50′	.4083	.5917	.4230	.5770	.0147	.9853	10′
15° 00′	9.4130	10.5870	9.4281	10.5719	10.0151	9.9849	75° 00′
10′	.4177	.5823	.4331	.5669	.0154	.9846	50′
20′	.4223	.5777	.4381	.5619	.0157	.9843	40′
30′	.4269	.5731	.4430	.5570	.0161	.9839	30′
40′	.4314	.5686	.4479	.5521	.0164	.9836	20′
50′	.4359	.5641	.4527	.5473	.0168	.9832	10′
16° 00′	9.4403	10.5597	9.4575	10.5425	10.0172	9.9828	74° 00′
10′	.4447	.5553	.4622	.5378	.0175	.9825	50′
20′	.4491	.5509	.4669	.5331	.0179	.9821	40′
30′	.4533	.5467	.4716	.5284	.0183	.9817	30′
40′	.4576	.5424	.4762	.5238	.0186	.9814	20′
50′	.4618	.5382	.4808	.5192	.0190	.9810	10′
17° 00′	9.4659	10.5341	9.4853	10.5147	10.0194	9.9806	73° 00′
10′	.4700	.5300	.4898	.5102	.0198	.9802	50′
20′	.4741	.5259	.4943	.5057	.0202	.9798	40′
30′	.4781	.5219	.4987	.5013	.0206	.9794	30′
40′	.4821	.5179	.5031	.4969	.0210	.9790	20′
50′	.4861	.5139	.5075	.4925	.0214	.9786	10′
18° 00′	9.4900	10.5100	9.5118	10.4882	10.0218	9.9782	72° 00′
10′	.4939	.5061	.5161	.4839	.0222	.9778	50′
20′	.4977	.5023	.5203	.4797	.0226	.9774	40′
30′	.5015	.4985	.5245	.4755	.0230	.9770	30′
40′	.5052	.4948	.5287	.4713	.0235	.9765	20′
50′	.5090	.4910	.5329	.4671	.0239	.9761	10′
19° 00′	9.5126	10.4874	9.5370	10.4630	10.0243	9.9757	71° 00′
10′	.5163	.4837	.5411	.4589	.0248	.9752	50′
20′	.5199	.4801	.5451	.4549	.0252	.9748	40′
30′	.5235	.4765	.5491	.4509	.0257	.9743	30′
40′	.5270	.4730	.5531	.4469	.0261	.9739	20′
50′	.5306	.4694	.5571	.4429	.0266	.9734	10′
20° 00′	9.5341	10.4659	9.5611	10.4389	10.0270	9.9730	70° 00′
	log cos θ	log sec θ	log cot θ	log tan θ	log csc θ	log sin θ	Angle θ

(Continued)

501

TABLE III | Four-Place Logarithms of Trigonometric Functions
Angle θ in Degrees

Attach -10 to logarithms obtained from this table

Angle θ	log sin θ	log csc θ	log tan θ	log cot θ	log sec θ	log cos θ	
20° 00′	9.5341	10.4659	9.5611	10.4389	10.0270	9.9730	70° 00′
10′	.5375	.4625	.5650	.4350	.0275	.9725	50′
20′	.5409	.4591	.5689	.4311	.0279	.9721	40′
30′	.5443	.4557	.5727	.4273	.0284	.9716	30′
40′	.5477	.4523	.5766	.4234	.0289	.9711	20′
50′	.5510	.4490	.5804	.4196	.0294	.9706	10′
21° 00′	9.5543	10.4457	9.5842	10.4158	10.0298	9.9702	69° 00′
10′	.5576	.4424	.5879	.4121	.0303	.9797	50′
20′	.5609	.4391	.5917	.4083	.0308	.9692	40′
30′	.5641	.4359	.5954	.4046	.0313	.9687	30′
40′	.5673	.4327	.5991	.4009	.0318	.9682	20′
50′	.5704	.4296	.6028	.3972	.0323	.9677	10′
22° 00′	9.5736	10.4264	9.6064	10.3936	10.0328	9.9672	68° 00′
10′	.5767	.4233	.6100	.3900	.0333	.9667	50′
20′	.5798	.4202	.6136	.3864	.0339	.9661	40′
30′	.5828	.4172	.6172	.3828	.0344	.9656	30′
40′	.5859	.4141	.6208	.3792	.0349	.9651	20′
50′	.5889	.4111	.6243	.3757	.0354	.9646	10′
23° 00′	9.5919	10.4081	9.6279	10.3721	10.0360	9.9640	67° 00′
10′	.5948	.4052	.6314	.3686	.0365	.9635	50′
20′	.5978	.4022	.6348	.3652	.0371	.9629	40′
30′	.6007	.3993	.6383	.3617	.0376	.9624	30′
40′	.6036	.3964	.6417	.3583	.0382	.9618	20′
50′	.6065	.3935	.6452	.3548	.0387	.9613	10′
24° 00′	9.6093	10.3907	9.6486	10.3514	10.0393	9.9607	66° 00′
10′	.6121	.3879	.6520	.3480	.0398	.9602	50′
20′	.6149	.3851	.6553	.3447	.0404	.9596	40′
30′	.6177	.3823	.6587	.3413	.0410	.9590	30′
40′	.6205	.3795	.6620	.3380	.0416	.9584	20′
50′	.6232	.3768	.6654	.3346	.0421	.9579	10′
25° 00′	9.6259	10.3741	9.6687	10.3313	10.0427	9.9573	65° 00′
10′	.6286	.3714	.6720	.3280	.0433	.9567	50′
20′	.6313	.3687	.6752	.3248	.0439	.9561	40′
30′	.6340	.3660	.6785	.3215	.0445	.9555	30′
40′	.6366	.3634	.6817	.3183	.0451	.9549	20′
50′	.6392	.3608	.6850	.3150	.0457	.9543	10′
26° 00′	9.6418	10.3582	9.6882	10.3118	10.0463	9.9537	64° 00′
10′	.6444	.3556	.6914	.3086	.0470	.9530	50′
20′	.6470	.3530	.6946	.3054	.0476	.9524	40′
30′	.6495	.3505	.6977	.3023	.0482	.9518	30′
40′	.6521	.3479	.7009	.2991	.0488	.9512	20′
50′	.6546	.3454	.7040	.2960	.0495	.9505	10′
27° 00′	9.6570	10.3430	9.7072	10.2928	10.0501	9.9499	63° 00′
	log cos θ	log sec θ	log cot θ	log tan θ	log csc θ	log sin θ	Angle θ

(Continued)

Attach −10 to logarithms obtained from this table

Angle θ	log sin θ	log csc θ	log tan θ	log cot θ	log sec θ	log cos θ	
27° 00′	9.6570	10.3430	9.7072	10.2928	10.0501	9.9499	63° 00′
10′	.6595	.3405	.7103	.2897	.0508	.9492	50′
20′	.6620	.3380	.7134	.2866	.0514	.9486	40′
30′	.6644	.3356	.7165	.2835	.0521	.9479	30′
40′	.6668	.3332	.7196	.2804	.0527	.9473	20′
50′	.6692	.3308	.7226	.2774	.0534	.9466	10′
28° 00′	9.6716	10.3284	9.7257	10.2743	10.0541	9.9459	62° 00′
10′	.6740	.3260	.7287	.2713	.0547	.9453	50′
20′	.6763	.3237	.7317	.2683	.0554	.9446	40′
30′	.6787	.3213	.7348	.2652	.0561	.9439	30′
40′	.6810	.3190	.7378	.2622	.0568	.9432	20′
50′	.6833	.3167	.7408	.2592	.0575	.9425	10′
29° 00′	9.6856	10.3144	9.7438	10.2562	10.0582	9.9418	61° 00′
10′	.6878	.3122	.7467	.2533	.0589	.9411	50′
20′	.6901	.3099	.7497	.2503	.0596	.9404	40′
30′	.6923	.3077	.7526	.2474	.0603	.9397	30′
40′	.6946	.3054	.7556	.2444	.0610	.9390	20′
50′	.6968	.3032	.7585	.2415	.0617	.9383	10′
30° 00′	9.6990	10.3010	9.7614	10.2386	10.0625	9.9375	60° 00′
10′	.7012	.2988	.7644	.2356	.0632	.9368	50′
20′	.7033	.2967	.7673	.2327	.0639	.9361	40′
30′	.7055	.2945	.7701	.2299	.0647	.9353	30′
40′	.7076	.2924	.7730	.2270	.0654	.9346	20′
50′	.7097	.2903	.7759	.2241	.0662	.9338	10′
31° 00′	9.7118	10.2882	9.7788	10.2212	10.0669	9.9331	59° 00′
10′	.7139	.2861	.7816	.2184	.0677	.9323	50′
20′	.7160	.2840	.7845	.2155	.0685	.9315	40′
30′	.7181	.2819	.7873	.2127	.0692	.9308	30′
40′	.7201	.2799	.7902	.2098	.0700	.9300	20′
50′	.7222	.2778	.7930	.2070	.0708	.9292	10′
32° 00′	9.7242	10.2758	9.7958	10.2042	10.0716	9.9284	58° 00′
10′	.7262	.2738	.7986	.2014	.0724	.9276	50′
20′	.7282	.2718	.8014	.1986	.0732	.9268	40′
30′	.7302	.2698	.8042	.1958	.0740	.9260	30′
40′	.7322	.2678	.8070	.1930	.0748	.9252	20′
50′	.7342	.2658	.8097	.1903	.0756	.9244	10′
33° 00′	9.7361	10.2639	9.8125	10.1875	10.0764	9.9236	57° 00′
10′	.7380	.2620	.8153	.1847	.0772	.9228	50′
20′	.7400	.2600	.8180	.1820	.0781	.9219	40′
30′	.7419	.2581	.8208	.1792	.0789	.9211	30′
40′	.7438	.2562	.8235	.1765	.0797	.9203	20′
50′	.7457	.2543	.8263	.1737	.0806	.9194	10′
34° 00′	9.7476	10.2524	9.8290	10.1710	10.0814	9.9186	56° 00′
	log cos θ	log sec θ	log cot θ	log tan θ	log csc θ	log sin θ	Angle θ

(Continued)

503

Attach -10 to logarithms obtained from this table

Angle θ	log sin θ	log csc θ	log tan θ	log cot θ	log sec θ	log cos θ	
34° 00′	9.7476	10.2524	9.8290	10.1710	10.0814	9.9186	56° 00′
10′	.7494	.2506	.8317	.1683	.0823	.9177	50′
20′	.7513	.2487	.8344	.1656	.0831	.9169	40′
20′	.7531	.2469	.8371	.1629	.0840	.9160	30′
40′	.7550	.2450	.8398	.1602	.0849	.9151	20′
50′	.7568	.2432	.8425	.1575	.0858	.9142	10′
35° 00′	9.7586	10.2414	9.8452	10.1548	10.0866	9.9134	55° 00′
10′	.7604	.2396	.8479	.1521	.0875	.9125	50′
20′	.7622	.2378	.8506	.1494	.0884	.9116	40′
30′	.7640	.2360	.8533	.1467	.0893	.9107	30′
40′	.7657	.2343	.8559	.1441	.0902	.9098	20′
50′	.7675	.2325	.8586	.1414	.0911	.9089	10′
36° 00′	9.7692	10.2308	9.8613	10.1387	10.0920	9.9080	54° 00′
10′	.7710	.2290	.8639	.1361	.0930	.9070	50′
20′	.7727	.2273	.8666	.1334	.0939	.9061	40′
30′	.7744	.2256	.8692	.1308	.0948	.9052	30′
40′	.7761	.2239	.8718	.1282	.0958	.9042	20′
50′	.7778	.2222	.8745	.1255	.0967	.9033	10′
37° 00′	9.7795	10.2205	9.8771	10.1229	10.0977	9.9023	53° 00′
10′	.7811	.2189	.8797	.1203	.0986	.9014	50′
20′	.7828	.2172	.8824	.1176	.0996	.9004	40′
30′	.7844	.2156	.8850	.1150	.1005	.8995	30′
40′	.7861	.2139	.8876	.1124	.1015	.8985	20′
50′	.7877	.2123	.8902	.1098	.1025	.8975	10′
38° 00′	9.7893	10.2107	9.8928	10.1072	10.1035	9.8965	52° 00′
10′	.7910	.2090	.8954	.1046	.1045	.8955	50′
20′	.7926	.2074	.8980	.1020	.1055	.8945	40′
30′	.7941	.2059	.9006	.0994	.1065	.8935	30′
40′	.7957	.2043	.9032	.0968	.1075	.8925	20′
50′	.7973	.2027	.9058	.0942	.1085	.8915	10′
39° 00′	9.7989	10.2011	9.9084	10.0916	10.1095	9.8905	51° 00′
10′	.8004	.1996	.9110	.0890	.1105	.8895	50′
20′	.8020	.1980	.9135	.0865	.1116	.8884	40′
30′	.8035	.1965	.9161	.0839	.1126	.8874	30′
40′	.8050	.1950	.9187	.0813	.1136	.8864	20′
50′	.8066	.1934	.9212	.0788	.1147	.8853	10′
40° 00′	9.8081	10.1919	9.9238	10.0762	10.1157	9.8843	50° 00′
10′	.8096	.1904	.9264	.0736	.1168	.8832	50′
20′	.8111	.1889	.9289	.0711	.1179	.8821	40′
30′	.8125	.1875	.9315	.0685	.1190	.8810	30′
40′	.8140	.1860	.9341	.0659	.1200	.8800	20′
50′	.8155	.1845	.9366	.0634	.1211	.8789	10′
41° 00′	9.8169	10.1831	9.9392	10.0608	10.1222	9.8778	49° 00′
	log cos θ	log sec θ	log cot θ	log tan θ	log csc θ	log sin θ	Angle θ

(Continued)

504

Attach -10 to logarithms obtained from this table

Angle θ	log sin θ	log csc θ	log tan θ	log cot θ	log sec θ	log cos θ	
41° 00′	9.8169	10.1831	9.9392	10.0608	10.1222	9.8778	49° 00′
10′	.8184	.1816	.9417	.0583	.1233	.8767	50′
20′	.8198	.1802	.9443	.0557	.1244	.8756	40′
30′	.8213	.1787	.9468	.0532	.1255	.8745	30′
40′	.8227	.1773	.9494	.0506	.1267	.8733	20′
50′	.8241	.1759	.9519	.0481	.1278	.8722	10′
42° 00′	9.8255	10.1745	9.9544	10.0456	10.1289	9.8711	48° 00′
10′	.8269	.1731	.9570	.0430	.1301	.8699	50′
20′	.8283	.1717	.9595	.0405	.1312	.8688	40′
30′	.8297	.1703	.9621	.0379	.1324	.8676	30′
40′	.8311	.1689	.9646	.0354	.1335	.8665	20′
50′	.8324	.1676	.9671	.0329	.1347	.8653	10′
43° 00′	9.8338	10.1662	9.9697	10.0303	10.1359	9.8641	47° 00′
10′	.8351	.1649	.9722	.0278	.1371	.8629	50′
20′	.8365	.1635	.9747	.0253	.1382	.8618	40′
30′	.8378	.1622	.9772	.0228	.1394	.8606	30′
40′	.8391	.1609	.9798	.0202	.1406	.8594	20′
50′	.8405	.1595	.9823	.0177	.1418	.8582	10′
44° 00′	9.8418	10.1582	9.9848	10.0152	10.1431	9.8569	46° 00′
10′	.8431	.1569	.9874	.0126	.1443	.8557	50′
20′	.8444	.1556	.9899	.0101	.1455	.8545	40′
30′	.8457	.1543	.9924	.0076	.1468	.8532	30′
40′	.8469	.1531	.9949	.0051	.1480	.8520	20′
50′	.8482	.1518	9.9975	.0025	.1493	.8507	10′
45° 00′	9.8495	10.1505	10.0000	10.0000	10.1505	9.8495	45° 00′
	log cos θ	log sec θ	log cot θ	log tan θ	log csc θ	log sin θ	Angle θ

TABLE IV

Powers and Roots

No.	Sq.	Sq. Root	Cube	Cube Root	No.	Sq.	Sq. Root	Cube	Cube Root
1	1	1.000	1	1.000	51	2,601	7.141	132,651	3.708
2	4	1.414	8	1.260	52	2,704	7.211	140,608	3.733
3	9	1.732	27	1.442	53	2,809	7.280	148,877	3.756
4	16	2.000	64	1.587	54	2,916	7.348	157,464	3.780
5	25	2.236	125	1.710	55	3,025	7.416	166,375	3.803
6	36	2.449	216	1.817	56	3,136	7.483	175,616	3.826
7	49	2.646	343	1.913	57	3,249	7.550	185,193	3.849
8	64	2.828	512	2.000	58	3,364	7.616	195,112	3.871
9	81	3.000	729	2.080	59	3,481	7.681	205,379	3.893
10	100	3.162	1,000	2.154	60	3,600	7.746	216,000	3.915
11	121	3.317	1,331	2.224	61	3,721	7.810	226,981	3.936
12	144	3.464	1,728	2.289	62	3,844	7.874	238,328	3.958
13	169	3.606	2,197	2.351	63	3,969	7.937	250,047	3.979
14	196	3.742	2,744	2.410	64	4,096	8.000	262,144	4.000
15	225	3.873	3,375	2.466	65	4,225	8.062	274,625	4.021
16	256	4.000	4,096	2.520	66	4,356	8.124	287,496	4.041
17	289	4.123	4,913	2.571	67	4,489	8.185	300,763	4.062
18	324	4.243	5,832	2.621	68	4,624	8.246	314,432	4.082
19	361	4.359	6,859	2.668	69	4,761	8.307	328,509	4.102
20	400	4.472	8,000	2.714	70	4,900	8.367	343,000	4.121
21	441	4.583	9,261	2.759	71	5,041	8.426	357,911	4.141
22	484	4.690	10,648	2.802	72	5,184	8.485	373,248	4.160
23	529	4.796	12,167	2.844	73	5,329	8.544	389,017	4.179
24	576	4.899	13,824	2.884	74	5,476	8.602	405,224	4.198
25	625	5.000	15,625	2.924	75	5,625	8.660	421,875	4.217
26	676	5.099	17,576	2.962	76	5,776	8.718	438,976	4.236
27	729	5.196	19,683	3.000	77	5,929	8.775	456,533	4.254
28	784	5.292	21,952	3.037	78	6,084	8.832	474,552	4.273
29	841	5.385	24,389	3.072	79	6,241	8.888	493,039	4.291
30	900	5.477	27,000	3.107	80	6,400	8.944	512,000	4.309
31	961	5.568	29,791	3.141	81	6,561	9.000	531,441	4.327
32	1,024	5.657	32,768	3.175	82	6,724	9.055	551,368	4.344
33	1,089	5.745	35,937	3.208	83	6,889	9.110	571,787	4.362
34	1,156	5.831	39,304	3.240	84	7,056	9.165	592,704	4.380
35	1,225	5.916	42,875	3.271	85	7,225	9.220	614,125	4.397
36	1,296	6.000	46,656	3.302	86	7,396	9.274	636,056	4.414
37	1,369	6.083	50,653	3.332	87	7,569	9.327	658,503	4.431
38	1,444	6.164	54,872	3.362	88	7,744	9.381	681,472	4.448
39	1,521	6.245	59,319	3.391	89	7,921	9.434	704,969	4.465
40	1,600	6.325	64,000	3.420	90	8,100	9.487	729,000	4.481
41	1,681	6.403	68,921	3.448	91	8,281	9.539	753,571	4.498
42	1,764	6.481	74,088	3.476	92	8,464	9.592	778,688	4.514
43	1,849	6.557	79,507	3.503	93	8,649	9.644	804,357	4.531
44	1,936	6.633	85,184	3.530	94	8,836	9.695	830,584	4.547
45	2,025	6.708	91,125	3.557	95	9,025	9.747	857,375	4.563
46	2,116	6.782	97,336	3.583	96	9,216	9.798	884,736	4.579
47	2,209	6.856	103,823	3.609	97	9,409	9.849	912,673	4.595
48	2,304	6.928	110,592	3.634	98	9,604	9.899	941,192	4.610
49	2,401	7.000	117,649	3.659	99	9,801	9.950	970,299	4.626
50	2,500	7.071	125,000	3.684	100	10,000	10.000	1,000,000	4.642

LIST OF SYMBOLS

Symbols	Meaning
P_x	The point on the line corresponding to the real number x
$\|P_xP_x'\|$	The distance between P_x and $P_x' = \|x - x'\|$
$\|AB\|$	The distance between A and B
P_xP_x'	The directed distance from P_x to $P_x' = x' - x$
$\left.\begin{array}{l}(x, y)\\ P(x, y)\end{array}\right\}$	The point with rectangular coordinates x and y
$\left.\begin{array}{l}c_1, c_2\\ c_1, c_2, c_3\\ l, m, n\end{array}\right\}$	Direction cosines
m	Slope
(A, B)	The arrow from A to B
$\left.\begin{array}{l}\mathbf{a, b, v}\\ \overrightarrow{AB}\end{array}\right\}$	Vectors
$\mathbf{0}$	Null vector
$\left.\begin{array}{l}\mathbf{i, j,}\\ \mathbf{i, j, k}\end{array}\right\}$	Unit base vectors
$\cong$	Is congruent to
$\left.\begin{array}{l}\|\mathbf{a}\|\\ \|\overrightarrow{AB}\|\end{array}\right\}$	The magnitude of the vector
R	The set of real numbers
$\left.\begin{array}{l}f: X \to Y\\ f: x \to y\\ X \xrightarrow{f} Y\\ x \xrightarrow{f} y\\ x \to f(x)\end{array}\right\}$	Notations for a function f
Id	Identity function
$\left.\begin{array}{l}\bar{x} = \overline{a + bi}\\ = a - bi\end{array}\right\}$	The complex conjugate of $x = a + bi$
$\langle a, b \rangle$	Open interval

507

$[a, b\rangle$ $\langle a, b]$	Half-open intervals
$[a, b]$	Closed interval
$\pm\infty$	Plus, or minus, infinity
e	The base for natural logarithms
f^{-1}	The inverse function to the function f
$\log_a$	The logarithm function with base a
$m(\angle AOB)$	The measure, in radians, of angle AOB, or where evident, also the measure in degrees
ϕ	The wrapping function, or standard map, from R to the unit circle
α, β, γ	Direction angles
$\mathbf{u} \cdot \mathbf{v}$	The scalar product of $\mathbf{u}$ and $\mathbf{v}$
$\mathbf{n}$	The unit normal
$\mathbf{a} \times \mathbf{b}$	The vector product of $\mathbf{a}$ and $\mathbf{b}$
(r, θ)	Polar coordinates
(r, θ, z)	Cylindrical coordinates
(r, θ, φ)	Spherical coordinates
f'	The derivative of f
Δx	The change in, or increment of, x
$\begin{pmatrix} a_{11} & a_{12} \\ a_{21} & a_{22} \end{pmatrix}$	A matrix
$\begin{vmatrix} a_{11} & a_{12} \\ a_{21} & a_{22} \end{vmatrix}$	A determinant.
N	The set of natural numbers
$\{a_n\}$	A sequence
$P(n, r)$ nPr	The number of permutations of n objects r at a time
$C(n, r)$ nCr $\binom{n}{r}$	The number of combinations of n objects r at a time

508

GREEK ALPHABET

Letters		Names	Letters		Names
A	α	Alpha	N	ν	Nu
B	β	Beta	Ξ	ξ	Xi
Γ	γ	Gamma	O	o	Omicron
Δ	δ	Delta	Π	π	Pi
E	ϵ	Epsilon	P	ρ	Rho
Z	ζ	Zeta	Σ	σ	Sigma
H	η	Eta	T	τ	Tau
Θ	θ	Theta	Υ	υ	Upsilon
I	ι	Iota	Φ	ϕ	Phi
K	κ	Kappa	X	χ	Chi
Λ	λ	Lambda	Ψ	ψ	Psi
M	μ	Mu	Ω	ω	Omega

INDEX